PEARSON

Richard T. Wright • Dorothy F. Boorse

Environmental Science
Toward a Sustainable Future

Second Custom Edition for De Anza College

Taken from:
Environmental Science: Toward a Sustainable Future, Twelfth Edition
by Richard T. Wright and Dorothy F. Boorse

ISBN 10: 1-269-52855-6
ISBN 13: 978-1-269-52855-9

BRIEF CONTENTS

ABOUT THE AUTHORS

Richard T. Wright is Professor Emeritus of Biology at Gordon College in Massachusetts, where he taught environmental science for 28 years. He earned a B.A. from Rutgers University and an M.A. and a Ph.D. in biology from Harvard University. For many years, Wright received grant support from the National Science Foundation for his work in marine microbiology, and in 1981, he was a founding faculty member of Au Sable Institute of Environmental Studies in Michigan, where he also served as Academic Chairman for 11 years. He is a Fellow of the American Association for the Advancement of Science, Au Sable Institute, and the American Scientific Affiliation. In 1996, Wright was appointed a Fulbright Scholar to Daystar University in Kenya, where he taught for two months. He is a member of many environmental organizations, including the Nature Conservancy, Habitat for Humanity, the Union of Concerned Scientists, and the Audubon Society, and is a supporting member of the Trustees of Reservations. He volunteers his services at the Parker River National Wildlife Refuge in Newbury, Massachusetts, and is an elder in First Presbyterian Church of the North Shore. Wright and his wife, Ann, live in Byfield, Massachusetts, and they drive a Toyota Camry hybrid vehicle as a means of reducing their environmental impact. Wright spends his spare time birding, fishing, hiking, and enjoying his three children and seven grandchildren.

Dorothy F. Boorse is a professor of biology at Gordon College in Wenham, Massachusetts. Her research interest is in drying wetlands, such as vernal pools and prairie potholes, and in salt marshes. Her research with undergraduates has included wetland and invasive species projects. She earned a B.S. in biology from Gordon College, an M.S. in entomology from Cornell University, and a Ph.D. in oceanography and limnology from the University of Wisconsin–Madison. Boorse teaches, writes, and speaks about biology, the environment, ecological justice, and care of creation. She was recently an author on a report on poverty and climate change. In 2005, Boorse provided expert testimony on wildlife corridors and environmental ethics for a congressional House subcommittee hearing. Boorse is a member of a number of ecological and environmental societies, including the Ecological Society of America, the Society of Wetland Scientists, the Nature Conservancy, the Audubon Society, the New England Wildflower Society, and the Trustees of Reservations (the oldest land conservancy group in the United States). She and her family live in Beverly, Massachusetts. They belong to Appleton Farms, a CSA (community-supported agriculture) farm. At home, Boorse has a native plant garden and has planted two disease-resistant elm trees.

ABOUT OUR SUSTAINABILITY INITIATIVES

Pearson recognizes the environmental challenges facing this planet, as well as acknowledges our responsibility in making a difference. This book is carefully crafted to minimize environmental impact. The paper is certified by the Forest Stewardship Council™ (FSC®). The binding, cover, and paper come from facilities that minimize waste, energy consumption, and the use of harmful chemicals. Pearson closes the loop by recycling every out-of-date text returned to our warehouse.

Along with developing and exploring digital solutions to our market's needs, Pearson has a strong commitment to achieving carbon-neutrality. In 2009, Pearson became the first carbon- and climate-neutral publishing company. Since then, Pearson remains strongly committed to measuring, reducing, and offsetting our carbon footprint.

The future holds great promise for reducing our impact on Earth's environment, and Pearson is proud to be leading the way. We strive to publish the best books with the most up-to-date and accurate content, and to do so in ways that minimize our impact on Earth. To learn more about our initiatives, please visit **www.pearson.com/responsibility**.

MIX
Paper from responsible sources
FSC® C100141
www.fsc.org

PEARSON

CONTENTS

ESSAY LIST

PREFACE

We are now well into the second decade of the 21st century, and it is promising to be a crucial decade. Globally, major changes are taking place in the atmosphere and climate, the human population and its well-being, and the Earth's natural resources. We are still recovering from a major global economic recession, pointing to the reach of globalization; societies are reeling from disasters such as the Japanese tsunami, the Haitian earthquake, and the huge oil leak in the Gulf of Mexico; there is no letup in the accumulating evidence of climate change, brought on by increased fossil fuel burning; terrorism and conflict continue to grip the Middle East; and crises in food and agricultural production, brought on by heat waves and extended drought in the United States, are leading to greater numbers of hungry and impoverished people.

In contrast to these and other disturbing trends, there are some changes that point to a brighter future. Renewable energy is ramping up swiftly in its share of the world's energy portfolio; many of the UN Millennium Development Goals (MDGs) are on track to be achieved by their target date of 2015; even though international accord on climate change is slow in coming, many countries are achieving major reductions in greenhouse gas emissions; death by tobacco use is being addressed in a global campaign; AIDS, tuberculosis, and malaria are on the defensive as public-health agencies expand treatment options and research; and population growth in the developing countries is continuing to decline.

The most profound change that must happen, and soon, is the transition to a sustainable civilization—one in which a stable human population recognizes the finite limits of Earth's systems to produce resources and absorb wastes, and acts accordingly. This is hard to picture at present, but it is the only future that makes any sense. If we fail to achieve it by our deliberate actions, the natural world will impose it on us in highly undesirable ways.

New to This Edition

To help implement our core values, we have made changes to the twelfth edition. The major changes are listed here, followed by a list of updates for each part and chapter. All of these changes were made in the hope of creating a book with a solid, rigorous framework that is also easily comprehensible.

- In this edition, Learning Objectives have been added to the beginning of each chapter. These objectives describe the knowledge or skills that students should have upon completing each chapter.
- The art program has been substantially updated. Each chapter features new photos and updated graphics.

- Content has been thoroughly updated: More than 45% of the research cited is from 2010 or later, and material has been carefully edited for currency.
- New Video Field Trips give students the chance to learn about wind power, invasive species, and campus sustainability in an all-new format.
- New Core Content and Data Analysis Coaching activities in MasteringEnvironmentalScience activities accompany the twelfth edition of the book.

Content Updates to the Twelfth Edition of *Environmental Science*

Part One—Framework for a Sustainable Future

Part One has a new opener that focuses on the vision of sustainability and the challenges facing us that are inconsistent with that vision. Chapter 1 (Science and the Environment) has a new opening story, the inspiring work of Rachel Carson and her seminal book, *Silent Spring*. Then, as we look at the state of the planet, we investigate the "environmentalist's paradox," where human well-being seems to be improving while the environment continues to decline. We then introduce the American environmental movement timeline, a new graphic that shows the major impacts of events, people, and policies. We continue with our three unifying themes (sustainability, sound science, and stewardship) and introduce hypothesis formation with a new essay, "When Oysters Became Canaries." The final section in Chapter 1 explores social and environmental changes in the context of globalization. Chapter 2 (Economics, Politics, and Public Policy) explores the concepts of a green versus a brown economy and incorporates results from a new World Bank study that updates the "wealth of nations" concept the bank introduced earlier. A new essay ("California's Green Economy") illustrates beneficial environmental policy impacts, and other benefits of environmental policy are updated. Because of its time-sensitive content, the section on politics and the environment has been heavily rewritten. If we only had a crystal ball. . .

Part Two—Ecology: The Science of Organisms and Their Environment

Chapters 3–5 were reorganized in the last edition, and that organization has been maintained in this one, with topics flowing from basic to more complex, small to large, and species to ecosystems and humans. Chapter 3 (Basic Needs of Living Things) has new material on the sulfur cycle—another geochemical cycle important to living things—and a new Sustainability essay ("Planetary Boundaries"). Chapter 4 (Populations and Communities) is somewhat reorganized and has additional material on Darwin's finches in a new Sound Science box ("Studying Finches: The Life of a Scientist"). An example that allows students to calculate population growth has been moved from the main text into a Sound Science essay ("The Story Behind the Numbers: It's a Wormy Project!") to make the text more readable. Chapter 5 (Ecosystems: Energy, Patterns and Disturbance) begins with a new opener—the effects of an Icelandic volcano—and includes a new Sustainability essay ("Ecological Restoration: Aldo Leopold and the Shack on the Prairie"). More-modern ecological studies are described, including the LTER and NEON programs. Chapter 6 (Wild Species and Biodiversity) begins with a new opener on the Ganges River dolphin. Two new essays describe the return of the Lake Erie Water snake (Stewardship, "Lake Erie's Island Snake Lady") and the use of DNA in forensic wildlife science (Sound Science, "Using DNA to Catch Wildlife Criminals"). The section on protecting species was reorganized to cover topics from individual to international scales, and the section on the consequences of losing biodiversity was reorganized to tie into the values of biodiversity. Citizen science is highlighted with several examples. Chapter 7 (The Value, Use, and Restoration of Ecosystems) has a new opener on the Caribbean reef. The chapter was reorganized, with restoration and conservation moved to the end. The chapter has an even greater focus on ecosystem goods and services and two new essays (Sustainability, "How Much for That Irrigation Water?", and Sound Science, "Restoration Science: Learning How to Restore").

Part Three—The Human Population and Essential Resources

Part 3 begins with a new section opener about world population hitting 7 billion in October 2011. Chapter 8 (The Human Population) includes a new essay on calculating an ecological footprint (Stewardship, "Lessening Your Ecological Footprint") and updated population profiles. The chapter returns throughout to three countries—Burkina Faso, Indonesia, and Sweden—which are introduced in the chapter opener. The section on the IPAT equation has been updated to include some newer concepts on calculating ecological impacts, and the concept of the GINI index of inequality is added to the chapter. Chapter 9 (Population and Development) has a new chapter opener on declining population growth rates in Thailand. The Stewardship essay on China ("Protecting People's Options") is expanded to include issues prior to the one-child policy and more information on human rights abuses. A new figure illustrates the concept of the speed of demographic change by contrasting different countries. The former chapter opener on Kerala, India, was updated and made into a Sustainability essay ("Looking at Change in India"). Chapter 10 (Water: Hydrologic Cycle and Human Use) has an new chapter opener on drought in China, a new essay on thermohaline circulation (Sound Science,

"What's New in the Water Cycle?"), and another on the connection between water, energy, and food (Stewardship, "The Energy/Water/Food Trade: Waste One, Waste Them All"). There is more material on impervious surfaces, extreme-distance transport of water, and the relationship of climate change and the water cycle. Chapter 11 (Soil: Foundation for Land Ecosystems) has a new chapter opener on the Dust Bowl as well as an essay on two-stage ditches in the American Midwest (Sustainability, "New Ditches Save Soil"). The effects of mining on soils, acid rain, soil and carbon storage, and nanoparticles are also added. Chapter 12 (The Production and Distribution of Food) was altered significantly, with an entirely new section on sustainable agriculture and cutting-edge agricultural techniques as well as a new chapter opener on urban agriculture. The chapter is organized around three ideas—production, environmental sustainability, and effective distribution—and with a new summary table on actions that increase or decrease food availability. The food pyramid has been updated with the new USDA food "plate." Golden rice, the subject of the former chapter opener, was moved to a new Stewardship essay ("Golden Rice"). A new Sustainabilty essay ("Preventing Food Crises") connects photographer Dorothea Lange and the Great Depression to modern food crises. Chapter 13 (Pests and Pest Control) has a new chapter opener on bedbugs, a new Sound Science essay on biofouling organisms ("Marine Fouling Organisms: Keeping One Step Ahead of the Barnacles"), and more information on stored product pests and on the decline of bees. The latter part of the chapter is reorganized to include policies regulating both pesticides and pests themselves, including more on the government agency APHIS and its role in monitoring pests. It should be mentioned that for all of these chapters, photos, graphics, and statistical data have been brought up to date.

Part Four—Harnessing Energy for Human Societies

Chapter 14 (Energy from Fossil Fuels) has a new part opener with bad news and good news and a new chapter opener on the Deepwater Horizon disaster in the Gulf of Mexico. A new figure plots the different kinds of power plants constructed in recent years, and a new energy flow scheme from Livermore Labs is employed. The discussion on oil sands is expanded, and the Keystone pipeline proposal is presented and illustrated. Natural gas and coal are given separate sections in this edition. Hydraulic fracturing (fracking) is explored, and mountaintop removal coal mining is presented under the heading "Mining Coal" (Section 14.4). Policy from the Recovery Act is added, and there is a new Sound Science essay ("Energy Returned on Energy Invested"). Chapter 15 (Nuclear Power) opens with the earthquake and tsunami that rocked northern Japan in March 2011, leading to the nuclear disaster at the Fukushima Daiichi power plant. This event is used as an illustration of the consequences of a loss-of-coolant accident. Yucca Mountain is revisited, and the President's Blue Ribbon Commission report of 2011 is presented. The relicensing situation for U.S. nuclear power plants is reviewed, and global nuclear power is summarized. Chapter 16 (Renewable

Energy) opens with the latest on Cape Wind and a look at portable solar travel bags. Then follows a new section ("Strategic Issues") that examines the issues surrounding calls for great changes in renewable energy, calls for achieving 80% of electricity by renewable sources within a few decades. The chapter highlights the utilities' trend toward large photovoltaic installations and reviews work by MIT scientists that for the first time connects solar cell power to water oxidation under standard conditions, something that could pave the way to major energy gains.

Part Five—Pollution and Prevention

Chapter 17 (Environmental Hazards and Human Health) opens with a reference to the movie *Contagion* and moves from there to some controversial research on the avian flu virus, a disease that has the potential for great harm. The obesity epidemic in the United States is highlighted, with a new graphic on body mass index. ToxCast and the new IRIS system are discussed, and new information on the causation of asthma is added. A new Sound Science essay is "The Grisly Seven," where neglected tropical diseases that affect millions are discussed. Chapter 18 (Global Climate Change) starts with a new opener on the threats of rising sea level to island populations. A new section on "The Atmosphere's Control Knob" gives a perspective on the key importance of CO_2. Another new section is "Skeptics, Deniers, and Ethics," where opposition to climate change is put into perspective. The major international climate conferences are summarized, and the gap between promised emission reduction pledges and what needs to be done is emphasized and illustrated. In Chapter 19 (Atmospheric Pollution), new material on ammonia points to the great importance of nitric acid in acid rain as sulfur dioxides are being brought under greater control. Mercury emissions are highlighted, and the new Mercury and Air Toxics Standards are presented as a highly important development in curbing pollution from older coal-burning power plants. Nitrous oxide is presented as the newly recognized key ozone-depleting substance of the 21st century. Chapter 20 (Water Pollution and Its Prevention) has new illustrations of sludge digesters and septic systems and documents changes in the Chesapeake Bay restoration efforts, ending with comments on partisan efforts in Congress to block EPA enforcement of water quality regulations. Chapter 21 (Municipal Solid Waste: Disposal and Recovery) has a new emphasis on composting, and single-stream recycling is described as the new trend in recycling. EPA's waste management hierarchy is added as an illustration. The opening story has a new focus: installing solar arrays on closed landfills. The Internet is referenced as a great way to accomplish resale and reuse, and options for getting rid of e-waste are presented. Chapter 22 (Hazardous Chemicals: Pollution and Prevention) has a new opener on the controversial issue of endocrine disruptors and bisphenol A. A new section ("Evaluating New Chemicals") illustrates the different approaches of TSCA and REACH in the United States and Europe. The many abandoned uranium mines on Navajo reservations provide a new example of environmental (in)justice.

Part Six—Stewardship for a Sustainable Future

Chapter 23 (Sustainable Communities and Lifestyles) begins with a new story on renewal in Atlanta, Georgia, exploring the Atlanta BeltLine. A new paragraph examines the Rust Belt as a way of understanding urban blight. A new paragraph on "Fixing Suburbia" presents two recent books on how to repair suburban sprawl. Finally, the essay on Tangier Island is updated with reference to a meeting between the islanders and a farming community in Pennsylvania.

Coauthors

Like the global scene, the field of environmental science evolves and continues to change, and so has this text. The most significant change has been the work of a coauthor, Dr. Dorothy Boorse. Boorse began as coauthor in the eleventh edition, and in the twelfth, she has taken responsibility for half of the book (Chapters 1 and 3–13). For Wright, this has been an especially gratifying development, as Boorse was his student at Gordon College and is now back at the college as Professor of Biology. It has been a delight to work together on this edition.

Core Values

Environmental science stands at the interface between humans and Earth and explores the interactions and relations between them. This relationship will need to be considered in virtually all future decision making. This text considers a full spectrum of views and information in an effort to establish a solid base of understanding and a sustainable formula for the future. What you have in your hands is a readable guide and up-to-date source of information that will help you to explore the issues in more depth. It will also help you to connect them to a framework of ideas and values that will equip you to become part of the solution to many of the environmental problems confronting us.

In this new edition, we hope to continue to reflect accurately the field of environmental science; in so doing, we have constantly attempted to accomplish each of the following objectives:

- To write in a style that makes learning about environmental science both interesting to read and easy to understand, without overwhelming students with details;

- To present well-established scientific principles and concepts that form the knowledge base for an understanding of our interactions with the natural environment;

- To organize the text in a way that promotes sequential learning yet allows individual chapters to stand on their own;

- To address all of the major environmental issues that confront our society and help to define the subject matter of environmental science;

- To present the latest information available by making full use of resources such as the Internet, books, and journals; every possible statistic has been brought up to date;
- To assess options or progress made in solving environmental problems; and
- To support the text with excellent supplements for instructors and students that strongly enhance the teaching and learning processes.

Because we believe that learning how to live in the environment is one of the most important subjects in every student's educational experience, we have made every effort to put in their hands a book that will help the study of environmental science come alive.

Reviewers

Eric C. Atkinson, *Northwest College*

William Brown, *State University of New York, Fredonia*

John S. Campbell, *Northwest College*

Kathy Carvalho-Knighton, *University of South Florida*

Christopher G. Coy, *Indiana Wesleyan University*

Christopher F. D'Elia, *Louisiana State University*

Lisa Doner, *Plymouth State University*

Matthew J. Eick, *Virginia Tech*

Carri Gerber, *Ohio State University Agricultural Technical Institute*

Nisse Goldberg, *Jacksonville University*

Sherri Hitz, *Florida Keys Community College*

Bryan Hopkins, *Brigham Young University*

David W. Hoferer, *Eastern University*

Aixin Hou, *Louisiana State University*

Melinda Huff, *Northeastern Oklahoma A&E College*

Ali Ishaque, *University of Maryland, Eastern Shore*

Owen Lawlor, *Northeastern University*

Charles A. McClaugherty, *University of Mount Union*

Blodwyn McIntyre, *University of the Redlands*

Karen E. McReynolds, *Hope International University*

Glynda Mercier, *Austin Community College*

Grace Ju Miller, *Indiana Wesleyan University*

Michael Moore, *Delaware State University*

Natalie Moore, *Lone Star College*

Carrie Morjan, *Aurora University*

Carole Neidich-Ryder, *Nassau Community College*

Virginia Rivers, *Truckee Meadows Community College*

Annelle Soponis, *Reading Area Community College*

Bradley Turner, *McLennan Community College*

Alison Kate Varty, *College of the Siskiyous*

Robert S. Whyte, *California University of Pennsylvania*

Todd Christian Yetter, *University of the Cumberlands*

Reviewers of Previous Editions

Clark Adams, *Texas A & M University*

Anthony Akubue, *St. Cloud State University*

Mary Allen, *Hartwick College*

Walter Arenstein, *San Jose State University*

Abbed Babaei, *Cleveland State University*

Kenneth Banks, *University of North Texas*

Raymond Beiersdorfer, *Youngstown State University*

Lisa Bonneau, *Metropolitan Community College*

Geralyn Caplan, *Owensboro Community and Technical College*

Kelly Cartwright, *College of Lake County*

Jason Cashmore, *College of Lake County*

Anne Ehrlich, *Stanford University*

Cory Etchberger, *Johnson County Community College*

Marcia Gillette, *Indiana University–Kokomo*

Sue Habeck, *Tacoma Community College*

Crista Haney, *Mississippi State University*

Les Kanat, *Johnson State College*

Barry King, *College of Santa Fe*

Cindy Klevickis, *James Madison University*

Steven Kolmes, *University of Portland*

Peter Kyem, *Central Connecticut State University*

Marcie Lehman, *Shippensburg University*

Kurt Leuschner, *College of the Desert*

Gary Li, *Cal State–East Bay Campus*

Kenneth Mantai, *SUNY Fredonia*

Heidi Marcum, *Baylor University*

Allan Matthias, *University of Arizona*

Dan McNally, *Bryant University*

Kiran Misra, *Edinboro University of Pennsylvania*

Robert Andrew Nichols, *City College–Gainesville Campus*

Tim Nuttle, *Indiana University of Pennsylvania*

Bruce Olszewski, *San Jose State University*

John Pleasants, *Iowa State University*

John Reuter, *Portland State University*

Kim Schulte, *Georgia Perimeter College*

Brian Shmaefsky, *Lone Star College–Kingwood*

Shamili Stanford, *College of DuPage*

Keith Summerville, *Drake University*

Todd Tarrant, *Michigan State University*

Dave Wartell, *Harrisburg Area Community College*

John Weishampel, *University of Central Florida*

Arlene Westhoven, *Ferris State University*

Danielle Wirth, *Des Moines Area Community College*

ACKNOWLEDGMENTS

More than 30 years ago, Bernard Nebel published the first edition of this text. He did it because he was frustrated with existing environmental science texts and was convinced he could produce a more readable and effective book—and he did! By the fourth edition, Richard Wright joined Nebel and collaborated for two more editions. From the seventh to tenth editions, Wright was responsible for the text, and now with the eleventh and twelfth editions, there are once again two authors. This is a good development, one that is already adding richness and a new voice to many of the chapters. We are deeply indebted to Nebel for his diligent work in developing the text and producing successive editions. We offer this new edition of the book as our contribution to the students who are now well into this new century, in the hope that they will join us in helping to bring about the environmental revolution—the transition to a sustainable society—that must come, we hope sooner rather than later.

Although the content and accuracy of this text are the responsibility of the authors, it would never have seen the light of day without the dedicated work of many other people. We want to express our heartfelt thanks to all those at Pearson Education who have contributed to the book in so many ways.

We salute our editor, Alison Rodal, for her encouragement in helping us reorganize and write this new edition. Our developmental and project editor, Leata Holloway, worked closely with us on every aspect of the book; thank you, Leata, for your good contributions. Katie Ostler at Element LLC was our production editor, keeping us focused on the details of transforming manuscript into a finished product. We are grateful to Gina Cheselka for her management and guidance and to Lee Ann Doctor for her work on the media. We'd also like to thank Lauren Harp for her help in marketing the text. Thanks also go to Jennifer Nonenmacher and Peter Jardim, photo researchers.

In addition, we thank Todd Tracy, Ed Zalisko, Trixi Beeker, Kayla Rihani, Thomas Pliske, and Heidi Marcum for their work on MasteringEnvironmentalScience and other text supplements.

I (Richard Wright) wish to offer some very personal thanks to my wife, Ann, who has been my companion since the beginning of my work in biology and has provided the emotional base and care without which I would be far less of a person and a biologist. Her love and patience have sustained me in immeasurable ways.

I (Dorothy Boorse) would like to thank my husband, Gary, my biggest supporter. I am also very thankful to my mentors—particularly Richard Wright, who has known me for years and helped me inestimably, and Calvin DeWitt of the University of Wisconsin–Madison, who has been one of the foremost figures in motivating young people to care about the environment and ethics.

Finally, it is our hope that this book can inspire a new generation to work toward bringing healing to a Creation suffering from human misuse.

Richard T. Wright
Dorothy F. Boorse

DEDICATION

This edition is dedicated to the memory of Wangari Muta Maathai (1940–2011) tireless advocate for the environment. Maathai became the voice of modern Africa, a voice of hope and strength protecting the environment for the next generation. We take pride in dedicating this edition to her memory.

Maathai became the first eastern African woman to get a PhD when she received a Doctorate in Anatomy from the University College of Nairobi, (now the University of Nairobi) where she also began her teaching career. There, she became an advocate for women's rights and the environment. She was convinced environmental degradation was the root of many of Kenya's problems. She served in Kenya's Parliament, became an assistant minister for Environment and Natural Resources and served international organizational roles. She is best known for founding the Green Belt Movement, an effort to help solve unemployment and deforestation while empowering women. To date, the organization has planted more than 47 million trees in Kenya.

Maathai received many international awards. She was a prolific author and frequent speaker. In 2004, she became the first African woman to receive the Nobel Peace Prize. It was the first awarded for work in protecting the natural world as a route to promoting justice and peace.

Maathai died of cancer in 2011. Her whole life, featured in the documentary film *Taking Root: The Vision of Wangari Maathai,* was dedicated to the poor and the land. In her Nobel acceptance speech, she said, "Today we are faced with a challenge that calls for a shift in our thinking, so that humanity stops threatening its life-support system. We are called to assist the Earth to heal her wounds and in the process heal our own—indeed, to embrace the whole creation in all its diversity, beauty and wonder."

MasteringEnvironmentalScience®
www.masteringenvironmentalscience.com

Mastering is the most effective and widely used online homework, tutorial, and assessment system for the sciences. It delivers self-paced tutorials that focus on your course objectives, provides individualized coaching, and responds to your individual progress. Mastering helps motivate you to learn outside of class and arrive prepared for lecture or lab.

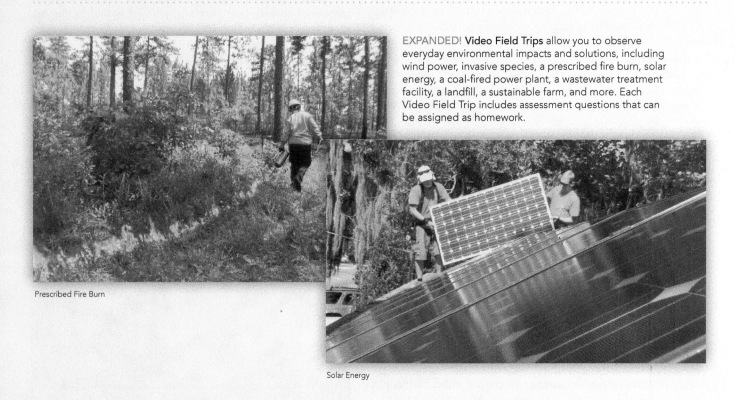

EXPANDED! Video Field Trips allow you to observe everyday environmental impacts and solutions, including wind power, invasive species, a prescribed fire burn, solar energy, a coal-fired power plant, a wastewater treatment facility, a landfill, a sustainable farm, and more. Each Video Field Trip includes assessment questions that can be assigned as homework.

Prescribed Fire Burn

Solar Energy

UPDATED! Current Events Quizzes are regularly updated and connect recent news articles to course topics.

EXPANDED! Concept Review Activities guide you through complex content with specific wrong answer feedback. New assignment options cover core topics in the environmental science course and include data analysis activities.

MasteringEnvironmentalScience®

Concept Review: Allopatric Speciation

Resources ▾

Concept Review: Allopatric Speciation

Part A

The arctic fox and gray fox evolved from the same species over thousands of years. Can you place these steps in the process of allopatric speciation along the timeline?

Drag each step in the process to its correct location.

Selective pressures favor foxes with thicker, lighter fur and shorter extremities.

Glaciation separates the population, forming northen and southern populations.

A single population of foxes exists in North America.

Selective pressures favor foxes with thinner, darker fur and longer extremities.

North (near Arctic Circle)

Long-term geographic isolation leads to divergence.

Eventually the arctic fox becomes a separate species, unable to breed with its southern counterpart.

Eventually the gray fox becomes a separate species, unable to breed with its northern counterpart.

South (near Equator)

First foxes evolve

Most recent glaciers cover central parts of North America

5–10 million years ago   100,000-10,000 years ago   Present day

↻ reset   ? help

Submit   My Answers   Give Up

Try Again

You labeled 5 of 5 targets incorrectly. Recall that a single population is the precondition for allopatric speciation. Where on the timeline should this precondition be located?

Additional Study Tools in MasteringEnvironmentalScience®

- The Pearson eText gives you access to the text whenever and wherever you can access the Internet. The eText pages look exactly like the printed text, and include powerful interactive and customization functions.

- Self Study Area offers a 24/7 study resource.

- GraphIt! Activities help you explore the data behind environmental issues and research.

- Reading Quizzes help you stay on track with your reading assignments and test your understanding of the content.

New to the Twelfth Edition

A revitalized art program makes the text more visually appealing and accessible with images and figures that teach more clearly. Learning Objectives also introduce you to important concepts that you should know.

NEW! Twelfth Edition

GLOBAL PRIMARY ENERGY SUPPLY

Coal	30.3%
Oil	33.1%
Natural Gas	23.7%
Nuclear	4.9%
Hydro	6.4%
Combustables, Renewables and Waste	1.6%

IMPROVED! **Bar Graphs and Data Figures** are more visually appealing and easier to interpret.

Corresponding Graph from Eleventh Edition

LEARNING OBJECTIVES

1. **Economics and the Environment:** Describe how economic activity relates to environmental goods and services, and differentiate between green and brown economies.

2. **Resources in a Sustainable Economy:** Summarize the components of the wealth a nation draws on to establish and maintain an economy, and identify new efforts to measure true economic progress.

3. **Environmental Public Policy:** Explain the kinds of policies employed to regulate the use of natural resources and deal with pollution, and describe a typical policy life cycle.

4. **Benefit-Cost Analysis of Environmental Public Policy:** Discuss how benefit-cost analysis is applied to environmental policy regulations, and give examples of the impact of regulations.

5. **Politics and the Environment:** Assess the role played by partisan politics in recent environmental public policy.

NEW! Twelfth Edition

Many hiding and resting places for small fish, etc.

Bacteria, protozoan insect larva attached to rocks

Good light penetration supports photosynthesis of attached algae, aquatic plants, and abundant food chains

(a) Stream ecosystem with LOW sediment load

Corresponding Figure from Eleventh Edition

NEW! **Learning Objectives** open each chapter to introduce key concepts that you should understand at the conclusion of the chapter.

PART ONE

Framework for a Sustainable Future

CHAPTER 1
Science and the Environment

NIGHTS SPENT POURING over blueprints, days looking at budgets, time spent deciding what parts need to be purchased and who will maintain a structure after it is built: you might imagine these activities being performed by professionals building a road or school, but they aren't. This is the work of a team of dedicated engineering undergraduates from Purdue University and their advisors. They are designing a small hydropower facility in Banyang, Cameroon, which will provide water and irrigation for a village.

THE PROJECT IS DESIGNED to promote sustainability—the ongoing thriving of people in a context of the natural world, living in such a way that doesn't use up resources, harm other creatures, or degrade our environment in the long term. Right now, there is evidence that we are not living sustainably: Our global economy relies on the use of fossil fuels and nuclear power, but continued emissions of carbon dioxide to the atmosphere and oceans are bringing major changes in the climate as Earth warms up and the oceans acidify. The global population will likely reach 9 billion by 2050, and the range and population size of many wild plant and animal species are declining. Food and clean water availability and basic health care remain low for the poorest people. Natural disasters such as the Japanese tsunami of 2011 interact with the built environment to cause radiation leaks and other problems. Human activities such as oil well drilling can interact with the natural environment to cause events such as the 2010 Gulf oil spill, which released 200 million gallons of crude oil into the Gulf, devastating sea life. We are all bound together: humanity, the other creatures, and the world around us.

We begin our framework for a sustainable future in Chapter 1, where we will introduce environmental science and what it might mean for you. In Chapter 2, we look at economics, politics, and public policy, three features of human societies that interact with science as we come to understand the environment and address the challenges we face.

CHAPTER 1

Science and the Environment

LEARNING OBJECTIVES

1. **The State of the Planet:** Explain the main reasons for concern about the health of our planet today.

2. **Environmental Science and the Environmental Movement:** Describe what the environmental movement has achieved in recent years, and explain how environmental science has greatly contributed to the environmental movement.

3. **Three Unifying Themes:** Define sustainability, sound science, and stewardship, the three unifying themes in environmental science.

4. **Moving Toward a Sustainable Future:** List trends that must be overcome in order to pursue a sustainable future and trends that promote sustainability.

"THERE WAS ONCE a town in the heart of America where all life seemed to live in harmony with its surroundings. The town lay in the midst of a checkerboard of prosperous farms, with fields of grain and hillsides of orchards where, in spring, white clouds of blossom drifted above the green fields. . . . The countryside was, in fact, famous for the abundance and variety of its bird life, and when the flood of migrants was pouring through in spring and fall people traveled from great distances to observe them. . . . So it had been from the days many years ago when the first settlers raised their houses, sank their wells, and built their barns.[1]"

These are words from the classic *Silent Spring*, written by biologist Rachel Carson (Fig. 1–1) to open her first chapter, titled "A Fable for Tomorrow." After painting this idyllic picture, the chapter goes on to describe "a strange blight" that began to afflict the town and its surrounding area. Fish died in streams, farm animals sickened and died, families were plagued with illnesses and occasional deaths. The birds had disappeared, their songs no longer heard—it was a "silent spring." And on the roofs and lawns and fields remnants of a white powder could still be seen, having fallen from the skies a few weeks before.

Rachel Carson explained that no such town existed, but that all of the problems she described had already happened somewhere, and that there was the very real danger that ". . . this imagined tragedy may easily become a stark reality we all shall know."[2] She published her book in 1962, during an era when pesticides and herbicides

---

[1]Rachel Carson, *Silent Spring*. Boston: Houghton Mifflin Company, pp. 1, 2.
[2]Ibid., p. 3.

Figure 1–1 **Rachel Carson.**

Figure 1–2 **Aerial spraying of pesticide on a tree farm.**

were sprayed widely on the landscape to control pests in agricultural crops, forests, and towns and cities (Fig. 1–2). In *Silent Spring*, Carson was particularly critical of the widespread spraying of DDT. This pesticide was used to control Dutch elm disease, a fungus that invades trees and eventually kills them. The fungus is spread by elm bark beetles, and DDT was used to kill the beetles. In towns that employed DDT spraying, birds began dying off, until in some areas people reported their yards were empty of birds. Many thousands of songbirds were recovered dead and analyzed in laboratories for DDT content; all had toxic levels in their tissues. DDT was also employed in spraying salt marshes for mosquito control, and the result was a drastic reduction in the fish-eating bald eagle and osprey.

FALLOUT. Rachel Carson brought two important qualities to her work: she was very careful to document every finding reported in the book, and she had a high degree of personal courage. She was sure of her scientific claims, and she was willing to take on the establishment and defend her work. In spite of the fact that her work was thoroughly documented, the book ignited a firestorm of criticism from the chemical and agricultural establishment. Even respected institutions such as the American Medical Association joined in the attack against her.

Despite this criticism, Carson's book caught the public's eye, and it quickly made its way to the President's Science Advisory Committee when John F. Kennedy read a serialized version of it in the *New Yorker*. Kennedy charged the committee with studying the pesticide problem and recommending changes in public policy. In 1963, Kennedy's committee made recommendations that fully supported Carson's thesis. Congress began holding hearings, public debate followed, and Carson's voice was joined by others who called for new policies to deal not only with pesticides, but also with air and water pollution and more protection for wild areas. Finally, in 1969, Congress passed a bill known as the Environmental Policy Act, the first legislation to recognize the interconnectedness of ecological systems and human enterprises. Shortly after that, a commission appointed by President Richard Nixon to study environmental policy recommended the creation of a new agency that would be responsible for dealing with air, water, solid waste, the use of pesticides, and radiation standards. The new agency, called the Environmental Protection Agency (EPA), was given a mandate to protect the environment against pressures from other governmental agencies and from industry, on behalf of the public. The year was 1970, the same year that 20 million Americans celebrated the first Earth Day.

In what must be seen as a triumph of Rachel Carson's work, DDT was banned in the United States and most other industrialized countries in the early 1970s. (The DDT story is more fully documented in Chapter 13.) Unfortunately, Rachel Carson did not live long after her world-shaking book was published; she died of breast cancer in 1964. Her legacy, however, is a lasting one: she is credited not only with major reforms in pesticide policy, but with initiating an environmental awareness that eventually led to the modern environmental movement and the creation of the EPA.

MOVING ON. This is a story of science and the environment, but it is more than that; it is a story of a courageous woman who changed the course of history. In this chapter, we briefly explore the current condition of our planet and then introduce three themes that provide structure to the primary goal of this text: *to promote a sustainable future.*

1.1 A Paradox: What Is the Real State of the Planet?

Paradox (n.): *A statement exhibiting contradictory or inexplicable aspects or qualities.*[3] A group of scientists from McGill University recently published a paper in which they identified a so-called **environmentalist's paradox**.[4] The paradox, they said, is this: over the past 40 years, human well-being has been steadily improving, while natural ecosystems (from which we derive many goods and services) have been declining.

To explain this paradox, the authors advanced four hypotheses:

1. The measurements of human well-being are flawed; it is actually declining.

2. Food production, a crucial ecosystem service that has been enhanced, outweighs the effects of declines in other ecosystem services.

3. Human technology makes us less dependent on ecosystem services.

4. There is a time lag between ecosystem decline and human well-being; the worst is yet to come.

We will take a brief look at four important global trends and keep in mind these hypotheses (the scientific method and hypotheses are explained later in the chapter) as we engage in our initial examination of the state of our planet: (1) human population and well-being, (2) the status of vital ecosystem services, (3) global climate change, and (4) a loss of biodiversity. Each of these is explored in greater depth in later chapters.

Population Growth and Human Well-Being

The world's human population, more than 7.1 billion in 2013, has grown by 2 billion in just the past 25 years. It is continuing to grow, at the rate of about 80 million persons per year. Even though the growth rate (now 1.2 %/year) is gradually slowing, the world population in 2050 could be 9.3 billion, according to the most recent projections from the United Nations (UN) Population Division (**Fig. 1–3**). The 2.2 billion persons added to the human population by 2050 will all have to be fed, clothed, housed, and, hopefully, supported by gainful employment. Virtually all of the increase will be in developing countries.

Human Development Index. Each year since 1990, the United Nations Development Program (UNDP) has published a Human Development Report.[5] A key part of the report is the *Human Development Index* (HDI), a comprehensive assessment of human well-being in most countries of

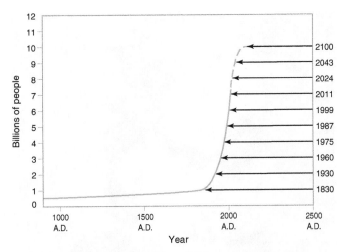

Figure 1–3 World population explosion. World population started a rapid growth phase in the early 1800s and has increased sixfold in the past 200 years. It is growing by 80 million people per year. (See Chapter 8.) Future projections are based on assumptions that birthrates will continue to decline. (Data from UN Population Division, 2010 revision, and from Population Reference Bureau reports.)

the world. With this index, well-being is measured in health, education, and basic living standards. In the 2010 report, worldwide trends in HDI were plotted over the 40 years since 1970 (**Fig. 1–4**). Even though there are some countries showing little or no progress, most of the 135 countries analyzed show marked improvement over the past 40 years. It is this overall progress that has provided one side of the environmentalist's paradox. During that time, life expectancy rose from 59 years to 70, school enrollment climbed from 55% to 70%, and per capita **gross domestic product** (GDP) doubled to more than $10,000. There has also been significant progress in the number of countries achieving democratic rule. Studies have shown that the HDI correlates well with other indicators of well-being, such as literacy, gender equality, and overall "happiness." As a result of these facts, the McGill team concluded that its first hypothesis is not supported; there are too many indications that human well-being has indeed improved markedly.

Is It All Good? However, overall progress can, and does, mask serious inequalities. Economic growth has been extremely unequal, both between and within countries. And there are huge gaps in human development across the world, as Figure 1–4 shows. For example, in developing countries, an estimated 1.29 billion people still experience extreme poverty, existing on an income of $1.25 a day. More than 925 million people—one out of every five in developing countries—remain undernourished. Some 8.1 million children per year do not live to see their fifth birthday. Addressing these tragic outcomes of severe poverty has been a major concern of the UNDP, and in 2000, all UN member countries adopted a set of goals—the **Millennium Development Goals (MDGs)**—to reduce extreme poverty and its effects on human well-being (see Table 9–2 for a list of the eight goals). If the goals are achieved by the target date of 2015, more than 400 million people will be lifted out of extreme

---

[3]From *Webster's II New College Dictionary*. Boston: Houghton Mifflin Company, 1995.
[4]Ciara Raudsepp-Hearne et al., Untangling the Environmentalist's Paradox: Why Is Human Well-Being Increasing as Ecosystem Services Degrade? *Bioscience* 60: 576–589. September 2010.
[5]United Nations Development Program, *Human Development Report 2010: The Real Wealth of Nations*. New York: UNDP. http://hdr.undp.org. August 30, 2011.

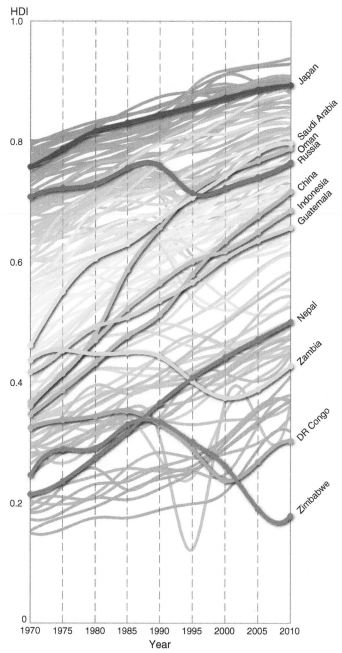

Figure 1–4 Human Development Index, 1970–2010. Advances in the HDI have occurred across all regions and almost all countries. The fastest progress has been in East Asia and the Pacific, followed by South Asia. All but three of the 135 countries have a higher level of human development today than in 1970.

poverty, and many millions of lives will be saved. Indeed, much progress has already been made in many developing countries, as signaled by the overall rise in the HDI values.

Virtually all of the discouraging issues outlined by the UNDP are most severe in developing countries, where population growth and fertility rates remain high. There is no doubt that these challenges will be easier to meet if population growth is brought down. When other countries have lowered their population growth, they have also made great advances in education, health care, and greater freedom and opportunities for women.

Is the prospect of 2.2 billion more people by 2050 a recipe for disaster? Can we feed that many more people? Certainly we have demonstrated our ability to continue to feed a growing human population, but at what cost to the environment? Are there enough energy and water and other ecosystem resources for 2.2 billion more of us?

Ecosystem Goods and Services

Natural and managed ecosystems support human life and economies with a range of goods and services. As crucial as they are, there is evidence that these vital resources are not being managed well. Around the world, human societies are depleting groundwater supplies, degrading agricultural soils, overfishing the oceans, and cutting forests faster than they can regrow. The world economy depends heavily on many renewable resources, as we exploit these systems for **goods**—fresh water (water with less than 0.1% salt), all of our food, much of our fuel, wood for lumber and paper, leather, furs, raw materials for fabrics, oils and alcohols, and much more. Just three sectors—agriculture, forestry, and fishing—are responsible for 50% of all jobs worldwide and 70% of all jobs in sub-Saharan Africa, eastern Asia, and the Pacific islands.

These same ecosystems also provide a flow of **services** that support human life and economic well-being, such as the breakdown of waste, regulation of the climate, erosion control, pest management, maintenance of crucial nutrient cycles, and so forth. In a very real sense, these goods and services can be thought of as capital—ecosystem capital. Human well-being and economic development are absolutely dependent on the products of this capital—its income, so to speak. As a result, the stock of ecosystem capital in a nation and its income-generating capacity represents a major form of the wealth of the nation (see Chapter 2). These goods and services are provided year after year, as long as the ecosystems producing them are protected.

Millennium Ecosystem Assessment. Launched on World Environment Day, 2001, the *Millennium Ecosystem Assessment* (ME) took four years to gather available information on the state of ecosystems across the globe. This monumental effort involved some 1,360 scientists from 95 countries gathering, analyzing, and synthesizing information from published, peer-reviewed research. The project focused especially on the linkages between ecosystem services and human well-being on global, regional, and local scales. Ecosystem goods and services (see Table 1–1) were grouped into *provisioning* services (goods like food and fuel), *regulating* services (processes like flood protection), and *cultural* services (nonmaterial benefits like recreation). The reports are now published and are also available on the Internet.

In a summary report,[6] the most prominent finding of the scientists was the widespread abuse and overexploitation of ecosystem resources. Humans have altered the

[6]Millennium Ecosystem Assessment, *Ecosystems and Human Well-Being: Synthesis.* Washington, DC: Island Press, 2005.

TABLE 1–1 **The Global Status of Ecosystem Services.** Human use has degraded almost two-thirds of these identified services; 20% are mixed, meaning they are degraded in some areas and enhanced in others; and 17% have been enhanced by human use.

Ecosystem Services	Degraded	Mixed	Enhanced
Provisioning (goods obtained from ecosystems)	Capture fisheries Wild foods Wood fuel Genetic resources Biochemicals Fresh water	Timber Fiber	Crops Livestock Aquaculture
Regulating (services obtained from the regulation of ecosystem processes)	Air quality regulation Regional and local climate regulation Erosion regulation Water purification Pest regulation Pollination Natural hazard regulation	Water regulation (flood protection, aquifer recharge) Disease regulation	Carbon sequestration (trapping atmospheric carbon in trees, etc.)
Cultural (nonmaterial benefits from ecosystems)	Spiritual and religious values Aesthetic values	Recreation and ecotourism	

Source: Millennium Ecosystem Assessment, *Ecosystems and Human Well-Being: Synthesis.* Washington, DC: Island Press, 2005.

world's ecosystems more rapidly and profoundly over the past 50 years than at any time in human history. More than 60% of the classes of ecosystem goods and services assessed by the team are being degraded or used unsustainably (Table 1–1). The scientists concluded that if this is not reversed, the next half-century could see deadly consequences for humans as the ecosystem services that sustain life are further degraded. The overall intent of the project is to build a knowledge base for sound policy decisions and management interventions; it remains for policy makers and managers to act on that knowledge.

However, one type of provisioning ecosystem services has actually been enhanced over recent years: the production of crops, livestock, and aquaculture. This production has more than kept pace with population growth, meeting the basic needs of people everywhere and improving nutrition for millions. Consequently, human well-being has benefited from the increased food provisioning services, as shown by increases in life expectancy and health improvements. These benefits apparently outweigh the costs of ecosystem decline, although the loss of certain goods and services has had serious impacts on human well-being.

Paradox Resolved? The McGill team set out to explain the environmentalist's paradox—the fact that human well-being has been improving while natural ecosystems have been declining. It rejected hypothesis 1, which stated that human well-being is actually declining. The team concluded that *hypothesis 2 was confirmed*: enhanced food production outweighs the effects of declines in other ecosystem services. Two further hypotheses remain: (3) our use of technology

to substitute for natural goods and services (e.g., irrigation, artificial fertilizers, improved sanitation), and (4) the existence of a time lag between the loss of goods and services and their impact on human well-being, with the possibility of exceeding limits and bringing on ecosystem collapse. The McGill University team concluded that these last two hypotheses also help explain the environmentalist's paradox, although not as clearly as hypothesis 2. They concluded that the paradox is not fully explained by any of the hypotheses, although hypothesis 1 was rejected. It also concluded that ecosystem conditions are indeed continuing to decline, with unknown and perhaps severe impacts on human well-being in the future. The most serious concern, one that affects all ecosystems, is global climate change.

Global Climate Change

The global economy runs on fossil fuel. Every day in 2012 we burned some 89 million barrels of oil, 340 billion cubic feet of natural gas, and 17 million tons of coal. All of this combustion generates carbon dioxide (CO_2), which is released to the atmosphere at a rate of 80 million tons a day. Because of past and present burning of fossil fuels, the CO_2 content of the atmosphere increased from 280 parts per million (PPM) in 1900 to 395 PPM in 2012. For the past decade, the level of atmospheric CO_2 has increased by 2 PPM per year, and given our dependency on fossil fuels, there is no end in sight.

Carbon dioxide is a natural component of the lower atmosphere, along with nitrogen and oxygen. It is required by plants for photosynthesis and is important to the Earth-atmosphere energy system. Carbon dioxide gas absorbs

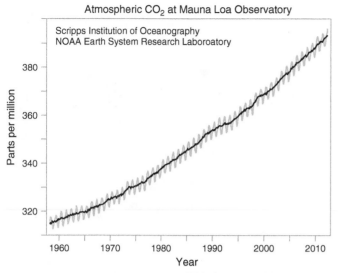

Figure 1–5 Atmospheric carbon dioxide concentrations. This record of CO₂ has been measured at the Mauna Loa Observatory since 1958. The atmospheric content of CO₂ has risen by 41% since the Industrial Revolution began.

(*Source:* Mauna Loa Observatory, Hawaii, NOAA Research Laboratory, Scripps Institution of Oceanography)

infrared (heat) energy radiated from Earth's surface, thus slowing the loss of this energy to space. The absorption of infrared energy by CO_2 and other gases warms the lower atmosphere in a phenomenon known as the **greenhouse effect**. This effect is well known, and the greenhouse gases keep Earth at hospitable temperatures as they trap heat. Although the concentration of CO_2 is a small percentage of the atmospheric gases, increases in the volume of this gas affect temperatures. **Figure 1–5** graphs changes in carbon dioxide from 1958 to the present, and **Figure 1–6** shows changes in global temperature since 1880. Both of these parameters are increasing—and rather steeply. This is not *proof* that the CO_2 caused the increase, but the argument based on the known greenhouse effect is quite convincing.

The Intergovernmental Panel on Climate Change (IPCC) was established by the UN in 1988 and given the

responsibility to report its assessment of climate change at five-year intervals. The latest of these assessments, the Fourth Assessment Report (FAR), was released during 2007. The work of thousands of scientific expert reviewers and hundreds of authors, this assessment produced convincing evidence of human-induced global warming that is already severely affecting global climate. Polar ice is melting at an unprecedented rate, glaciers are retreating, storms are increasing in intensity, and sea level is rising. Because the oceans are absorbing half of the CO_2 being emitted, the seawater is becoming more acid; the Sound Science essay "When Oysters Became Canaries" (see p. 8) explores one consequence of ocean acidification. The IPCC concluded that future climate change could be catastrophic if something is not done to bring the rapidly rising emission of CO_2 and other greenhouse gases under control. With few exceptions, the scientists who have studied these phenomena have reached a clear consensus: this is a huge global problem, and it must be addressed on a global scale.

Responses. There are real solutions to this problem, but they are not easy. The most obvious need is to reduce global CO_2 emissions (called **mitigation**). At issue for many countries is the conflict between the short-term economic impacts of reducing the use of fossil fuels and the long-term consequences of climate change for the planet and all its inhabitants. Future climate changes are likely to disrupt the ecosystem goods and services essential to human well-being, and because the extreme poor depend especially on natural ecosystems, they will suffer disproportionately. International agreements to reduce greenhouse gas emissions have been forged, and some limited mitigation has been achieved.

Most observers believe that the best course forward is to aim toward an effective, binding international treaty to reduce emissions, but on a more immediate scale, for countries to act independently. The United States has backed away from any binding treaties, but the government is moving forward to regulate greenhouse gas emissions under existing air pollution laws and to encourage renewable energy development.

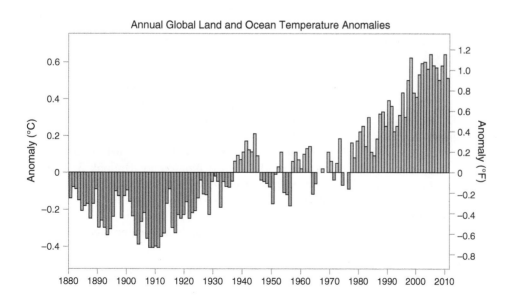

Figure 1–6 Global temperatures since 1880. This plot shows the course of global temperatures as recorded by thousands of stations around the world. The baseline, or zero point, is the 20th century average temperature.

(*Source:* National Climatic Data Center, NOAA, 2011)

SOUND SCIENCE

When Oysters Became Canaries

Oysters are big business on the U.S. West Coast, netting some $85 million a year and employing 3,000 workers. The oyster of choice on that coast is *Crassostrea gigas*, a native of Japanese waters imported many years ago and planted in many coastal waters. Because this oyster species needs warm water in order to spawn and West Coast waters are cold, oyster farms purchase so-called "seed, " young oysters 2 to 3 mm in diameter that are raised in hatcheries (see illustration). They then "plant" the seed on selected sandy banks or in special trays that are suspended in coastal embayments, and the oysters grow to maturity in a year or two as they feed on natural food in the saline waters. Sue Cudd, co-owner of Whiskey Creek Shellfish Hatchery on Netarts Bay, Oregon, ships out millions of oyster seed on a good day to oyster farmers.

At Whiskey Creek, oysters spawn under laboratory conditions. A female oyster produces millions of eggs, which are then fertilized by male oysters. The fertile eggs, now held in tanks, develop into swimming larvae, which start to form shells as they grow. The larvae settle down as they grow into "seed" oysters; all this time they have been bathed in filtered coastal seawater and provided with microscopic algae for food.

Unfortunately, the good days at Whiskey Creek came to a halt in the summer of 2007. During this time, oyster larvae and seed oysters began dying off, sometimes simply disappearing from the incubation tanks. Owners Cudd and her husband, Mark Wiegardt, immediately started looking for the culprit; they quickly identified a naturally occurring pathogenic bacterium, *Vibrio tubiashii*, that had become established in their tanks. They installed an expensive filtration system that removed the bacteria from incoming water, but the larvae continued to die. So it wasn't a pathogen killing the baby oysters.

Then, in July 2008, all of the remaining larvae in their tanks suddenly died. At the same time, the bay water brought into the tanks had turned acidic and colder. The timing was the key; this was water that had recently been brought up to the surface as offshore winds pushed the warmer surface water away, a process called upwelling. The pH of the upwelled water was in the range of 7.5; normal surface seawater pH is around 8.5, a 10-fold difference in acidity. The reason for the acidic waters was high concentrations of CO_2, released as plankton died and sank to the deeper waters and decomposed. However, new studies by oceanographers showed that waters rising from Pacific Ocean depths hold the CO_2 from normal decomposition plus CO_2 absorbed from the atmosphere of past decades; the oceans have been acidified as they have been absorbing atmospheric CO_2. It has been well understood for some years now that the oceans have taken up at least half of the CO_2 released as fossil fuels have been burned over the past 250 years. Now it begins to appear that ocean acidification is well under way and is now beginning to affect shellfish.

The solution for the Whiskey Creek Hatchery owners was now clear; they had to avoid the acidic waters that could simply dissolve away the thin shells of the young oysters. They installed chemical monitors that measured the CO_2 and pH of incoming waters and were able to time water withdrawals to daytime hours when natural algae were removing CO_2 from the water for photosynthesis and avoid recently upwelled and nighttime hours where CO_2 levels were elevated and pH lowered. Whiskey Creek Hatchery has recovered, and seed oysters are being shipped out once again. For a time, their oyster larvae were the "canary in the cage," a term that refers to the old practice by coal miners of bringing cages of canaries down into the mines with them. Because canaries are more sensitive to coal gas than are humans, the miners would quickly leave the mines if the canaries began dying. The oyster larvae were an early sign of a process that is now under way and looks to become increasingly serious—ocean acidification. As acidification intensifies, it is likely that more sturdy shellfish will succumb to the rising acid conditions, and whole coastal and coral ecosystems could be degraded, perhaps to the point of no return. The solution? Reduce the carbon emissions from burning fossil fuels (see Chapter 18).

Without doubt, this is one of the defining environmental issues of the 21st century. (Chapter 18 is wholly devoted to exploring the many dimensions of global climate change.)

Loss of Biodiversity

The Convention on Biological Diversity (CBD) defines biodiversity as "the variability among living organisms from all sources including terrestrial, marine, other aquatic ecosystems, and the ecological complexes of which they are part; this includes diversity within species, between species and of ecosystems."[7] The rapidly growing human population, with its growing appetite for food, water, timber, fiber, and fuel, is accelerating the conversion of forests, grasslands, and wetlands to agriculture and urban development. The inevitable result is the loss of many of the wild plants and animals that occupy those natural habitats. Pollution also degrades habitats—particularly aquatic and marine habitats—eliminating the species they support. Further, hundreds of species of mammals, reptiles, amphibians, fish, birds, and butterflies, as well as innumerable plants, are exploited for their commercial value. Even when species are protected by law, many are hunted, killed, and marketed illegally. According to the Global Biodiversity Outlook 3 (GBO 3) assessment,[8] the majority of wild plant and animal species are declining in their range and/or population size.

As a result, Earth is rapidly losing many of its species, although no one knows exactly how many. About 2 million

[7]Convention on Biological Diversity. Text of Convention, Article 2. Use of Terms. http://www.cbd.int/convention/articles/?a=cbd-02

[8]Secretariat of the Convention on Biological Diversity, *Global Biodiversity Outlook 3*. Montreal. 2010. www.cbd.int/gbo3. September 5, 2011.

species have been described and classified, but scientists estimate that 5 to 30 million species may exist on Earth. Because so many species remain unidentified, the exact number of species becoming extinct can only be estimated. However, GBO 3 reported that the abundance of vertebrate species fell by nearly a third between 1970 and 2006. The most dramatic declines have occurred in the tropics, in both ground-dwelling and ocean species.

Risks of Losing Biodiversity. Why is losing biodiversity so critical? Biodiversity is the mainstay of agricultural crops and of many medicines. The loss of biodiversity can only curtail development in these areas. Biodiversity is also a critical factor in maintaining the stability of natural systems and enabling them to recover after disturbances such as fires or volcanic eruptions. Most of the essential goods and services provided by natural systems are derived directly from various living organisms, and we threaten our own well-being when we diminish the biodiversity within those natural systems. These goods and services are especially important in sustaining the poor in developing countries. There are also aesthetic and moral arguments for maintaining biodiversity. Shall we continue to erase living species from the planet, or do we have a moral responsibility to protect and preserve the amazing diversity of life on Earth? Once a species is gone, it is gone forever. Finding ways to protect the planet's biodiversity is one of the key challenges of environmental science. (Chapter 6 covers loss of biodiversity.)

1.2 Environmental Science and the Environmental Movement

As you read this book, you will encounter descriptions of the natural world and how it works. You will also encounter a great diversity of issues and problems that have arisen because human societies live in this natural world. We use materials from it (goods taken from natural ecosystems); we convert parts of it into the built environment of our towns, cities, factories, and highways; and we transform many natural ecosystems into food-producing agricultural systems. We also use the environment as a place to dump our wastes—solids, liquids, gases—all proceeding from human activities, most of them legitimate, but all of them affecting the environment. The **environment**, then, includes the natural world, human societies, and the human-built world; it is an extremely inclusive concept.

Environmental Science

Things go wrong in the environment, sometimes badly. We have already considered four trends (human population growth, ecosystem decline, global climate change, loss of biodiversity) that signal to us that we are creating problems for ourselves that we ignore at our peril. Lest you think that all we do is create problems, however, consider some of the great successes human societies have achieved. We have learned how to domesticate landscapes and ecosystems, converting them into highly productive food-producing systems that provide

sustenance for 7 billion people. We have learned how to convert natural materials into an endless number of manufactured goods and structures, all useful for the successful building of cities, roadways, vehicles, and all that makes up a 21st-century human world. We have successfully tapped into the abundant pool of carbon-based fuels laid down in the geological past, using it for energy to produce electricity, heat our homes, power our vehicles, and manufacture our products. All of these successes, however, carry with them hazards. Burning fossil fuels creates air pollutants that can make us sick and even raise the temperature of our planet; using chemicals to control diseases and pests leaves a residue of contaminants that can poison whole food chains—and ourselves; overharvesting forests and fisheries can lead to their collapse, erasing vital services that natural ecosystems provide.

Human actions have negative effects on the environment in two broad categories: cumulative impacts and unintended consequences. Sometimes we simply do too much of any one activity—too much burning, too much tree cutting, too much mining on steep slopes. Activities that would not pose a problem if a few people engaged in them are big problems if millions of people do. Sometimes it isn't the accumulation of an activity; it is that we are not paying attention to how the world works. There are unintended consequences of using chemical pesticides, as we've seen, or of putting trash dumps in wetlands. These two concepts, cumulative impacts and unintended consequences, will come up in the chapters ahead. This is where environmental science comes in. Simply put, **environmental science** is the study of how the world works. Scientists help figure out ways to lower the negative impacts of our actions, to find alternative ways to meet the same needs, and to better anticipate the likely effects of what we are doing.

All sorts of disciplines contribute to environmental science: history, engineering, geology, physics, medicine, biology, and sociology, to name a few. It is perhaps the most multidisciplinary of all sciences. As you study environmental science, you have an opportunity to engage in something that can change your life and that will certainly equip you to better understand the world you live in now and will encounter in the future.

The Environmental Movement

To understand how the world works today, we need some sense of history. Although what we now term the environmental movement began less than 60 years ago, it had its roots in the late 19th century, when some people realized that the unique, wild areas of the United States were disappearing.

The history of the environmental movement in the United States has been one in which environmental degradation, resource misuse, and disastrous events sparked scientific study and sometimes grassroots action. Scientific study yielded information on how the world works. Individuals and groups worked as stewards to make changes. Policies were put into place to better protect resources and people from environmental degradation. **Figure 1–7** (on the next page) is a timeline of some of the events and scientific findings, people, and policies of the American environmental movement that will come up throughout the book.

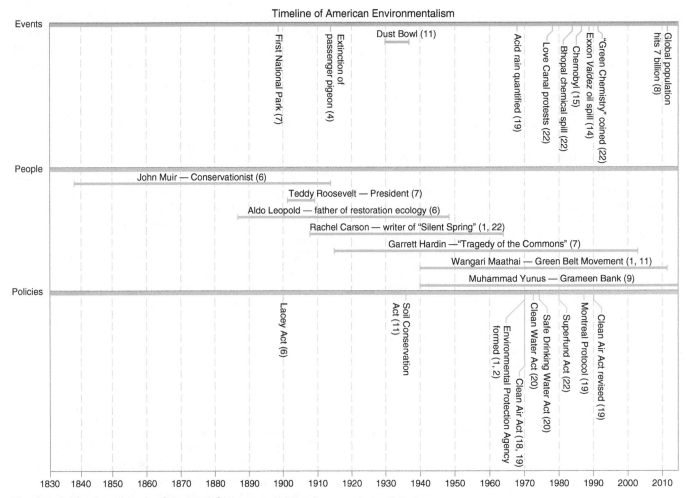

Figure 1–7 The American Environmental Movement. Selected events and scientific findings, people, and policies of the environmental movement in the United States. Numbers next to them are the chapters in which they are covered.

In the late 19th century, the indiscriminate killing of birds and animals and the closing of the frontier sparked a reaction. Around that time, several groups devoted to conservation formed: the National Audubon Society, the National Wildlife Federation, and the Sierra Club, which was founded in California by naturalist John Muir, who helped popularize the idea of wilderness. President Theodore Roosevelt promoted the conservation of public lands, and the national parks were formed.

The first half of the 20th century was marked by increasing awareness of the environment. Unwise agricultural practices following World War I eventually helped create an environmental crisis—the Dust Bowl of the 1930s (enormous soil erosion in the American and Canadian prairielands). During the Great Depression (1930–1936), conservation provided a means of both restoring the land and providing work for the unemployed, such as workers in the Civilian Conservation Corps (CCC), who built trails and did erosion control in national parks and forests.

The two decades following World War II (1945–1965) were full of technological optimism. New developments, ranging from rocket science to computers and from pesticides to antibiotics, were redirected to peacetime applications. How-

ever, although economic expansion enabled most families to have a home, a car, and other possessions, certain problems became obvious. The air in and around cities was becoming murky and irritating to people's eyes and respiratory systems. Rivers and beaches were increasingly fouled with raw sewage, garbage, and chemical wastes from industries, sewers, and dumps. Conspicuous declines occurred in many bird populations (including that of our national symbol, the bald eagle), aquatic species, and other animals. The decline of the bald eagle and other bird populations was traced to the accumulation in their bodies of DDT, the long-lasting pesticide that had been used in large amounts since the 1940s. In short, it was clear that we were seriously contaminating our environment.

The Modern Environmental Movement. In 1962, biologist Rachel Carson wrote *Silent Spring*, presenting her scenario of a future with no songbirds. Carson's voice was soon joined by others, many of whom formed organizations to focus and amplify the voices of thousands more in demanding a cleaner environment. This was the beginning of the modern **environmental movement**, in which a newly motivated citizenry demanded the curtailment of pollution, the cleanup of polluted environments, and the protection of pristine areas.

Pressured by concerned citizens, Congress created the Environmental Protection Agency (EPA) in 1970 and passed numerous laws promoting pollution control and wildlife protection, including the National Environmental Policy Act of 1969, the Clean Air Act of 1970, the Clean Water Act of 1972, the Marine Mammals Protection Act of 1972, the Endangered Species Act of 1973, and the Safe Drinking Water Act of 1974. A disastrous hazardous waste problem in Love Canal, New York, prompted the Superfund Act of 1980; scientific studies on acid rain, the decline of the ozone layer, and global climate change caused more environmental groups to form and policies to be put into place. Concerns about hazardous waste disposal triggered the rise of the Green Chemistry Movement. You will read more about these and more recent laws and their effects later in this book.

Persons and organizations with a strong focus on environmental concerns became known as **environmentalists,** and the resulting widespread development of this movement is often called **environmentalism.** As a result of these efforts, the air in our cities and the water in our lakes and rivers are far cleaner than they were in the late 1960s. Without a doubt, absent the environmental movement, our air and water would now be a toxic brew. By almost any measure, the environmental movement has been successful, at least in solving some pollution problems.

Environmentalism Acquires Critics. In the early stages of the environmental movement, sources of problems were specific and visible, and the solutions seemed relatively straightforward: install waste treatment and pollution control equipment and ban the use of very toxic pesticides, substituting safer pesticides, for example. At first, many industries conformed to the reforms, but as regulatory demands increased, a number of the more polluting industries, such as mining and utilities, pressed for a halt in regulation, and some began demanding significant deregulation.

Today, there are political battles surrounding almost every environmental issue. Bitter conflicts have emerged over issues involving access to publicly owned resources such as water, grazing land, and timber. The Endangered Species Act, which protects wild plants and animals whose existence is threatened, has been a lightning rod for controversy. When the EPA develops regulations to address air and water pollution, for example, some business special interests oppose the regulations and often environmental special interests support them. Climate change has been so controversial that it has triggered a host of antienvironmental groups. Instead of civility and persuasive discussion, discourse on environmental issues has become one of polemics and anger. As environmental public policies are developed and enforced, the controversies that accompany those policies remind us that politics always accompanies policy.

1.3 Three Unifying Themes

What will it take to move our civilization in the direction of a long-term sustainable relationship with the natural world? The answer to this question is not simple, but we would like to present three themes that provide coherence to the issues and topics covered in this text. In reality, these themes deal with how we should conceptualize our task of forging a sustainable future (Fig. 1–8). Each theme is a concept that we believe is essential to environmental science. The first theme is **sustainability**—the practical goal toward which our interactions

Figure 1–8 **Three unifying themes.** Sustainability, stewardship, and sound science are three vital concepts or ideals that can move societies toward a sustainable future if they are applied to public policies and private environmental actions.

with the natural world should be working. The second is **sound science**—the basis for our understanding of how the world works and how human systems interact with it. The third theme is **stewardship**—the actions and programs that manage natural resources and human well-being for the common good. These themes will be applied to public policy and individual responsibility throughout the text and will also be explored in brief essays within each chapter. As each chapter of this text develops, the concepts behind these themes will come into play at different points. At the end of each chapter, we will revisit the themes, summarizing their relevance to the chapter topics and often adding our own perspective. We explore each of these themes here, appropriately beginning with sustainability.

Sustainability

A system or process is sustainable if it can be continued indefinitely, without depleting any of the material or energy resources required to keep it running. The term was first applied to the idea of **sustainable yields** in human endeavors such as forestry and fisheries. Trees, fish, and other biological species normally grow and reproduce at rates faster than those required just to keep their populations stable. This built-in capacity allows every species to increase or replace a population following some natural disaster.

It is possible, then, to harvest a certain percentage of trees or fish every year without depleting the forest or reducing the fish population below a certain base number. As long as the number harvested stays within the capacity of the population to grow and replace itself, the practice can be continued indefinitely. The harvest then represents a sustainable yield. It becomes unsustainable only when trees are cut or fish are caught at a rate that exceeds the capacity of their present population to reproduce and grow. The concept of a sustainable yield can also be applied to freshwater supplies, soils, and the ability of natural systems to absorb pollutants without being damaged.

The notion of sustainability can be extended to include ecosystems. Sustainable ecosystems are entire natural systems that persist and thrive over time by recycling nutrients, maintaining a diversity of species, and using the Sun as a source of sustainable energy. As we'll see, ecosystems are enormously successful at being sustainable (Chapters 3, 4, and 5).

Sustainable Societies. Applying the concept of sustainability to human systems, we say that a **sustainable society** is a society in balance with the natural world, continuing generation after generation, neither depleting its resource base by exceeding sustainable yields nor producing pollutants in excess of nature's capacity to absorb them. Many primitive societies were sustainable in this sense for thousands of years.

When the concept of sustainability is applied to modern societies, we generally picture certain desirable, healthy characteristics of the people, their communities, and the ecosystems on which they depend. Many of our interactions with the environment are *not* sustainable, however. This is demonstrated by such global trends as the decline

of biodiversity and essential ecosystems and the increased emissions of greenhouse gases. Although population growth in industrialized countries has almost halted, these countries are using energy and other resources at unsustainable rates, producing pollutants that are accumulating in the atmosphere, water, and land. In contrast, developing countries are experiencing continued population growth, yet are often unable to meet the needs of many of their people in spite of heavy exploitation of natural resources. As our modern societies pursue continued economic growth and consumption, we are apparently locked into an unsustainable mode. How do we resolve this dilemma? One answer is the concept of sustainable development.

Sustainable Development. **Sustainable development** is a term that was first brought into common use by the World Commission on Environment and Development, a group appointed by the United Nations. The commission made sustainable development the theme of its final report, *Our Common Future*, published in 1987. The report defined sustainable development as a form of development or progress that "meets the needs of the present without compromising the ability of future generations to meet their own needs." The concept arose in the context of a debate between the respective *environmental* and *developmental* concerns of groups of developed and developing countries. **Development** refers to the continued improvement of human well-being, usually in the developing countries. Both developed and developing countries have embraced the concept of sustainable development, although the industrialized countries are usually more concerned about environmental sustainability, while the developing countries are more concerned about economic development. The basic idea, however, is to maintain and improve the well-being of both humans and ecosystems.

The concept of sustainable development is now so well entrenched in international circles that it has become almost an article of faith. It sounds comforting, so people want to believe that it is possible, and it appears to incorporate some ideals that are sorely needed, such as **equity**—whereby the needs of the present are actually met and future generations are seen as equally deserving as those living now. Sustainable development means different things to different people, however, as illustrated by the viewpoints of three important disciplines traditionally concerned with the processes involved. Economists are concerned mainly with growth, efficiency, and the optimum use of resources. Sociologists mainly focus on human needs and on concepts like equity, empowerment, social cohesion, and cultural identity. Ecologists show their greatest concern for preserving the integrity of natural systems, for living within the carrying capacity of the environment, and for dealing effectively with pollution. It can be argued, however, that sustainable solutions will be found mainly where the concerns of these three groups intersect, as illustrated in **Figure 1–9**.

There are many dimensions to sustainable development— environmental, social, economic, political—and no societies today have achieved it. Nevertheless, as with justice,

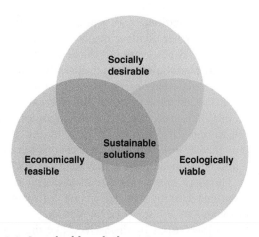

Figure 1–9 Sustainable solutions. If the concerns of sociologists, economists, and ecologists can be brought into intersection, sustainable solutions in a society are much more achievable.

equality, and freedom, it is important to uphold sustainable development as an ideal—a goal toward which all human societies need to be moving, even if we have not achieved it completely anywhere. For example, policies and actions in a society that reduce infant mortality, increase the availability of family planning, improve the air quality, provide abundant and pure water, preserve and protect natural ecosystems, reduce soil erosion, reduce the release of toxic chemicals to the environment, and restore healthy coastal fisheries are all moving that society in the right direction—toward a sustainable future. At the same time, these actions are all quite measurable, so progress in achieving sustainable development can be assessed. Communities and organizations are forging sustainable development indicators and goals to track their progress, such as the Environmental Sustainability Index (produced by Yale University, 1999–2005), which evaluated a society's natural resources and its stewardship of those resources and the people they support.

An Essential Transition. The transition to a truly sustainable civilization is hard to picture at present. It requires achieving a stable human population that recognizes the finite limits of the ability of Earth's systems to produce resources and absorb wastes and that acts accordingly. To achieve sustainability will require a special level of dedication and commitment to care for the natural world and to act with justice and equity toward one another. What will it take to make the transition to a sustainable future? There is broad agreement on the following major points:

- A population transition from a continually increasing human population to one that is stable or even declining.

- A resource transition to an economy that is not dedicated to growth and consumption, but instead relies on nature's income and protects ecosystem capital from depletion.

- A technology transition from pollution-intensive economic production to environmentally friendly processes—in particular, moving from fossil fuel energy to renewable energy sources.

- A political/sociological transition to public policies that embrace a careful and just approach to people's needs and that eliminate large-scale poverty.

- A community transition from the present car-dominated urban sprawl of developed countries to the "smart growth" concepts of smaller, functional settlements and more livable cities.

This is not an exhaustive list, but it does give a glimpse of what a sustainable future might look like. One thing is certain: we cannot continue on our present trajectory and hope that everything will turn out well. The natural world—our life support system—is being degraded, its ecosystem capital eroded. One essential tool for achieving sustainability is sound science.

Sound Science

Some environmental issues are embroiled in controversies so polarized that no middle ground seems possible. On the one side are those who argue using seemingly sound scientific facts and well-found theories. On the other are those who disagree and present opposing explanations of the same facts. Both groups may have motives for arguing their case that are not all apparent to the public. In the face of such controversy, many people are understandably left confused. It is our objective to give first a brief overview of the nature of science and the scientific method so that you can evaluate for yourself the two sides of such controversies and then to show how science forms the foundation for understanding controversial issues.

The Scientific Method. In its essence, science is simply a way of gaining knowledge; that way is called the **scientific method**. The term **science** further refers to all the knowledge gained through that method. We employ the term **sound science** to distinguish legitimate science from what can been called **junk science**, information that is presented as valid science but that does not conform to the rigors of the methods and practice of legitimate science. Sound science involves a disciplined approach to understanding how the natural world works, an approach that has become known as the scientific method.

Assumptions. To begin, the scientific method rests on four basic assumptions that most of us accept without argument. The first assumption is that what we perceive with our basic five senses represents an objective reality; that is, our perceptions are not some kind of mirage or dream. The second assumption is that this "objective reality" functions according to certain basic principles and natural laws that remain consistent through time and space.

The third assumption, which follows directly from the second, is that every result has a cause and every event in turn will cause other events. In other words, we assume that events do not occur without reason and that there is an explainable cause behind every happening. The fourth and final assumption is that, through our powers of observation, manipulation, and reason, we can discover and understand the basic principles and natural laws by which the universe functions.

Although assumptions, by definition, are premises that are simply accepted, the fact is that the assumptions underlying science have served us well and are borne out by everyday experience. For example, we suffer severe consequences if we do not accept our perception of fire as real. Similarly, our experience confirms that gravity is a predictable force acting throughout the universe and that it is not subject to unpredictable change. And the same can be said for any number of other phenomena that we observe. If our car fails to start, we know that there is a logical reason (such as lights left on), and we can get it jump-started.

Thus, whether we are conscious of the fact or not, we all accept the basic assumptions of science in the conduct and understanding of our everyday lives. Scientists and scientific investigations focused on the natural world (the **natural sciences**) extend the boundaries of everyday experience, deepen our understanding of cause-and-effect relationships, and enable us to have a greater appreciation of the principles and natural laws that seem to determine the behavior of all things, from the outcome of a chemical reaction to the functioning of the biosphere.

Observation. The foundation of all science and scientific discovery is **observation**. Indeed, many branches of science, such as natural history (the study of where and how various plants and animals live, mate, reproduce, etc.), astronomy, anthropology, and paleontology, are based almost entirely on observation because experimentation is either inappropriate or impossible. For example, it simply is impossible to conduct experiments on stars or past events. **Figure 1–10** shows how observations alone can lead to answers or explanations of some natural phenomena.

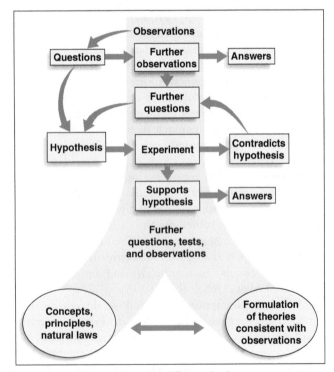

Figure 1–10 Steps of the scientific method. The process leading to the formation of theories and the postulation of natural laws and concepts is a continual interplay among observations, hypotheses, tests (experiments), explanations or theories, and further refinement.

Even experimentation, as we will discuss shortly, is conducted to gain another window of observation. Simply put, in all science, careful observation is the keystone. So how can we be sure that observations are accurate? Well, as a matter of fact, not every reported observation is accurate, for reasons ranging from honest misperceptions or instrument error to calculated mischief. Therefore, an important aspect of science, and a trait of scientists, is to be *skeptical* of any new report until it is *confirmed* or verified. As observations are confirmed by more and more investigators, they gain the status of factual data. Things or events that do not allow such confirmation—a reported visit by Martian aliens, for example—are very questionable from a scientific standpoint.

Various observations by themselves, like the pieces of a puzzle, are often put together into a larger picture—a **model** of how a system works. To give a simple example, we observe that water evaporates and leads to moist air and that water from moist air condenses on a cool surface. We also observe clouds and precipitation. Putting these observations together logically, we derive the concept of the hydrologic cycle, described later (Chapter 10). Water evaporates and then condenses as air is cooled, condensation forms clouds, and precipitation follows. Water thus makes a cycle from the surface of Earth into the atmosphere and back to Earth (Fig. 10–3). Note how this simple example incorporates the four assumptions described previously: there is an objective reality, it operates according to principles, every result has a cause, and we can discover the principles according to which reality operates. Note also how the example broadens our everyday experiences of the evaporation of water and the falling of rain into an understanding of a cycle involving both.

So, the essence of science and the scientific method may be seen as a process of making observations and logically integrating those observations into a model of how some natural system works. To be sure, many areas of science get more complex and difficult to comprehend. Still, the basic process—constructing a logically coherent picture of causes and effects from basic observations—is the same.

Where, then, does experimentation, that additional hallmark of science, fit in?

Experimentation. **Experimentation** is simply setting up situations to make more systematic observations regarding causes and effects. For example, the number of chemical reactions one can readily observe in nature is limited. However, in the laboratory it is possible to purify elements or compounds, mix them together in desired combinations and proportions, and carefully observe and measure how they react (or fail to react). From the way chemicals react, chemists have constructed a coherent cause-and-effect picture, the **atomic theory**, and they have determined the attributes of each element. Similarly, biologists put organisms into specific situations in which they can carefully observe and measure their responses to particular conditions or treatments (Fig. 1–11). To solve a particular problem (e.g., What is the cause of *this* event?), a more or less systematic line of experimentation is used. This is where the sequence consisting of observation, hypothesis, test (experiment), and explanation comes in.

Figure 1–11 Experiment demonstrating the importance of mycorrhizae. Mycorrhizae is a root–fungus symbiosis that greatly enhances the ability of a plant to absorb nutrients. The pine seedlings shown were grown under identical conditions, except that the seedling on the left was grown with mycorrhizal fungi and the one on the right was grown without the fungi.

Hypotheses. Let's consider the problem of the death of oyster larvae at the Whiskey Creek hatchery (see Sound Science, p. 8). What was killing the oyster larvae in the incubation tanks? The first step in solving the problem was to make educated guesses as to the cause. Each such educated guess is a **hypothesis**. Each hypothesis is then tested by making further field observations or conducting experiments to determine whether or not the hypothesis really accounts for the observed effect. The owners found high numbers of pathogenic bacteria in the tanks (hypothesis: the bacteria were killing the larvae). They installed a new filtration system that removed bacteria before they could multiply, essentially an experiment. The larvae still died. They rejected that hypothesis. Then a crucial observation was made about the timing of the bay water brought into the tanks, water that had come from recently upwelled coastal surface water. This water had higher acidity (lower pH) than usual (hypothesis: acid waters were killing the larvae by dissolving their shells). By monitoring the pH of incoming water, the owners were able to avoid the acid waters and time water withdrawals to daytime hours when the pH was higher. The results were dramatic: the larvae were able to thrive and grow. The hypothesis was confirmed, and the larval death was satisfactorily explained. The experimental results brought what started out as a hypothesis to the status of a satisfactory explanation. Figure 1–10 shows how such a process moves from observations to hypotheses, experiments, and a satisfactory answer.

Theories. We have already noted how various specific observations (e.g., evaporation, precipitation) may fit together to give a logically coherent conceptual framework (e.g., the hydrologic cycle). At first, the conceptual framework is termed a hypothesis because it is really a tentative explanation as to how various observations are related. It becomes a **theory** only after much testing and confirmation showing that it is logically consistent with all observations (Fig. 1–10).

Through logical reasoning, theories will generally suggest or predict certain events. If an event predicted by a theory is indeed observed, the observation provides evidence for the truth of the theory. Predictions require experiments, testing, further data gathering, and more observation. When theories reach a state of providing a logically consistent framework for all relevant observations and when they can be used to reliably predict outcomes, they deserve to be accepted. For example, we have never seen atoms directly (or, until recently, even indirectly), but innumerable observations and experiments are coherently explainable by the theory that all gases, liquids, and solids consist of various combinations of slightly over a hundred kinds of atoms. Hence, we fully accept the atomic theory of matter.

Science has successfully brought us a high degree of understanding of the natural world and has also brought a host of technologies based on that understanding. Doesn't this success mean that our theories about how the world works must be true? A philosopher of science would answer, "No, not necessarily." The best we can do is to establish a theory beyond a reasonable doubt. Theories are always less than absolutely certain, because we can never know whether some other theory exists that will do a better job of explaining the data. Generally speaking, our confidence in scientific explanations should be proportional to the evidence supporting them.

Natural Laws and Concepts. Like a theory, the second assumption underlying science—that the universe functions according to certain basic principles and natural laws that remain consistent through time and space—cannot be established with absolute certainty. Still, every observation and test that scientists have performed up to the present have borne it out. All our observations, whether direct or through experimentation, demonstrate that matter and energy behave neither randomly nor even inconsistently, but in precise and predictable ways. We refer to these principles by which we can define and precisely predict the behavior of matter and energy as **natural laws.** Examples are the *Law of Gravity*, the *Law of Conservation of Matter*, and the various *Laws of Thermodynamics*. Our technological success in space exploration and many other fields is in no small part due to our recognition of these principles and our precise calculations based on them. Conversely, trying to make something work in a manner contrary to a natural law invariably results in failure.

In many situations, the outcome of scientific work results in well-established explanations that must be expressed in the mathematical language of probability and statistics. This is especially true of biological phenomena such as predator–prey relationships and the effects of pesticides. Accordingly, here it is appropriate to speak of concepts rather than laws. **Concepts** are perfectly valid explanations of data gathered from the natural world, and they can also be predictive, but they don't reach the status of laws. They model the way we believe the natural world works and enable us to make qualified predictions of future outcomes. Thus, we might say that, on the basis of our understanding of the effects of DDT (a potent pesticide) on mosquitoes and on the basis of our observation that mosquitoes can, and do, develop resistance to DDT, continued spraying of the local salt marshes with DDT to eradicate unwelcome mosquitoes is likely to result in the development of a more resistant mosquito population in the future, an unwelcome outcome. Here the concept of pest resistance may be used to modify public policy. In general, explanations in biology do not lead to the development of statements with such high predictability that we are justified in calling them laws.

The Role of Instruments in Science. Complex instrumentation is another hallmark of science, one that often gives it an aura of mystery. Yet, regardless of complexity, all scientific **instruments** perform one of three basic functions. First, they may extend our powers of observation, as do telescopes, microscopes, X-ray machines, and CAT scans, for example. Second, instruments are used to quantify observations—that is, they enable us to measure exact quantities. For example, we may feel cold, but a thermometer enables us to measure and quantify exactly how cold it is. Comparisons, communication, and verification of different observations and events would be impossible if it were not for such measurement and quantification. Third, instruments such as growth chambers and robots help us achieve conditions and perform manipulations required to make certain observations or perform certain experiments.

All instruments used in science need to be subjected to testing and verification to be sure that they are giving as accurate a representation of reality as we can attain with their use. The need for this can be seen in the case of instruments measuring ocean temperatures (see Sound Science "Getting It Right," in Chapter 18). Failure to calibrate the instruments properly led to a serious underestimation of ocean temperature changes. It is safe to say that modern scientific instruments have made possible many important discoveries that were out of reach of the human senses.

The Scientific Community. It is important to understand that science and its outcomes take place in the context of a scientific community and a larger society. There is no single authoritative source that makes judgments on the validity of scientific explanations. Instead, it is the collective body of scientists working in a given field who, because of their competence and experience, establish what is sound science and what is not. They do so by communicating their findings to each other and to the public as they publish their work in peer-reviewed journals. The process of peer review is crucial; it requires experts in a given field to analyze the results of their colleagues' work. Careful scrutiny is given to research publications, with the objective of rooting out poor or sloppy science and affirming work that is clearly meritorious.

Controversies. Even with these checks and balances that work to establish scientific knowledge and with all the procedures of the scientific method, controversies arise that pit one group against another, with both groups claiming that they have science on their side. For example, we will make the claim that the global climate is changing because of human activities (Chapter 18). A few scientists disagree with this claim, although for most the evidence is convincing. There are at least four reasons why such controversies occur.

1. **New information.** We are continually confronted by new observations—the hole in the ozone layer, for instance (see Chapter 19). It takes some time before all the hypotheses regarding the cause of what we have observed can be adequately tested. During this time, there may be honest disagreement as to which hypothesis is most likely. Such controversies are gradually settled by further observations and testing, but the process leads into the second reason for continuing controversy.

2. **Complex phenomena.** Certain phenomena, such as the hole in the ozone layer, do not lend themselves to simple tests or experiments. Therefore, it is difficult and time consuming to confirm the causative role of one factor or to rule out the involvement of another. Gradually, different lines of evidence come together to support one hypothesis and exclude another, enabling the issue to be resolved. When is there enough evidence to say unequivocally that one hypothesis is right and another wrong? At some point, the scientists working in the appropriate field will reach a consensus in making that judgment.

3. **Multiple perspectives.** The third reason for controversy is that multiple perspectives may be involved. This is particularly true in environmental science because many issues have social, economic, or political ramifications. For example, there is no controversy regarding nuclear power, as long as it is considered at the purely scientific level of physics. However, when it comes to deciding whether to promote the further use of nuclear energy to generate electrical power, controversy arises because different groups have different perspectives about the relative costs, risks, and benefits involved.

4. **Bias.** The fourth reason for controversy is that there are many vested interests that wish to maintain and promote disagreement because they stand to profit by doing so. For example, tobacco interests argued for years that the connection between smoking and illness had not been established and that more studies were necessary. By harping on the absence of absolute proof (a scientific impossibility anyway) and downplaying the overwhelming body of evidence supporting the connection between smoking and illness, the tobacco lobby succeeded in keeping the issue controversial and thereby delayed regulatory restrictions on smoking. In fact, some businesses hire "product-defense firms," whose strategy is to do everything possible to challenge scientific evidence damaging to their products or interests.

Some controversy is the inevitable outcome of the scientific process itself, but much of it is attributable to less-noble causes. Unfortunately, the media and the public may be unaware of the true nature of the information and will often give equal credibility to opposing views on an issue. This can be seen, for example, in the media's coverage of global climate change, where the opinions of a few industry-sponsored deniers are often given equal coverage with the overwhelming scientific consensus. This leads us to the topic of junk science.

Junk Science. Junk science traditionally refers to information that is presented as scientifically valid but that does not conform to the rigors imposed by the scientific community. In recent years, another use of this term has appeared that has created some confusion. In some cases, people with a bias have used *junk science* to refer to anything that threatens their preferred viewpoint; conversely, *sound science* becomes anything that supports their viewpoint. One example of this is the use of the term "junk science" by people who do not support the Endangered Species Act. They label as "junk science" the legitimate use of computer models to make predictions about the survival of endangered species. This limits scientific input to a much smaller number of studies and could mean we make decisions without the full range of information we might have.

In contrast, true junk science can take many forms: the presentation of selective results (picking and choosing only those results that agree with one's preconceived ideas), politically motivated distortions of scientifically sound information, and the publication of poor work in quasi-scientific (unreviewed) journals and books. Quite often, junk science is generated by special interest groups trying to influence the public debate about science-related concerns. The result is that the junk science may be given equal respectability with the sound science in the public arena. Information presented by the Tobacco Institute, for example, is clearly suspect, due to its corporate-related funding. In particular, junk science has been heavily employed in the debate surrounding climate change and what to do about it in the United States.

Evaluating Issues. Whether scientist or layperson, we can use facets of the scientific method to deal with controversies and to develop our own capacity for logical reasoning. Here are some basic questions to ask:

- What are the data underlying a particular claim? Can they be satisfactorily confirmed?

- Do the explanations and theories follow logically from the data?

- Are there reasons that a particular explanation is favored? Who profits from having that explanation accepted broadly?

- Is the conclusion supported by the community of scientists with the greatest competence to judge the work? If not, it is highly suspect.

In sum, sound science is absolutely essential to forging a sustainable relationship with the natural world. Our planet is dominated by human beings—our activities have reached such an intensity and such a scale that we are now one of the major forces affecting nature. Our influence on the natural ecosystems that support most of the world economy and process our waste is strong and widespread, and we need to know how to manage the planet so as to maintain a sustainable relationship with it. As a result, the information gathered by scientists needs to be accurate, credible, and communicated clearly to policy makers and the public, and the policy makers need to handle that information responsibly (the interaction between science and politics is explored in Chapter 2).

Stewardship

The third of our themes is **stewardship**—the actions and programs that manage natural resources and human well-being for the common good. Stewardship is a concept that can be traced back to ancient civilizations. A steward was put in charge of his master's household, responsible for maintaining the welfare of the people and the property of the owner. Because a steward did not own the property himself, the steward's ethic involved caring for something on behalf of someone else.

Applying this concept to the world today, stewards are those who care for something—from the natural world or from human culture—that they do not own and that they will pass on to the next generation. Modern-day environmental stewardship, therefore, incorporates an ethic that guides actions taken to benefit the natural world and other people. It recognizes that even our ownership of land is temporary; the land will be there after we die, and others will own it in turn. Stewardship is compatible with the goal of sustainability, but it is different from it, too, because stewardship deals more directly with how sustainability is to be achieved—what actions are taken, and what values and ethical considerations are behind those actions. (See Stewardship, "Exploring a Stewardship Ethic." p. 19.)

Who Are the Stewards? How is stewardship achieved? Sometimes stewardship leads people to try to stop the destruction of the environment or to stop the pollution that is degrading human neighborhoods and health. For example, Rachel Carson (from our opening story) was a steward who alerted the public about the dangers of pesticides and their role in decimating bird populations. Francisco Pineda (Fig. 1–12, on the next page) is a farmer in El Salvador who organized rural communities to protest the damages to local irrigation streams by Canadian mining giant Pacific Rim. Their challenges led the Salvadoran government to stop the mining by Pacific Rim, and Pineda received the 2011 Goldman Environmental Prize. Stewardship is not without risks, however: Pineda is under 24-hour police protection because three of his colleagues have been murdered by supporters of the mining project. The late Wangari Maathai (the first Kenyan woman to earn a Ph.D.) founded the Green Belt Movement to help rural Kenyan women. The grassroots movement eventually

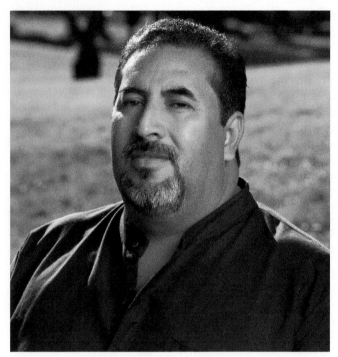

Figure 1–12 Goldman Prize winner, 2011. At the risk of his life, Francisco Pineda organized opposition to a damaging mining operation by the Canadian mining company Pacific Rim. "My work is as an environmentalist; this is the principle for my life. When I began to understand the impact of the mining exploration, I couldn't stay quiet."

(*Source:* Goldman Environmental Prize).

Figure 1–13 Stewardship at work. Wangari Maathai receiving the 2004 Nobel Peace Prize from Ole Danbolt Mjøs, chairman of the Norwegian Nobel Committee. She is an example of unusual environmental stewardship at work.

involved more than 6,000 groups of women, who planted 47 million trees in Kenya. Maathai was beaten and jailed when she went on to protest government corruption. Eventually, she was appointed deputy environment minister under a new Kenyan president and received the Nobel Peace Prize in 2004 (Fig. 1–13)—the first environmental activist to receive that honor.

More often, stewardship is a matter of everyday people caring enough for each other and for the natural world that they do the things that are compatible with that care. These include participating fully in recycling efforts, purchasing cars that pollute less and use less energy, turning off the lights in an empty room, refusing to engage in the conspicuous consumption constantly being urged on them by commercial advertising, supporting organizations that promote sustainable practices, staying informed on environmentally sensitive issues, and expressing their citizenship by voting for candidates who are sympathetic to environmental concerns and the need for sustainable development.

Justice and Equity. The stewardship ethic is concerned not only with caring for the natural world, but also with establishing just relationships among humans. This concern for justice is seen in the United States in the *environmental justice movement*. The major problem addressed by the movement is **environmental racism**—the placement of waste sites and other hazardous industries in towns and neighborhoods where most of the residents are nonwhite.

The flip side of this problem is seen when wealthier, more politically active, and often predominantly white communities receive a disproportionately greater share of facility improvements, such as new roads, public buildings, and water and sewer projects.

People of color are seizing the initiative to correct these wrongs, creating citizen groups and watchdog agencies to bring effective action and to monitor progress. For example, Chattanooga's Southside community is populated largely by African Americans. This part of Chattanooga was bypassed when the city underwent a huge renewal that changed its reputation from being the dirtiest city in America to the "Renaissance City of the South" (see Chapter 23). Formed in 2010 by Southside community members, Chattanooga Organized for Action (COA) has quickly become a voice for social justice. In 2011, COA organized the restoration of funding for family planning programs for low-income and minority women and forced a more thorough cleanup of a former chemical plant site in Southside owned by Velsicol Chemical Corporation, among other actions.

Justice is especially crucial for the developing world, where unjust relationships often leave people without land, with inadequate food, and in poor health. Extreme poverty is the condition of more than a billion people; this poverty is often brought on by injustices within societies where wealthy elites maintain political power and, through corruption and nepotism, steal money and give corporations preferential treatment. It takes significant government reform to turn this situation around so that the poor can achieve justice in securing property rights and gain greater access to ecosystem goods and services.

Some of the poverty of the developing countries can be attributed to unjust economic practices of the wealthy

STEWARDSHIP

One of the major concerns of philosophers is the development of codes of practice and thought that define right and wrong, known as ethics. Ethics is about the good—those values and virtues we should encourage—and about the right—our moral duties as we face practical problems. Ethics, therefore, is a "normative" discipline—it tells us what we ought to do. Some things are right, and some things are wrong. How do we know what we ought to do? In other words, how does an ethic work? A fully developed ethic has four ingredients:

1. **Cases.** These refer to specific acts and ask whether a particular act is morally justified. The answer must be based on moral rules.

2. **Moral rules.** These are general guidelines that can be applied to various areas of concern, such as the rules that govern how we should treat endangered species.

3. **Moral principles.** Moral rules are based on more-general principles, which are the broadest ethical concepts. They are considered to be valid in all cases. An example is the principle of distributive justice, which states that all persons should be treated equitably.

4. **Bases.** Ethical principles are justified by reference to some philosophical or theological basis. This is the foundation for an ethical system.

A stewardship ethic is concerned with right and wrong as they apply to actions taken to care for the natural world and the people in it. Because a steward is someone who cares for the natural world on behalf of others, we might ask, "To whom is the steward responsible?" Many would answer, "The steward is responsible to present and future generations of people who depend on the natural world as their life-support system." For people with religious convictions, stewardship stems from a belief that the world and everything in it belongs to a higher being; they may be stewards on behalf of a higher power. For others, stewardship becomes a matter of concern that stems from a deep understanding and love of the natural world and the necessary limitations on our use of that world.

Is there a well-established stewardship ethic? Insofar as human interests are concerned, ethical principles and rules are fairly well established, even if they are often violated by public and private acts. However, there is no firmly established ethic that deals with care for natural lands and creatures for their own sake. Most of our ethic concerning natural things really deals with how those things serve human purposes; that is, our current ethic is highly anthropocentric. For example, a basic ethical principle from the UN Declaration on Human Rights and the Environment is "All persons have the right to a secure, healthy, and ecologically sound environment." Here, the point of the healthy environment is for humanity. There are several underlying reasons for a stewardship ethic, some stronger than others. Ethics for protection of other species will be covered later (Chapter 6).

Many organizations have developed stewardship principles for their own guidance, and these principles can sometimes serve as broader guidelines for society, although they usually address specific areas of concern and are often anthropocentric. One excellent group is the Forest Service Employees for Environmental Ethics (www.fseee.org), with a mission of protecting national forests and bringing reform to the U.S. Forest Service by advocating environmental ethics. The group is active in halting unauthorized logging and protecting Forest Service employees from unjust disciplinary actions, as well as lobbying in Congress to maintain stewardship of the National Forests.

Here are some of the issues that a stewardship ethic must grapple with in order to be truly helpful in accomplishing our stated goal of providing the "actions and programs that manage natural resources and human well-being for the common good":

1. How to define the common good in cases where conflicting needs emerge, such as the economic need to extract resources from natural systems versus the need to maintain those systems in a healthy state.

2. How to balance the needs of present generations against those of future generations.

3. How to preserve species when doing so clearly means limiting some of the property rights commonly enjoyed by people and organizations.

4. How to encourage people and governments to exercise compassion and care for others who suffer profoundly from a lack of access to the basic human needs of food, shelter, health, and gainful work.

5. How to promote virtues that are conducive to stewardship of the natural world, such as benevolence, accountability, frugality, and responsibility. (There are many others.)

6. How to limit excessive consumption while at the same time allowing people the freedom to choose their lifestyles. In other words, how do you balance individual environmental rights and responsibilities with those of the broader community?

industrialized countries. The current pattern of international trade is a prime example. The industrialized countries have maintained inequities that discriminate against the developing countries by taxing and restricting imports from the developing countries and by flooding the world markets with agricultural products that are subsidized (and, therefore, priced below real cost). This is the number one issue at every meeting of the World Trade Organization, where global trade agreements are negotiated (see Chapter 2). Such barriers deprive people in developing countries of jobs and money that would go far to improve their living conditions. Although international justice is a thorny issue, it is part of the mission of stewardship to address it.

1.4 Moving Toward a Sustainable Future

Without doubt, one of the dominant trends of our times is globalization—the accelerating interconnectedness of human activities, ideas, and cultures. For centuries, global connections have brought people together through migration, trade, and the exchange of ideas. What is new about the current scene is the increasing intensity, speed, extent, and impact of connectedness, to the point where its consequences are profoundly changing many human enterprises. These changes are most evident in the globalization of economies, cultural patterns, political arrangements, environmental resources, and pollution. For many in the world, globalization has brought undeniable improvements in well-being and health: as economic exchanges have connected people to global markets, information exchanges have improved public health practices, and agricultural research has improved crop yields. For others, however, globalization has brought the dilution and even destruction of cultural and religious ideals and norms and has done little to improve economic well-being. Whether helpful or harmful, globalization is taking place, and it is important not only to recognize its impacts, but also to point out where its impacts are harmful or undesirable. Moving toward a sustainable future will occur in the context of globalization.

Social Changes

The major elements of globalization may be the economic reorganization of the world and changes wrought by social media. These transformations have been facilitated by the globalization of communication, whereby people are instantly linked through the Internet, satellite, and cable. Social media play a role not only in the economy, but also in the rapid mobilization of people during times of change such as the 2011 riots in Egypt, Greece, and Libya. Other components of the global economic reorganization are the relative ease of transportation and financial transactions and the dominance of transnational corporations (e.g., Nokia, Roche, Philips Electronics, Nestlé) with unprecedented wealth and power. Moreover, economic changes bring cultural, environmental, and technological changes (to name a few) in their wake. Western diet, styles, and culture are marketed throughout the world, to the detriment of local customs and diversity.

Environmental Changes

On the one hand, the increased dissemination of information has made it possible for environmental organizations and government agencies to connect with the public and has enabled people to become politically involved with current issues. It has also enabled consumers to find more environmentally friendly consumer goods and services, such as shade-grown coffee and sustainably harvested timber. On the other hand, globalization has contributed to some notoriously harmful outcomes, such as the worldwide spread of emerging diseases like the SARS virus, H1N1 swine influenza, and AIDS; the global dispersion of exotic species; the trade in hazardous wastes; the spread of persistent organic pollutants; the radioactive fallout from nuclear accidents; the exploitation of oceanic fisheries; the destruction of the ozone layer; and global climate change. These outcomes must be addressed in the move toward a sustainable future.

A New Commitment

People in all walks of life—scientists, sociologists, workers and executives, economists, government leaders, and clergy, as well as traditional environmentalists—are recognizing

that "business as usual" is not sustainable. Many global trends are on a collision course with the fundamental systems that maintain our planet as a tolerable place to live. A finite planet cannot continue to grow by 80 million persons annually without significant detrimental effects. The current degradation of ecosystems, atmospheric changes, losses of species, and depletion of water resources inevitably lead to a point where resources are no longer adequate to support the human population without significant changes in the way we live.

The news is not all bad, however. Food production has improved the nutrition of millions in the developing world, life expectancy continues to rise, and the percentage of individuals who are desperately poor continues to decline. Population growth rates continue to fall in many countries. A rising tide of environmental awareness in the industrialized countries has led to the establishment of policies, laws, and treaties that have improved environmental protection. Professional groups such as ecologists, climatologists, and engineers are proposing scientific and technological solutions to environmental problems.

Numerous caring people are beginning to play an important role in changing society's treatment of Earth. For example, in January 2011, a group of 70 engineers produced a report proposing engineering development goals[9] and stated, ". . . the engineers of today, and the future, will need to be innovative in the application of sustainable solutions and increasingly engaged with the human factors that influence their decisions." Likewise, people in business have formed the Business Council for Sustainable Development, economists have formed the International Society for Ecological Economics, religious leaders have formed the National Religious Partnership for the Environment, and environmental philosophers are calling for a new ethic of "caring for creation."

The movement toward sustainability is growing as people, businesses, and governments slowly but surely begin to change direction. Some examples: wind energy is the fastest-growing source of electricity; cap-and-trade markets are being established to curb carbon emissions; car-sharing companies are springing up in our cities; chemists have embraced the initiatives of "green chemistry"; microfinance is opening up people's small-scale business opportunities; "green investments" are attracting increasing capital; and the nations of the world are working on agreements to bring down greenhouse gas emissions. These developments show that people's behavior toward the environment *can* be transformed from exploitative to conserving.

---

[9]Institution of Mechanical Engineers, Population: One Planet, Too Many People? 2011. http://www.imeche.org/Libraries/2011_Press_Releases/Population_report.sflb.ashx. September 21, 2011.

REVISITING THE THEMES

It will be our practice in each chapter to revisit the three themes that we have introduced in this chapter, summarizing the ways in which the chapter topics have connected to the themes and sometimes adding editorial comments.

Sustainability

The story of DDT and other chemicals widely broadcast over vast areas of land only to be revealed later as serious water and soil pollutants is a great example of unsustainable actions. Many unsustainable practices result from a combination of cumulative impacts and unintended consequences. For example, we did not expect that DDT would affect the food chain. At first, DDT seemed a wise way to protect food supplies and eliminate malaria. As we gathered more information, we discovered the unintended consequences of those actions. Likewise, as the human population expands, the effects of individuals are multiplied. Both natural and managed ecosystems are being pressed to provide increasing goods and services. We may have reached the limit in some resources, and most of the ways we use the other resources are currently unsustainable. In addition, we extract and burn fossil fuels much faster than they could ever be replenished, bringing on global climate change, and we tolerate the continued loss of biodiversity. Many suffer from hunger and other effects of poverty. The Millennium Development Goals are moving us in a better direction, but it remains to be seen if those goals will be met. A movement toward sustainability is under way, and it will occur within the context of globalization.

Sound Science

Our brief look at the global environment was based largely on the information uncovered by sound science. The Millennium Ecosystem Assessment and the Intergovernmental Panel on Climate Change demonstrate the crucial value of scientific study of the status of and trends in global ecosystems and the ways in which human systems affect them. Environmental science itself is a multidisciplinary enterprise, one that can readily lead to disputes and misuse. To understand these, it is essential to understand the scientific method as a disciplined way to investigate the natural world. Rachel Carson is a good example of a scientist who communicated sound science to popular audiences. The issue of "junk science" points to the importance of a functioning scientific community and the need for an educated public able to evaluate opposing claims of scientific support for a given issue.

Stewardship

Although current cultures and religions place some value on stewardship, it is not always a fundamental part of the way we think about caring for the natural world and for our fellow humans. If it were, there would not be the widespread degradation of essential ecosystems and the devastating impacts of poverty and injustice. However, many people work toward care for the natural world and its human inhabitants. Rachel Carson is an example of a person using her expertise to promote stewardship and advocating for policies that would better reflect sustainability. Francisco Pineda and Wangari Maathai also exemplify stewardship in this chapter. As we will see throughout the book, it is no easy matter to establish a valid stewardship ethic to guide the actions and programs that manage natural resources and human well-being for the common good.

REVIEW QUESTIONS

1. What information made Rachel Carson concerned about chemical pollution?

2. What is the paradox of human population and well-being?

3. Cite four global trends that indicate that the health of planet Earth is suffering.

4. Define *environment*, and describe the general development and successes of modern environmentalism.

5. What are the concepts behind each of the three unifying themes—sound science, sustainability, and stewardship?

6. Explain the role of assumptions, observation, experimentation, and theory formation in the operation of scientific research and thinking.

7. Cite some reasons for the existence of controversies within science, and carefully distinguish between sound science and junk science.

8. Define *sustainability* and *sustainable development*. What is a sustainable society?

9. List five transitions that are necessary for a future sustainable civilization.

10. Describe the origins of stewardship and its modern applications.

11. What is an ethic, and what are some of the difficult questions confronting the stewardship ethic?

12. What are the concerns of the environmental justice movement?

13. How does justice become an issue between the industrialized countries and the developing countries?

14. What is globalization? What are its most significant elements?

15. Cite some of the recent developments in the movement toward sustainability.

THINKING ENVIRONMENTALLY

1. Imagine a class debate between people representing the developing countries and people representing the developed countries. Characterize the arguments of the two sides in terms of the issues surrounding population growth, energy use, resource use, and sustainable development. Then describe what should be the common interests between the two.

2. Some people say that the concept of sustainable development either is an oxymoron or represents going back to some kind of primitive living. Develop an argument contradicting this opinion, and give your own opinion on sustainable development.

3. Study Table 1–1, pick one of the vital ecosystem services listed there, and investigate the reasons why it is placed where it is by the Millennium Ecosystem Assessment.

4. Set up a debate between proponents and opponents of building a new coal-fired power plant. Use the strategies of sound science and junk science to conduct the debate, and show how a perverted use of these terms can help to obscure the real issues. Other interesting debate options include the "ozone hoax" and global warming; the Internet can provide ample material for both sides of the debate.

MAKING A DIFFERENCE

1. Find out whether there is an environmental organization or club on your campus or in your community. Join it if there is, or help to create one if there isn't. Once in the organization, join efforts to maintain awareness of important environmental issues and problems.

2. Use letters to the local newspapers or visits to town meetings to raise awareness in your community about sustainable systems and sustainable societies. Examples of issues to raise include smart growth; cluster zoning, which provides a healthy mix of open space and buildings; recycling; and ways to encourage public transit systems.

3. Encourage sound science on a national level by researching and voting in favor of political candidates who support your environmental viewpoint. Share your views with your friends and relatives.

4. Investigate the placement of waste-treatment facilities and industrial plants in your city or community, especially if they are in the planning stage. If they are aimed at poorer or largely nonwhite communities, join the local population in protesting these situations.

MasteringEnvironmentalScience®

Go to **www.masteringenvironmentalscience.com** for practice quizzes, Pearson eText, videos, current events, and more.

PART TWO

Ecology:
The Science of Organisms and Their Environment

E VEN IF YOU'VE never stepped foot in one, you probably know that tropical rain forests are humid, warm, dense, and full of unusual plants and animals. You might not know, however, that they are home to a greater diversity of living things than anywhere else on Earth; that they are the result of millions of years of adaptive evolution; and that they store more carbon than is in the entire atmosphere. Nor can you see with your eyes how energy flows through these forests or how nitrogen and phosphorus are cycled and recycled. This knowledge comes from the work of many scientists who have been asking basic questions about how such natural systems function, how they came to be, and how they relate to the rest of the world.

HOW IMPORTANT IS the knowledge that comes from these scientists? In this second part of the text, we'll see that information about how the natural world works is absolutely crucial to understanding how to manage and protect it. In Part 2, we will look at the science underlying how living things survive in the world and how matter and energy move throughout systems. We will use a hierarchical approach: we will start small and move large—from the molecules necessary for life and the solar energy that sustains it to how plants return to a habitat after a fire and why large regions of the world have different vegetation (such as forests, desert, and grassland). Understanding environmental science begins with an understanding of how living organisms are structured, survive, relate to their environment (and each other), and change over time.

CHAPTER 3

Basic Needs of Living Things

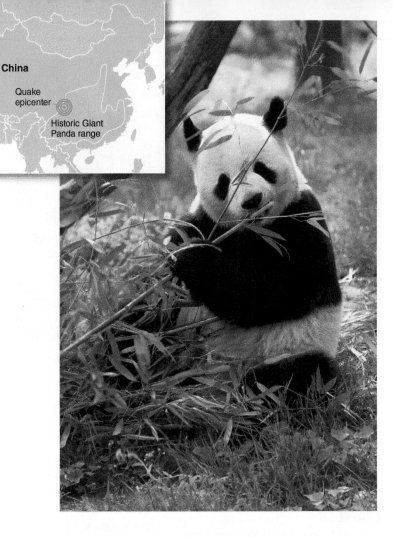

China
Quake epicenter
Historic Giant Panda range

LEARNING OBJECTIVES

1. **Organisms in Their Environment: Explain how the science of ecology can be described as a hierarchy of questions; describe the questions different types of ecologists ask, and anticipate different experiments they might do, all within the same natural systems.**

2. **Environmental Factors: Explain how organisms need specific conditions and resources to survive; define an organism's niche.**

3. **Matter in Living and Nonliving Systems: Explain how living things need materials to build tissues and energy to carry out life processes such as photosynthesis and cellular respiration.**

4. **Matter and Energy: List the simple laws that control the transformation of energy from one type to another and its flow through Earth's systems and back into space.**

5. **The Cycling of Matter in Ecosystems: Explain the biogeochemical cycles of matter (particularly the elements of carbon, phosphorus, nitrogen, and sulfur) as they cycle through living and nonliving spheres.**

O N May 12, 2008, a massive earthquake shook Sichuan Province, China. It closed roads, caused buildings to collapse, and triggered mudslides. The earthquake and an estimated 11,600 aftershocks over the next several weeks left more than 88,000 dead or missing and up to 5 million people homeless.

The earthquake also damaged two reserves for China's giant pandas: the Wolong Giant Panda Reserve Center in southwest Sichuan Province and the nearby Chengdu Panda Breeding and Research Center. Enclosures were destroyed, pandas were frightened and escaped, and food was difficult to obtain. Although most of the pandas were unharmed in the earthquake, one was missing, and an adult female named Maomao was killed. In the face of this bad news, two weeks after the earthquake, to the relief of keepers and the great rejoicing of panda conservationists, a pregnant female gave birth. Eventually, the pandas in the earthquake area had to be moved to other facilities.

A SAD DAY. China's sorrow and concern for the pandas made international news. Maomao's funeral was covered on the Internet and television. Why so much concern about pandas in a disaster that harmed so many humans? The giant panda is a cultural icon of China, beloved and found in books and stories. Sadly, it is endangered, with only about 1,600 pandas still alive in the wild, many in small reserves, and another approximately 270 in captivity. Despite their endangered species status, giant pandas remain under pressure from habitat loss and poaching. To many Chinese citizens, the loss of a giant panda and the fear that they might be even closer to extinction after the earthquake were sorrows added to the tremendous loss of human life. The survival of most of the protected pandas brought joy in a time of despair.

PANDA SURVIVAL. The giant panda lives on bamboo, found in broad-leaved forests in a decreasing habitat in China. Care for the declining panda population involves not only care for their individual health and the interbreeding population, but also protection of their habitat, including their food source. Often populations decline because damage is done to a habitat or food resource rather than to individuals directly. The panda and its food, bamboo, give us an opportunity to look at the fundamental science behind the survival of organisms in their natural spaces.

In this chapter, we will follow the panda and the bamboo as examples of organisms living in their environment. All organisms get nutrients and energy from the environment and use them to build their body tissues and carry out activities such as moving, getting food, protecting themselves, reproducing, and getting rid of wastes. Pandas and bamboo both need ways to deal with the conditions under which they live—the amount of light, food, and water available, for example. We will see how the basic functions of organisms fit into the scientific discipline of ecology. We will explore basic physical rules about matter and energy and how they control the lives of organisms in their environments. To do this, we will need to understand some basic chemistry and physics. At the chapter's end, we will look at the global movements of important nutrients and how those huge cycles both affect individual organisms and are affected by human activities.

3.1 Organisms in Their Environment

Bamboo is a group of about 1,000 related types in the grass family, but unlike most grasses you may be familiar with, bamboos are woody and evergreen. As a group, bamboo is the fastest-growing plant on Earth. The areas in which bamboo is found are a function of several factors—its habitat requirements, its evolutionary history (where it first developed), and its interactions with other organisms, including humans. Bamboo needs certain resources (such as sunlight and water) to survive. A panda also needs certain resources to survive, including bamboo (as a food source). The distribution and abundance of the giant panda are likewise functions of its requirements for survival, its growth, and the history of interaction between pandas and other species, especially humans. To understand why giant pandas are in decline and what conditions bamboo requires for growth, we turn to the science of ecology.

The Hierarchy of Ecology

Ecology (from *Oikos*, meaning "house or home") is *the study of all processes influencing the distribution and abundance of organisms and the interactions between living things and their environment.* A very basic understanding of ecological terms and concepts will help later as we look at how changes in the environment affect living things.

Ecologists studying the conservation of giant pandas ask an array of different questions. They investigate what type of soil bamboo requires to grow most rapidly or look for the factors that influence successful breeding. They might also study land use around Sichuan Province to see how it affects giant panda habitat. Any of these inquiries constitutes an ecological question, and several different branches of ecology exist to address them. Ecology can be described as a group

of different, but related, disciplines: a hierarchy of studies. Scientists in different branches of the discipline might operate at different scales and ask different questions about the same system. The concept of ecological hierarchy is depicted in **Figure 3–1**.

As we investigate the science of ecology, we will look at these different levels in the hierarchy. We start by examining individual organisms at the species level. We will see how species are grouped into larger categories and how these groups interact. Species exist in specific habitats because those habitats provide the nutrients and other factors that a species needs to survive; we will look at how those needs are met. Lastly, we will take a broader view of matter and energy, and how energy and nutrients cycle through the various systems on Earth. All of these different processes are interlinked. Ecologists study the connections as well as the whole.

Species. A **species** is a group of individuals that share certain characteristics distinct from other such groups (robins versus redwing blackbirds, for example). Species are classified into closely related groups called *genera* (singular, *genus*), and they in turn are grouped into *families*. These are grouped into larger groups: *orders, classes, phyla* (singular, *phylum*), *kingdoms*, and *domains*. The official scientific name of any species is always Latin and has two parts: the genus name and the species epithet, or descriptive term. For example, the giant panda's name, *Ailuropoda melanoleuca* ("black-and-white cat-foot"), tells us first the genus (*Ailuropoda*) and second a descriptive word (the species epithet, *melanoleuca*). Although the giant panda is in the bear family (*Ursidae*), it is considered so different from other bears that it is the only species in this genus. In contrast, when we say "bamboo," we actually mean a group of about 1,000 related species in the same subcategory of the grass family. The bamboo eaten by the giant panda is composed of members of two of these bamboo species.

Levels of organization within an organism

Biome

Biosphere

Landscape

Ecosystem
organisms,
sun, and rain.

Organism

Population

Organ

Tissue

Cell

Community

Figure 3–1 **The hierarchy of life.** Organisms can be seen as a hierarchy of complex systems from cells to tissues to organs to systems to whole individuals. Likewise, individuals function in a set of increasingly complex systems that make up the disciplines of ecology. These include populations, communities, ecosystems, and landscapes. The very largest regions are called biomes. Together, all living things make up the biosphere.

Sometimes it is difficult to determine exactly what constitutes a species. The biological definition of a species is *all members that can interbreed and produce fertile offspring*. Members of different species generally do not interbreed. This definition is good for many organisms, but does not work for those that do not need to mate to produce offspring. In those cases, scientists use a variety of other classification methods. New species can arise over periods of time through evolution, and species classifications are occasionally altered to reflect this.

Populations. Each species in a biotic community is represented by a certain **population**—that is, by a certain number of individuals that make up the interbreeding, reproducing group. The distinction between population and species is that *population* refers only to those individuals of a certain species that live within a given area—for example, all of the gray wolves in Yellowstone National Park. *Species* is all inclusive, such as all of the gray wolves in the world.

Biotic Communities. The grouping of populations we observe when studying a forest, grassland, or pond is referred to as the area's **biota** (*bio* means "living") or **biotic community**. The biota includes all vegetation, from large trees through microscopic algae, and all animals, from large mammals, birds, reptiles, and amphibians through earthworms, tiny insects, and mites. It also includes microscopic creatures such as bacteria, fungi, and protozoans.

The particular kind of biotic community found in a given area is, in large part, determined by **abiotic** (nonliving, chemical, and physical) factors. Abiotic factors include the amount of water or moisture present, climate, salinity (saltiness), and soil type. Sometimes, we quickly refer to a community by its most obvious members, such as the dominant plants. For example, we might describe a "hemlock/beech forest" or an "oak/hickory forest" (Fig. 3–2). This is because vegetation is easily observed (it doesn't usually run away) and is a strong indicator of the environmental conditions of a site.

The species within a community depend on one another. For example, certain animals will not be present unless certain plants that provide food and shelter are also present. In this way, the plant community supports (or limits by its absence) the animal community. In addition, every plant and animal species is adapted to cope with the abiotic factors of its region. For example, every species that lives in a temperate region is adapted in one way or another to survive the winter season, which includes a period of freezing temperatures (Fig. 3–3). These interactions among organisms and their environments will be discussed later. For now, keep in mind that the populations of different species within a biotic community are constantly interacting with each other and with the abiotic environment.

Ecosystems. An **ecosystem** is an interactive complex of communities and the abiotic environment affecting them within a particular area. Forests, grasslands, wetlands, sand dunes, and coral reefs each contain specific species in particular spatial areas and are all distinct ecosystems. Humans are parts of ecosystems, too, and some branches of ecology, such as urban ecology, focus on human-dominated

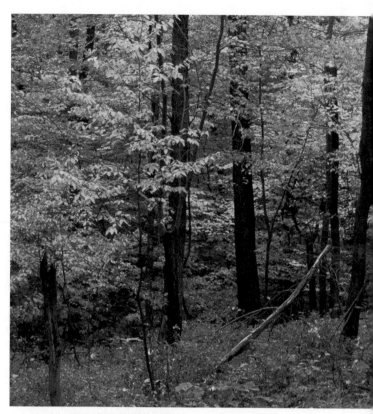

Figure 3–2 Predictable vegetation. An oak/hickory forest is dominated by oak and hickory trees, which define the type of forest habitat other species experience.

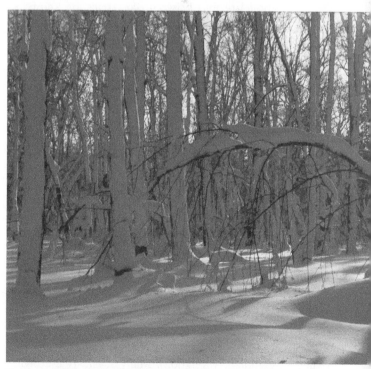

Figure 3–3 Winter in the forest. Many trees and other plants of temperate forests are so adapted to the winter season that they actually require a period of freezing temperature in order to grow again in the spring.

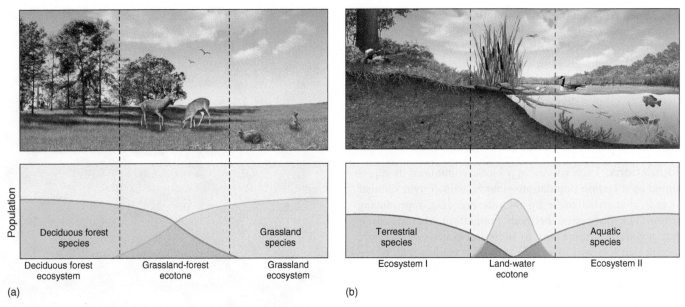

(a)   (b)

Figure 3–4 Ecotones. (a) Ecosystems are not isolated from one another. One ecosystem blends into the next through a transitional region—an ecotone—that contains many species common to both systems, though in lower numbers than in those systems. (b) An ecotone may create a unique habitat that harbors specialized species not found in either of the ecosystems bordering it. For example, cattails, reeds, and lily pads typically grow in the ecotone between land and freshwater ponds.

systems. Other ecologists study the interaction between humans and non-human ecosystems, such as salt marshes or the open ocean, which are deeply affected by humans.

While it is convenient to divide the living world into different ecosystems, you will find that there are seldom distinct boundaries between them and that they are not totally isolated from one another. Many species occupy (and are a part of) two or more ecosystems or, as in the case of migrating birds, may move from one ecosystem to another at different times.

Transitional regions between ecosystems are known as **ecotones**. An ecotone shares many of the species and characteristics of both ecosystems it passes through. Ecotones may lack unique (and contain fewer overall) species than bordering ecosystems, as in the ecotone between grassland and forest shown in **Figure 3–4a**. Alternatively, ecotones may also house and support more different species than those they pass through, as in the marshy ecotone that often occurs between the open water of a lake and dry land (Fig. 3–4b).

Landscapes and Biomes. Clusters of interacting ecosystems like forests, open meadows, and rivers together constitute **landscapes**. Landscape ecologists study issues such as how much suitable habitat will be left for fish to lay eggs in a riverbed if the surrounding forest is clear-cut or how far squirrels will be able to travel if the forest is broken into small segments. Landscapes are usually on a scale humans can envision; for example, if you look out at the horizon and see a forest merge into a field or meadow, you are seeing a landscape. However, landscapes can also be observed on a large scale: one could also pull back from Earth and look at large areas of its surface that have similar characteristics (such as dominant vegetation). Many scientists use digital technology tools such as **Geographic Information Systems (GIS)** to study landscape features. They also use **remote sensing**, including images from satellites **(Fig. 3–5)**.

Tropical rain forests, grasslands, and deserts are **biomes** (discussed in Chapter 5). A biome is a large area of Earth's surface that shares climate and has similar vegetation. Biomes are much larger than landscapes. For example, grasslands (such as prairies) are geographical regions whose locations can be predicted by their rainfall and temperatures. On different continents, they may have different particular species, but they are still grasslands, described by the dominant type of vegetation. As with ecosystems, there are generally no sharp boundaries between biomes. Instead, one grades into the next through transitional regions. The term *biome* is limited to terrestrial systems. There are major categories of aquatic and wetland ecosystems that are determined primarily by the depth, salinity, and permanence of water in them (Chapter 5).

Figure 3–5 Landscape Ecology. Here a researcher demonstrates a mapping tool used in landscape ecology. This is a prototype of a Geographical Information System (GIS) called Soilfit.

Biosphere. Regardless of how we choose to categorize and name different ecosystems, they are interconnected and interdependent. Terrestrial ecosystems are connected by the flow of rivers and by migrating animals. Sediments and nutrients washing from the land may nourish or pollute the ocean. Seabirds and marine mammals connect the oceans with the land, and all biomes share a common atmosphere and water cycle. All the species on Earth live in ecosystems, and ecosystems are interconnected so that all living things form one huge system called the **biosphere**. This concept is analogous to the idea that the cells of our bodies form tissues, tissues form organs, organs are connected into organ systems, and all are interconnected to form the whole body.

3.2 Environmental Factors

Let's look back at the giant panda eating bamboo at the reserve. Why are pandas living there and not in another part of the world? The answer is both the environment and history. The bamboo and the panda have evolved to live in the environment of the reserve, with the physical, chemical, and biological factors it contains. As already discussed, we describe these factors as either biotic (living) or abiotic (nonliving). The factors can be further characterized as either conditions or resources. **Conditions** are any factors that vary in space and time, but that are not used up or made unavailable to other species. These include temperature (extremes of heat and cold as well as average temperature), wind, pH (acidity), salinity (saltiness), and fire. **Resources** are any factors—biotic or abiotic—that are consumed by organisms. These include water, chemical nutrients (like nitrogen and phosphorus), light (for plants), oxygen, food (like the bamboo for the panda), and space for resting or nesting.

Some factors can be conditions in one situation and resources in another. For example, plants in the desert compete for water as a *resource*; however, in a pond, water is a *condition* for which plants like water lilies and cattails need special adaptations and for which they are not competing.

The degree to which each factor is present or absent profoundly affects the ability of organisms to survive. However, each species may be affected differently by each factor, and its response determines whether or not it will occupy a given region.

Optimums, Zones of Stress, and Limits of Tolerance

Different species thrive with different combinations of environmental factors. This principle applies to all living things, both plants and animals. Bamboo thrives in full sun and warm temperatures, with plenty of water and well-drained, nitrogen-rich soil. In contrast, desert cacti are generally adapted for low amounts of water, poor soil fertility, and extremes of heat and cold. Aquatic systems also vary in their environmental factors and residents—for example, the amounts of freshwater and saltwater determine the varieties of fish and other organisms present.

Organismal ecologists study the adaptations of organisms to specific environmental factors. Organisms can be grown under controlled conditions in which one factor is varied while other factors are held constant. Such experiments demonstrate that, for every factor, there is a certain level at which the organisms grow or survive most; an **optimum** (plural, *optima*). At higher or lower levels than the optimum, the organisms do less well, and at further extremes, they may not be able to survive at all (Fig. 3–6). This pertains to almost any abiotic factor that might be tested.

The point at which the best response occurs is the optimum, but this may be a range of several degrees (or other units), so it is common to speak of an *optimal range*. The entire span that allows any growth at all is called the **range of tolerance**. The points at the high and low ends of the range of tolerance are called the **limits of tolerance**. Between the optimal range and the high or low limit of tolerance are **zones of stress**. In other words, as the factor is raised or lowered from the optimal range, the organisms experience increasing stress, until, at either limit of tolerance, they cannot survive.

A Fundamental Biological Principle. Based on the consistency of observations and experiments, the following is considered to be a fundamental biological principle: *Every species has an optimal range, zones of stress, and limits of tolerance with respect to every abiotic factor, and these characteristics vary between species.* For instance, some plants cannot tolerate any freezing temperatures; others can tolerate slight freezing; and some actually require several weeks of freezing temperatures to complete their life cycles. Some species have a very broad range of tolerance, whereas others have a much narrower range.

The range of tolerance for any factor affects more than just the growth of individuals. Because the health and vigor of individuals affect their ability to reproduce, the survival of the next generation is also affected, which in turn influences the population as a whole. Consequently, the population density (individuals per unit area) of a species is greatest where all conditions are optimal, and it decreases as any one or more conditions depart from the optimum. You expect to see the most bamboo in the places where all conditions are best for bamboo and less where conditions are not so favorable.

Law of Limiting Factors. In 1840, Justus von Liebig studied the effects of chemical nutrients on plant growth. He observed that restricting any one of the many different nutrients at any given time had the same effect: it limited growth. A factor that limits growth is called (not surprisingly) a **limiting factor**. If any one factor is outside the optimal range, it will cause stress and limit the growth, reproduction, or even survival of a population. This observation is referred to as the **law of limiting factors** or Liebig's law of the minimum.

A limiting factor may be a problem of *too much* instead of a problem of *too little*. For example, plants may be stressed or killed not only by underwatering or underfertilizing, but also by overwatering or overfertilizing, which are common pitfalls for beginning gardeners. Note also that the limiting factor may change from one time to another and that if one limiting factor is corrected, growth will increase only until another factor comes into play. For instance, temperature may

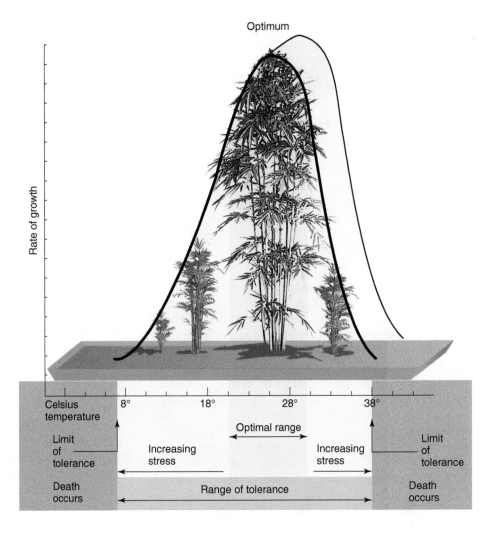

Figure 3–6 **Survival curve.** For every factor influencing growth, reproduction, and survival, there is an optimum level. Above and below the optimum, stress increases until survival becomes impossible at the limits of tolerance. The total range between the high and low limits is the range of tolerance.

be limiting in the early spring, nutrients may be limiting in the winter, and water may be limiting if a drought occurs.

While one factor may be limiting at a given time, several factors outside the optimum may combine to cause additional stress or even death. In particular, pollutants may act in a way that causes organisms to become more vulnerable to disease or drought. Such cases are examples of **synergistic effects,** or **synergisms,** which are defined as two or more factors interacting in a way that causes an effect much greater than one would anticipate from each of the two acting separately.

Habitat and Niche. Habitat refers to the kind of place—defined by the plant community and the physical environment—where a species is biologically adapted to live. For example, deciduous forests, swamps, and grassy fields are types of habitats. Different types of forests (for instance, coniferous versus tropical) provide markedly different habitats and support different species of wildlife. Because some organisms operate on very small scales, we use the term *microhabitat* for things like puddles, spaces sheltered by rocks, and holes in tree trunks that might house their own small community (Fig. 3–7).

Even when different species occupy the same habitat, competition may be slight or nonexistent because each species has its own niche. An ecological **niche** is the sum of all of the conditions and resources under which a species can live: what and where it feeds, what it feeds on, where it finds shelter and nests, and how it responds to abiotic factors.

Similar species can coexist in the same habitat but have separate niches. Competition is minimized because potential competitors are using different resources. For example, bats and swallows both feed on flying insects, but they do not compete because bats feed on night-flying insects and swallows feed during the day.

In the next section, we will see how organisms take these materials from the environment and use them to grow and maintain their bodies and do activities necessary for survival.

3.3 Matter in Living and Nonliving Systems

Living organisms need to be able to take in matter and energy from their environment to grow and function. For example, the bamboo that grows in the panda reserve can survive only because it is able to take the Sun's energy and combine it with materials from the soil, air, and water around it to make the basic building blocks of its own tissues and to power its cellular activities. In turn, the giant panda will eat

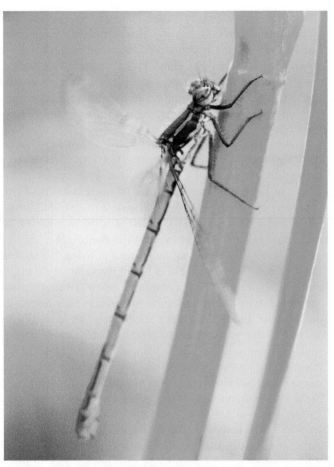

Figure 3–7 Habitat and niche. For part of their lives, these damselflies live in the pool of water trapped by a type of tropical plant; the tiny pool is a microhabitat. The specific conditions required by the damselfly, such as the pool and the types of food it eats there or where it lays its eggs as an adult, are its niche.

the bamboo and get energy and matter necessary to build its own tissues and to do the work it needs to do in each of its cells. To understand this simple ecological relationship, we need to know some basic chemistry and physics. Later, we will explore what happens to energy and matter as they move through the biosphere.

Basic Units of Matter

Matter is defined as anything that occupies space and has mass. This definition covers all solids, liquids, and gases as well as all living and nonliving things. Matter is composed of **atoms**—very small pieces—that are combined to form molecules, which in turn can be combined into more complex structures.

Atoms. The basic building blocks of all matter are atoms. Only 94 different kinds of atoms occur in nature, and these are known as the naturally occurring **elements.** Atoms are made up of protons, neutrons, and electrons, which in turn are made up of still smaller particles. For example, lead (Pb) is an element. An atom of lead is the smallest amount of lead existing that has the characteristics of lead. A lead atom has a characteristic number of protons (positive particles), neutrons (neutral particles), and electrons (negative particles).

How can these relatively few building blocks make up the countless materials of our world, including the tissues of living things? Picture each kind of atom as a different-sized Lego® block. Like Legos, atoms can build a great variety of things. Also like Legos, natural materials can be taken apart into their separate constituent atoms, and the atoms can then be reassembled into different materials. All chemical reactions, whether occurring in a test tube, in the environment, or inside living things (and whether they occur very slowly or very quickly), involve rearrangements of atoms to form different kinds of matter.

Atoms do not change during the disassembly and reassembly of different materials. A carbon atom will always remain a carbon atom. In chemical reactions, atoms are neither created nor destroyed. The same number and kind of different atoms exist before and after any reaction. This constancy of atoms is regarded as a fundamental natural law, the **Law of Conservation of Matter.** Nuclear reactions differ from the chemical reactions we are discussing and can result in the splitting of an atom of one element into multiple atoms of another element. However, this is a very specific, rare instance and is not a chemical reaction. (Nuclear reactions will be discussed in Chapter 15.)

Now we turn our attention to the ways atoms are put together, which atoms make up the bulk of the bodies of living organisms, and how atoms are incorporated into organisms.

Molecules and Compounds. A molecule consists of two or more atoms (either the same kind or different kinds) bonded in a specific way. The properties of a material depend on the exact way in which atoms are bonded to form molecules as well as on the atoms themselves. A **compound** consists of two or more *different* kinds of atoms that are bonded. For example, the fundamental units of oxygen gas, which consist of two bonded oxygen atoms, are molecules (O_2) but not compounds. By contrast, when an oxygen atom binds with hydrogen atoms to create water, it is both a molecule and a compound (H_2O).

On the chemical level, the cycle of growth, reproduction, death, and decay of organisms is a continuous process of using various molecules and compounds from the environment (food), assembling them into living organisms (growth), disassembling them (decay), and repeating the process.

Four Spheres

During growth and decay, atoms move from the environment into living things and then return to the environment. To picture this process, think of the environment as three open, nonliving systems, or "spheres," interacting with the biosphere (Fig. 3–8). The **atmosphere** is the thin layer of gases (including water vapor) separating Earth from outer space. The **hydrosphere** is water in all of its liquid and solid compartments: oceans, rivers, ice, and groundwater. The **lithosphere** is Earth's crust, made up of rocks and minerals. Matter is constantly being exchanged within and between these four spheres.

Figure 3–8 The four spheres of Earth's environment. The biosphere is all of life on Earth. It depends on, and interacts with, the atmosphere (air), the hydrosphere (water), and the lithosphere (soil and rocks).

(*Source*: Adapted from *Geosystems*, 5th ed., by Robert W. Christopherson, © 2005 Pearson Education, Inc.)

Atmosphere. The lower atmosphere is a mixture of molecules of three important gases—oxygen (O_2), nitrogen (N_2), and carbon dioxide (CO_2)—along with water vapor and trace amounts of several other gases. The gases in the atmosphere are normally stable, but under some circumstances, they react chemically to form new compounds. For example, ozone is produced from oxygen in the upper atmosphere (Chapter 18). Plants take carbon dioxide in from the atmosphere, usually through their leaves. Animals usually take oxygen in through some type of specialized organ such as a lung, but some, like earthworms, can simply absorb oxygen through their skin.

Hydrosphere. While the atmosphere is a major source of carbon and oxygen for organisms, the hydrosphere is the source of hydrogen. Each molecule of water consists of two hydrogen atoms bonded to an oxygen atom, so the chemical formula for water is H_2O. A weak attraction known as *hydrogen bonding* exists between water molecules.

Water is an important molecule for living things and usually needs to be available in liquid form. Water occurs in three different states. At temperatures below freezing, hydrogen bonding holds the molecules in position with respect to one another, and the result is a solid **crystal** structure (ice or snow). At temperatures above freezing but below vaporization, hydrogen bonding still holds the molecules close but allows them to move past one another, producing the liquid state. Vaporization (evaporation) occurs as hydrogen bonds break and water molecules move into the air independently. As temperatures are lowered again, all of these changes of state go in the reverse direction. Generally, water undergoes melting and evaporation, but sometimes water molecules leave snow or ice and go directly into the air. This is *sublimation* (Fig. 3–9). Moving from one state to another either releases or requires a great deal of energy. This is one reason why many animals sweat to cool off: changing from

Figure 3–9 Water and its three states. (a) Water consists of molecules, each of which is formed when two hydrogen atoms bond to an oxygen atom (H_2O). (b) In water vapor, the molecules are separate and independent. (c) In liquid water, the weak attraction between water molecules known as hydrogen bonding gives the water its liquid property. (d) At freezing temperatures, hydrogen bonding holds the molecules firmly, giving the solid state—ice.

Figure 3–10 **Minerals.** Minerals (hard, crystalline compounds) are composed of dense clusters of atoms of two or more elements. The atoms of most elements gain or lose one or more electrons, becoming negative (−) or positive (+) ions, and form a predictable pattern held closely together. This photograph is of a mineral, gypsum in a mine in Texas.

the liquid to gas state requires heat and removes it from the organism. Despite the changes of state, the water molecules themselves retain their basic chemical structure of two hydrogen atoms bonded to an oxygen atom; only the *relationship* between the molecules changes.

Lithosphere. All the other elements that are required by living organisms, as well as the approximately 72 elements that they do not require, are found in the lithosphere, in the form of rock and soil minerals. A **mineral** is a naturally occurring solid, made by geologic processes; it is a hard, crystalline structure of a given chemical composition (Fig. 3–10). Most rocks are made up of relatively small crystals of two or more minerals, and soil generally consists of particles of many different minerals. Each mineral is made up of dense clusters of two or more kinds of atoms bonded by an attraction between positive and negative charges on the atoms (Appendix C).

Interactions. Air, water, and minerals interact with each other in a simple, but significant, manner. Gases from the air and ions (charged atoms) from minerals may dissolve in water. Therefore, natural water is inevitably a **solution** containing variable amounts of dissolved gases and minerals. This solution is constantly subject to change because various processes may remove any dissolved substances in it or additional materials may dissolve in it. Molecules of water enter the air by evaporation and leave it again via condensation and precipitation (see the hydrologic cycle, Chapter 10). Thus, the amount of moisture in the air fluctuates constantly. Wind may carry dust or mineral particles, but the amount changes constantly because the particles gradually settle out from the air. These interactions are summarized in Figure 3–11. The materials in these three spheres interact with the biosphere as living organisms take materials from the spheres and use them to create complex molecules in their bodies. We will discuss the process of building these molecules next.

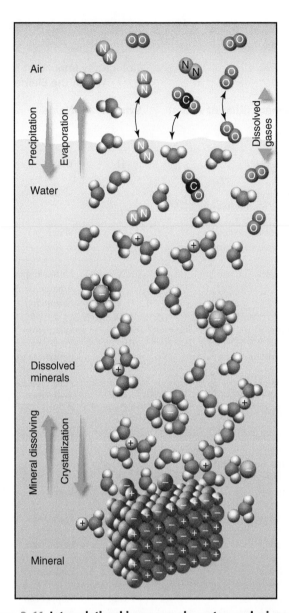

Figure 3–11 **Interrelationship among air, water, and minerals.** Minerals and gases dissolve in water, forming solutions. Water evaporates into air, causing humidity. These processes are all reversible: minerals in solution recrystallize, and water vapor in the air condenses to form liquid water.

Organic Compounds

Your body, like that of the panda or even the bamboo it eats, is composed of relatively large chemical compounds in a number of broad categories, such as proteins, carbohydrates (sugars and starches), lipids (fatty substances), and nucleic acids (DNA and RNA). These compounds usually contain six key elements: carbon (C), hydrogen (H), oxygen (O), nitrogen (N), phosphorus (P), and sulfur (S) (Table 3–1). Living things need other elements as well, sometimes in smaller, but no less important, amounts.

Unlike the relatively simple molecules that occur in the environment (such as CO_2, H_2O, and N_2), the key chemical elements in living organisms bond to form very large, complex molecules. The chemical compounds making up

TABLE 3–1 Elements Found in Living Organisms and the Locations of Those Elements in the Environment

Element (Kind of Atom)	Biologically Important Molecule or Ion in Which the Element Occurs[a]			Location in the Environment[b]		
	Symbol	Name	Formula	Atmosphere	Hydrosphere	Lithosphere
Carbon	C	Carbon dioxide	CO_2	X	X	X (CO_3)
Hydrogen	H	Water	H_2O	X	(Water itself)	
Atomic oxygen (required in respiration)	O	Oxygen gas	O_2	X	X	
Molecular oxygen (required in photosynthesis)	O_2	Water	H_2O		(Water itself)	
Nitrogen	N	Nitrogen gas	N_2	X	X	Via fixation
		Ammonium ion	NH_4		X	X
		Nitrate ion	NH_3		X	X
Sulfur	S	Sulfate ion	SO_4^2		X	X
Phosphorus	P	Phosphate ion	PO_4^3		X	X
Potassium	K	Potassium ion	K^+		X	X
Calcium	Ca	Calcium ion	Ca^2		X	X
Magnesium	Mg	Magnesium ion	Mg^2		X	X
Trace Elements[c]						
Iron	Fe	Iron ion	Fe^2, Fe^3		X	X
Manganese	Mn	Manganese ion	Mn^2		X	X
Boron	B	Boron ion	B^3		X	X
Zinc	Zn	Zinc ion	Zn^2		X	X
Copper	Cu	Copper ion	Cu^2		X	X
Molybdenum	Mo	Molybdenum ion	Mo^2		X	X
Chlorine	Cl	Chloride ion	Cl^-		X	X

Note: These elements are found in *all* living organisms—plants, animals, and microbes. Some organisms require certain elements in addition to the ones listed. For example, humans require sodium and iodine.

[a]A molecule is a chemical unit of two or more atoms that are bonded. An ion is a single atom or group of bonded atoms that has acquired a positive or negative charge as indicated.

[b]X means that element exists in the indicated sphere.

[c]Only small or trace amounts of these elements are required.

the tissues of living organisms are referred to as **organic.** Some of these molecules may contain millions of atoms. These molecules are constructed mainly from carbon atoms bonded into chains, with hydrogen and oxygen atoms attached. Nitrogen, phosphorus, or sulfur may be present also, but the key common denominator is carbon–carbon and carbon–hydrogen or carbon–oxygen bonds. **Inorganic,** then, refers to molecules or compounds with neither carbon–carbon nor carbon–hydrogen bonds. While this is the general rule, some exceptions occur; by convention, a few compounds that contain carbon bonds, such as carbon dioxide, are still considered inorganic.

All plastics and countless other human-made compounds are also based on carbon bonding and are, chemically speaking, organic compounds. To resolve any confusion this may cause, the compounds making up living organisms are referred to as **natural organic compounds** and the human-made ones as **synthetic organic compounds.** The term *organic* can have a completely different meaning, such as in *organic farming* (Chapter 12).

To summarize: the elements essential to life (C, H, O, and so on) are present in the atmosphere, hydrosphere, or lithosphere in relatively simple molecules. In the living organisms of the biosphere, on the other hand, these elements are organized into highly complex organic compounds. In the case of the panda and bamboo, simple molecules and atoms in the soil, air, and water are combined to form the tissues of bamboo and eaten, digested, and recombined to make the tissues of the giant panda. When the bamboo or panda dies, the reverse process occurs through decomposition and decay. Each of these processes is discussed in more detail later in the chapter. Next, we discuss energy, the force that helps change chemical matter into substances that support life.

3.4 Matter and Energy

The universe is made up of matter and energy. Recall that matter is *anything that occupies space and has mass.* By contrast, light, heat, movement, and electricity do not have mass, nor do they occupy space. These are the common forms of

energy that you are familiar with. What do the various forms of energy have in common? They affect matter, causing changes in its *position* or *state.* For example, the release of energy in an explosion causes things to go flying—a change in position. Heating water causes it to boil and change to steam, a change of state. On a molecular level, changes of state are actually also movements of atoms or molecules. For instance, the degree of heat energy contained in a substance is a measure of the relative vibrational motion of the atoms and molecules of the substance. Therefore, we can define **energy** as *the ability to move matter.*

Energy Basics

Energy can be categorized as either kinetic or potential **(Fig. 3–12). Kinetic energy** is *energy in action or motion.* Light, heat, physical motion, and electrical current are all forms of kinetic energy. **Potential energy** is *energy in storage.* A substance or system with potential energy has the capacity, or potential, to release one or more forms of kinetic energy. A stretched rubber band has potential energy; it can send a paper clip flying. Numerous chemicals, such as gasoline and other fuels, release kinetic energy— heat, light, and movement—when ignited. The potential energy contained in such chemicals and fuels is called **chemical energy.**

FORMS OF ENERGY

Kinetic Energy

Light and other forms of radiation

Heat

Motion

Electrical power

Potential Energy

Reservoir behind hydroelectric dam

High pressure

Four Types of Chemical Potential Energy

Battery

Gasoline

Firewood

Explosives

Figure 3–12 **Forms of energy.** Energy is distinct from matter in that it neither has mass nor occupies space. It has the ability to act on matter, though, changing the position or the state of the matter. Kinetic energy is energy in one of its active forms. Potential energy is the potential that systems or materials have to release kinetic energy.

Figure 3–13 **Energy conversions.**
Any form of energy except heat can spontaneously transform into any other form. Heat is a form of energy that flows from one system or object to another because the two are at different temperatures; therefore, heat can spontaneously transform only to something cooler.

Energy may be changed from one form to another in innumerable ways (Fig. 3–13). Besides understanding that potential energy can be converted to kinetic energy, it is especially important to recognize that kinetic energy can be converted to potential energy. (Consider, for example, charging a battery or pumping water into a high-elevation reservoir.) We shall see later in this section that photosynthesis does just that.

Because energy does not have mass or occupy space, it cannot be measured in units of weight or volume. Instead, energy is measured in other kinds of units. One of the most common energy units is the **calorie,** which is defined as the amount of heat required to raise the temperature of 1 gram (1 milliliter) of water 1 degree Celsius. This is a very small unit, so it is frequently more convenient to use the kilocalorie (1 kilocalorie = 1,000 calories), the amount of thermal (heat) energy required to raise 1 liter (1,000 milliliters) of water 1 degree Celsius. Kilocalories are sometimes denoted as "Calories" with a capital "C." Food Calories, which measure the energy in given foods, are actually kilocalories. *Temperature* measures the molecular motion in a substance caused by the kinetic energy present in it.

If energy is defined as the ability to move matter, then no matter can be moved *without* the absorption or release of energy. Indeed, no change in matter—from a few atoms coming together or apart in a chemical reaction to a major volcanic eruption—can be separated from its respective change in energy.

Laws of Thermodynamics. Because energy can be converted from one form to another, numerous would-be inventors over the years have tried to build machines that produce more energy than they consume. One common idea was to use the output from a generator to drive a motor that in turn would be expected to drive a generator to keep the cycle going and yield additional power in the bargain (a perpetual-motion machine). Unfortunately, all such devices have one feature in common: They don't work. When all the inputs and outputs of energy are carefully measured, they are found to be equal. There is no net gain or loss in total energy. This observation is now accepted as a fundamental natural law, the **Law of Conservation of Energy.** It is also called the **First Law of Thermodynamics,** and it can be expressed as follows: *Energy is neither created nor destroyed, but may be converted from one form to another.* What this law really means is that you can't get something for nothing.

Imaginative "energy generators" fail for two reasons: First, in every energy conversion, a portion of the energy is converted to heat energy. Second, there is no way of trapping and recycling heat energy without expending even more energy in doing so. Consequently, in the absence of energy inputs, any and every system will sooner or later come to a stop as its energy is converted to heat and lost. This is now accepted as another natural law, the **Second Law of Thermodynamics,** and it can be expressed as follows: *In any energy conversion, some of the usable* *energy is always lost.* Thus, you can't get something for nothing (the first law), and in fact, you can't even break even (the second law)!

Entropy. The principle of increasing entropy underlies the loss of usable energy and its transformation to heat energy. Entropy is *a measure of the degree of disorder in a system,* so increasing entropy means increasing disorder. Without energy inputs, everything goes in one direction only—toward increasing entropy.

The conversion of energy and the loss of usable energy to heat are both aspects of increasing entropy. Heat energy is the result of the random vibrational motion of atoms and molecules. It is the lowest (most disordered) form of energy, and its spontaneous flow to cooler surroundings is a way for that disorder to spread. Therefore, the Second Law of Thermodynamics may be more generally stated as follows: *Systems will go spontaneously in one direction only—toward increasing entropy* (Fig. 3–14). The second law also states that systems will go spontaneously only toward lower potential energy, a direction that releases heat from the systems.

It is possible to pump water uphill, charge a battery, stretch a rubber band, and compress air. All of these require the input of energy in order to increase the potential energy of a system. The verbs *pump, charge, stretch,* and *compress* reflect the fact that energy is being put into the system. In contrast, flow in the opposite direction (which releases energy) occurs spontaneously (Fig. 3–15).

Whenever something gains potential energy, therefore, keep in mind that the energy is being obtained from somewhere else (the first law). Moreover, the amount of usable energy lost from that "somewhere else" is greater than the amount gained (the second law). We now relate these concepts of matter and energy to organic molecules, organisms, ecosystems, and the biosphere.

Energy Changes in Organisms

Picture someone building a fire in a fireplace. The wood is largely composed of complex organic molecules. These molecules required energy to form, and therefore, their chemical bonds contain high potential energy. Lighting a fire causes a series of reactions that break these molecules and release energy. When released, the energy contained in those bonds can be used to do work. This chemical reaction involves **oxidation**, a loss of electrons, usually accomplished by the addition of oxygen (which causes *burning*). The heat and light of the flame are the potential energy being released as kinetic energy. In contrast, most inorganic compounds, such as carbon dioxide, water, and rock-based minerals, are nonflammable because they have very low potential energy. Thus, the production of organic material from inorganic material represents a gain in potential energy. Conversely, the breakdown of organic matter *releases* energy. Inside the cells of the giant panda eating bamboo, the reaction that

Figure 3–14 Entropy. Systems go spontaneously only in the direction of increasing entropy. This spray can illustrates the idea. It took energy to concentrate a liquid in the can. Once it is dispersed, the energy is dissipated and entropy is increased.

takes place is similar to that of burning wood in a fireplace, except that it occurs in a set of small steps and is much more controlled.

Producers and Photosynthesis. The relationship between the formation and breakdown of organic matter, where energy is gained and released from chemical bonds, forms the basis of the energy dynamics of ecosystems. **Producers** (primarily green plants) make *high-potential-energy organic molecules* for their needs from *low-potential-energy raw materials* in the environment—namely, carbon dioxide, water, and a few dissolved compounds of nitrogen, phosphorus, and other elements (Fig. 3–16). This "uphill" conversion is possible because producers use chlorophyll to absorb light energy, which "powers" the production of the complex, energy-rich organic molecules. On the other hand, **consumers** (all organisms that live on the production of others) obtain energy for movement and growth from *feeding on and breaking down organic matter made by producers* (Fig. 3–17 on page 65).

Green plants use the process of **photosynthesis** to make sugar (glucose, which contains stored chemical energy) from carbon dioxide, water, and light energy (Fig. 3–16). This process, which also releases oxygen gas as a by-product, is described by the following chemical equation:

Photosynthesis
(An energy-demanding process)

$$6\,CO_2 + 12\,H_2O \xrightarrow{\text{light energy}} C_6H_{12}O_6 + 6\,O_2 + 6\,H_2O$$

carbon dioxide   water   light energy   glucose   oxygen   water
(gas)   input   (gas)
(low potential energy)   (high potential energy)

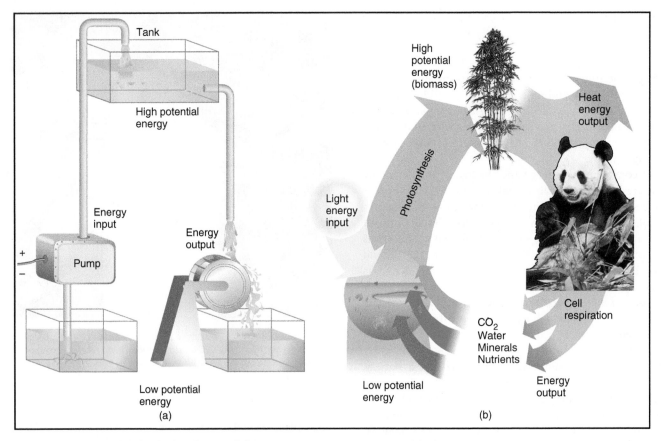

Figure 3–15 Storage and release of potential energy. (a) A simple physical example of the storage and release of potential energy. (b) The same principle applied to ecosystems.

Figure 3–16 Producers as chemical factories. Using light energy, producers make glucose from carbon dioxide and water, releasing oxygen as a by-product. Breaking down some of the glucose to provide additional chemical energy, they combine the remaining glucose with certain nutrients from the soil to form other complex organic molecules that the plant then uses for growth.

Figure 3–17 Consumers.
Only a small portion of the food ingested by a consumer is assimilated into body growth and repair. Some food provides energy in chemical bonds that are broken by the process of cell respiration: this is the reverse process of photosynthesis, and waste products are carbon dioxide, water, and various mineral nutrients. A third portion is not digested and becomes fecal waste.

Chlorophyll in the plant cells absorbs the kinetic energy of light and uses it to remove the hydrogen atoms from water (H_2O) molecules. The hydrogen atoms combine with carbon atoms from carbon dioxide to form a growing chain of carbons that eventually becomes a glucose molecule. After the hydrogen atoms are removed from water, the oxygen atoms that remain combine with each other to form oxygen gas, which is released into the air. Water appears on both sides of the equation because 12 molecules are consumed and 6 molecules are newly formed during photosynthesis.

The key energy steps in photosynthesis take the hydrogen from water molecules and join carbon atoms together to form the carbon–carbon and carbon–hydrogen bonds of glucose. These steps convert the low-potential-energy bonds in water and carbon dioxide molecules to the high-potential-energy bonds of glucose.

Within the Plant. The glucose produced in photosynthesis serves three purposes in the plant: (1) Glucose, with the addition of other molecules, can be the backbone used for making all the other organic molecules (proteins, carbohydrates, and so on) that make up the stem, roots, leaves, flowers, and fruit of the plant. (2) It takes energy to run the cell activities of plants, such as growth. This energy is obtained when the plant breaks down a portion of the glucose to release its stored energy in a process called *cell respiration*, which is discussed later. (3) A portion of the glucose produced may be stored for future use. For storage, the glucose is generally converted to starch, as in potatoes or grains, or to oils, as in many seeds. This stored energy is what is available to be eaten by consumers (Fig. 3–17).

None of these reactions, from the initial capture of light by chlorophyll to the synthesis of plant structures, takes place automatically. Each step is catalyzed by specific **enzymes**, *proteins that promote the synthesis or breaking of chemical bonds*. The same is true of cell respiration.

Cell Respiration. Inside each cell, organic molecules may be broken down through a process called **cell respiration** to release the energy required for the work done by that cell. Most commonly, cell respiration involves the breakdown of glucose, and the overall chemical equation is basically the reverse of that for photosynthesis:

Cell Respiration
(An energy-releasing process)

$$C_6H_{12}O_6 + 6\,O_2 \;\rightarrow\; 6\,CO_2 \;+\; 6\,H_2O \;+\; \text{energy}$$

glucose   oxygen   carbon dioxide   water
(high potential energy)   (low potential energy)

The purpose of cell respiration is to release the potential energy contained in organic molecules to perform the activities of the organism. Note that oxygen is *released* in photosynthesis but *consumed* in cell respiration to break down glucose to carbon dioxide and water. All organisms need to perform cell respiration, even producers like bamboo. In order to have the oxygen they need, animals like giant pandas eating bamboo, and deer grazing on grass (Fig. 3–17), must obtain oxygen through some type of respiratory organ. This means that their ability to use food depends on the availability not only of food, but also of oxygen. Many animals, such as deer, use lungs to obtain oxygen and release carbon dioxide. Oxygen is more limited in water, and fish use gills to obtain it, but many aquatic places are severely oxygen limited.

In keeping with the Second Law of Thermodynamics, converting the potential energy of glucose to the energy required to do the body's work is not 100% efficient. The energy released from glucose is stored in molecules that work like compressed springs—that is, they store the energy so that the body can use it in cells later. But the number of "energy units" that come from respiration is not nearly as high as the amount of solar energy required for the photosynthesis of glucose. Cell respiration is only 40–60% efficient. This is a great example of the Second Law of Thermodynamics at work. The rest of the energy is released as waste heat, and this is the source of body heat. This heat output can be measured in animals (cold-blooded or warm-blooded) and in plants.

Gaining Weight. The basis of weight gain or loss becomes apparent in this context. If you consume more calories from food than your body needs, the excess may be converted to fat and stored, and you gain weight as a result. In contrast, the principle of dieting is to eat less and exercise more, to create an energy demand that exceeds the amount of energy contained in your food.

The overall reaction for cell respiration is the same as that for simply burning glucose. Thus, it is not uncommon to speak of "burning" our food for energy. There are other ways of releasing stored energy from food that do not require oxygen. Such anaerobic respiration includes fermentation, as in the process used to make wine. Yeast cells use anaerobic respiration to convert grape sugars into usable energy, releasing alcohol as a by-product. However, these methods are less efficient than oxidation, and organisms that use them do not thrive unless oxygen is severely limited.

Photosynthesis and cell respiration are necessary for life on Earth to survive. In the next section, we will see how the energy that fuels photosynthesis moves through Earth's systems after traveling from the Sun.

One-Way Flow of Energy

What happens to all the solar energy entering ecosystems? Most of it is absorbed by the atmosphere, oceans, and land, heating them in the process. The small fraction (2–5%) captured by living plants is either passed along to the consumers and **detritivores** (organisms that live on dead or decaying organisms) that eat them or degraded into the lowest and most disordered form of energy—heat—as the plants decompose. Eventually, all of the energy entering ecosystems escapes as heat. According to the laws of thermodynamics, no energy will actually be lost. So many energy conversions are taking place in ecosystem activities, however, that entropy is increased, and all the energy is degraded to a form unavailable to do further work. That heat energy may stay in the atmosphere for some period of time, but will eventually be re-radiated out into space. The ultimate result is that *energy flows in a one-way direction through ecosystems* and eventually leaves Earth; it is not lost to the universe, but it is no longer available to ecosystems, so it must be continually resupplied by sunlight.

Energy flow is one of the two fundamental processes that make ecosystems work. In contrast with the *flow* of energy, we talk about the *cycling* of nutrients and other elements, which are continually reused from those already available on Earth.

3.5 The Cycling of Matter in Ecosystems

Earlier we saw that the molecules that make up cells, which in turn make up tissues, contain certain key elements. In bamboo, for example, all organic molecules contain carbon; photosynthesis requires water (hydrogen and oxygen) and carbon dioxide (carbon and oxygen); potassium is part of the energy-holding mechanism in each cell; nitrogen is contained

in every protein; and sulfur bonds help proteins stay in the right shape. There are many other necessary nutrients. Some are only necessary in very small amounts. For example, to make the protein hemoglobin, which carries oxygen in blood, small amounts of iron are needed.

According to the Law of Conservation of Matter, atoms cannot be created or destroyed, so recycling is the only possible way to maintain a dynamic system. To see how recycling takes place in the biosphere, we now focus on the pathways of four key elements heavily affected by human activities: carbon, phosphorus, nitrogen, and sulfur. Because these pathways are circular and involve biological, geological, and chemical processes, they are known as the **biogeochemical cycle**. (The water, or hydrologic, cycle is just as important, but it will be covered in Chapter 10).

The Carbon Cycle

The global carbon cycle is illustrated in **Figure 3–18**. Boxes represent major "pools" of carbon, and arrows represent the movement, or flux, of carbon from one compartment to another. For descriptive purposes, it is convenient to start the carbon cycle with the "reservoir" of carbon dioxide (CO_2 molecules present in the air). Through photosynthesis and further metabolism, carbon atoms from CO_2 become the carbon atoms of the organic molecules making up a plant's body. The carbon atoms can then be eaten by an animal, such as the panda, and become part of the tissues of all the other organisms in the ecosystem. About half of the carbon-containing molecules are respired by plants and animals, and half are deposited to the soil (a large reservoir) in the form of **detritus** (dead plant and animal matter). Respiration by organisms in the soil that eat dead matter returns more carbon to the atmosphere (as CO_2). The cycle is different in the oceans: Photosynthesis by phytoplankton and macroalgae removes CO_2 from the huge pool of inorganic carbonates in seawater, and feeding moves the organic carbon through marine food webs. Respiration by the biota returns the CO_2 to the inorganic carbon compounds in solution.

Some other significant processes exist. The figure indicates two in particular: (1) diffusion exchange between the atmosphere and the oceans; and (2) the combustion of fossil fuels, which releases CO_2 to the atmosphere. Some geological processes of the carbon cycle are not shown in Figure 3–18. For example, the fossilization of dead plants and animals produced coal deposits in many areas of Earth. This process removed vast amounts of carbon dioxide from the atmosphere and trapped it underground. Burning the coal and oil created by this process releases the CO_2 to the atmosphere. For another example, limestone (such as that formed by ancient corals) also keeps carbon out of circulation; however, the weathering of exposed limestone releases carbon into the aquatic system.

Because the total amount of carbon dioxide in the atmosphere is about 765 Gt (gigaton, or 1,000 metric tons) and photosynthesis in terrestrial ecosystems removes about

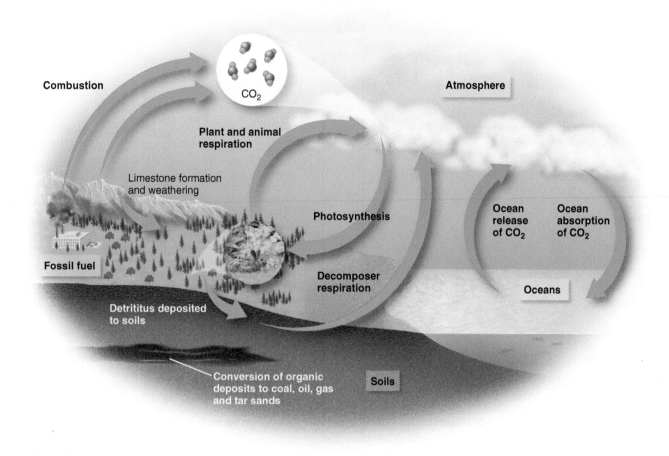

Figure 3–18 **The global carbon cycle.** Boxes in the figure refer to pools of carbon, and arrows refer to the movement, or flux, of carbon from one pool to another.

120 Gt/year, a carbon atom cycles from the atmosphere through one or more living things and back to the atmosphere about every six years.

Human Impacts. Human intrusion into the carbon cycle is significant. As we will see shortly, we are diverting (or removing) 40% of the photosynthetic productivity of land plants to support human enterprises. By burning fossil fuels, we have increased atmospheric carbon dioxide by 35% over preindustrial levels (Chapter 18). In addition, until the mid-20th century, deforestation and soil degradation released significant amounts of CO_2 to the atmosphere. However, more recent reforestation and changed agricultural practices have improved this somewhat.

The Phosphorus Cycle

The phosphorus cycle is similar to the cycles of other mineral nutrients—those elements that have their origin in the rock and soil minerals of the lithosphere, such as iron, calcium, and potassium. We focus on phosphorus because its shortage tends to be a limiting factor in a number of ecosystems and its excess can stimulate unwanted algal growth in freshwater systems.

The phosphorus cycle is illustrated in **Figure 3–19**. Like the carbon cycle, it is depicted as a set of pools of phosphorus and fluxes to indicate key processes. Phosphorus exists in various rock and soil minerals as the inorganic ion phosphate (PO_4^{3-}). As rock gradually breaks down, phosphate and other ions are released in a slow process. Plants absorb PO_4^{3-} from the soil or from a water solution, and once the phosphate is incorporated into organic compounds by the plant, it is referred to as **organic phosphate**. Moving through food chains, organic phosphate is transferred from producers to the rest of the ecosystem. As with carbon, at each step it is highly likely that the organic compounds containing phosphate will be broken down in cell respiration or by decomposers, releasing PO_4^{3-} in urine or other waste material. Phosphate is then reabsorbed by plants to start the cycle again.

Phosphorus enters into complex chemical reactions with other substances that are not shown in this simplified version of the cycle. For example, PO_4^{3-} forms solid, insoluble compounds with a number of cations (positively charged ions),

Figure 3–19 **The global phosphorus cycle.** Phosphorus is a limiting factor in many ecosystems. Note that the cycle is not connected to the atmosphere, which limits biosphere recycling.

such as iron (Fe^{3+}), aluminum (Al^{3+}), and calcium (Ca^{3+}). Phosphorus can bind with these ions to form chemical precipitates (solid, insoluble compounds) that are largely unavailable to plants. The precipitated phosphorus can slowly release PO_4^{3-} as plants withdraw naturally occurring PO_4^{3-} from soil, water, or sediments.

Human Impacts. The most serious human intrusion into the phosphorus cycle comes from the use of phosphorus-containing fertilizers. Phosphorus is mined in several locations around the world (e.g., Florida in the United States) and is then made into fertilizers, animal feeds, detergents, and other products. Phosphorus is a common limiting factor in soils and, when added to croplands, can greatly stimulate production.

Unfortunately, human applications have tripled the amount of phosphorus reaching the oceans. This increase is roughly equal to the global use of phosphorus fertilizer in agriculture. Humans are accelerating the natural phosphorus cycle as it is mined from the earth and as it subsequently moves from the soil into aquatic ecosystems, creating problems as it makes its way to the oceans. There is essentially no way to return this waterborne phosphorus to the soil, so the bodies of water end up overfertilized. This leads in turn to a severe water pollution problem known as eutrophication (Chapter 17). Eutrophication can cause the overgrowth of algae, too many bacteria, and the death of fish.

The Nitrogen Cycle

The nitrogen cycle (**Fig. 3–20**) has similarities to both the carbon cycle and the phosphorus cycle. Like carbon, nitrogen has a gas phase; like phosphorus, nitrogen acts as a limiting factor in plant growth. Like phosphorus, nitrogen is in high demand by both aquatic and terrestrial plants.

The nitrogen cycle is otherwise unique. Most notably, unlike in the other cycles, bacteria in soils, water, and sediments perform many of the steps of the nitrogen cycle.

The main reservoir of nitrogen is the air, which is about 78% nitrogen gas (N_2). This form of nitrogen is called **nonreactive nitrogen**; most organisms are not able to use it in chemical reactions. The remaining forms of nitrogen are called **reactive nitrogen** (Nr) because they are used by most organisms and can make chemical reactions more easily.

Plants in terrestrial ecosystems ("non-N-fixing producers" in Figure 3–20) take up Nr as ammonium ions (NO_4^+) or nitrate ions (NO_3^-). The plants incorporate the nitrogen into essential organic compounds such as proteins and nucleic acids. The nitrogen then moves from producers through consumers and, finally, to decomposers (organisms that live on dead plant and animal matter are referred to as "heterotrophs" in Figure 3–20). At various points, nitrogen wastes are released, primarily as ammonium compounds. A group of soil bacteria, the *nitrifying bacteria*, oxidizes the ammonium to nitrate in a process that yields energy for the

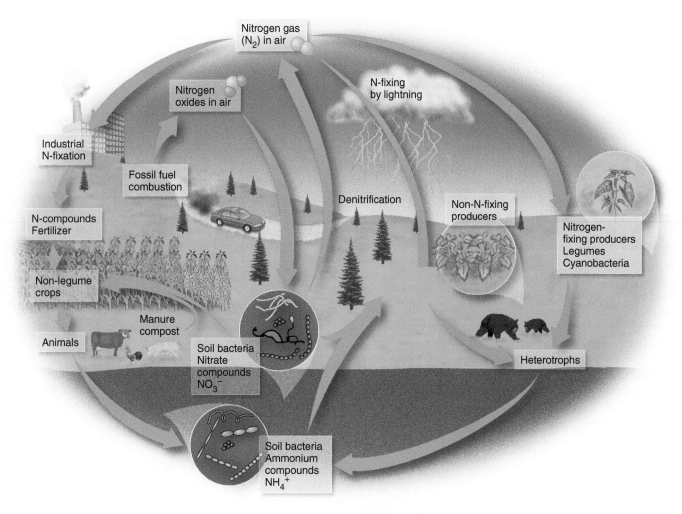

Figure 3–20 The global nitrogen cycle. Like phosphorus, nitrogen is often a limiting factor. Its cycle heavily involves different groups of bacteria.

bacteria. At this point, the nitrate is once again available for uptake by green plants—a local ecosystem cycle within the global cycle. In most ecosystems, the supply of Nr is quite limited, yet there is an abundance of nonreactive N—if it can be accessed. The nitrogen cycle in aquatic ecosystems (not shown in Figure 3–20) is similar.

Nitrogen Fixation. A number of bacteria and cyanobacteria (chlorophyll-containing bacteria, formerly referred to as blue-green algae) can use nonreactive N through a process called biological **nitrogen fixation**. In terrestrial ecosystems, the most important among these nitrogen-fixing microbes live in nodules on the roots of legumes, the plant family that includes peas and beans. The legume provides the bacteria with a place to live and with food (carbohydrates and proteins) and gains a source of nitrogen in return. From legumes, nitrogen enters the food web. The legume family includes a huge diversity of plants. Without them, plant production would be sharply impaired due to a lack of available nitrogen.

Three other important processes also "fix" nitrogen. One is the conversion of nitrogen gas to the ammonium form by discharges of lightning in a process known as *atmospheric*

nitrogen fixation; the ammonium then comes down with rainfall. The second is the *industrial fixation* of nitrogen in the manufacture of fertilizer; the Haber-Bosch process converts nitrogen gas and hydrogen to ammonia, by an industrial process using fossil fuels. This is the main source of agricultural fertilizer. The third is a consequence of the *combustion of fossil fuels*, during which nitrogen from coal and oil is oxidized; some nitrogen gas is also oxidized during high-temperature combustion. These last two processes lead to nitrogen oxides (NO_x) in the atmosphere, which are soon converted to nitric acid and then brought down to Earth as acid precipitation (Chapter 19).

Denitrification. Denitrification is a microbial process that occurs in soils and sediments depleted of oxygen. A number of microbes can take nitrate (which is highly oxidized) and use it as a substitute for oxygen. In so doing, the nitrogen is reduced (it gains electrons) to nitrogen gas and released back into the atmosphere. In sewage treatment systems, denitrification is a desirable process and is promoted to remove nitrogen from the wastewater before it is released in soluble form to the environment (Chapter 20).

Human Impacts.   Human involvement in the nitrogen cycle is substantial. Many agricultural crops are legumes (peas, beans, soybeans, alfalfa), so they draw nitrogen from the air, thus increasing the rate of nitrogen fixation on land. Crops that are nonleguminous (corn, wheat, potatoes, cotton, and so on) are heavily fertilized with nitrogen derived from industrial fixation. Both processes benefit human welfare profoundly. Also, fossil fuel combustion fixes nitrogen from the air (Fig. 3–19). However, human actions more than double the rate at which nitrogen is moved from the atmosphere to the land.

The consequences of this global nitrogen fertilization are serious. Nitric acid (and sulfuric acid, produced when sulfur is also released by burning fossil fuels) has destroyed thousands of lakes and ponds and caused extensive damage to forests (Chapter 19). Nitrogen oxides in the atmosphere contribute to ozone pollution, global climate change, and stratospheric ozone depletion (Chapter 18). Surplus nitrogen has led to "nitrogen saturation" of many natural areas, whereby nitrogen can no longer be incorporated into living matter and is released into the soil. Washed into surface waters, nitrogen makes its way to estuaries and coastal areas of oceans, where, just like phosphorus, it triggers a series of events leading to eutrophication, resulting in dead seafood, detriments to human health, and areas of oceans that are unfit for fish (Chapter 20). This complex of ecological effects has been called the **nitrogen cascade**, in recognition of the sequential impacts of Nr as it moves through environmental systems, creating problems as it goes.

The Sulfur Cycle

Sulfur is the last element we will investigate. Sulfur is important to living things because it is a component of many proteins, hormones, and vitamins. Sulfur is often linked in nature with oxygen atoms, as in sulfate (SO_4) (Fig. 3–21). Most of Earth's sulfur is found in rocks and minerals, including deep ocean sediments. Weathering of rocks and volcanic activity sends sulfur into the atmosphere or soil. Sulfur also gets into the air when fossil fuels are burned and when mined metals are processed. In soil, sulfate can be taken up by plants and microorganisms. In air, sulfur dioxide (SO_2) contributes to acid rain when it combines with water vapor and forms sulfuric acid. Sulfates are added to water bodies as sulfur compounds fall from the atmosphere or are weathered from rocks. There they can be serious pollutants.

Human Impacts.   The largest human impact of the sulfur cycle is the addition of sulfur oxides to the atmosphere and the addition of sulfates to water. Unlike phosphorus and

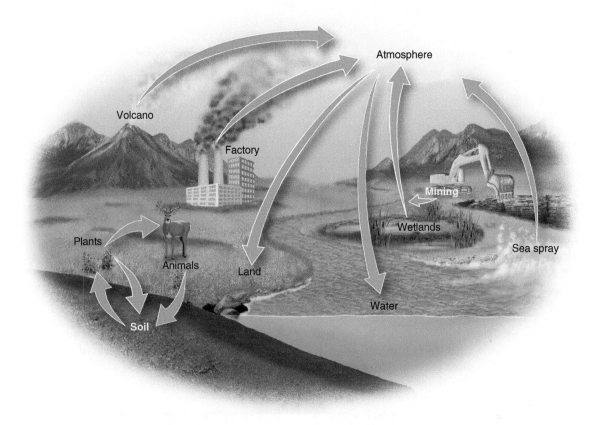

Figure 3–21 The global sulfur cycle. Sulfur spends little time in the atmosphere. Part of the cycle does rely on bacteria, but less than nitrogen's cycle. Like all three other cycles, the sulfur cycle is sped up by human activity.

SUSTAINABILITY Planetary Boundaries

Ancient peoples thought that Earth had an edge—if you took a ship too far, perhaps you and your crew would fall right off. Today, some scientists suggest that Earth has a metaphorical edge: a boundary where use of a particular resource becomes so great that it alters natural cycles and changes ecosystems. Reaching a point where dramatic changes are likely is called the tipping point, and the levels of change at which this might occur are called planetary boundaries, a term coined by Johann Rockström and his colleagues at Stockholm University, who together published a paper in 2009 entitled "Planetary Boundaries: Exploring the Safe Operating Space for Humanity." In that paper, they estimate that a safe boundary for nitrogen would be to "limit industrial and agricultural fixation of N_2 to 35 Tg N/yr."[1] (A terragram (Tg) is one billion kilograms.)

The innovation of the Haber-Bosch process for fixing nitrogen allowed humans to produce more food on the same amount of land than was possible previously. One estimate is that without nitrogen fertilizer, we would have needed four times the agricultural land in 2000 that we did in 1900 and half of all continental land would be needed for agriculture. The downside of so much fertilizer is that it washes into oceans, where it and other pollutants produce "dead zones" where oxygen is limited and most life cannot survive. Likewise, the use of fossil fuels has brought advantages to humans, but the acid rain created by the burning of these fuels kills lake fish.

Humanity might be reaching planetary boundaries or tipping points—where we suddenly experience ecological change that is difficult to reverse and that causes great changes to our ability even to feed ourselves. Just as a ship might have a lookout, scientists have an important role in helping us understand the world so that we can recognize when we are approaching or have passed planetary boundaries. If we have a way to estimate the consequences of what we are trying to do, such as this paper suggests, then both scientists and others will be involved in measuring those consequences and finding solutions for problems that arise. One place to start is to calculate your own nitrogen footprint. Just like a carbon footprint, a nitrogen footprint is calculated from your activities and tells you something about your own effect on the globe. You can find resource footprint calculators by searching on the Web. Scientists play a role in helping to make more efficient use of fertilizer and to make technologies to remove nitrogen from smoke in burning of fossil fuels. These advancements, coupled with the will of individuals to consume less and be wise consumers, are parts of the solution to avoid taking our global ship across a planetary boundary.

[1]Rockström, J. et al., 2009. "Planetary Boundaries: Exploring the Safe Operating Space for Humanity." *Ecology and Society* *14*(2): 32.

nitrogen, sulfur is not usually directly added to soils in order to improve their fertility. However, soil and water sulfate levels are increased by human action. Acid rain and water pollution are the major effects. For example, in heavily developed areas of the Everglades, the percent of sulfates in water is 60 times what it would normally be expected to be (Chapter 19). Sulfate compound aerosols (small particles or drops) also play a role in the climate. They act to temporarily cool the atmosphere, although the compounds cause other problems when they fall to earth.

Comparing the Cycles

The four cycles we have looked at in depth differ in some important ways (Table 3–2). Carbon is found in large amounts in the atmosphere in a form that can be directly taken in by plants, so carbon is rarely the limiting factor in the growth of vegetation. Both nitrogen and phosphorus are often limiting factors in ecosystems. Phosphorus has no gaseous atmospheric component (though it can be found in airborne dust particles) and thus, unless added to an ecosystem artificially, enters very slowly. Nitrogen is unique because of the importance of bacteria in driving the cycle forward. Sulfur can get into the atmosphere, but only for a short time. It is also different from the others because of its concentration in mining runoff.

All four cycles have been sped up considerably by human actions. Nitrogen compounds in the atmosphere

TABLE 3–2 Major Characteristics of the Carbon, Phosphorus, and Nitrogen Cycles

Nutrient	Major Source	Interesting Feature	Human Impact
Carbon	Air	Taken in directly by plant leaves	Burning fuel moves it to air from underground
Phosphorus	Rock	No atmospheric component	Fertilizer use adds it to waterways
Nitrogen	Soil/Air	Bacteria drive the cycle	Fertilizer moves it to soil, burning moves it to air
Sulfur	Rock	Spends only a short time in the atmosphere	Burning moves it to air, rain and mining move it to soil and water

contribute to acid rain, and carbon dioxide is being moved from underground storage in carbon molecules to the atmosphere, where it acts as a greenhouse gas. Both nitrogen and phosphorus are put on soil as fertilizer or get into water from sewage and runoff. Both act in water to promote overgrowth

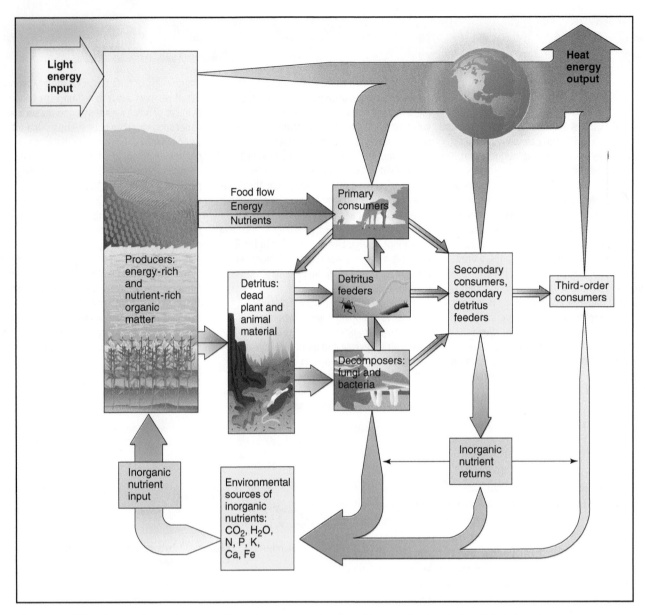

Figure 3–22 Nutrient cycles and energy flow. The movement of nutrients (blue arrows), energy (red arrows), and both (brown arrows) through the ecosystem. Nutrients follow a cycle, being used over and over. Light energy absorbed by producers is released and lost as heat energy as it is "spent."

of algae (Chapter 20). Sulfur adds to acid rain and to water pollution.

Although we have focused on carbon, phosphorus, nitrogen, and sulfur, cycles exist for oxygen, hydrogen, iron, and all the other elements that play a role in living things. While the routes taken by distinct elements may differ, all of the cycles are going on simultaneously, and all come together in the tissues of living things. As elements cycle through ecosystems, energy flows in from the Sun and through the living members of the ecosystems. The links between these two fundamental processes of ecosystem function are shown in **Figure 3–22**.

In this chapter, we introduced the various fields of ecology and showed that the science of ecology encompasses living things and their relationships with each other and the environment. We looked at two ecological levels in greater detail in this chapter—what is happening with individuals (organismal ecology) and what is happening to the large-scale movement of matter and energy through the biosphere (ecosystem ecology). To understand the flow of matter and energy, we also included some background on the basics of atoms, molecules, and the laws of energy. Later, we will investigate the other subdisciplines of ecology introduced here, especially population ecology and community ecology.

REVISITING THE THEMES

Sound Science

Ecology is the science of living things and the abiotic and biotic components interacting with them. Ecologists can study on a variety of levels. In this chapter, we looked at organismal ecology and ecosystem ecology—that is, how materials work in individual animals and how matter and energy flow throughout the world.

Much of this chapter is about how the basic processes of the natural world work, focusing on matter and energy. Both matter and energy are limited. Matter cycles in the form of molecules (sets of atoms) through living things and the abiotic environment. Energy flows in one direction—from the Sun, through activities on Earth, and back out into space. Using the giant panda and its food (the bamboo plant) as our examples, we demonstrated basic principles of organization within their bodies and the flow of energy and materials through their systems. The bamboo plant has a specific niche, or set of parameters, within which it needs to live. These resources and conditions include the amount of rainfall and nutrients it needs, for example. Because it has chlorophyll, bamboo is able to undergo photosynthesis. In this chemical process, inorganic building blocks are turned into more-complex organic molecules whose bonds contain more chemical energy than their original components do. This energy can be released when the panda eats the bamboo and its body burns those molecules through a controlled process of cellular respiration. Energy is lost at each step of this energy path. In order to build the bodies of the bamboo and its consumer, the panda, a number of nutrients need to be available. The cycles for four of these (carbon, phosphorus, nitrogen, and sulfur) were described. Humans affect these biogeochemical cycles by actions such as the burning of fossil fuels and the fertilization of agricultural land.

Sustainability

The science in this chapter that leads to specific management actions is primarily that surrounding the needs of individual species in terms of habitat and niche, the consequences of limits on nutrients and energy, and the impacts of human effects on biogeochemical cycles. These ideas will be more thoroughly explored later. For instance, the science surrounding habitat and niche underlies our understanding of why some types of organisms are particularly vulnerable to extinction (Chapter 4). The science underlying the nitrogen and phosphorus cycles is important to management decisions about water pollution (Chapter 20). Finally, the science about carbon and nitrogen cycles aids in our understanding of air pollution and global climate change (Chapters 18 and 19). The sustainability essay provides a good example of how science is used to identify boundaries, and this can be used to manage our global environment—in this case, the nitrogen cycle.

The giant panda helps us look at basic processes within organisms and the flow of matter and energy. Later, we will look at ways individuals relate to members of their own species (population ecology) and ways species relate to other species (community ecology).

Stewardship

The giant panda, focused on throughout this chapter, is in decline. It has a particular habitat, which is shrinking because of competition with human activities. As stewards, the panda conservationists in China and around the world are protecting not only the panda, but also its habitat. Human activity also speeds up biogeochemical cycles, and this can have global effects. All of us have to be stewards not only of the nutrients in our world, but also of the natural processes that move chemicals from one part of a cycle to another. Stewardship involves protecting not only resources but ecosystem functions. We will look at some of the ethical and justice implications of these scientific realities in other chapters. We will ask, "Why protect other species?" (Chapter 6). We will also look at the implications of energy loss at every transfer and apply those principles to human population growth and the need for food (Chapter 8).

REVIEW QUESTIONS

1. Distinguish between the biotic community and the abiotic environmental factors of an ecosystem.

2. Define and compare the terms *species*, *population*, and *ecosystem*.

3. Compared with an ecosystem, what are an ecotone, a landscape, a biome, and a biosphere?

4. How do the terms *organic* and *inorganic* relate to the biotic and abiotic components of an ecosystem?

5. What are the six key elements in living organisms?

6. What features distinguish between organic and inorganic molecules?

7. In one sentence, define *matter* and *energy*, and demonstrate how they are related.

8. Give four examples of potential energy. In each case, how can the potential energy be converted into kinetic energy?

9. State two energy laws. How do they relate to entropy?

10. What is the chemical equation for photosynthesis? Examine the origin and destination of each molecule referred to in the equation. Do the same for cellular respiration.

11. Describe the biogeochemical cycle of carbon as it moves into and through organisms and back to the environment. Do the same for phosphorus, nitrogen, and sulfur.

12. What are the major human impacts on the carbon, phosphorus, and nitrogen cycles?

THINKING ENVIRONMENTALLY

1. From local, national, and international news, compile a list of ways humans are altering abiotic and biotic factors on a local, regional, and global scale. Analyze ways in which local changes may affect ecosystems on larger scales and ways in which global changes may affect ecosystems locally.

2. Use the laws of conservation of matter and energy to describe the consumption of fuel by a car. That is, what are the inputs and outputs of matter and energy? (*Note:* Gasoline is a mixture of organic compounds containing carbon–hydrogen bonds.)

3. Using your knowledge of photosynthesis and cell respiration, draw a picture of the hydrogen cycle and the oxygen cycle. (*Hint:* Consult the four cycles in the book for guidance.)

4. Look up everything you can find about iron seeding of the oceans, and see if you can decide what you think we should do.

MAKING A DIFFERENCE

1. Find the closest farm that does not use artificial fertilizer. Many are listed on Web sites under the terms "community supported agriculture" or "CSA." See if you can arrange a visit. See what they do to lower their impact on the nitrogen and phosphorus cycles and still maintain fertile soil.

2. Visit the EPA's Web site to find out how you can help protect your local watershed. Its project database allows you to get involved in monitoring, cleanups, and restorations in your area.

3. Take one of the biogeochemical cycles and try to track your impact on it. This is most easily done with carbon. Search on the Web under "carbon footprint."

MasteringEnvironmentalScience®

Go to **www.masteringenvironmentalscience.com** for practice quizzes, Pearson eText, videos, current events, and more.

Volcano. Iceland's Eyjafjallajökull volcano shut down airspace for days in April 2010, injecting millions of tons of ash into the air but did not kill people or spew lava as many volcanoes do.

CHAPTER 5

Ecosystems:
Energy, Patterns, and Disturbance

LEARNING OBJECTIVES

1. **Characteristics of Ecosystems:** Describe how matter and energy flow through ecosystems by moving from one trophic level to another.

2. **The Flow of Energy Through the Food Web:** Explain three main ideas relating trophic pyramids with the relative numbers and biomasses of different levels in a food chain.

3. **From Ecosystems to Global Biomes:** Define and recognize characteristics of major broad regions called biomes, major aquatic regions, and factors that determine their placement on the globe.

4. **Ecosystem Reponses to Disturbance:** Explain the effects of ecological disturbances, such as a fire or volcanic eruption, which are normal in ecosystems and can even be beneficial.

5. **Human Values and Ecosystem Sustainability:** Describe ways that humans alter ecosystem services both positively and negatively, and explain why we need to manage ecosystems to protect their components from overuse.

C LOUDS OF SMOKE and ash accompanied rumblings of the earth as Iceland's volcano at Eyjafjallajökull ("EY-ya-fyat-lah-YOH-kuht") belched awake on April 14, 2010. The tremblors that had affected the area over the previous month increased, and a billowing cloud of ash erupted into a plume that rose 9 kilometers (30,000 feet) into the air. The ash spread across Western Europe, clouding the sky and closing down all air travel for days, the largest air traffic disruption since World War II. Thousands of travelers were stranded as the volcano spewed particles and gases into the atmosphere. Ash fell on the ground for miles, making the grasses unfit for consumption by cattle and horses and making driving impossible. Even so, Eyjafjallajökull was a moderate volcano, without the massive lava flows and mudslides that accompany many volcanic eruptions. People were relatively safe and, except for the cessation of air travel, life returned to normal quickly.

PREPARATION. The eruption of Mount Pinatubo on June 15, 1991, in the Philippines was larger and had more-serious global effects (Fig. 5–1). The eruption of this volcano, with no recorded history of eruptions, blew the top of the densely forested mountain into the air. This was the beginning of a process that spilled between 6 and 16 cubic kilometers of ash

(a)

(b)

Figure 5–1 Recovery from volcanic eruption. (a) The eruption of Mt. Pinatubo in 1991. (b) Changes in the ecosystem from that eruption continued even 15 years later. Sections of the hillsides remain denuded as intermittent landslides removed vegetation.

into the atmosphere, along with 20 million tons of sulfur dioxide and 10 billion metric tons of magma. Small particles known as aerosols were thrown into the air and traveled around the globe, blocking sunlight and lowering the global temperature by 0.5°C (0.9°F). More aerosols were produced by this volcanic eruption than any since Krakatoa in 1883. The sulfur found in the aerosols combined with water to form sulfuric acid, a component of acid rain. Fortunately, even though the volcano had not

erupted in years prior to the event, scientists were able to predict that it would, as seismic activity picked up in the months before the eruption, and they successfully prompted the largely successful evacuation of 60,000 people. Unfortunately, people did die in the aftermath, when typhoon rains and wet ash combined to collapse roofs and from illness due to crowded emergency housing. Today, years after the eruption, parts of Mount Pinatubo still lie denuded as periodic landslides move material down the hillside.

REBUILDING. Volcanoes, triggered by the movements of tectonic plates, relieve pressure building under the earth's crust and spread minerals into the soil. They may build new lands altogether by causing islands, such as the Hawaiian Islands, to rise out of the ocean. Often, volcanic eruptions kill many of the organisms living in their immediate vicinity, but such organisms return and recolonize in a process of succession. In this chapter, we will look at ecosystems and how they function, including the processes that occur after a disturbance like a wild fire, large flood, volcano, or retreat of a glacier. These processes offer us a chance to better understand the workings of an ecosystem.

Earlier, the focus was on the components of ecosystems (Chapters 3 and 4). We considered the environmental conditions and resources required by living things, the basic movement of energy and nutrients that sustain living things, and how populations work and relate to populations of other species. Now, we will look at how basic processes such as photosynthesis and respiration in individuals play out in complex systems and how energy moves from one part of the community to another. We will see how concepts like ranges of tolerance and limiting factors, which we applied to individuals, apply to large groups and control their distributions over large portions of Earth (Chapter 3). We will also look at how ecosystems change over time as a result of disturbances such as volcanoes. We'll see how vital ecosystems are to human well-being and look at efforts to assign value to the goods and services we derive from them. We will also see that ecosystem sustainability is being severely challenged by human use.

It is a popular belief that nature will be in balance if left alone. You will learn in this chapter, however, that an ecosystem is a dynamic system in which changes are constantly occurring. The notion of a balanced ecosystem, then, must be carefully defined. We will ask questions about balance, or equilibrium, in ecosystems: What does it mean for an ecosystem to be "in balance"? Are populations normally in a state of equilibrium? What happens when a major disturbance (like a fire) interrupts the "balance" in an ecosystem? Can ecosystems and the natural populations in them change over time yet maintain the important processes that make them sustainable?

Our objective in this chapter is to examine more of the basic mechanisms that underlie the sustainability of all ecosystems, including those heavily influenced by human use. We will look at the values, goods, and services of ecosystems and their importance to humans. The chapter concludes with some perspectives on the challenge of managing ecosystems and a summary of ecosystem sustainability issues.

5.1 Characteristics of Ecosystems

Mt. Pinatubo is located on the island of Luzon in the Philippines, an area with one of the largest forests in the country and home to some of the few remaining individuals of the national bird, the highly endangered Philippine eagle. We will look at this area to better understand the characteristics of ecosystems. The forest around Mt. Pinatubo, like all ecosystems, contains communities of interacting species and their abiotic factors. However, the species living in this ecosystem, or any other ecosystem, may function on very different scales, which makes it difficult to delineate a fixed boundary for ecosystems. For example, the lowland rain-forest ecosystem contains migratory birds that live there only seasonally. Some species inhabiting the ecosystem may also have little to no interaction with each other, such as the orchids high on branches of trees and organisms that live in leaf litter.

The rain forest around Mt. Pinatubo contrasts sharply with the treeless spaces of Iceland, where Eyjafjallajökull sent ash into the air. As we will see later in the chapter, what lives in an ecosystem is a function not only of characteristics of the regional climate, but of the landscape's history—including the actions of humans. Even so, there are predictable patterns to the distribution of ecosystems around the globe. Ecosystems that have a similar type of vegetation and similar climactic conditions are grouped into broader areas called **biomes,** such as the tropical rain-forest biome. (We will look at biomes in more depth in Section 5.4.)

Just as the study of communities raises questions about relationships that cannot be answered by looking at species separately, the study of ecosystems allows us to understand concepts that cannot be predicted by understanding community interactions alone. For example, community relationships such as predation and parasitism (discussed in Chapter 4) provide the mechanisms for the flow of energy—as well as the flow of carbon, nitrogen, and phosphorus—through the natural world (discussed in Chapter 3). But these community relationships may not tell us about ecosystem properties, such as how much photosynthesis occurs in all plants or how much water can be absorbed by all of the plants at once. In this chapter, we will pull together the concepts presented in the previous two chapters, abiotic forces and biotic interactions, to look at characteristics of ecosystems—specifically, **trophic levels, productivity,** and **consumption.**

Trophic Levels, Food Chains, and Food Webs

Imagine a grassy meadow containing a variety of plants. As discussed in previous chapters, plants use energy from the Sun through the process of photosynthesis to produce complex chemical chains from more-simple molecules such as carbon dioxide and water. These plants can then be eaten by their predators, such as grasshoppers, mice, or even elk (remember that herbivory is a subset of predation). In turn, the grasshopper could be eaten by its predator, a bird; the

mouse eaten by an owl; and the elk fed on by a parasite or eaten by a wolf. Energy in the form of chemical bonds and nutrients in the form of molecules in the bodies of the prey are then used by the next **trophic level** (feeding level)—the predators—for energy and other physiological needs. This breakdown of chemical bonds to release energy is called cellular respiration. Recall that plants need to respire, too.

You can imagine two things from this. First, organisms can be linked into feeding chains—the grass to the mouse, to the snake, to the eagle, for example. Such **food chains** describe where the energy and nutrients go as they move from one organism to another. We usually refer to this as energy moving "up" the food chain. Second, you can imagine that the energy and nutrients are not all passed up the chain from one level to the next. Because of the energy laws we discussed, there is inefficiency every time one organism eats another (Chapter 3). While it is interesting to trace these feeding pathways, it is important to recognize that food chains seldom exist as isolated entities. Mice feed on several kinds of plants, are preyed on by several kinds of animals, and so on. Some organisms, including humans, eat at more than one level in the food chain. Consequently, virtually all food chains are interconnected and form a complex web of feeding relationships—the **food web** (Fig. 5–2).

Rather than simply asking what predators are eating snakes and how they affect the snake population or what mice are eating and how food availability affects mice, we ask different types of questions in ecosystem ecology—those that focus on trophic levels in general, in order to study bigger trends in the movement of energy and materials. Examples of these questions include the following: How much of the Sun's energy do the plants in the meadow trap? How much do they use, and how much is available to plant eaters? How many predators can the ecosystem support? These questions emphasize the broader aspects of the flow of energy and materials through ecosystems, not through individual species. In order to answer these questions, ecologists divide members in the food web into categories.

Trophic Categories

All organisms in the biosphere can be categorized as either autotrophs or heterotrophs, depending on whether they produce the organic compounds they need to survive and grow. Green plants, photosynthetic single-celled organisms, and chemosynthetic bacteria are **autotrophs** (*auto* = self; *troph* = feeding) because they produce their own organic material from inorganic constituents in their environment through the use of an external energy source. They are also referred to as producers. Organisms that must consume organic material to obtain energy are **heterotrophs** (*hetero* = other; *troph* = feeding). Heterotrophs may be divided into numerous categories, the two major ones being consumers (which eat living prey) and **decomposers** (which break down dead organic material and can include scavengers, detritus feeders, and chemical decomposers). Together, producers, consumers, and decomposers produce food, pass it along

(a)

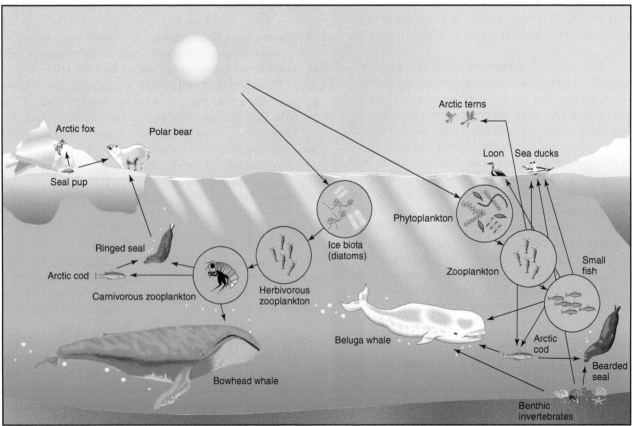

(b)

Figure 5–2 Food webs. (a) The arrows show herbivores feeding on plants and carnivores feeding on herbivores. Specific pathways, such as that from nuts to squirrels to foxes, are referred to as *food chains*. A food web
is the collection of all food chains, which are invariably interconnected. (b) The marine food web in the offshore
Beaufort Sea (north of Alaska and Canada) in spring.

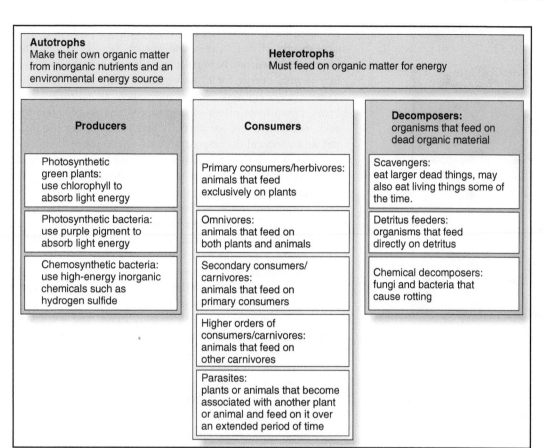

Figure 5–3 Trophic categories. A summary of how living organisms are ecologically categorized according to how they get their energy.

food chains, and return the starting materials to the abiotic parts of the environment (Fig. 5–3).

Producers. As we have seen, producers are organisms that capture energy from the Sun or from chemical reactions to convert carbon dioxide (CO_2) to organic matter (Chapter 3). Most producers are green plants. Through the process of photosynthesis, these plants use light energy to convert CO_2 and water to organic compounds such as glucose (a sugar) and then release oxygen as a by-product. Plants use a variety of molecules to capture light energy in photosynthesis, but the most predominant of these is **chlorophyll**, a green pigment. Hence, plants that photosynthesize are easily identified by their green color. In some producers, additional red or brown photosynthetic pigments (in red and brown algae, for example) may mask the green. Producers range in diversity from microscopic photosynthetic bacteria and single-celled algae through medium-sized plants such as grass, daisies, and cacti to gigantic trees. Every major ecosystem, both aquatic and terrestrial, has its particular producers that are actively engaged in photosynthesis.

Interestingly, there are bacteria, including some in the hot springs at Yellowstone National Park, that are able to use the energy in some inorganic chemicals to form organic matter from CO_2 and water. This process is called **chemosynthesis**, and the organisms using it are producers, too. Producers are absolutely essential to every ecosystem. The photosynthesis and growth of producers such as green plants constitute the **primary production** of organic matter, which sustains all other organisms in the ecosystem.

Consumers. All organisms other than producers in an ecosystem feed on organic matter as their source of energy. These heterotrophs include not only all animals, but also fungi (mushrooms, molds, and similar organisms) and most bacteria. For ease of discussion, heterotrophs are often divided into consumers, which eat living prey, and decomposers, which break down dead organic material. Consumers encompass a wide variety of organisms, ranging in size from plankton to blue whales. Among consumers are such diverse groups as protozoans, worms, fish, shellfish, insects, reptiles, amphibians, birds, and mammals (including humans).

For the purpose of understanding ecosystem structure, consumers are divided into various subgroups according to their food source. Animals—as large as elephants or as small as mites—that feed directly on producers are called **primary consumers** or **herbivores** (*herb* = grass). Animals that feed on primary consumers are called **secondary consumers**. Thus, mice, which feed on vegetation, are primary consumers, whereas snakes are secondary consumers because they feed on mice (Fig. 5–4). There may also be third (tertiary), fourth (quaternary), or even higher levels of consumers. Many animals occupy more than one position on the consumer scale. For instance, humans are primary consumers when they eat vegetables, secondary consumers when they eat beef, and tertiary consumers when they eat fish that feed on smaller fish that feed on algae. Secondary and higher-order consumers are also called **carnivores** (*carni* = meat). Consumers that feed on both plants and animals are called **omnivores** (*omni* = all).

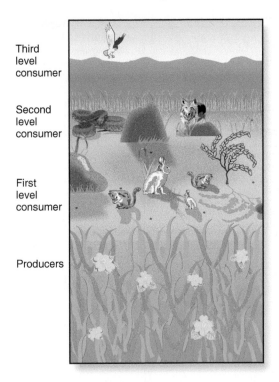

Figure 5–4 **A grassland food chain.** A grassland food chain, showing the producers (plants) and the first-, second-, and third-order consumers (mouse, snake, and hawk, respectively).

Decomposers. A very large proportion of the primary producer trophic level is not consumed in the grazing food web. As this material dies (leaves drop, grasses wither, and so on), it is joined by the fecal wastes and dead bodies from higher trophic levels and is referred to as *detritus*. This represents the starting point for a separate food web. In many cases, most of the energy in an ecosystem flows through the detritus food web (**Fig. 5–5**).

Detritus is composed largely of cellulose because it consists mostly of dead leaves, the woody parts of plants, and animal fecal wastes. Nevertheless, it is still organic and high in potential energy for those organisms that can digest it—namely, decomposers. Scavengers, such as vultures, help break down large pieces of organic matter; detritus feeders, such as earthworms, eat partially decomposing organic matter; and chemical decomposers (various species of fungi and bacteria as well as a few other microbes) break down dead material on the molecular scale. Decomposers act as any other consumer does, using the organic matter as a source of both energy and nutrients. Some, such as termites, can digest woody material because they maintain decomposer microorganisms in their guts in a mutualistic, symbiotic relationship. The termite (a detritus feeder) provides a cozy home for microbes (chemical decomposers) and takes in cellulose, which the microbes digest for both their own and the termites' benefit (**Fig. 5–6**). The decomposers, breaking down detritus, serve as the primary consumers in this food chain. The detritus is similar to the "producer" trophic level, and the decomposers have their own predators that form higher trophic levels.

Most decomposers use oxygen for cell respiration, which breaks detritus down into carbon dioxide, water, and mineral nutrients. Likewise, there is a release of waste heat, which you may observe as the "steaming" of a manure or compost pile on a cold day. The release of nutrients by decomposers is vitally important to the primary producers because it is the major source of nutrients in most ecosystems. However, some decomposers (certain bacteria and yeasts) meet their energy needs through the partial breakdown of glucose, which can occur in the absence of oxygen. This modified form of cell respiration, called **fermentation**, results in end products such as ethyl alcohol, methane gas,

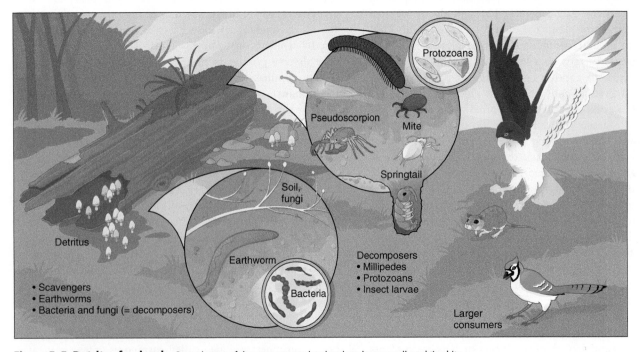

Figure 5–5 **Detritus food web.** Several types of decomposers work to break up large, small, and tiny bits of dead organic matter. These organisms in turn are eaten by other, higher-level consumers. In the detritus food web, the role of the producer is played by dead plant and animal matter.

Figure 5–6 Termite gut. Termites can live on cellulose-based woody matter because their guts contain a consortium of symbiotic microbes able to digest cellulose. In this electron micrograph, the symbionts are on the left and the termite intestinal wall is on the right.

in a mutualistic, symbiotic relationship similar to that just described for termites. As a result, both cattle and termites release methane.

Limits on Trophic Levels. How many trophic levels are there? Usually, there are no more than three or four in terrestrial ecosystems and sometimes five in marine systems (Fig. 5–2). This answer comes from straightforward observations. If you were to capture all of the organisms on each trophic level over a particular area or volume, dry them, and weigh them, you would find a pattern: The **biomass,** or total combined (net dry) weight, would be roughly 90% less at each higher trophic level for a terrestrial ecosystem (Fig. 5–7). For example, if you dried and weighed all of the grass and other producers in an acre of grassland, you might have 907 kilograms (1 ton or 2,000 lbs) per acre. If you could capture, dry, and weigh all of the herbivores (everything from grasshoppers to bison) in the same acre, you would find the biomass of herbivores would be about 90.7 kilograms (200 lbs) per acre. Following that pattern, the same acre would yield about 9.7 kilograms (20 lbs) of primary carnivores (animals living on grasshoppers and bison) if you captured, dried, and weighed them. At this rate, you can't go through very many trophic levels before the biomass approaches zero. If you graphed the different levels of producer and consumer mass, you would have what is commonly called a **biomass pyramid** (Fig. 5–7). We'll see the reason for this pattern as we look at where energy and nutrients go.

and acetic acid. In nature, **anaerobic,** or oxygen-free, environments commonly exist in the sediments of lakes, marshes, and swamps and in the guts of animals, where oxygen does not penetrate readily. Methane gas is commonly produced in these locations. A number of large grazing animals, including cattle, maintain fermenting bacteria in their digestive systems

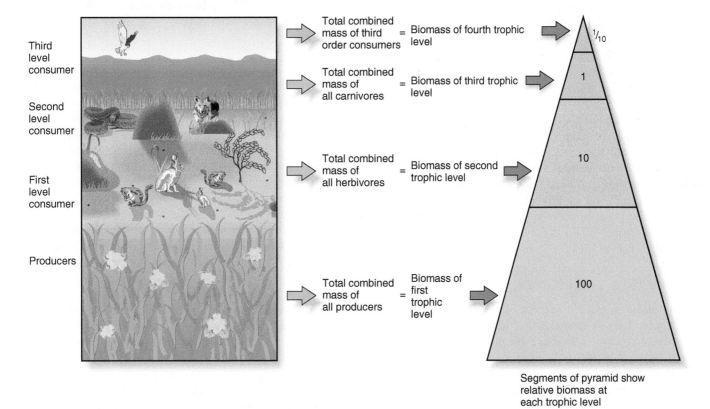

Figure 5–7 A biomass pyramid. A graphical representation of the biomass (the total combined mass of organisms) at successive trophic levels has the form of a pyramid, with about 10% of the energy contained in one trophic level being incorporated into the bodies of the next trophic level, giving each level a smaller biomass.

5.2 The Flow of Energy in Ecosystems

In most ecosystems, sunlight (or solar energy) is the initial source of energy absorbed by producers through the process of photosynthesis. The only exceptions are rare ecosystems, such as those near the ocean floor, where the producers are chemosynthetic bacteria. Primary production—the production of organic molecules from the Sun's energy through photosynthesis—captures only about 2%, at most, of incoming solar energy. Even though this seems like a small fraction, the resulting terrestrial net production—estimated at some 120 gigatons (billion metric tons, 1.1 billion U.S. tons) of organic matter per year—is enough to fuel all of the life in a biome. In a given ecosystem, the actual biomass of primary producers at any given time is referred to as the standing-crop biomass. Both biomass and primary production vary greatly in different ecosystems. For example, a forested ecosystem maintains a very large biomass compared with tropical grassland because so much carbon is captured in the wood of trees. However, the rate of primary production could be higher in the grassland; grazing animals might simply eat the produced organic matter. Consequently, standing biomass is not always a good measure of productivity.

The Fate of Food

Whereas 60–90% of the food that consumers eat, digest, and absorb is oxidized (burned) for energy, the remaining 10–40%, which is converted to the body tissues of the consumer, is no less important. This is the fraction that enables a body to grow, maintain, and repair itself. A portion of what is ingested by consumers is not digested, but simply passes through the digestive system and out as fecal wastes. For consumers that eat plants, this waste is largely **cellulose**, the material of plant cell walls. It is often referred to as fiber, bulk, or roughage, and some of it is a necessary part of the diet. The intestines need to push some fiber through them so that they can stay clean and open. Waste products can also include compounds of nitrogen, phosphorus, and any other elements present, in addition to the usual carbon dioxide and water. These by-products are excreted in the urine (or as similar waste in other kinds of animals) and returned to the environment. This process was illustrated previously (Chapter 3, Figure 3–17).

Energy Flow and Efficiency

As the biomass pyramid suggests, when energy flows from one trophic level to the next, only a small fraction is actually passed on. This is due to three things: (1) Much of the preceding trophic level is biomass that is not consumed by herbivores, (2) much of what is consumed is used as energy to fuel the heterotroph's cells and tissues, and (3) some of what is consumed is undigested and passes through the organism as waste (e.g., feces). Thus, there is a tremendous inefficiency at each trophic level, and energy is lost to the food web. In an ecosystem, therefore, only the portion of food that becomes the body tissue of the consumer can become food for the next organism in the food chain. Incorporating matter and energy from a lower trophic level into the body of a consumer is often referred to as secondary production, and like primary production, it can be expressed as a rate (the amount of growth of the consumer, or consumer trophic level) over time.

The inefficiency of trophic levels means two things. First, individuals at higher levels in the biomass pyramid represent a greater amount of the Sun's energy for the same amount of body tissue. For example, a pound of hamburger requires a great deal more photosynthesis to create than a pound of soybeans. This may be counterintuitive, because we just saw that there is less energy at each trophic level, but it requires a great deal more energy to produce a top-order consumer than a mid-level consumer and, likewise, more energy to produce a mid-level consumer than a producer of the same body weight. It usually also takes a longer time to produce a top-order consumer than a mid-level consumer or a producer. The top-order consumer also requires more water and other resources for a unit of body weight. In later chapters, as we look at food production in a crowded world, we will see why this matters.

Second, some materials are difficult to get rid of (such as chemicals that dissolve in fat) and therefore remain throughout an organism's life. These chemicals remain in the bodies of predators at higher rates than in their prey and thus biomagnify or **bioaccumulate** (build up in the tissues) as you go up the food chain. This is the reason, as we will see later, that some toxins build up in the tissues of higher-order consumers such as eagles and tuna.

Aquatic Systems

For simplicity, the focus of this chapter has been on terrestrial ecosystems. Keep in mind, though, that exactly the same processes occur in aquatic ecosystems. As aquatic plants and algae absorb dissolved carbon dioxide and mineral nutrients from the water, they use photosynthesis to produce food and dissolved oxygen that sustain consumers and other heterotrophs. Likewise, aquatic heterotrophs return carbon dioxide and mineral nutrients to the aquatic environment.

There are two differences between aquatic and terrestrial systems in this regard, however. First, the transfer of energy is often more efficient in an aquatic system. There are also more cold-blooded animals here, and less energy is required to run the bodies of cold-blooded creatures than warm-blooded creatures. It also takes less energy to support body weight in water than on land or in the air. Consequently, when less energy is used at each level, more energy is available to the next level, and food chains can be longer.

Second, aquatic systems do not always result in the same kind of biomass pyramid as terrestrial systems. If you went out to a lake and captured all of the algae, all of the zooplankton eating the algae, all of the fish that live on

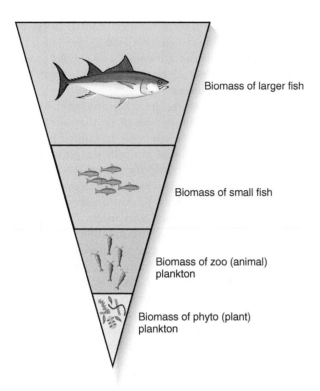

Figure 5–8 Reverse pyramid in aquatic systems. In aquatic systems such as this lake, there is a small amount of algae and a much greater biomass of large fish at any one moment. This is because the turnover is very high and life spans are so short at the lower trophic levels. The longer life spans of the upper trophic levels mean that the biomass of a fish, for example, includes all of its growth over a period of time.

zooplankton, and all of the fish that live on fish, and if you then dried and weighed them in their group, you might find a reverse biomass pyramid **(Fig. 5–8)**. The reason for this upside-down pyramid is that the fish that live on fish are the oldest and largest and the algae have very short life spans and turn over rapidly. Thus, there might be more biomass in the fish, but they had to eat many times that amount of algae to form that tissue. The algae actually in the water at any one time can be small, but they have an extremely rapid rate of new production.

5.3 From Ecosystems to Global Biomes

Just as photosynthesis processes and basic energy laws translate into broad patterns in food chain length in an ecosystem, broad patterns in ecosystems translate into a pattern we see all over the globe: There is a predictable set of organisms that live under particular conditions, such as deserts occurring in dry areas and rain forests occurring in very wet areas, for example. We can now use the concepts of optimums and limiting factors and the concepts of differences in light and productivity to gain a better understanding of why different

regions (or even localized areas) may have distinct biotic communities, creating an amazing variety of ecosystems, landscapes, and biomes.

A **biome** can be defined as a large geographical biotic community, controlled by climate. They are usually named after the dominant type of vegetation, such as deciduous forest or grassland. While the Greater Yellowstone region is an ecosystem (and possibly could be viewed as more than one), it is contained within a vast geographical region, or global biome, called the northern temperate forest. Like ecosystems, biomes have fuzzy edges. Aquatic areas such as the tidal zone and the open ocean can also be characterized by temperature and light and divided into categories. These are not typically called biomes, but function similarly.

The Role of Climate

The climate of a given region is a description of the average temperature and precipitation—the weather—that may be expected on each day throughout the entire year. Climates in different parts of the world vary widely. Equatorial regions are continuously warm, with high rainfall and no discernible seasons. Above and below the equator, temperatures become increasingly seasonal (characterized by warm or hot summers and cool or cold winters); the farther we go toward the poles, the longer and colder the winters become, until at the poles it is perpetually cold. Likewise, colder temperatures are found at higher elevations, so that there are even snowcapped mountains on or near the equator **(Fig. 5–9)**.

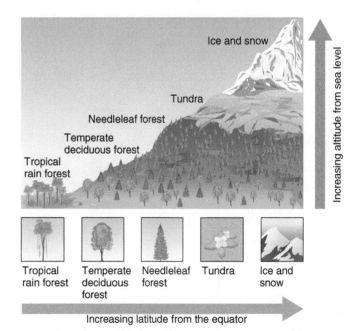

Figure 5–9 Effects of latitude and altitude. Decreasing temperatures, which result in the biome shifts depicted, occur with both increasing latitude (distance from the equator) and increasing altitude. (*Source:* Redrawn from *Geosystems,* 5th ed., by Robert W. Christopherson. Copyright © 2005 by Pearson Prentice Hall, Inc., Upper Saddle River, NJ 07458.)

Annual precipitation in an area also may vary greatly, from virtually zero to well over 250 centimeters (100 in.) per year. Precipitation may be evenly distributed throughout the year or concentrated in certain months, dividing the year into wet and dry seasons. A given climate will support only those species that find the temperature and precipitation levels within their ranges of tolerance. Population densities will be greatest where conditions are optimal and will decrease as any condition departs from the optimum (Chapter 3, Fig. 3–7). A species will be excluded from a region (or local areas) where any condition is beyond its limit of tolerance. How will this variation affect the biotic community?

Biome Examples. Individual ranges of tolerance, particularly for temperature and precipitation, determine where dominant species can live. In turn, the distribution of these species describes the placement of the biomes. To illustrate, let us consider six major types of biomes and their global distribution. Table 5–1 describes these terrestrial biomes and their major characteristics, and Figure 5–10 shows the distribution of the biomes as they occur globally. Within the temperate zone (between 30° and 50° of latitude), the amount of rainfall is the key limiting factor. The **temperate deciduous forest** biome is found where annual precipitation is 75–200 centimeters (30–80 in.). Where rainfall tapers off or is highly seasonal (25–150 cm or 10–60 in. per year), the **grassland** and **prairie** biomes are found, and regions receiving an average of less than 25 centimeters (10 in.) per year are occupied by a **desert biome.**

The effect of temperature, the other dominant parameter of climate, is largely superimposed on that of rainfall. That is, 75 centimeters (30 in.) or more of rainfall per year will usually support a forest, and generally temperature will determine the type of forest that grows there. For example, broad-leaved evergreen species, which are extremely vigorous and fast growing but cannot tolerate freezing temperatures, predominate in the **tropical rain forest.** By dropping their leaves and becoming dormant each autumn, deciduous trees are well adapted to freezing temperatures. Therefore, wherever rainfall is sufficient, deciduous forests predominate in temperate latitudes. Most deciduous trees, however, cannot tolerate the extremely harsh winters and short summers that occur at higher latitudes and higher elevations. These northern regions and high elevations are occupied by the **coniferous forest biome,** because conifers are better adapted to those conditions.

Temperature by itself limits forests only when it becomes low enough to cause **permafrost** (permanently frozen subsoil). Permafrost prevents the growth of trees, because

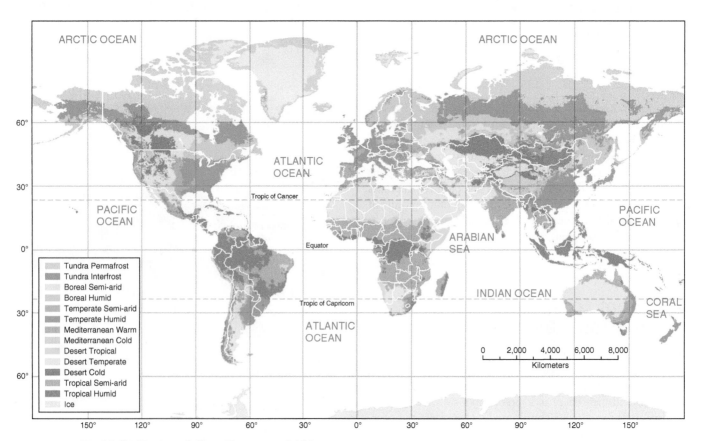

Figure 5–10 World distribution of the major terrestrial biomes. Photos and climate data for these biomes are maintained by the National Aeronautics and Space Administration's Earth Observatory.

USDA Natural Resources Conservation Service

roots cannot penetrate deeply enough in these conditions to provide adequate support. However, a number of grasses, clovers, and other small flowering plants can grow in the topsoil above permafrost. Consequently, where permafrost sets in, the coniferous forest biome gives way to the **tundra biome** (Table 5–1). At still colder temperatures, the tundra gives way to permanent snow and ice cover.

The same relationship of rainfall effects being primary and temperature effects secondary applies in deserts. Any region receiving less than about 25 centimeters (10 in.) of rain per year will be a desert, but the unique plant and animal species found in hot deserts are different from those found in cold deserts. A summary of the relationship between biomes and

temperature and rainfall conditions is given in Figure 5–11. The average temperature for a region varies with both **latitude** (distance from equator) and **altitude** (distance from sea level), as shown in Figure 5–9.

Examples of Aquatic Systems. The biome category is reserved exclusively for terrestrial systems. However, there are major categories of aquatic and wetland ecosystems similar to biomes that are determined primarily by the depth, salinity, and permanence of water in them. Among these ecosystems are lakes, marshes, streams, rivers, estuaries, bays, and ocean systems. As units of study, these aquatic systems may be viewed as ecosystems, as parts of landscapes, or as major

TABLE 5–1 Major Terrestrial Biomes

Biome	Climate and Soils	Dominant Vegetation	Dominant Animal Life	Geographic Distribution
Deserts	Very dry; hot days, cold nights; rainfall less than 10 in. (25 cm)/yr; soils thin and porous	Widely scattered thorny bushes and shrubs, cacti	Rodents, lizards, snakes, numerous insects, owls, hawks, small birds	North and southwest Africa, parts of the Middle East and Asia, Southwestern North America
Grasslands and Prairies	Seasonal rainfall, 10 to 60 in. (25–152 cm)/yr; fires frequent; soils rich and often deep	Grass species, both tall and short; bushes and woodlands in some areas	Large grazing mammals (bison, wild horses; kangaroos); prairie dogs, coyotes, lions; termites important	Central North America, central Asia, subequatorial Africa and South America, southern India, northern Australia
Tropical Rain Forests	Nonseasonal; annual average temperature 28°C; rainfall frequent, heavy; average over 95 in. (240 cm)/yr; soils thin, poor in nutrients	High diversity of broad-leafed evergreen trees, dense canopy, vines	Enormous biodiversity; exotic, colorful insects, amphibians, birds, snakes; monkeys, tigers, jaguars	Northern South America, Central America, western central Africa, islands in Indian and Pacific Oceans, Southeast Asia
Temperate Forests	Seasonal; temperature below freezing in winter; summers warm, humid; rainfall from 30–80 in. (76–203 cm)/yr; soils well developed	Broad-leafed deciduous trees, some conifers; shrubby undergrowth, ferns, mosses	Squirrels, raccoons, opossums, skunks, deer, foxes, black bears, snakes, amphibians, many soil organisms, birds	Western and central Europe, eastern Asia, eastern North America
Coniferous Forests	Seasonal; winters long, cold; precipitation light in winter, heavier in summer; soils acidic, with leaf litter	Coniferous trees (spruce, fir, pine, hemlock), some deciduous trees (birch, maple)	Large herbivores (mule deer, moose, elk); mice, hares, squirrels; lynx, bears, foxes; nesting area for migrating birds	Northern portions of North America, Europe, Asia, extending southward at high elevations
Tundra	Bitter cold, except for short growing season with long days and moderate temperatures; precipitation low; soils thin—and below, permafrost	Low-growing sedges, dwarf shrubs, lichens, mosses, and grasses	Year round: lemmings, arctic hares, arctic foxes, lynx, caribou; summers: abundant insects, many migrant shorebirds	North of the coniferous forest in Northern Hemisphere, extending southward at elevations above the coniferous forest

Note: See http://earthobservatory.nasa.gov/Experiments/Biome/index.php and click on the links for different biomes for photos and climatic data.

Figure 5–11 Climate and major biomes. Moisture is generally the overriding factor determining the type of biome that may be supported in a region. Given adequate moisture, an area will likely support a forest. Temperature, however, determines the kind of forest. The situation is similar for grasslands and deserts. At cooler temperatures, there is a shift toward less precipitation because lower temperatures reduce evaporative water loss. Temperature becomes the overriding factor only when it is low enough to sustain permafrost. (*Source*: Redrawn from *Geosystems*, 5th ed., by Robert W. Christopherson. Copyright © 2005 by Pearson Prentice Hall, Inc., Upper Saddle River, NJ 07458.)

biome-like features such as seas or oceans. Table 5–2 (on page 114) lists the six major aquatic systems and their primary characteristics.

Microclimate and Other Abiotic Factors

A specific site may have temperature and moisture conditions that are significantly different from the overall climate of the region in which it is located. For example, a south-facing slope, which receives more direct sunlight in the Northern Hemisphere, will be relatively warmer and hence drier than a north-facing slope (Fig. 5–12). Similarly, the temperature range in a sheltered ravine will be narrower than that in a more exposed location, and so on. The conditions found in a specific localized area are referred to as the **microclimate** of that location. In the same way that different climates determine the major biome of a region, different microclimates result in variations of ecosystems within a biome. For example, while the Greater Yellowstone region may be in the northern temperate forest biome, it includes areas of grassland and, above the tree line on mountains, areas of permafrost. This pattern of changing habitat with elevation means that the tops of mountains function ecologically as if they were more polar than their actual latitude (Fig. 5–9).

Soil type and topography also contribute to the diversity found in a biome, because these two factors affect the availability of moisture. In the eastern United States, for example, oaks and hickories generally predominate on rocky, sandy soils and on hilltops, which retain little moisture, whereas beeches and maples are found on richer soils, which hold more moisture, and red maples and cedars inhabit low, swampy areas. In the transitional region between desert and grassland, with 25–50 centimeters (10–20 in.) of rainfall per year, a soil capable of holding water will support grass, but a sandy soil with little ability to hold water will support only desert species.

Biome Productivity. All biomes have varying levels of primary productivity. Those that have high productivity may help support organisms from other biomes. For example, many seabirds migrate through salt marshes and live off the vast productivity there before traveling to other places. Highly productive biomes, like rain forests, also remove carbon dioxide from the atmosphere and trap it (Chapter 18). Biomes with high productivity aren't better than others, though. Low-productivity biomes can have other important roles, such as habitat for rare species.

Why are some biomes or types of ecosystems more productive than others? **Figure 5–13** presents (a) the average

Figure 5–12 Microclimates. Abiotic factors such as terrain, wind, and type of soil create different microclimates by influencing temperature and moisture in localized areas.

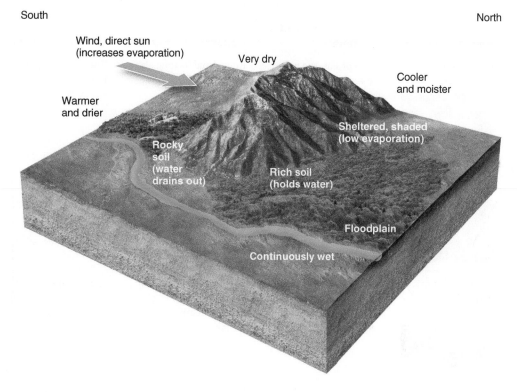

NORTHERN HEMISPHERE

South

North

Wind, direct sun (increases evaporation)

Very dry

Cooler and moister

Warmer and drier

Sheltered, shaded (low evaporation)

Rocky soil (water drains out)

Rich soil (holds water)

Floodplain

Continuously wet

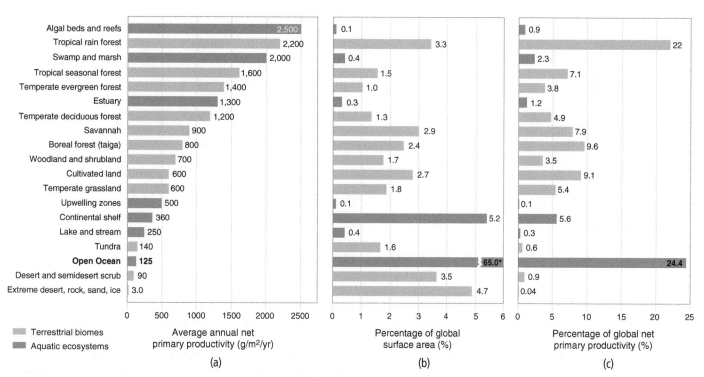

Figure 5–13 **Productivity of different ecosystems.** (a) The annual net primary productivity of different ecosystems, (b) the percentage of different ecosystems over Earth's surface area, and (c) the percentage of global net primary productivity. The outlined column for open ocean in (b) shows that the open ocean is such a high percentage of Earth's surface that it is off the scale relative to all of the other ecosystems. (*Source: Biology: Concepts and Connections,* 4th Edition, by Neil A. Campbell, Jane B. Reece, Lawrence G. Mitchell and Martha R. Taylor. Copyright © 2003 by Pearson Education. Reprinted with permission.)

TABLE 5–2 Major Aquatic Systems

Aquatic Systems	Major Environmental Parameters	Dominant Vegetation	Dominant Animal Life	Distribution
Lakes and Ponds (freshwater)	Bodies of standing water; low concentration of dissolved solids; seasonal vertical stratification of water	Rooted and floating plants, phytoplankton	Zooplankton, fish, insect larvae, turtles, ducks, geese, swans, wading birds	Physical depressions in the landscape where precipitation and groundwater accumulate
Streams and Rivers (freshwater)	Flowing water; low level of dissolved solids; high level of dissolved oxygen; often turbid from runoff	Attached algae, rooted plants	Insect larvae, fish, amphibians, otters, raccoons, wading birds, ducks, geese	Landscapes where precipitation and groundwater flow by gravity toward oceans or lakes
Inland Wetlands (freshwater)	Standing water, at times seasonally dry; thick organic sediments; high nutrients	Marshes (grasses, reeds); cattail swamps (water-tolerant trees); bogs (sphagnum moss, shrubs)	Amphibians, snakes, numerous invertebrates, wading birds, alligators, turtles	Shallow depressions, poorly drained, often occupy sites of lakes and ponds that have filled in
Estuaries (mixed)	Variable salinity; tides create two-way currents; often rich in nutrients, turbid	Phytoplankton, rooted grasses (salt-marsh grass), mangrove swamps in tropics with salt-tolerant trees, shrubs	Zooplankton, rich shellfish, worms, crustaceans, fish, wading birds, sandpipers, ducks, geese	Coastal regions where rivers meet the ocean; may form bays behind sandy barrier islands
Coastal Ocean (saltwater)	Tidal currents promote mixing; nutrients high	Phytoplankton, large benthic algae, turtle grass, symbiotic algae in corals	Zooplankton; rich bottom fauna of worms, shellfish, crustaceans; coral colonies, jellyfish, fish, turtles, gulls, terns, sea lions, seals, dolphins, penguins, whales	From coastline outward over continental shelf; coral reefs abundant in tropics
Open Ocean (saltwater)	Great depths (to 11,000 m, 36,100 ft); all but upper 200 m (656 ft) dark and cold; poor in nutrients except in upwelling regions	Phytoplankton, sargassum weed	Zooplankton and fish adapted to different depths; seabirds, whales, tuna, sharks, squid, flying fish	Covering 70% of Earth, from edge of continental shelf outward

annual net primary productivity, (b) the percentage of different ecosystems over Earth's surface, and (c) the percentage of global net primary productivity attributed to 19 of the most important ecosystems. Some key relationships between abiotic factors and specific ecosystems can be seen in the data. Tropical rain forests both are highly productive and contribute considerably to global productivity; they cover a large area of the land and are characterized by ideal climatic conditions for photosynthesis—warm temperatures and abundant rainfall. The open oceans cover 65% of Earth's surface, so they account for a large portion of global productivity, yet their actual rate of production is low enough that they are veritable biological deserts. Although light, temperature, and water are abundant, primary production in the oceans is limited by the scarcity of nutrients—a good lesson in the significance of limiting factors. The seasonal effects of differences in latitude can also be seen by comparing productivity in tropical, temperate, and boreal (coniferous) forests.

The biosphere consists of a great variety of environments, both aquatic and terrestrial. In each environment, plant, animal, and microbial species are adapted to all the abiotic factors. In addition, they are adapted to each other, in various feeding and nonfeeding relationships. Each environment supports a group of organisms interacting with each other and with the environment in a way that perpetuates or sustains the entire group. Every ecosystem is tied to others through species that migrate from one system to another and through exchanges of air, water, and minerals common to the whole planet.

5.4 Ecosystem Responses to Disturbance

People often picture ecosystems at equilibrium, as stable environments in which species interact constantly in well-balanced predator-prey and competitive relationships. This idea has led to the popular idea of "the balance of nature": natural systems maintain a delicate balance over time that lends them great stability. A more recent understanding of ecosystems, however, shows that they operate in a dynamic, changing way. Species' abundances and ecosystem characteristics are not unchanging. Rather, the landscape is composed of a shifting mosaic of patches, much like patches of lava and unburned areas after a volcano. Volcanoes such as those in Iceland and the Philippines give us a great example of how ecosystems respond to a disturbance—a significant change that kills or displaces many community members.

Ecological Succession

After a disturbance like a fire or volcanic eruption, new plants grow from the soil, new trees sprout, and eventually the original forest stands are replaced by new and different stands. First, however, these communities go through a series of intermediate stages. This phenomenon of transition from one biotic community to another is called ecological succession. Ecological succession occurs because the physical environment may be gradually modified by the growth of a biotic community itself, such that the area becomes more favorable to another group of species and less favorable to the current occupants. Views on ecological succession have changed over time as scientists have done studies on changes near retreating glaciers and moving dune ecosystems. In the past, succession was viewed as a very predictable and orderly process through a series of stages to a stable end point. That view is useful for understanding generally how ecosystems change. However, new work, particularly through large-scale studies at Long Term Ecological Research (LTER) sites or the National Ecological Observatory Network (NEON)

project, suggests that succession is more complicated, something we will discuss shortly.

In the most basic version of succession, pioneer species—the first to colonize a newly opened area in the aftermath of a fire, flood, volcanic lava flow, or other large disturbance—start the process. As these grow, they create conditions that are favorable to longer-lived colonizers, and succession is driven forward by the changing conditions that pave the way for other species. Driving succession forward by improving conditions for subsequent species is known as **facilitation.**

The succession of species does not go on indefinitely. A stage of development is eventually reached in which there appears to be a dynamic balance between all of the species and the physical environment. In the past, this final state was called a **climax ecosystem** because the assemblage of species continues on in space and time. The term *climax ecosystem* is still used, but many ecologists are moving away from its use because they believe it implies more stability than actually occurs in nature. In the real world, even climax communities experience change. Also, within the area of a climax ecosystem there may be patches of disturbance that open spaces for new growth. Some parts of the ecosystem may be in an earlier stage of succession; sometimes there are several "final" stages, with adjoining ecosystems in the same environment at different stages. We will discuss some of these alternatives later in the chapter.

Three classic examples of succession are presented next: primary and secondary succession on land and succession in aquatic ecosystems.

Primary Succession. If an area lacks plants and soil—such as might occur after volcanic eruption or the recession of a glacier—the process of initial invasion and progression from one biotic community to the next is called **primary succession.** An example is the gradual invasion of a bare rock or gravel surface by what eventually becomes a climax forest ecosystem. Bare rock is an inhospitable environment. It has few places for seeds to lodge and germinate or for seedlings to survive. However, certain species, such as some mosses, are able to exploit this environment. Their tiny spores (specialized cells that function reproductively) can lodge and germinate in minute cracks, and moss can withstand severe drying simply by becoming dormant. With each bit of moisture, moss grows and gradually forms a mat that acts as a sieve, catching and holding soil particles as they are broken from the rock or as they blow or wash by. Thus, a layer of soil gradually accumulates, held in place by the moss (Fig. 5–14).

The mat of moss and soil provides a suitable place for seeds of larger plants to lodge. The larger plants in turn collect and build additional soil, and eventually there is enough soil to support shrubs and trees. In the process, the fallen leaves and other litter from the larger plants smother and eliminate the moss and most of the smaller plants that initiated the process. Thus, there is a gradual succession from

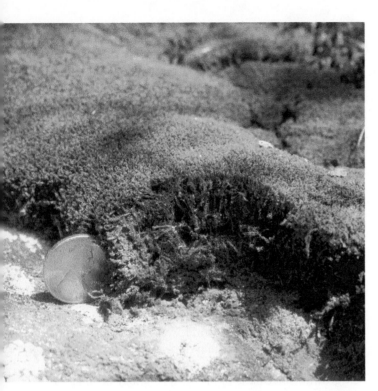

Figure 5–14 Primary succession on bare rock. Moss invades bare rock and acts as a collector, accumulating a layer of soil sufficient for additional plants to become established.

moss through small plants and, finally, to trees or whatever the regional climate supports, yielding the biomes typical of different climatic regions.

Secondary Succession. When an area has been cleared by fire, human activity, or flooding and then left alone, plants and animals from the surrounding ecosystem may gradually reinvade the area—through a series of distinct stages called **secondary succession.** The major difference between primary and secondary succession is that secondary succession starts with preexisting soil. Thus, the early, prolonged stages of soil building are bypassed. Hence, the process of reinvasion begins with different species. The steps leading from abandoned agricultural fields in the eastern United States back to deciduous forests provide a classic example of secondary succession **(Fig. 5–15).**

Aquatic Succession. Natural succession also takes place in lakes or ponds. Succession occurs because soil particles inevitably erode from the land and settle out in ponds or lakes, gradually filling them. Aquatic vegetation produces detritus that also contributes to the filling process. As the buildup occurs, terrestrial species from the surrounding

	Year	
Crab-grass	0–1	
Tall grass-herba-ceous plants	1–3	
Pines come in	3–10	
Pine forest	10–30	
Hard-woods come in	30–70	
Hard-wood forest climax	70+	

(a)

(b)

Figure 5–15 Secondary succession. (a) Reinvasion of an agricultural field by a forest ecosystem occurs in the stages shown. (b) Hardwoods (in this case, species of oak) are growing up underneath and displacing pines in eastern Maryland.

Figure 5–16 **Aquatic succession.** In this photograph, taken in Banff National Park in the Canadian Rockies, you can visualize the lake that used to exist in the low-level area. It is now filled with sediment and covered by scrub willow. Spruce and fir forest is gradually encroaching.

ecosystem can advance in the ecotone and aquatic species must move farther out into the lake. In time, the shoreline advances toward the center of the lake until, finally, the lake disappears altogether (Fig. 5–16). Here the climax ecosystem may be a bog or a forest. Just as disturbances affect terrestrial ecosystems, disturbances such as droughts—or even large floods and erosion—can send **aquatic succession** back to an earlier stage.

Disturbance and Resilience

In order for natural succession to occur, the spores and seeds of various invading plants and the breeding populations of various invading animals must already be present in the vicinity. Ecological succession is not a matter of new species developing or even old species adapting to new conditions; it is a matter of populations of existing species taking advantage of a new area as conditions become favorable. Where do these early-stage species come from if their usual fate is to be replaced by late-stage or climax species? They come from surrounding ecosystems in the early stages of succession. Similarly, the late-stage species are recruited from ecosystems in the later stages of succession. In any given landscape, therefore, all stages of succession are likely to be represented in the ecosystems. This is the case because disturbances constantly create gaps or patches in the landscape. When a variety of successional stages is present in a landscape, as opposed to one single climax stage, a greater diversity of species can be expected; in other words, biodiversity is enhanced by disturbance.

If certain species have been eliminated, natural succession will be blocked or modified. For example, Iceland was colonized by the Norse in the 11th century, and, as a result, trees were cut until, in 1850, not a tree was left standing (Fig. 5–17). Iceland had become a barren, tundra-like habitat. Succession was unable to proceed naturally, and Iceland has remained treeless. (See Sustainability, "Ecological Restoration: Aldo Leopold and the Shack on the Prairie.")

Fire and Succession. Fire is an abiotic factor that has particular relevance to succession. It is a major form of disturbance common to terrestrial ecosystems, as we saw in the Yellowstone National Park example. About 80 years ago, forest managers interpreted the potential destructiveness of fire to mean that all fire was bad, whereupon they embarked on fire prevention programs that eliminated fires from many areas. Unexpectedly, fire prevention did not preserve all ecosystems in their existing state. In pine forests of the southeastern United States, for instance, economically worthless scrub oaks and other broad-leaved species began to displace the more valuable pines. Grasslands were gradually taken over by scrubby, woody species that hindered grazing. Pine forests of the western United States that were once clear and open became cluttered with the trunks and branches of trees that had died in the normal aging process. This deadwood became the breeding ground for wood-boring insects that

Figure 5–17 **Iceland.** Forests that originally covered much of this island nation were totally stripped for fuel in the 18th and 19th centuries. With natural succession impossible, Iceland has remained barren and tundra-like, as seen here.

proceeded to attack live trees. In California, the regeneration of redwood seedlings began to be blocked by the proliferation of broad-leaved species.

Scientists now recognize that fire, which is often started by lightning, is a natural and important abiotic factor. As with all abiotic factors, different species have different degrees of tolerance to fire. In particular, the growing buds of grasses and pines are located deep among the leaves or needles, where they are protected from most fires. By contrast, the buds of broad-leaved species, such as oaks, are exposed, so they are sensitive to damage from fire. Consequently, in regions where these species coexist and compete, periodic fires tip the balance in favor of pines, grasses, or redwood trees. In relatively dry ecosystems, where natural decomposition is slow, fire may also help release nutrients from dead organic matter. Some plant species even depend on fire. The cones of lodgepole pine, for example, will not release their seeds until they have been scorched by fire.

Ecosystems that depend on the recurrence of fire to maintain their existence are referred to as **fire climax ecosystems.** The category includes various grasslands and pine forests (Fig. 5–18). Fire is being increasingly used as a tool in the management of such ecosystems. In pine forests, if ground fires occur every few years, relatively little deadwood accumulates. With only small amounts of fuel, fires usually just burn along the ground, harming neither pines nor wildlife significantly.

Crown fires, such as the fierce Yellowstone fires that occurred in 1980, sometimes occur naturally because not every area is burned on a regular basis. In fact, exceedingly dry conditions can make a forest vulnerable to crown fires even when no large amounts of deadwood are present. Even crown fires, however, serve to clear deadwood and sickly trees, release nutrients, and provide for a fresh ecological start. Burned areas soon become productive meadows as secondary succession starts anew. Thus, periodic crown fires create a patchwork of meadows and forests at different stages of succession that lead to a more-varied, healthier

Figure 5–18 Ground fire. Periodic ground fires are necessary to preserve the balance of pine forests. Such fires remove excessive fuel and kill competing species.

habitat that supports a greater diversity of wildlife than does a uniform, aging conifer forest.

Long-Term Ecosystem Studies. A great deal of our understanding of ecosystem changes comes from studies of changes in fields after fires, on mountain slopes after volcanoes, and near retreating glaciers. However, as human-caused changes to the environment have become global in scope, our studies have had to become longer and cover wider areas. Two ongoing research efforts of note help us to better understand ecosystems. The first is a system of ecosystems designated as Long-Term Ecological Research (LTER) sites. These 26 sites represent different types of ecosystems and different levels of human disturbance. At each site and between sites, research projects focus on five core areas:

1. Pattern and control of primary production;

2. Spatial and temporal distribution of populations selected to represent trophic structure;

3. Pattern and control of organic matter accumulation in surface layers and sediments;

4. Patterns of inorganic inputs and movements of nutrients through soils, groundwater, and surface waters;

5. Patterns and frequency of site disturbances.

Some of these sites, such as the Hubbard Brook Experimental Station, which was critical to the discovery of the problem of acid rain, have been studied for decades.

The second ecosystem study initiative, funded by the National Science Foundation, is the National Ecological Observatory Network (NEON), a network operating in the United States and Puerto Rico. It is a system for collecting data about ecosystems and climate, pulling them together, and making them available for scientists to study. The data will be available to the public as well. NEON's mission is to "enable understanding and forecasting of the impacts of climate change, land-use change and invasive species on continental-scale ecology—by providing infrastructure and consistent methodologies to support research and education in these areas."[1] Planned for years, construction on NEON infrastructure was begun in 2011.

Resilience. The ability of an ecosystem to return to normal functioning after a disturbance, such as a fire or flood, is called its **resilience.** Fire can appear to be a highly destructive disturbance to a forested landscape. Nevertheless, fire releases nutrients that nourish a new crop of plants, and in a short time, the burned area is repopulated with trees and is indistinguishable from the surrounding area. The processes of replenishment of nutrients, dispersion by surrounding plants and animals, rapid regrowth of plant cover, and succession to a forest can all be thought of as **resilience mechanisms** (Fig. 5–19). Resilience helps maintain the sustainability of ecosystems.

[1]NEON. 2012. Mission. http://www.neoninc.org/about/mission477. May11, 2012.

Figure 5–19 Resilience in ecosystems. Disturbances in ecosystems are usually ameliorated by a number of resilience mechanisms that restore normal ecosystem function in a short time.

Ecosystem resilience has its limits, however. If forests are removed from a landscape by human intervention and the area is prevented from undergoing reforestation by overgrazing, the soil may erode, leaving a degraded state that carries out few of the original ecosystem's functions. As in Iceland, some disturbances may be so profound that they can overcome normal resilience mechanisms and create an entirely new and far less productive ecosystem. This new ecosystem can also have its own resilience mechanisms, which may resist any restoration to the original state. We can view this as a "tipping point"—a situation in an ecosystem where a small action catalyzes a major change in the state of the system.

Tipping points act as levers that can change a system to be better able—or less able—to function as an ecosystem. They stimulate the action of **feedback loops,** where system dynamics influence a system in ways that amplify (positive loop) or dampen (negative loop) the behavior of the system. For example, predator-prey cycles function as negative feedback loops that keep both populations from exploding in terms of numbers and then crashing. Removal of predators (to favor the prey species) would be a tipping point that could allow the positive feedback of prey reproduction to bring devastation to their plant food supply.

You might wonder why it matters if an ecosystem such as the forests of Iceland moves into an alternative state, such as an Iceland with no trees, and stays there. After all, don't

treeless, cold places exist? As we will see below, ecosystems provide a number of services valuable to humans and other species. These include large-scale effects such as lowering flood surges, maintaining soil, maintaining even ground temperatures, and taking up carbon dioxide.

If just a few parts of the planet moved from one type of ecosystem to another, it really wouldn't matter. The problem is one of frequency. Large-scale human actions tend to lower ecosystem services such as flood control, wind-erosion control, and carbon dioxide storage. They tend to produce ecosystems either with very low productivity or with high primary productivity but low food chain length (such as a lake with too many nutrients). Such ecosystems tend to have less physical complexity and lower biological diversity. We will see this more when we discuss the problem of desertification (Chapter 11).

5.5 Human Values and Ecosystem Sustainability

Ecosystems have existed for millions of years, maintaining natural populations of biota and the processes that these carry out (which in turn sustain the ecosystems). One of the reasons for studying natural ecosystems is that they are models of sustainability. In this chapter, we started with trophic levels

SUSTAINABILITY

Ecological Restoration: Aldo Leopold and the Shack on the Prairie

Conservationist Aldo Leopold (1887–1948) sat in a converted chicken coop writing at a table. His essays on the value of nature and the damage inflicted by unthinking use and his scientific papers on the impacts of fire and of predator suppression were to change the course of history. Around him lay acres of degraded farmland, its sandy soil depleted by years of unrelenting use, its plants gone, sparse grasses standing as tufts across the eroded fields. In 1935, Leopold had bought this land near the Wisconsin River and begun its restoration. For years, he brought friends, neighbors, and students to the farm, encouraging them to sow seeds of prairie plants and promote the use of fire as a restoring agent. Gradually, the agricultural weed pests were outcompeted by the native grasses, shrubs, and flowers. Wild lupine, its purple flowers flecking the horizon, vied for space with purple coneflower and wild indigo. Native butterflies returned, along with the prairie voles and 13 lined ground squirrels. The work he did at the "shack," as his home away from home was called, paralleled the restoration of native prairie at the University of Wisconsin Madison Arnold Arboretum, begun by Leopold and other scientists. It was the beginning of the field of restoration ecology.

The potential for restoration of any ecosystem rests on the following three assumptions: (1) abiotic factors must have remained unaltered or, if not, can at least be returned to their original state; (2) viable populations of the species formerly inhabiting the ecosystem must still exist; and (3) the ecosystem must not have been upset by the introduction of one or more foreign species that cannot be eliminated and that may preclude the survival of reintroduced native species. If these conditions are met, revival efforts have the potential to restore the ecosystem to some semblance of its former state.

Restoration ecologists use a set of actions described in a primer on ecological restoration published by the Society for Ecological Restoration in 2004.* The basic processes include taking an *inventory*, developing a *model* of the desired ecosystem in structural and functional terms, setting goals for the restoration efforts, designing an *implementation plan*, and carrying out the plan. For example, it may be necessary to remove all herbaceous vegetation and then plow and plant the land with native grasses. To maintain the prairie, it may be necessary to burn it regularly or, in the case of larger landholdings, to introduce bison. Clear *performance standards* should be stated, along with the means of evaluating progress. Finally, the results of the implementation plan should be monitored and strategies developed for the long-term protection and maintenance of the restored ecosystem.

Leopold practiced these strategies on his own land in Wisconsin, bringing a broken and eroded abandoned farm back to a health it had not seen for years. In his well-known *Sand County Almanac*, as well as his other essays, Leopold wrote of this goal of understanding the natural world and caring for it. Leopold died trying to control a brush fire, but his work

lives on in a whole field of endeavor. We will discuss more on his contribution to conservation biology when we look at the ethical principles that underlie efforts to protect species and their habitats (Chapter 6).

---

*Society for Ecological Restoration, International Science and Policy Working Group, *The SER International Primer on Ecological Restoration (2004).* Available at www.ser.org.

and then examined the flow of energy and nutrients in an ecosystem. These discussions have focused on how natural ecosystems work in theory. In reality, however, it is Earth's specific ecosystems that we depend on for goods and services (also known as **ecosystem capital**). Is our use of natural and managed ecosystems a serious threat to their long-term sustainability? Many ecosystem scientists believe that it is.

Appropriation of Energy Flow

As we have seen, it is the Sun that energizes the processes of energy flow and nutrient cycling. Humans make heavy use of the energy that starts with sunlight and flows through natural and agricultural ecosystems. Agriculture, for example, provides most of our food. To produce food, we have converted almost 11% of Earth's land area from forest and grassland biomes to agricultural ecosystems. Grasslands sustain our domestic animals for labor, meat, wool, leather, and milk. Forest biomes provide us with 3.3 billion cubic meters (117 billion cubic feet) of wood annually for fuel, building material, and paper. Finally, some 15% of the world's energy consumption is derived directly from plant material, like firewood and peat.

Calculations of the total annual global net primary production of land ecosystems range around 120 petagrams (1 petagram = 1 billion metric tons) of dry matter, including agricultural as well as the more natural ecosystems (Fig. 5–20).

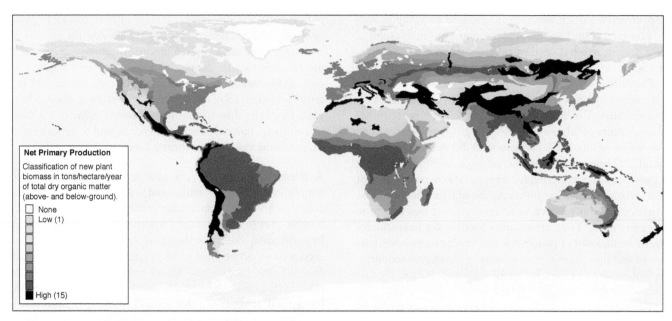

Figure 5–20 Global primary productivity in terrestrial ecosystems. The primary production values range from 1 ton/hectare/year (yellow) to 15 tons/hectare/year (black) of dry organic matter. The global annual total is 120 billion metric tons (1 billion metric tons = 1 petagram). (*Source*: Bazilevich global primary productivity map, NOAA Satellite and Information Service.)

In 1986, researchers calculated that humans appropriate around 30% of this total production for agriculture, grazing, forestry, and human-occupied lands.[2] More-recent calculations have supported this figure.[3] These estimates indicate that humans are using a large fraction of the whole. Further, because humans convert many natural and agricultural lands to urban and suburban housing, highways, dumps, factories, and the like, we cancel out an additional 8% of potential primary production. Thus, we appropriate about 40% of the land's primary production to support human needs. In using this much, we have become the dominant biological force on Earth, despite representing about 5% of the biomass. As ecologist Stuart Pimm put it, "Man eats Planet! Two-fifths already gone!"[4]

Involvement in Nutrient Cycling

Nutrients are replenished in ecosystems through the breakdown of organic compounds and the release of the chemicals that make them up—processes we have described as biogeochemical cycles. This maintains the sustainability of ecosystems indefinitely. However, human intrusion into these natural cycles is substantial, and it is bound to increase. As we have seen, our alterations of the nutrient cycles have

long-term consequences (Chapter 3). Climate change is one consequence of these alterations.

Currently, global climate change is one of the most serious environmental issues facing society. The burning of fossil fuels has increased the level of carbon dioxide in the atmosphere to the point where, by the mid–21st century, it will have doubled since the beginning of the Industrial Revolution. Methane is also released from the drying and decomposition of areas that used to be permafrost and from cattle. Because both carbon dioxide and methane are powerful greenhouse gases, a general warming of the atmosphere is occurring, leading to many other effects on Earth's climate (Chapter 20). Numerous ecosystems are being affected by the changes, and it is questionable whether they can function sustainably in the face of such rapid changes. The threat of disturbance on such an enormous scale is a major reason why many nations of the world have begun to take steps to reduce emissions of greenhouse gases.

Value of Ecosystem Capital

How much are natural ecosystems worth to us? To the poor in many developing countries, the products of natural ecosystems keep life going and may enable them to make economic gains that can lift them from deep poverty. Theirs is a direct and absolute dependence. For example, 1.6 billion people, many of them the world's poorest, depend on forests for much of their sustenance (in the form of fuelwood, construction wood, wild fruits, herbs, animal fodder, and bush meat). Their access to these ecosystem goods is often uncertain. Those of us in the developed world, however, are susceptible to a very different

[2]Peter Vitousek, Paul R. Ehrlich, Anne H. Ehrlich, and Pamela Matson, "Human Appropriation of the Products of Photosynthesis," *BioScience* 36, No. 6. (June 1986): 368–373.
[3]N. Ramankutty, A. T. Evan, C. Monfreda, and J. A. Foley, "Farming the Planet: 1. Geographic Distribution of Global Agricultural Lands in the Year 2000," *Global Biogeochemical Cycles* 22 (2008): GB1003.
[4]Pimm, Stuart. 2001. *The World According to Pimm: A scientist audits the Earth.* McGraw-Hill.

perspective: We often assign little thought or value to natural ecosystems and are unconcerned about (and insulated from) human impacts on natural ecosystems. This perspective can have dangerous consequences.

Recall that we defined the goods and services we derive from natural systems as ecosystem capital (Chapter 1). In a first-ever attempt of its kind, a team of 13 natural scientists and economists collaborated in 1997 to produce a report titled "The Value of the World's Ecosystem Services and Natural Capital."[5] Their reason for making such an effort was that the goods and services provided by natural ecosystems are not easily seen in the market (meaning the market economy that normally allows us to place value on things) or may not be in the market at all. Thus, clean air to breathe, the formation of soil, the breakdown of pollutants, and similar items never pass through and thus are not given a value by the market economy. People are often not even aware of their importance. Because of this, these things are undervalued or not valued at all.

The team identified 17 major ecosystem goods and services that provide vital functions we depend on. The team also identified the ecosystem functions that actually carry out the vital human support and gave examples of each (Table 5–3). They made the point that it is useless to consider human welfare without these ecosystem services; so, in one sense, their value as a whole is infinite. However, the **incremental value** of each type of service can be calculated. That is, changes in the quantity or quality of various types of services may influence human welfare, and an economic value can be placed on that relationship. For example, removing a forest will affect the ability of the forest to provide lumber in the future, as well as to perform other services, such as soil formation and promotion of the hydrologic cycle. The economic value of this effect can be calculated. By calculating incremental values, making many approximations, and collecting data from other researchers who have worked on individual processes, the research team tabulated the annual global value of ecosystem services performed by all types of ecosystems. According to their calculations, the total value to human welfare of a year's services amounts to $41 trillion (in 2004 dollars)—and that is considered a conservative estimate. This is close to the $55 trillion calculated for the gross world economic product in 2004.

Using Ecosystem Value in Decision Making. The real power of the team's analysis lies in its use for making local decisions. For instance, the value of wetlands cannot be represented solely by the amount of soybeans that could be grown on the land if it were drained. Instead, wetlands provide other vital ecosystem services, and these should be balanced against the value of the soybeans in calculating the costs and benefits of a proposed change in land use. The bottom line of their analysis is, in their words, "that ecosystem services provide an important portion of the total contribution to human welfare on this planet." For this reason, the ecosystem capital stock (the ecosystems and the populations in them, including the lakes and wetlands) must be given adequate weight in public-

policy decisions involving changes to that stock. However, because these ecosystem services are outside the market and uncertain, they are too often ignored or undervalued, and the net result is human changes to natural systems whose social costs far outweigh their benefits. For example, coastal mangrove forests in Thailand are often converted to shrimp farms, yet an analysis showed that the economic value of the forests (for timber, charcoal, storm protection, and fisheries support) exceeded the value of the shrimp farms by 70%.

A New Look. In 2002, a new team looked at the 1997 team's calculation of value and examined the benefit-cost consequences of converting ecosystems to more-direct human uses (e.g., converting a wetland to a soybean field).[6] In every case, the net balance of value was a loss—that is, services lost outweighed services gained. The team examined five different biomes and found consistent losses in ecosystem capital, running at –1.2% per year. Based on the calculated total ecosystem value of $41 trillion, this percentage represents an annual loss of $250 billion through habitat conversion alone. If this is so, the authors asked, why is this conversion still happening? They suggested that the benefits of conversion were often exaggerated through various government subsidies, seriously distorting the market analysis. Thus, the market does not adequately measure many of the benefits from natural ecosystems, nor does it deal well with the fact that many major benefits are realized on regional or global scales, while the benefits of conversion are narrowly local. Other analyses, including a National Research Council report published in 2005[7] that investigated the value of wild nature and ecosystem services, support the idea that conservation is more achievable when the real costs of harming ecosystems are included in our thinking. Beyond conservation, our tremendous dependence on natural systems should lead, logically, to proper management of those systems, a topic discussed later in this chapter.

Can Ecosystems Be Restored?

The human capacity for destroying ecosystems is well established. To some degree, however, we also have the capacity to restore them (see Sustainability, "Ecological Restoration: Aldo Leopold and the Shack on the Prairie"). In many cases, restoration simply involves stopping the abuse. For example, after pollution is curtailed, water quality often improves, and fish and shellfish gradually return to previously polluted lakes, rivers, and bays. Similarly, forests may gradually be restored to areas that have been cleared. Humans can speed up the process by seeding and planting seedling trees and by reintroducing populations of fish and animals that have been eliminated.

In some cases, however, specific ecosystems have been destroyed or disturbed to such an extent that they require the efforts of a new breed of scientist: the restoration ecologist.

[5]Robert Costanza et al., "The Value of the World's Ecosystem Services and Natural Capital," *Nature* 387 (1997): 253–260.

[6]Andrew Balmford et al., "Economic Reasons for Conserving Wild Nature," *Science* 297 (August 9, 2002): 950–953.
[7]National Research Council, *Valuing Ecosystem Services: Toward Better Environmental Decision-Making* (Washington, D.C.: National Academies Press, 2005).

TABLE 5–3 Ecosystem Services and Function

Ecosystem Service	Ecosystem Functions	Examples
Gas regulation	Regulation of atmospheric chemical composition	CO_2–O_2 balance, O_3 for UVB protection, and SO_x levels
Climate regulation	Regulation of global temperature, precipitation, and other biologically mediated climatic processes at global or local levels	Greenhouse gas regulation, dimethylsulfoxide production affecting cloud formation
Disturbance regulation	Capacitance, damping, and integrity of ecosystem response to environmental fluctuations	Storm protection, flood control, drought recovery, other aspects of habitat response to environmental variability controlled mainly by vegetation structure
Water regulation	Regulation of hydrological flows	Provisioning of water for agricultural (such as irrigation) or industrial (such as milling) processes or transportation
Water supply	Storage and retention of water	Provisioning of water by watersheds, reservoirs, and aquifers
Erosion control and sediment retention	Retention of soil within an ecosystem	Prevention of loss of soil by wind, runoff, or other removal processes; storage of silt in lakes and wetlands
Soil formation	Soil-formation processes	Weathering of rock and the accumulation of organic material
Nutrient cycling	Storage, internal cycling, processing, and acquisition of nutrients	Nitrogen fixation, N, P, and other elemental or nutrient cycles
Waste treatment	Recovery of mobile nutrients and removal or breakdown of excess nutrients and compounds	Waste treatment, pollution control, detoxification
Pollination	Movement of floral gametes	Provisioning of pollinators for the reproduction of plant populations
Biological control	Trophic-dynamic regulations of populations	Keystone predator to control prey species, reduction of herbivory by top predators
Refuges	Habitat for resident and transient populations	Nurseries, habitat for migratory species, regional habitats for locally harvested species, or overwintering grounds
Food production	The portion of primary production extractable as food	Production of fish, game, crops, nuts, and fruits by hunting, gathering, subsistence farming, or fishing
Raw materials	That portion of primary production extractable as raw materials	The production of lumber, fuel, or fodder
Genetic resources	Sources of unique biological materials and products	Medicine, products for science, genes for resistance to plant pathogens and crop pests, ornamental species (pets and horticultural varieties of plants)
Recreation	Provision of opportunities for recreational activities	Ecotourism, sport fishing, and other outdoor recreational activities
Cultural	Provision of opportunities for noncommercial uses	Aesthetic, artistic, educational, spiritual, or scientific values of ecosystems

Source: Reprinted, by permission, from Robert Costanza, Ralph d'Arge, Rudolf de Groot, Stephen Farber, Monica Grasso, Bruce Hannon, Karin Limburg, Shahid Naeem, Robert V. O'Neill, Jose Paruelo, Robert G. Raskin, Paul Sutton, and Marjan van den Belt, "The Value of the World's Ecosystem Services and Natural Capital," *Nature* 387 (1997): 253–260.

Unfortunately, sometimes the ecosystem is too greatly disturbed for scientists to repair. In a prairie, for example, lack of grazing by native herbivores, overgrazing by cattle or sheep, and suppression of regular fires can lead to much woody vegetation. Exotic species may abound in the region and can continuously disperse seeds on the experimental prairie, and there may be no remnants of the original prairie grasses and herbs on the site. Such sites may take intensive efforts to bring back any native species or may continue in an alternative ecosystem.

Why should we restore ecosystems? Restoration ecologists Steven Apfelbaum and Kim Chapman cite several reasons.[8] First, we should do so for aesthetic reasons. Natural ecosystems are often beautiful, and the restoration of something beautiful and pleasing to the eye is a worthy project that can be uplifting to many people. Second, we should do so for the benefit of human use. The ecosystem services of a restored wetland, for example, can be enjoyed by present and future generations. The degradation of ecosystems robs them of their ecosystem capital, and restoring them returns their value. Finally, we should do so for the benefit of the species and ecosystems themselves. It can be argued that nature has value separate from human use and that people should act to preserve and restore ecosystems and species in order to preserve that value.

The Future

On a global scale, the future growth of the human population and its rising consumption levels will severely challenge ecosystem sustainability. Over the next 50 years, the world's population is expected to increase by at least 2.5 billion people (see Chapter 8). The needs and demands of this expanded human population will create unprecedented pressures on the ability of Earth's systems to provide goods and services. Estimates based on current trends indicate that impacts on the nitrogen and phosphorus cycles will raise the amounts of these nutrients being added to the land and water to two to three times current levels. Demands on agriculture will likely require at least 15% more agricultural land; irrigated land area is expected to double, greatly stressing an already strained hydrologic cycle. Such growing demands cannot be met without facing serious trade-offs between different goods and services. More agricultural land means more food, but less forest—and, therefore, less of the important services forests perform. More water for irrigation means more rivers will be diverted, so less water will be available for domestic use and for sustaining the riverine ecosystems. These dire projections are not necessarily predictions, and they don't have to be inevitable outcomes. By looking ahead, we may choose other alternatives if we clearly understand the consequences of simply continuing present practices. There is a powerful

need to understand how essential natural and managed ecosystems are for human well-being and to bring to bear the wisdom and political will necessary to promote their sustainability.

Ecosystems are resilient, living units of the landscape, often subject to natural disturbances and capable of changing over time. They also provide essential goods and services that improve the quality of human life and, in many areas, allow those in poverty to improve their lot. However, we have seen that ecosystem goods and services are routinely undervalued, with the result that, as the Millennium Ecosystem Assessment found, ecosystem capital is being degraded and overexploited in many areas of the world. To turn human efforts in a sustainable direction, we need to protect or manage the natural environment in a way that maintains the goods and services vital to the human way of life, and we need to manage ourselves. The two aspects are interrelated.

Managing Ecosystems

Virtually no ecosystem can escape human impact. We depend on ecosystems for vital goods and services—and by using ecosystems, we are in fact managing them. Forests are a good example. Management can be a matter of fire suppression (or, more recently, controlled burns), clear-cutting, or selective harvesting. The objective of management can be to maximize profit from logging or to maintain the forest as a sustainable and diverse ecosystem that yields multiple products and services. Good ecosystem management is based on understanding how ecosystems function, how they respond to disturbances, and what goods and services they can best provide to the human societies living in or around them. Since 1992, the U.S. Forest Service, the U.S. Bureau of Land Management, the U.S. Fish and Wildlife Service, the U.S. National Park Service, and the U.S. Environmental Protection Agency have all officially adopted ecosystem management as their management paradigm. What, then, is ecosystem management?

Ecosystem management is composed of several main principles. First, it looks at ecosystems on both small and large scales. For example, the impact of logging on a single river and the impact of that logging on the entire watershed are both considered in managing the ecosystem. Good management preserves the range of possible landscapes in an ecosystem instead of allowing one type to take over the area. In addition, management is not static—managers are given the opportunity to learn from experiments and to employ new knowledge from forestry and landscape science in their practice. Such "managers" can be volunteer land stewards or neighborhood groups, not just government agencies. As part of adapting to changing circumstances, management must also look at the human element of these ecosystems. The valuable goods and services of ecosystems are recognized, and through active involvement in monitoring and management, all stakeholders (all people with a stake in the ecosystem's health) are included as important elements in stewardship of the resources (see Stewardship, "Ecosystem Stakeholders").

---

[8]Steven I. Apfelbaum and Kim Alan Chapman, "Ecological Restoration: A Practical Approach," in *Ecostem Management: Applications for Sustainable Forest and Wildlife Resources*, ed. Mark S. Boyce and Alan Haney (New Haven, CT: Yale University Press, 1997).

STEWARDSHIP

Ecosystem Stakeholders

The pressures on ecosystems illustrate why it is crucially important to understand how ecosystems work and how human societies interact with them. Although many pressures are large-scale—even global—the decisions (and decision makers) that will most directly determine ecosystem sustainability are local or regional. The Millennium Ecosystem Assessment identifies a number of "drivers of change": factors that bring about alterations in ecosystems, such as changes in land use, species introductions, and resource harvesting. Decision makers are those who are responsible for these "drivers." To understand how and why they make the decisions they do, it is useful to employ the concept of **stakeholders.** People who have an interest in or may be affected by a given approach to environmental management, including government decision makers, are all considered to be stakeholders. They have a stake in the ecosystem resource and what happens to it. Primary stakeholders are those most dependent on the resource; secondary stakeholders may be those living near the resource, but not greatly dependent on it; government officials; scientists studying the resource; and conservation organizations.

People living within and adjacent to an ecosystem are usually the primary stakeholders.

In ecosystems of the developing world, these are among the world's poorest people, and their dependence on what has been called environmental income is almost absolute. Primary stakeholders may remove vegetation, harvest wood, withdraw water, harvest game animals, and so on. They may use these products in their own households; or where markets exist, they may sell them for cash or exchange them for services. Their local decisions will have both intended and unintended consequences. If they harvest firewood from a forest (intended), soil erosion may increase (unintended). If many local decision makers make similar decisions, the impacts may have cumulative undesirable regional and, eventually, global consequences. Preventing such outcomes requires effective management of the ecosystem so as to maintain its sustainability and at the same time meet the needs of the various stakeholders.

One way to promote good stewardship of resources is to involve the stakeholders in management. One example of a case where poor rural communities were able to pursue community-based natural resource management and restore and manage crucial environmental resources is documented in the World Resources Institute report titled *The Wealth of the Poor: Managing Ecosystems to Fight Poverty.** The Shinyanga region of Tanzania was once an abundant woodland environment that supported

the Sukuma people with subsistence agriculture and forage for livestock. An indigenous natural resource management system of maintaining protected vegetation enclosures was removed by government decree in the 1970s, and the result was devastating to the region. Land and soil were overused, wood was difficult to find, and traditional wild fruit and plants became scarce. In 1986, the Tanzanian government reversed its approach and promoted the revival of the original indigenous scheme of enclosures. As a result, people exerted local ownership over the natural resources, and gradually, the landscape changed from an eroded, dry land to one where vegetation and wildlife have been restored on more than 350,000 hectares (860,000 acres). The outcome greatly improved livelihoods for the Sukuma, with dividends in fuelwood, construction timber, fodder for animals, and traditional foods. In this situation, the involvement of the primary stakeholders in decisions affecting local ecosystems was the key to restoration. One conclusion of the World Resources Institute report was that democratic reform may be the most important step toward sustainable use of ecosystem goods and services, particularly in developing countries.

---

*World Resources Institute, *World Resources 2005: The Wealth of the Poor: Managing Ecosystems to Fight Poverty* (Washington, D.C.: World Resources Institute, 2005).

Above all, the paradigm incorporates the objective of ecological sustainability.

The U.S. Forest Service is responsible for managing some 192 million acres (77.7 million hectares) of national forests and is a key player in overseeing public natural resources. A decade ago, the Forest Service convened an interdisciplinary committee of scientists to advise the service on what sound science would recommend for managing national lands. According to the committee's report, "the first priority for management is to retain and restore the ecological sustainability of watersheds, forests, and rangelands for present and future generations. The Committee believes that the policy of sustainability should be the guiding star for stewardship of the national forests and grasslands to assure the continuation of this array of benefits" (referring to the goods and services

provided by the national lands).[9] These were fine words, but have they been followed?

The governing board of the Millennium Ecosystem Assessment process examined the findings of the more than 1,350 experts who produced the many reports of the assessment and issued its own statement of the key messages to be derived from the process. The title of this work is significant: *Living Beyond Our Means: Natural Assets and Human Well-Being.*[10] As stated in the first few lines of this document: "At the heart of this assessment is a stark warning. Human activity is putting such strain on the natural functions of Earth that the ability of the planet's ecosystems to sustain future generations can no longer be taken for granted." The following are the key messages from the governing board:

- Everyone in the world depends on nature and ecosystem services to provide the conditions for a decent, healthy, and secure life.

- Humans have made unprecedented changes to ecosystems in recent decades, to meet growing demands for food, fresh water, fiber, and energy.

---

[9]Committee of Scientists, Department of Agriculture, *Sustaining the People's Lands: Recommendations for Stewardship of the National Forests and Grasslands into the Next Century* (1999). Available at www.fs.fed.us/news/science.
[10]Millennium Ecosystem Assessment, *Living Beyond Our Means: Natural Assets and Human Well-Being* (Statement of the Millennium Assessment Board, 2005). Available at www.millenniumassessment.org/en/Products.BoardStatement.aspx.

- These changes have helped to improve the lives of billions, but at the same time, they have weakened nature's ability to deliver other key services such as the purification of air and water, protection from disasters, and the provision of medicines.

- Among the outstanding problems identified by this assessment are the dire state of many of the world's fish stocks; the intense vulnerability of the 2 billion people living in dry regions to the loss of ecosystem services, including water supply; and the growing threat to ecosystems from climate change and nutrient pollution.

- Human activities have taken the planet to the edge of a massive wave of species extinctions, further threatening our own well-being.

- The loss of services derived from ecosystems is a significant barrier to the achievement of the Millennium Development Goals to reduce poverty, hunger, and disease.

- The pressures on ecosystems will increase globally in coming decades unless human attitudes and actions change.

- Measures to conserve natural resources are more likely to succeed if local communities are given ownership of them, share the benefits, and are involved in decisions.

- Even today's technology and knowledge can reduce considerably the human impact on ecosystems. They are unlikely to be deployed fully, however, until ecosystem services cease to be perceived as free and limitless and their full value is taken into account.

- Better protection of natural assets will require coordinated efforts across all sections of governments, businesses, and international institutions. The productivity of ecosystems depends on policy choices in the areas of investment, trade, subsidy, taxation, and regulation, among others.

We are living off the future, in other words. Our current well-being is apparently dependent on drawing down the ecosystem capital that provides the goods and services; as a result, agricultural soils erode, fish stocks decline, forests shrink, and pollution of land, water, and air increases. This situation is unsustainable.

REVISITING THE THEMES

Sound Science

Ecosystems have natural processes that drive their functions. They are not static entities—change is a fundamental property of ecosystems. They can stand alone or be grouped into large global areas called biomes, which are predicted largely by precipitation and temperature. Ecosystems can also include sub-ecosystems, caused by variations or microclimates. Ecosystems can be characterized by their primary productivity and how that energy and the associated nutrients move up through a food chain or food web. These structures contain several trophic levels of organisms that gain their energy from their prey (or in the case of producers, primarily from the Sun). Ecosystems pull together several concepts we saw in earlier chapters. The concepts of energy and matter (and the inefficiency of their transfer) play out in forming the biomass pyramid and determining the length of food chains. Individual limits on distribution of species are the cause of large predictable areas of Earth having similar ecosystems—the biomes. The relationships between species determine the trophic levels in ecosystems. A functioning ecosystem and its food webs are resilient to disturbance—indeed, some even depend on disturbances to reset succession and allow diversity. However, extremely large or unusual disturbances might tip an ecosystem into an altered state from which it might not recover. In some instances, this leads to much lower productivity or diversity, and in others, sound environmental management can tip a degraded ecosystem back into a restored state. Scientists and others study the processes of restoring degraded ecosystems to health, as did Aldo Leopold.

Sustainability

The message of the Millennium Ecosystem Assessment is that human impacts on the resilient natural world are so unprecedented and extensive that we crossed the line into unsustainable consumption some time ago and are now depleting ecosystem capital stock instead of living off its sustainable goods and services. Converting ecosystems into farms and other human uses has frequently depleted their ability to provide us with pivotal assets. We are just beginning to calculate the lost economic value of these altered landscapes, not to mention their lost aesthetic and natural value. Any attempt at sustainability will need to include monitoring the world's ecosystems, setting international policies to protect them, and involving all stakeholders in their management. Basic science will inform much of the policy making and other solutions for sustainability discussed in later chapters.

Stewardship

Ecosystem management has shown us that we need to monitor the impacts we have on our ecosystems, because, while they are resilient, large disturbances can do irreparable damage. Indeed, stewardship means, first of all, understanding how ecosystems, such as the Greater Yellowstone Ecosystem, do just what they do and then stepping back and restraining our activities to allow ecosystems to continue to provide us with essential goods and services. Human agency has become the dominant force on Earth, affecting living systems all over the planet. In the process, we have the ability to drastically reduce biodiversity, or we have the ability to act as responsible stewards of our environment. Ecosystem management is, above all, a stewardship approach to the natural world. As the U.S. Forest Service's Committee of Scientists put it, "the policy of sustainability should be the guiding star" for our actions, fittingly linking sustainability and stewardship.

REVIEW QUESTIONS

1. How did the described volcanoes in Iceland and the Philippines change the environment to lesser or greater extents?

2. Name and describe the attributes of the two categories into which all organisms can be divided based on how they obtain nutrition.

3. Name and describe the roles of the three main trophic categories that make up the biotic structure of every ecosystem. Give examples of organisms from each category.

4. Give four categories of consumers in an ecosystem and the role that each plays.

5. Describe different members of the decomposition food web.

6. Differentiate among the concepts of *food chain, food web,* and *trophic levels.*

7. Relate the concept of the biomass pyramid to the fact that all heterotrophs depend on autotrophic production.

8. Describe how differences in climate cause Earth to be partitioned into major biomes.

9. What are three situations that might cause microclimates to develop within an ecosystem?

10. Identify and describe the biotic and the abiotic components of the biome of the region in which you live.

11. Define the terms *ecological succession* and *climax ecosystem*. How do disturbances allow for ecological succession?

12. What role may fire play in ecological succession, and how may fire be used in the management of certain ecosystems?

13. What is meant by ecosystem *resilience*? What can cause it to fail? How does this relate to environmental tipping points?

14. What is meant by the term *stakeholder*? How does ecosystem management involve stakeholders?

15. Succinctly describe ecosystem management.

16. Can ecosystems be restored? What has to happen for that to work?

17. How much of Earth's primary productivity is used or preempted by humans?

18. Examine the key messages from the Millennium Ecosystem Assessment's governing board, and evaluate how these points affect you now and will affect you and your children in the future.

THINKING ENVIRONMENTALLY

1. Write a scenario describing what would happen to an ecosystem or to the human system in the event of one of the following: (a) all producers are killed through a loss of fertility of the soil or through toxic contamination, or (b) decomposers and detritus feeders are eliminated. Support all of your statements with reasons drawn from your understanding of the way ecosystems function.

2. Look at the following description of a broad global region, and describe what the biome name and main biota would be and how you know that: 40 centimeters (16 in.) of precipitation a year, seasons, frozen much of the year, high winds.

3. Consider the plants, animals, and other organisms present in a natural area near you, and then do the following: (a) Imagine how the area may have undergone

ecological succession, and (b) analyze the population-balancing mechanisms that are operating among the various organisms. Choose one species, and predict what will happen to it if two or three other native species are removed from the area. Then predict what will happen to your chosen species if two or three foreign species are introduced into the area.

4. Consult the Web site www.ecotippingpoints.org, and read several of the success stories from the site. Compare the tipping points as presented, and explain the common properties of the tipping points.

5. Explore how the human system can be modified into a sustainable ecosystem in balance with (i.e., preserving) other natural ecosystems without losing the benefits of modern civilization.

MAKING A DIFFERENCE

1. Find out where the nearest wilderness area or national park is to where you live. If possible, make a plan to visit it. Find out what management issues the park has. Do they have advisories about fire risk, invasive species, or other ecosystem management issues?

2. Using an online map, find out what river drains your watershed and where that water goes. Is there a watershed stewardship group for the river? Who might be looking out for the protection of the ecosystem? If you are interested, organize a group volunteer activity.

3. In your area, is there a citizens' group for restoring any degraded ecosystems? There are many such small groups of citizens in the United States and elsewhere. See if you can link to a citizens' group. Volunteer if you can. One such activity is the annual CoastSweep, usually held in September, in which people all over the world clean up beaches. If you are coastal, see if you can help.

MasteringEnvironmentalScience®

Go to **www.masteringenvironmentalscience.com** for practice quizzes, Pearson eText, videos, current events, and more.

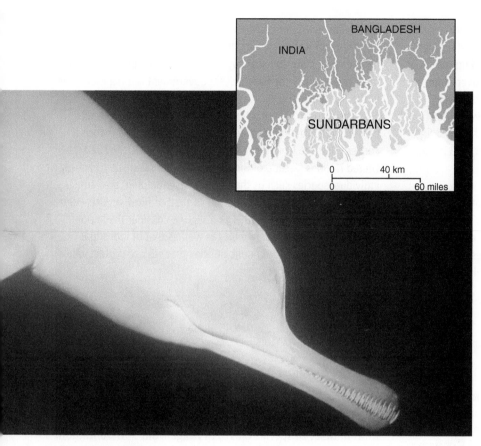

Indus River dolphin

CHAPTER 6

Wild Species and Biodiversity

A BROWN RIVER WINDS slowly past mangroves filled with flocking birds, carrying with it plankton, crustaceans, and young fish that will support a vast food chain. A fisherman in a boat casts a net to the side. The place is the Sundarbans, the largest mangrove forest in the world. The long nose of a Ganges River dolphin (*Platanista gangetica gangetica*) breaks the water surface in the early morning mist. This endangered cetacean swims past mangrove roots and edges past a fishing net, its body narrowly avoiding entanglement.

THREATENED. This area of the Bay of Bengal is home to populations of two of the most endangered cetaceans in the world: the Ganges River dolphin (*Platanista gangetica gangetica*) and a related subspecies, the Indus River dolphin (*Platanista gangetica minor*). These rare beasts are nearly blind and swim sideways to get hints of sunlight through the water as they find their prey by echolocation. Freshwater dolphins, like their saltwater cousins, live on fish. Because they live in rivers instead of oceans, they are in some of the most populous areas of the world. These rivers may be highly polluted, in habitats heavily divided by dams, and in places already crowded with fishermen.

River dolphins are among the most threatened large vertebrates in the world. In fact, another species of river dolphin, the Baiji, in China,

LEARNING OBJECTIVES

1. **The Value of Wild Species and Biodiversity:** Define and give examples of both instrumental and intrinsic value of wild species.

2. **Biodiversity and Its Decline:** Explain the causes, extent, relation to human activities, and impacts of the tremendous loss of species occurring today.

3. **Saving Wild Species:** Describe how cutting-edge science, policies for protection, and changes in the way people think can be used to protect wild species.

4. **Protecting Biodiversity Internationally:** Explain at least three international efforts to protect wild species.

was declared extinct, to the great sorrow of conservationists worldwide. The Baiji, nicknamed "the goddess of the Yangtze," declined because of loss of habitat, pollution, crowding, and injury from contact with fishing vessels, as well as overharvest. The species, once spread throughout several large rivers in China, became rarer and rarer. In 2006, an extensive 45-day search by experts with sonar and other equipment failed to find any in the last areas the Baiji was known to inhabit, and it was declared extinct.

AREAS OF IMPORTANCE. Recently, to protect the Ganges and Indus river dolphins from the same fate, Bangladesh has identified dolphin **hot spots,** areas of importance, within the sprawling Sundarbans mangrove forest. Three of these areas are being set aside as breeding and feeding areas for dolphins. Inten-

sive multicountry protections are needed to keep these unique animals from further decline. In an area already crowded with people, protecting species may seem impossible, but it is important. The effort of the Bangladeshi government is a hopeful move in the right direction.

The focus in this chapter is wild species. The world is experiencing a dramatic decline in wild organisms. This is such a concern that the United Nations has designated 2011–2020 the United Nations Decade of Biodiversity. While scientists can study individual species such as the Ganges River dolphin, they can also work on species decline in the context of biodiversity—the variety of life on Earth. In this chapter, we consider the importance of biodiversity as a whole, as well as that of individual species, and look at the public policies that seek to protect wild species and biodiversity.

6.1 The Value of Wild Species and Biodiversity

Recall that ecosystem capital is the sum of all the goods and services provided to human enterprises by natural systems (Chapter 1). This capital is enormously valuable to humankind. The 1997 mean estimate of ecosystem capital by Robert Constanza and his coauthors was $46.7 trillion, adjusted for 2009 dollars (see Chapter 5). Such a value is so difficult to pull together that there is no subsequent estimate of the same set of parameters. However, in 2008, economist Pavan Sukhdev reported that capital loss from the worldwide financial crisis stood at $1–$1.5 trillion, and capital loss from ecosystem degradation was estimated to be $2–$4.5 trillion per year.[1] The basis of much of our natural capital is ecosystems, and the basis of ecosystems is the plants, animals, and microbes—the wild species—that make them work. To maintain the sustainability of these ecosystems, their integrity must be preserved; this means maintaining their resilience, natural processes, and biodiversity, among other things. Placing a high priority on protecting wild species and the ecosystems in which they live is therefore crucial.

Even those who agree on the need to protect wild species, however, may disagree on the kind of protection that should be afforded to them. Some want wildlife protected so as to provide recreational hunting. Others feel strongly that hunting for sport should be banned. Many have a deeper concern for the ecological survival of wild species, and they view the ongoing loss of biodiversity as an impending tragedy. In the developing world, however, many collect or kill wild species in order to eat or make money, so their personal survival is at stake. All of these attitudes stem from the values we place on wild species. Can the differing values be reconciled in a way that still leads to sustainable management of these important natural resources?

Biological Wealth

The Millennium Ecosystem Assessment states that about 2 million species of plants, animals, and microbes have been examined, named, and classified, but that many more species have not yet been found or cataloged. Most estimates of the total number of species on Earth range from 5 to 30 million. The most recent estimate is around 8.7 million (+/− 1.3 million). About 15,000 new species are described each year. A 2011 survey of habitats on Luzon Island and surrounding waters in the Philippines revealed more than 300 new species, including an "inflatable" shark that swells by filling its belly with water **(Fig. 6–1)**.

These natural species of living things, collectively referred to as **biota,** are responsible for the structure and maintenance of all ecosystems. They, and the ecosystems that they form, represent wealth—the **biological wealth**—that makes up most of the ecosystem capital that sustains human life

Figure 6–1 The "inflatable shark." New species are being discovered regularly. These sharks were among 300 new species discovered in the Philippines in 2011.

[1]Pavan Sukhdev, *The Economics of Ecosystems and Biodiversity* (Interim Report funded by the German Ministry for Environment and the European Commission on the Economics of Ecosystems and Biodiversity). Presented at the UN's Convention on Biological Diversity, November 2008.

and economic activity with goods and services. From this perspective, the biota found in each country can represent a major component of the country's total wealth. More broadly, this richness of living species constitutes Earth's biodiversity.

Humans have always depended on Earth's wild species for food and materials. Approximately 12,000 years ago, however, our ancestors began to select certain plant and animal species from the natural biota and propagate them, and the natural world has never been the same. Forests, savannas, and plains were converted to fields and pastures as the human population grew and human culture developed. In time, many living species were exploited to extinction, and others disappeared as their habitats were destroyed. The Center for Biological Diversity has reported that 631 species and subspecies went extinct in North America between 1642 and 2001. A 2008 report said that global biodiversity loss costs as much as $4.5 trillion a year.[2] We have been drawing down our biological wealth, with unknown consequences.

For many Americans who live in cities and suburbs and get all their food from supermarkets, the connection between everyday life and nature may seem remote. That is an illusion, however. Our interactions with the natural world may have changed, but we still depend on biological wealth. Moreover, millions of our neighbors in the developing world are not so insulated from the natural world; they draw sustenance and income directly from forests, grasslands, and fisheries. For them, "environmental income" is often the safety net that sustains them during lean times and can enable them in good times to generate wealth to improve their well-being. However, these people, too, are often engaged in practices that draw down their biological wealth. A root source of this problem is the way we regard and value wild nature.

Two Kinds of Value

In the 19th century, hunters on horseback could ride out to the vast herds of bison roaming the North American prairies and shoot them by the thousands, often taking only the tongues for markets back in the east. The passenger pigeons that once darkened the skies in huge flocks were killed at their roosts to fill a lively demand for their meat, until the species was gone. Plume hunters decimated the populations of egrets and other shorebirds to satisfy the demands of fashion in the late 1800s. Appalled at this wanton destruction, 19th-century naturalists called for an end to the slaughter, and the U.S. public became sensitized to the losses. People began to see natural species as worthy of preservation, and naturalists began to look for ways to justify their calls to conserve nature. Thus, there was an emerging sense that species should not be hunted to extinction. But why not? Their problem then, and ours now, is to establish the thesis

that wild species have some value that makes it essential to preserve them. If we can identify that value, then we will be able to assess what our moral duties are in relation to wild species.

Instrumental Value. Philosophers who have addressed this problem identify two kinds of value that should be considered. The first is **instrumental value.** A species or individual organism has instrumental value if its existence or use benefits some other entity (by providing food, shelter, or a source of income). This kind of value is usually anthropocentric; that is, the beneficiaries are human beings. Many species of plants and animals have instrumental value to humans and will tend to be preserved (conserved, that is) so that we can continue to enjoy the benefits derived from them.

Intrinsic Value. The second kind of value that must be considered is **intrinsic value.** Something has intrinsic value when it has value for its own sake; that is, it does not have to be useful to us to possess value. How do we know that something has intrinsic value? This is a philosophical question and comes down to a matter of moral reasoning. People often disagree about intrinsic value, as illustrated by the controversies about the rights of animals. Some people argue that animals have certain rights and should be protected, for example, from being used for food, fur and hides, or experimentation. On the other side, some people hold that animals are simply property and have no rights at all. Others, probably the majority, hold an intermediate position: They agree that cruelty to animals is wrong, but they do not believe that animals should be given rights approaching those afforded to humans (**Fig. 6–2**).

Many people believe that no species on Earth except *Homo sapiens* has any intrinsic value. Accordingly, they then find it difficult to justify preserving species that are apparently insignificant. Still, in spite of the problems of

Figure 6–2 Intrinsic value. Do species like this Blandings turtle have value separate from their value to humans? The question of intrinsic value is one of debate amongst philosophers.

[2]Ibid.

establishing intrinsic value for species, support is growing in favor of preserving species that not only may appear useless to humans, but also may never be seen by anyone except a few naturalists or taxonomists (biologists who are experts on classifying organisms).

The value of natural species can be categorized as follows:

- Value as sources for food and raw materials,
- Value as sources for medicines and pharmaceuticals,
- Recreational, aesthetic, and scientific value, and
- Value for their own sake (intrinsic value).

Sources for Food and Raw Materials

Most of our food comes from agriculture, rather than being collected directly from wild populations, so it is tempting to falsely believe that food is independent of natural biota. In nature, both plants and animals are continuously subjected to the rigors of natural selection. Only the fittest survive. Consequently, wild populations have numerous traits for competitiveness, resistance to parasites, tolerance to adverse conditions, and other aspects of vigor.

In contrast, populations grown for many generations under the "pampered" conditions of agriculture tend to lose these traits because they are selected for production, not resilience. For example, a high-producing plant that lacks resistance to drought is irrigated, and the resistance to drought is ignored. Also, in the process of breeding plants for maximum production, virtually all genetic variation is eliminated. Indeed, the cultivated population is commonly called a cultivar (for *culti*vated *vari*ety), indicating that it is a highly selected strain of the original species, with a minimum of genetic variation. When provided with optimal water and fertilizer, cultivars produce outstanding yields under the specific climatic conditions to which they are adapted. With their minimum genetic variation, however, they have virtually no capacity to adapt to any other conditions. For example, winter wheat varieties with high yields may be less winter hardy or more prone to pests and disease.

Wild Genes. To maintain vigor in cultivars and to adapt them to different climatic conditions, plant breeders comb wild populations of related species for the desired traits. When found, these traits are introduced into the cultivar through crossbreeding or, more recently, biotechnology (Chapter 12). For example, in the 1970s, the U.S. corn crop was saved from blight by genes from a wild strain of maize. The point is that this trait came from a related wild population—that is, from natural biota. Another area in which wild species have instrumental value to humans is pest control. Later, we will discuss the tremendous and invaluable opportunities there are to control pests by increasing genetic resistance (Chapter 13). Genes for increasing this resistance can come only from natural biota. If wild populations are lost, the options for continued improvements in food plants will be greatly reduced.

New Food Plants. The potential for developing new agricultural cultivars would also be lost if wild populations were destroyed. From the hundreds of thousands of plant species existing in nature, humans have used perhaps 7,000 in all, and modern agriculture has tended to focus on only about 30. Of these, three species—wheat, maize (corn), and rice—fulfill about 50% of global food demands. This limited diversity in agriculture makes modern plants ill suited to production under many different environmental conditions. For example, arid regions are generally considered to be unproductive without irrigation, but there are wild plants, including many wild species of the bean family, that produce abundantly under dry conditions.

Scientists estimate that 30,000 plant species with edible parts could be brought into cultivation. Many of these could increase production in environments that are less than ideal. For example, every part of the winged bean, a native of New Guinea, is edible: pods, flowers, stems, roots, and leaves. Recently introduced into many developing countries, this legume has already contributed significantly to improving nutrition. Loss of biological diversity undercuts similar future opportunities.

Woods and Other Raw Materials. Because species are selected from nature for animal husbandry, forestry, and aquaculture, essentially all the same arguments apply to those important enterprises, too. For example, nearly 3 billion people rely on wood for fuel for heating and cooking. Wood products rank behind only oil and natural gas as commodities on the world market. Demand for wood is increasing so rapidly that scientists are predicting a "timber famine" or "fuelwood crisis" in the next decade. Products such as rubber, oils, nuts, fruits, spices, and gums also come from forests (Fig. 6–3). All of these products are part of the value of wild species for humans, and forests are only one example of ecosystems that provide wild and natural living resources.

Figure 6–3 Forest products. These are all nonwood forest products developed to increase income in African forested areas. (*Source:* FAO.)

Banking Genes. Living organisms can be thought of as a bank in which the gene pools of all the species involved are deposited. Thus, biota is frequently referred to as a **genetic bank.** Because of concerns about agriculture, many scientists suggest that wild relatives of cultivated crops be conserved. In Kew, England, the Royal Botanic Gardens house the Millennium Seed Bank (MSB). In 2007, the MSB banked the billionth seed in its vast collection of the genetic diversity of world plants—the largest wild seed collection in the world. There is also the massive Svalbard Global Seed Vault, built into the permafrost deep in a mountain on a remote arctic island in Norway. This ultimate seed bank officially opened in 2008 and holds seeds that will act as a backup for seed banks around the world. Similarly, zoos act as a type of genetic bank for animals, and many zoos are active in conservation and captive breeding. In the United Kingdom, the Frozen Ark Project is collecting cells and DNA from species likely to go extinct in the near future. This collaborative effort with organizations around the world is designed to preserve genetic diversity while we try to stabilize species and slow currently high extinction rates.

Sources for Medicine

Earth's genetic bank is also important for the field of medicine. For thousands of years, the indigenous people of the island of Madagascar used an obscure plant, the rosy periwinkle, in their folk medicine (Fig. 6–4). If this plant, which grows only on Madagascar, had become extinct before 1960, hardly anyone outside Madagascar would have cared. In the 1960s, however, scientists extracted two chemicals with medicinal properties—vincristine and vinblastine—from the plant. These chemicals have revolutionized the treatment of childhood leukemia and Hodgkin's disease. Before their discovery, leukemia was almost always fatal in

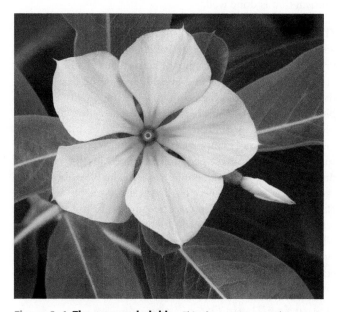

Figure 6–4 The rosy periwinkle. This plant, native to Madagascar, is a source of two anticancer agents that are highly successful in treating childhood leukemia and Hodgkin's disease.

children; today, with vincristine treatment, there is a 99% chance of remission.

The story of the rosy periwinkle is just one of hundreds. Chinese star anise, a tree in the magnolia family, yields star-shaped fruits that are harvested and processed to produce shikimic acid, the raw material for making Tamiflu®, an effective treatment against influenza viruses. Paclitaxel (trade name Taxol®), an extract from the bark of the Pacific yew, has proven valuable for treating ovarian, breast, and small-cell cancers. For a time, this use threatened to decimate the Pacific yew because six trees were required to treat one patient for a year. Now, the substance is extracted from the leaves of the English yew tree, a horticultural plant that is easy to maintain. Today, Taxol® is the most prescribed antitumor drug.

Stories like these have created a new appreciation for the field of *ethnobotany*, the study of the relationships between plants and people. To date, more than 3,000 plants have been identified as having anticancer properties. Drug companies have been financing field studies of the medicinal use of plants by indigenous peoples (called *bioprospecting*) for years. The search for beneficial drugs in the tropics has led to the creation of parks and reserves to promote the preservation of natural ecosystems that are home to both the indigenous people and the plants they use in traditional healing. In Surinam, for example, a consortium made up of drug companies, the U.S. government, and several conservationist and educational groups has created the Central Surinam Reserve, a 4-million-acre (1.64-million-hectare) protected area. Table 6–1 lists a number of well-established drugs that were discovered as a result of analyzing the chemical properties of plants used by traditional healers. Who knows what other medicinal cures are out there?

Recreational, Aesthetic, and Scientific Value

The species in natural ecosystems also provide the foundation for numerous recreational and aesthetic interests, ranging from sportfishing and hunting to hiking, camping, bird-watching, photography, and more (Fig. 6–5). Periodically, the U.S. government conducts a survey on outdoor recreation; the latest was carried out from 2005 to 2006. Of all people age 16 and older who were surveyed, an estimated 87.5 million were involved in some form of outdoor recreation. The largest activity was viewing natural scenery, an activity reported by 71.1 million people. Very likely, much of the public support for preserving wild species and habitats stems from the aesthetic and recreational enjoyment people derive from them. While hunting has declined in recent decades, other outdoor activities remain popular. A 2006 U.S. Fish and Wildlife Service survey on fishing, hunting, and wildlife found that 87.5 million U.S. resident adults (age 16 and older) participated in wildlife-centered recreation. This number included 30 million people who fished, 12.5 million who hunted, and 71.1 million who did some type of wildlife observation such as bird-watching. Hunting, fishing, and wildlife-watching result in employment for 2.6 million people—nearly as

Figure 6–5 **Recreational, aesthetic, and scientific uses.** Natural biota provides numerous values, a few of which are depicted here.

many as employed by the computer industry—and produce $108 billion in revenues in the United States.

Recreational and aesthetic values constitute a very important source of support for maintaining wild species, because activities inspired by these values also support commercial interests. **Ecotourism**—whereby tourists visit a place in order to observe wild species or unique ecological sites—represents the largest foreign-exchange-generating enterprise in many developing countries. Because some percentage of recreational dollars will be spent on activities related to the natural environment, any degradation of that environment affects commercial interests. As the national surveys indicated, recreational, aesthetic, and scientific activities involve a great number of people and represent a huge economic enterprise.

Scientific value comes from our need to have living things available so we can learn basic laws of nature, the way ecosystems function, and the way the world works generally. Societies have long held that such "pure science" is valuable. Many scientists are engaged in this endeavor by sheer curiosity about the world, including about the functioning of individual types of organisms, and biota provides the nature that we get to study. Realistically, though, most of the science done with these species aims for more-pragmatic goals—new medicines, protection from gene loss in agriculture and forestry, and other outcomes already discussed.

A Cautionary Note. The use of wild species and biodiversity for instrumental value can raise some problems of justice as we navigate the needs of people with competing claims. For example, while the rosy periwinkle was a success story because of its effectiveness in combating cancer, little of the money returned to Madagascar, a very poor country. In other cases, such as the case of turmeric (a spice commonly used in India), ancient herbal remedies have been patented by large companies. While the patent on turmeric was eventually overturned, the patent on the rosy periwinkle was not, and money from the rosy periwinkle came to Madagascar only when the patent ran out. The indigenous people in the

areas where biodiversity is highest may not be the ones to benefit from their resources. The Nagoya Protocol on Access and Benefit Sharing is a recent International Treaty designed to protect the interests of indigenous peoples as products are discovered in wild sources.

Similarly, ecotourism may bring money to poor areas of the world, but such tourism can also increase pollution, directly harm wildlife, or alter local societies in negative ways. For example, whale-watching boats on the St. Lawrence River disrupt the feeding of whales. Tourist boats on Mexican lakes frighten flocks of flamingoes and reduce their feeding time. In the Caribbean, coral reefs are damaged by divers, boat anchors, and shopkeepers who remove coral to sell. Ecotourism can marginalize indigenous people as part of the scenery, or they can remain poor while tourism operators gain wealth. Nonetheless, there is sustainable tourism, and people intending to travel in the hopes of promoting conservation can find tourism that is done well.

The Loss of Instrumental Value. Overall, a loss of biodiversity has a tremendous negative effect on the world in real, practical ways. The Economics of Ecosystems and Biodiversity (TEEB) report, released in May 2008, was the first international report to detail the economic and life-quality effects of biodiversity loss. Researchers have estimated that the loss of ecosystem services and biodiversity costs $78 billion annually and, even more importantly, that these costs are higher for the world's poorest people. Continued loss of biological diversity, the report said, could halve the income of the poorest billion and a half people. Because the people who benefit most from the rapid use of resources are not the people who are most harmed by the loss of those resources, many ethicists believe such an outcome to be morally wrong. Thus, even the instrumental values of Earth's resources have an ethical component.

Value for Their Own Sake

The usefulness (instrumental value) of many wild species is apparent. But instrumental value alone may not be a

TABLE 6–1 Modern Drugs from Traditional Medicines

Drug	Medical Use	Source	Common Name
Aspirin	Reduces pain and inflammation	*Filipendula ulmaria*	Queen of the meadow
Codeine	Eases pain; suppresses coughing	*Papaver somniferum*	Opium poppy
Ipecac	Induces vomiting	*Psychotria ipecacuanha*	Ipecac
Pilocarpine	Reduces pressure in the eye	*Pilocarpus jaborandi*	Jaborandi plant
Pseudoephedrine	Reduces nasal congestion	*Ephedra sinica*	*Ma-huang* shrub
Quinine	Combats malaria	*Cinchona pubescens*	Cinchona tree
Reserpine	Lowers blood pressure	*Rauwolfia serpentina*	Rauwolfia
Scopolamine	Eases motion sickness	*Datura stramonium*	Jimsonweed
Theophylline	Opens bronchial passages	*Camellia sinensis*	Tea
Tubocurarine	Relaxes muscles during surgery	*Chondrodendron tomentosum*	Curare vine
Vinblastine	Combats Hodgkin's disease	*Catharanthus roseus*	Rosy periwinkle

compelling reason to protect many wild species. What about the species that have no obvious value to anyone—including many plant and animal species? Another strategy for preserving all wild species is to emphasize the intrinsic value of species rather than their unknown or uncertain ecological and economic values. From this viewpoint, the extinction of any species is an irretrievable loss of something valuable.

Environmental ethicists argue that the long-established existence of species means they have a right to continued existence. Living things have ends and interests of their own, and the freedom to pursue them is often frustrated by human actions. Do humans have the right to terminate a species that has existed for thousands or millions of years? Environmental philosopher Holmes Rolston III puts it this way: "Destroying species is like tearing pages out of an unread book, written in a language humans hardly know how to read, about the place where they live."[3] Some support this view by arguing that there is value in every living thing and that one kind of living thing (e.g., humans) has no greater value than any other. This argument, however, can lead to some difficulties, such as having to defend the rights of pathogens and parasites. A more common viewpoint held by ethicists is that, because humans have the ability to make moral judgments, they also have a special responsibility toward the natural world, and that this responsibility includes concern for other species.

Religious Support. Many ethicists find their basis for intrinsic value in religious thought. For example, in the Jewish and Christian traditions, Old Testament writings express God's concern for wild species when he created them. Judeo-Christian scholars maintain that by declaring his creation good and giving it his blessing, God was saying that all wild things have intrinsic value and, therefore, deserve moral consideration and stewardly care. In the story of Noah, described in the Hebrew Bible, God makes a covenant not only with humans, but also with all creatures, "every living thing." Similarly, in the Islamic tradition, the Quran (Koran) proclaims that the environment is the creation of Allah and should be protected because its protection praises the Creator. Many Native American religions have a strong environmental ethic (a system of moral values or beliefs); for example, the Lakota hold that humans and other forms of life should interact like members of a large, healthy family. Drawing on Hindu philosophy, the Chipko movement of northern India represents a strong grassroots environmentalism. Ethical concern for wild species underlies several religious traditions and represents a potentially powerful force for preserving biodiversity. Even if species have no demonstrable use to humans, it can still be argued that they have a value and a right to exist and that humans thus have a responsibility to protect them from harm that results from human actions.

The Land Ethic. Further, there is an ethic about the preservation not just of species, but also of their ecosystems. This view of nature was most famously described by conservationist Aldo Leopold in an essay published in 1949 entitled "The Land Ethic." Leopold is known for being one of the first scientists to understand the importance of both fire and predators in maintaining ecosystem health. He advocated for protection of wild places—*wilderness*—as well as for better care of agricultural and other human-dominated land. Leopold wrote a number of essays and is well known in the literary community as well as among conservationists. *A Sand County Almanac*, in which "The Land Ethic" appeared, sold more than 2 million copies and is printed in nine languages. "The Land Ethic" was instrumental in generating interest in the protection of wilderness. In it, Leopold describes his viewpoint: "A thing is right when it tends to preserve the integrity, stability, and beauty of the biotic community. It is wrong when it tends otherwise."[4]

---

[3]Holmes Rolston III. *Environmental Ethics: Duties to and Values in the Natural World* (Philadelphia: Temple University Press, 1988), p. 129.

[4]Aldo Leopold. "The Land Ethic," in *A Sand County Almanac and Sketches Here and There* (Oxford, England: Oxford University Press, 1949). Available at http://www.luminary.us/leopold/land_ethic.html.

6.2 Biodiversity and Its Decline

In the introduction to this chapter, biodiversity was defined simply as the variety of life on Earth. We can be more specific than that. The dimensions of biodiversity include the genetic diversity within a species and the variety of species as well as the range of communities and ecosystems. When scientists use the term *biodiversity*, however, sometimes they mean a characteristic that they can calculate and compare between habitats. In this definition, scientists use two measures to calculate biodiversity—the number of species and a measure of how "even" the species are. A habitat has low biodiversity if it is dominated by only one species, with few members of other species, because those few might easily leave or die out. Given the same number of species, diversity is considered to be higher in habitats where the dominance by any single species is low. In this chapter, our main focus is the diversity of species. Recall that over long periods of time, natural selection leads to speciation (the creation of new species) as well as extinction (the disappearance of species) (Chapter 4). Now, we are interested in how humans interact with wild species and impact biodiversity over a relatively short time.

How Many Species?

Almost 2 million species have been discovered and described, and certainly many more than that exist. Most people are completely unaware of the great diversity of species that occurs within any given taxonomic category. Groups especially rich in species are the flowering plants (270,000 species) and the insects (950,000 species), but even less-diverse groups, such as birds or ferns, are rich with species that are unknown to most people (Table 6–2). Groups that are conspicuous or commercially important—such as birds, mammals, fish, and trees—are much more fully explored and described than, say, insects and very small invertebrates (such as soil nematodes, fungi, and bacteria). Taxonomists are aware that their work in finding and describing new species is incomplete. Trained researchers who can identify major groups of organisms are few, and the task of fully exploring the diversity of life would require a major, sustained effort in systematic biology. For example, Costa Rica, less than half the size of New York State, is estimated to contain at least 5% of all living species. Estimates of unknown species keep rising as taxonomists explore the rain forests more and more. Whatever the number of species, the planet's biodiversity represents an amazing and diverse storehouse of biological wealth.

The Decline of Biodiversity

Biodiversity is declining in the United States as well as around the world. Because U.S. ecosystems are well studied, the trends that show themselves here (including the decline of many plant and animal species) may represent larger global

TABLE 6–2 Known and Estimated Species on Earth

Domain	Eukaryote kingdoms	No. of described species	Estimated total
Archaea		175	?
Bacteria		10,000	?
Eukarya			
	Animalia		1,320,000
	Craniata (vertebrates), total	52,500	55,000
	Mammals	4,630	
	Birds	9,750	
	Reptiles	8,002	
	Amphibians	4,950	
	Fishes	25,000	
	Mandibulata (insects and myriapods)	963,000	8,000,000
	Chelicerata (arachnids, etc.)	75,000	750,000
	Mollusca	70,000	200,000
	Crustacea	40,000	150,000
	Nematoda	25,000	400,000
	Fungi	72,000	1,500,000
	Plantae	270,000	320,000
	Protoctista	80,000	600,000
Total		1,750,000	14,000,000

Notes: This table presents estimates of the number of species of living organisms in the high-level groups recognized and in some selected groups within them. Vertebrate classes are distinguished because of the general interest in these groups. The described species column refers to species named by taxonomists. Most groups lack a formal list of species. All estimates are approximations. They are inevitably inaccurate because new species will have been described since publication of any checklist; more are continually being described, and other names turn out to be redundant synonyms. In general, the diversity of microorganisms, small-sized species, and those from habitats difficult to access are likely to be seriously underestimated. Among Archaea and Bacteria, the figures of 175 and 10,000 are very rough estimates of "species" defined on features shown in culture; there appears to be no sound estimate of the total amount of prokaryote diversity. The estimated total column includes provisional working estimates of the number of described species plus the number of unknown species; the total figure is highly imprecise. Only a small selection of animal phyla is shown, but the figure for Animalia applies to all. Figures in the total row are for all species in all domains.

Source: Groombridge B. and Jenkins M.D. (2002) *World Atlas of Biodiversity.* Prepared by the UNEP World Conservation Monitoring Centre. University of California Press, Berkeley, USA.

trends. **Endemic** species (those found in only one habitat and nowhere else) are especially at risk. Some areas of the country and of the world are particularly vulnerable to species loss. These areas are often the focus of special conservation efforts.

North America. The biota of the United States is as well known as any. Even so, not much is known about most of the 200,000-plus species of plants, animals, and microbes estimated to live in the nation. At least 500 species native to the United States, including at least 100 vertebrates, are known to have gone extinct (or have "gone missing" and are believed to have gone extinct) since the early days of colonization. An inventory of 20,897 wild plant and animal species in the 50 states, carried out in the late 1990s by a team of biologists from the Nature Conservancy and the National Heritage Network (and more recently Nature-Serve), concluded that one-third are vulnerable (threatened), imperiled (endangered), or already extinct. In the United States, mussels, crayfish, fishes, and amphibians—all species that depend on freshwater habitats—are at greatest risk. In part, this potential for loss stems from the high number of endemic aquatic species in the American Southeast. For example, there are close to 200 species of freshwater mussels and clams in North America, giving these bivalves the greatest species diversity of any freshwater bivalve group in the

world. Flowering plants are also of great concern, with one-third of their numbers in decline in North America.

Species populations are a more important element of biodiversity than even the species' existence. Populations of species that occupy different habitats and ranges contribute to biological wealth, as they provide goods and services important in ecosystems. Across North America, even populations of well-studied species are in decline. Commercial landings of many species of fish are down, puzzling reductions in amphibian populations are occurring all over the world, and many North American songbird species (such as the Cerulean warbler, wood thrush, and scarlet tanager) are declining and have disappeared entirely from some local regions. These birds are neotropical migrants; that is, they winter in the neotropics of Central and South America and breed in temperate North America. According to a report from the National Audubon Society, more than one-fourth of North American birds are already declining or are in danger of doing so.

Global Outlook. Worldwide, the loss of biodiversity is even more disturbing. One of the most recent global analyses of biodiversity is the third *Global Biodiversity Outlook*, published by the UN (2010). **Figure 6–6**, from this assessment, shows groups from a comprehensive survey of more than 47,000 species, categorized by level of risk

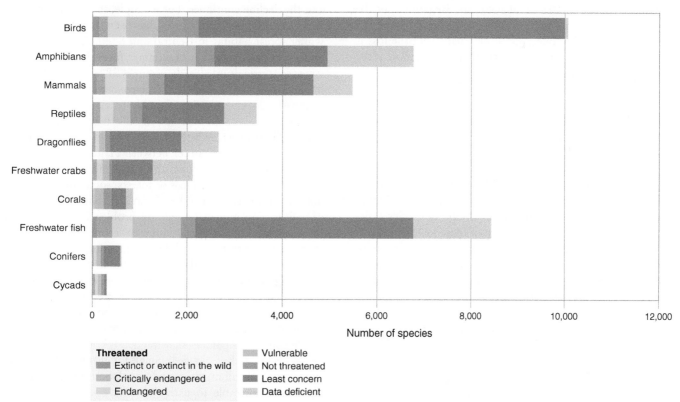

Figure 6–6 Who is going extinct? This bar graph shows groups from a comprehensive survey of more than 47,000 species, categorized by level of risk of extinction.

(Source: Global Biodiversity Outlook 3.)

of extinction. Estimates of extinction rates in the past show alarming increases in loss of species. For mammals, the background (past) extinction rate was less than one extinction every thousand years, although rates were higher during five great extinction events. (Scientists estimate the background extinction rate from the fossil record of marine animals and from rates of change in DNA.) This rate can be compared with known extinctions of the past several hundred years (for mammals and birds, 20 to 25 species per hundred years and, for all groups, 850 species over about 500 years), indicating that the current rate is 100 to 1,000 times higher than past rates.

The International Union for Conservation of Nature (IUCN) keeps a running list of threatened species. In 2011, approximately 23% (1,138) of mammal species and 12% (1,253) of bird species were globally threatened. These two groups have been thoroughly studied.[5] The status of all other groups of organisms is much less well known. The majority of threatened species are concentrated in the tropics, where biodiversity is so rich as to be almost unimaginable. Biologist Edward O. Wilson identified 43 species of ants on a single tree in a Peruvian rain forest, a level of diversity equal to the entire ant fauna of the British Isles.[6] Other scientists found 300 species of trees in a 1-hectare (2.5-acre) plot and almost 1,000 species of beetles on 19 specimens of a species of tree in Panama.[7] Unfortunately, the same tropical forests that hold such high biodiversity are also experiencing the highest rate of deforestation. Because the inventory of species in these ecosystems is so incomplete, it is virtually impossible to assess extinction rates in such forests. Regardless of the exact rates, numerous species are in decline, and some are becoming extinct. No one knows how many, but the loss is real, and species loss represents a continuing depletion of the biodiversity of our planet.

Reasons for the Decline

Extinctions of the distant past were caused largely by processes of climate change, plate tectonics, and even asteroid impacts. Current threats to biodiversity are sometimes described with the acronym **HIPPO**, which refers to five factors: habitat destruction, **invasive species**, pollution, population, and overexploitation. Many declining species experience combinations of several or all of these factors. Indeed, global climate change in particular increases the effects of some of these factors. We will discuss each factor in more detail below. Future losses will be greatest in the developing world, where biodiversity is greatest and human population growth is highest. Africa and Asia have lost almost two-thirds of their original natural habitat. People's desire for a better way of life, the desperate poverty of rural populations, and the global market for timber and other natural resources are powerful forces that will continue to draw down biological wealth on those continents.

One key to slowing the loss of biodiversity lies in bringing human population growth down (Chapter 8). If the human population increases to 10 billion, as some demographers believe that it will, the consequences for the natural world may be frightening. Another key is to pull individual consumption down to sustainable levels in parts of the world with high consumption of energy and materials. These two concepts will be vital to solving several environmental issues and will be further discussed throughout the rest of the book.

Habitat Change. By far the greatest source of biodiversity loss is the physical alteration of habitats through the processes of conversion, fragmentation, simplification, and intrusion. Habitat destruction has already been responsible for 36% of the known extinctions and is the key factor in the currently observed population declines. Natural species are adapted to specific habitats, so if the habitat changes or is eliminated, the species go with it.

Conversion. Natural areas are commonly converted to farms, housing subdivisions, shopping malls, marinas, and industrial centers. When a forest is cleared, for example, destruction of the trees is not the only result; every other plant or animal that occupied the destroyed ecosystem, either permanently or temporarily (e.g., migrating birds), also suffers. Global forest cover has been reduced by 40% already, and the decline continues. For example, the decline in North American songbird populations has been traced to the loss of winter forest habitat in Central and South America and the increasing fragmentation of summer forest habitat in North America. Agriculture already occupies 38% of land on Earth; habitats like croplands that replace natural habitats such as grasslands are quite inhospitable to all but a few species that tend to be well adapted to the new managed landscapes. Haiti provides one extreme example of habitat loss. Figure 6–7 shows the border between Haiti and the Dominican Republic, with Haiti on the left. Land use in Haiti has resulted in a tremendous loss of forests, something important not only in the context of loss of species, but also as a driver of soil erosion and water quality problems (as we will see in later chapters). In the Dominican Republic, social trends such as greater stability and democratization have helped the country avoid unrest and environmental destruction.

Fragmentation. Natural landscapes generally have large patches of habitat that are well connected to other similar patches. Human-dominated landscapes, however, consist of a mosaic of different land uses, resulting in small, often geometrically configured patches that frequently contrast highly with neighboring patches (Fig. 6–8). Small fragments of habitat can support only small numbers and populations of species, making them vulnerable to extermination. Species that require large areas are the first to go; those that grow slowly or have naturally unstable populations are also vulnerable.

Reducing the size of a habitat creates a greater proportion of **edges**—breaks between habitats that expose species

[5]Red List Category summary for all animal classes and orders, IUCN Red List version 2011.2: Table 4a. http://www.iucnredlist.org/documents/summarystatistics/2011_2_RL_Stats_Table4a.pdf. March 3, 2012.
[6]Edward O. Wilson. "The Arboreal Ant Fauna of Peruvian Amazon Forests: A First Assessment," *Biotropica* 19 (1987): 245–251.
[7]T. L. Erwin. "The Tropical Forest Canopy: The Heart of Biotic Diversity." In *Biodiversity,* edited by E. O. Wilson, National Academy Press, Washington, D.C., pp. 123–129.

Figure 6–7 The border of Haiti and the Dominican Republic. Severe deforestation in Haiti, on the left, leads to habitat loss for many species. It also causes a number of problems for humans. The forested area on the right is the Dominican Republic.

Figure 6–8 Fragmentation. Development usually leads to the breaking up of natural areas, resulting in a mosaic of habitats that may not support local populations of species.

to predators. Increased edge favors some species but may be detrimental to others. For example, the Kirtland's warbler is an endangered species that is highly dependent on large patches of second-growth jack pines in Michigan. The species is endangered because its habitat has been greatly fragmented, creating edges that favor the brown-headed cowbird, a nest parasite that can invade the forest and lay its eggs in the nest of the rare warbler. Edges also favor species that prey on nests, such as crows, magpies, and jays. These predators are thought to be partly responsible for declines in many neotropical bird populations.

Roadways offer particular dangers to wildlife. The number of animals killed on roadways now far exceeds the number killed by hunters. As rural areas are developed, the increasing numbers of animals found on roadways are a serious hazard to motorists. With 5.7 million miles (9.2 million km) of paved roadways in the United States, more than a million animals a day become roadkill. Overpasses and tunnels are increasingly being built to provide wildlife with safe corridors. A 2008 study at Purdue University identified amphibians as especially affected by road mortality.[8] More than 95% of the roadkill that researchers identified over 11 months along a stretch of road in the Midwest were amphibians.

Simplification. Human use of habitats often simplifies them. Removing fallen logs and dead trees from woodlands for firewood, for example, diminishes an important microhabitat on which species ranging from woodpeckers to germinating forest trees depend. When a forest is managed for the production of one (or a few) species of tree, tree diversity declines, and as a result, so does the diversity of the plant and animal species that depend on the less favored trees. Streams are sometimes "channelized"—their beds are cleared of fallen trees and stony riffle areas (places with more rapidly moving water), and sometimes the stream is straightened out by dredging the bottom. Such alterations inevitably reduce the diversity of fish and invertebrates that live in the stream.

Intrusion. Birds use the air as a highway, especially as they migrate north and south in the spring and fall. Recently, telecommunications towers have presented a new hazard to birds. Although television towers have been around for decades, new towers are sprouting up on hilltops and in countrysides in profusion. Cell phone signal towers are also common. The lights often placed on these towers can attract birds, which usually migrate at night, and the birds simply collide with the towers and supporting wires. In 2000, a study estimated that the towers kill somewhere between 5 and 50 million birds a year.[9] Three organizations petitioned the Federal Communications Commission (FCC) to incorporate bird mortality in its decisions about new towers in 2002, but nothing was done. The scientific research from the study gave environmentalists the power to go to court to

force the FCC to consider risk to birds when making decisions. Finally, a federal appeals court ruled in 2008 that the FCC did in fact have to come up with a plan to protect birds. This ruling resulted in a meeting of five agencies with the FCC in June of 2008. A draft plan followed in 2011, with a time for public comment and hopes of an agreement to make more-bird-friendly towers. The clear surfaces of windows are one of the greatest dangers for birds. Ornithologist Daniel Klem estimated that between 100 million and 1 billion birds die every year from crashing into glass windows. Birds are just one example of organisms harmed by the intrusion of structures into habitats. Any solution to wild species' decline must include creative ways to lower the impact of human structures on other organisms.

Invasive Species. An exotic, or alien, species is one that is introduced into an area from somewhere else, often a different continent (see Chapter 4, where they were covered extensively). Because the species is not native to the new area, it is frequently unsuccessful in establishing a viable population and quietly disappears. Such is the fate of many pet birds, reptiles, and fish that escape or are deliberately released. Some exotic species establish populations that remain at low levels without becoming pests. Occasionally, however, an alien species finds the new environment to be very favorable, and it becomes an **invasive species** thriving, spreading out, and perhaps eliminating native species by predation or competition for space or food. You will learn that most of the insect pests and plant parasites that plague agricultural production were accidentally introduced (Chapter 13). Invasive species are major agents in driving native species to extinction and are responsible for an estimated 39% of all animal extinctions since 1600.

Accidental Introductions. As humans travelled around the globe in the days of sailing ships and exploration, they brought with them more than curiosity and dreams of exotic lands. They brought rats and mice to ports all over the world. As a result, rats are the most invasive mammal worldwide. The two most common invasive rat species are the black rat (*Rattus rattus*, called the ship rat) and the brown rat (*Rattus norvegicus*, called the Norway rat). Fleas infesting black rats carried the bubonic plague bacterium to Europe, eventually killing a third of Europe's human population in the Middle Ages. In terms of species loss, the arrival of rats is especially deadly to birds. One report found that rats have been found preying on nearly one-quarter of seabird species. Thirty percent of seabirds are threatened with extinction, and rats are the biggest single cause. Rats also eat crops, destroy property, and cause other harm directly to humans, but their effect on other species is profound. Rats are only one example of accidental introduction of non-native species. Figure 6–9 shows another: the red imported fire ant (*Solenopsis invicta*), which arrived in Mobile, Alabama, from South America, possibly in shipments of wood. The fire ant is a major pest across the southern United States, inflicting damage to crops and domestic animals. It also contributes to the decline of wild species. In Texas, it is estimated that fire ants kill a fifth of songbird babies before they leave the nest.

[8]D. J. Glista, T. L. DeVault, and J. A. DeWoody. "Vertebrate Road Mortality and Its Impact on Amphibians," *Herpetological Conservation and Biology* 3 (2008): 77–87.
[9]G. Shire. *New Report Documents Hundreds of Thousands of Birds Killed at Communications Towers* (2000). Available from the American Bird Conservancy at www.abcbirds.org/newsandreports/releases/000629.html.

Figure 6–9 The red imported fire ant. This ant, *Solenopsis invicta*, has invaded the southern United States, where it kills other animals and sometimes starves them by eating their prey.

Figure 6–10 Japanese knotweed. Japanese knotweed can break foundations and walkways, shade other plants, and grow without seeds from a tiny bit of root or underground stem.

May I Introduce . . . Deliberate introductions sanctioned by the U.S. Natural Resources Conservation Service (in the interest of "reclaiming" eroded or degraded lands) have brought us kudzu and other runaway plants, such as the autumn olive and multiflora rose (Chapter 4). Salt cedar was introduced in the American Southwest for erosion control and has taken over riverbanks there. Many other exotic plants are introduced as horticultural desirables (Fig. 6–10). *Fallopia japonica*, Japanese knotweed, is a good example. Tall, with attractive flowers, it originated in Asia and is now found in North America and Europe. It forms dense patches and outcompetes native plants. Unfortunately, the strong underground stem (rhizome) and root systems cause the plant to spread even when it does not produce seeds. Whole plants can grow from tiny fragments of root. In the United Kingdom, it is illegal to dispose of Japanese knotweed except by burning or placement in a landfill. Japanese knotweed is on the World Conservation Union's list of 100 worst invasive species. The site of the 2012 Olympics in London had a large infestation, which was removed over a period of years in a process estimated to cost 70 million pounds (more than $110 million).

There are specific instances of both deliberate and accidental introductions in **aquaculture**—the farming of shellfish, seaweed, and fish—which produces one-third of all seafood consumed worldwide. More than 100 species of aquatic plants and animals are raised in aquaculture in the United States, most of which are not native to the farming locations. Parasites, seaweeds, invertebrates, and pathogens have been introduced together with the desired aquaculture species, often escaping from the pens or ponds and entering the sea or nearby river system. For example, Asian black carp are used in raising catfish because the carp eat snails that harbor parasites capable of ruining the catfish meat. So far, no carp are known to have escaped in the United States, but everywhere else that they have been used in farming, they have escaped and spread. Sometimes the aquaculture species itself is a problem. Atlantic salmon,

for example, are now raised along the Pacific Coast, and many have escaped from the pens and have been breeding in some West Coast rivers, where they compete with native species and spread diseases.

Over Time. The transplantation of species by humans has occurred throughout history, to the point where most people are unable to distinguish between the native and exotic species living in their lands. European colonists brought hundreds of weeds and plants to the Americas, and now most of the common field, lawn, and roadside plant species in eastern North America are exotics. For example, almost one-third of the plants in Massachusetts are alien or introduced—about 725 species, of which 66 have been specifically identified as invasive or likely to become so. In Europe, there are about 11,000 alien species, 15% of which harm biodiversity. Among the animals introduced to North America, the most notorious have been the house mouse and the Norway rat; others include the wild boar, the starling, the horse, and the nutria. One of the most destructive exotics is the house cat: Studies in the 1990s showed that the millions of domestic and feral cats in the United States are highly efficient at catching small mammals and birds (Fig. 6–11). They kill an estimated 1 billion small mammals (chipmunks, deer mice, and ground squirrels, as well as rats) and hundreds of millions of birds annually. One report calculates the annual cost of invasive species in the United States to be $137-billion.[10]

Species originating in the Americas can cause havoc in other places, too. For example, the North American gray squirrel is invasive in Europe, where it outcompetes the native red squirrels and may be infecting them with a fatal virus. The gray squirrel is one of the 100 most invasive species worldwide.

[10]D. Pimental, L. Lach, R. Zuniga, and D. Morrison. "Environmental and Economic Costs of Nonindigenous Species in the United States," *BioScience 50* (2000): 53–65.

Figure 6–11 The house cat. House cats allowed to roam freely kill more than a billion small animals every year.

Invasive Species and Trophic Levels. Plants provide food for herbivores that in turn provide food for carnivores. Non-native plants may be difficult for herbivores to eat and thus may keep energy and materials from passing up the food chain, even if a species has been in a new ecosystem for a long time. For example, the Norway maple was introduced to North America in 1756, but in spite of being in the United States for hundreds of years, these maples provide much less food up the food chain for herbivores (like caterpillars) and their predators (like songbirds) than native trees do.

Pollution. Another factor that decreases biodiversity is pollution, which can directly kill many kinds of plants and animals, seriously reducing their populations. For example, nutrients (such as phosphorus and nitrogen) that travel down the Mississippi River from the agricultural heartland of the United States have created a fluctuating "dead zone" in the Gulf of Mexico, an area of more than 6,765 square miles (in 2011) where oxygen completely disappears from depths below 20 meters every summer[11] (see Chapter 20). Shrimp, fish, crabs, and other commercially valuable sea life are either killed or forced to migrate away from this huge area along the Mississippi and Louisiana coastline.

Pollution destroys or alters habitats, with consequences just as severe as those caused by deliberate conversions. Every oil spill kills seabirds and often sea mammals, sometimes by the thousands (water pollution is discussed further in Chapter 20). Some pollutants, such as the pesticide DDT, can travel up food chains and become more concentrated in higher consumers (Chapter 5). Acid deposition and air pollution kill forest trees; sediments and large amounts of nutrients kill species in lakes, rivers, and bays; and global climate change, brought on by greenhouse gas emissions, is already having an impact on many species. Climate change is likely to accelerate in the next 50 years (discussed in depth in Chapter 18).

Pollution can spread disease. Human wastes can spread pathogenic microorganisms to wild species, a threat called pathogen pollution. For example, the manatee (an endangered aquatic mammal) has been infected by human papillomavirus, cryptosporidium, and microsporidium, with fatal outcomes. Pollution can also disrupt hormones and other body functions. Fish exposed to polluted river water may develop tumors or deformed organs. Sometimes they develop both male and female tissues, a condition called "intersex" (Fig. 6–12). The recent and rapid rise in the incidence of these deformities has been traced to habitats that have been altered by human use, specifically run-off, industry, and sewage in populated areas.

Population. Human population growth puts pressure on wild species through several mechanisms—through direct use of wild species, through conversion of habitat into agriculture or other use, through pollution, and through having to compete for resources with growing human populations (human population trends will be described in depth in Chapters 8 and 9). Overconsumption is tied to overpopulation and to the concept of overexploitation—the last letter in the HIPPO acronym—which will be discussed next. Even if each person using a resource used a modest amount, large numbers of people might still use too much, leading to a total overconsumption. Thus, overpopulation is a problem even if people use few resources individually. However, a small group of people can also overuse resources. Indirectly, overconsumption can drive pollution, conversion of habitat, and other effects that harm wildlife. In a world in which some individuals own literally billions of times the money and resources that

Figure 6–12 Intersex fish. Up to 80% of male fish in some rivers are found to have a condition where they also have female tissues, such as eggs developing in their testes. This appears to result from pollution.

[11]Conners, D. (2011). 2011 Gulf of Mexico dead zone smaller than scientists predicted. EarthSky. http://earthsky.org/earth/2011-gulf-of-mexico-dead-zone-smaller-than-scientists-predicted.

others own, people with the most consumptive lifestyles have a disproportionate effect on the environment. Differences in level of consumption and in sheer numbers of people drive some of the tensions among the high-, middle-, and low-income countries (see Chapter 8).

Overexploitation. The overharvest of a particular species is known as overexploitation. Removing whales, fish, or trees faster than they can reproduce will lead to their ultimate extinction. In addition, overuse of individual species harms ecosystems. Overexploitation is estimated to have caused 23% of recent extinctions (past 500 years) and is often driven by a combination of greed, ignorance, and desperation. Poor resource management often leads to a loss of biodiversity. Forests and woodlands are overcut for firewood, grasslands are overgrazed, game species are overhunted, fisheries are overexploited, and croplands are overcultivated. These practices not only deplete the resource in question, but also often set into motion a cycle of erosion and desertification, with effects far beyond the exploited area (this problem is explored in depth in Chapter 7).

Trade in Exotics. One prominent form of overuse is the trafficking in wildlife and in products derived from wild species. Much of this "trade" is illegal. Worldwide, the International Criminal Police Organization (Interpol) estimates that it generates at least $12 billion a year, making it the third-largest illicit income source, after drugs and guns. This illegal activity flourishes because some consumers are willing to pay exorbitant prices for furniture made from tropical hardwoods (like teak), exotic pets, furs from wild animals, traditional medicines from animal parts, and innumerable other "luxuries," including polar-bear rugs, ivory-handled knives, and reptile-skin handbags. For example, some Indonesian and South American parrots sell for up to $10,000 in the United States, and a panda-skin rug can bring in $25,000.

One example of illegal wildlife trade that still continues is that of rhinoceros horn. In 2011, the West African rhino was declared extinct. In October 2011, the Javan rhino was declared extinct in mainland Asia, only surviving in a small population in Indonesia. Rhino species are all very rare because of the high value placed on their horn. Rhino horn is valued as a traditional medicine in Asia and used for ornamental knife handles in the Middle East.

Rhinos have suffered, as have all large African mammals, from loss of habitat and increasing human population. However, the biggest danger to rhinos is direct illegal killing (Fig. 6–13). In November 2011, customs agents in Hong Kong seized $2.2 million worth of rhino horns along with ivory from elephant tusks. The horns represented the deaths of 17 rhinos. The news is not all bad, however. In 2011, a survey of one-horned rhinos in Nepal found that conservation efforts and protection was working and that a small population was increasing. That small glimmer of hope shows us what conservation can do if poaching can be stopped.

Greed. The long-term prospect of extinction does not curtail the activities of exploiters because, to them, the prospect of a huge immediate profit outweighs it. Even when the species is protected, the economic incentive is such that poaching and black-market trade continue. Particularly severe is the growing fad for exotic pets—fish, reptiles, birds, and houseplants. In many cases, these plants and animals are taken from the wild; often, only a small fraction even survives the transition. When animals and plants are removed from their natural breeding populations, these individuals are no better than dead when it comes to maintaining the species. At least 40 of the world's 330 known species of parrots are threatened because of this fad. Many pet stores carry imported species. Not purchasing wild-caught species is one way individuals can help preserve biodiversity.

In 1992, the United States, the largest importer of exotic birds, adopted the Wild Bird Conservation Act, a law designed to stop wild capture of declining birds, uphold international treaties in wildlife trade, and support sustainable breeding programs. In 2004, more than 200 nongovernmental organizations (NGOs) signed the European Union Wild Bird Declaration, a call for wild bird protection in the European Union (EU). In a huge step forward in bird conservation, in 2007 the EU decided unanimously to prohibit the import of wild birds.

(a)

(b)

Figure 6–13 Black rhino and rhino horn products. (a) Rhino horn is prized in traditional Asian medicine and as ornamentation. (b) The black rhino is often killed by poachers for its horn.

Consequences of Losing Biodiversity

Why is biodiversity loss a concern? The answer goes back to the values of wild species. Intrinsic value is self-explanatory: the loss of species matters simply because that species is valuable, regardless of human benefit. However, much of the discussion about the consequences of losing species is focused on instrumental value—on the fact that we humans need biodiversity. We need wild species for all the reasons we value them: we use them directly for food, fiber, fuel; we value them aesthetically, want medicines from them, want recreation in natural habitats, or need them to maintain healthy ecosystems. It is this last reason that most people understand the least. The complexity of ecosystems means that the loss of diversity causes them to break down.

The Millennium Ecosystem Assessment team agreed: biodiversity is essential for the ecosystem services and goods that human societies derive from the natural world. For example, richly diverse mangrove forests and coral reefs are buffers against coastal storms and floods. The well-being of millions of rural poor in the developing world is tied to the provision of products of natural ecosystems, especially during economic hard times. In fact, biodiversity loss threatens the achievement of virtually all of the Millennium Development Goals (see Chapter 8). Nature-based tourism would not happen without the rich diversity of wildlife and flora that attract and delight people; for many countries of sub-Saharan Africa, nature-based tourism represents the largest earner of foreign currency.

Can ecosystems lose some species and still retain their functional integrity? Research evidence indicates that the dominant plants and animals determine major ecosystem processes such as energy flow and nutrient cycling. Thus, simplifying ecosystems by driving rare species to extinction will not necessarily lead to ecosystem decline. This has risks, however: It is possible to lose keystone species—species whose role is absolutely vital to the survival of many other species in an ecosystem (see Chapter 4). For example, through felling trees and building dams, beavers make local habitats that undergo succession as beavers move throughout the landscape, increasing ecosystem diversity in a region. Alternatively, the keystone species in an ecosystem may be a predator at the top of a food chain that keeps herbivore populations under control. Sometimes keystone species are the largest animals in the ecosystem, and because of their size, they have the greatest demands for unspoiled habitat. Thus, wolves, elephants, tigers, moose, and other large animals are considered "umbrella" species for whole ecosystems.

As we have seen, one thing many declining species have in common is that they are often long-lived, large, and older at first reproduction and have high parental care of offspring (as *K*-strategists are) (Chapter 4). Thus, they are vulnerable to rapid changes in the environment. Sometimes species go

---

STEWARDSHIP   Lake Erie's Island Snake Lady

A three-foot-long grayish-tan snake basks on a rock at the shoreline of an island in Lake Erie, Pennsylvania. As is warms itself, the sun glints on its scales. Slowly it moves, one coil sliding over another, and quietly glides into the water. Head still, it watches a small round goby fish (*Neogobius melanostomus*). Suddenly, it strikes. The goby caught, the snake swallows slowly and slithers off to resume basking in the sun. The snake is the Lake Erie water snake *Nerodia sipedon insularum*, and it is endemic to the area. It was once endangered and limited to only 1,000 individuals and was subject to conservation measures.

Out of the vegetation steps a woman in field gear. Kristen Stanford, known as the "Island Snake Lady," is the water snake recovery plan coordinator for this rare reptile, working out of the Ohio State University Stone Laboratory. Over the past several years, she and her colleagues caught, measured, tagged, and protected water snakes; as a result, the small snake recovered in numbers.

The hard work of scientists, policy makers, and enthusiasts paid off. The snake, returning to a population of 12,000 individuals, was taken off of the threatened species list in 2011. Species are placed on the threatened and endangered species lists when they are already so rare that, for many, recovery is a long, drawn-out process. The rapid recovery of the snake is great news for conservationists.

What makes populations of one species increase rapidly and causes populations of another to decline? How do species relate to the other species around them? In the case of the water snake, intensive human killing and loss of habitats were the main causes of decline. Ironically, the presence of large numbers of invasive goby fish helped the snake come back from the brink of extinction. This unexpected benefit is not the norm for invasive species, however.

Many people find it hard to feel concerned about a declining snake. They may feel that snakes are threatening or are unattractive. Many people need a reason to care for a species in decline and find it much easier to relate to rabbits, whales, a beautiful bird like the whooping crane, or perhaps the rare and majestic Bengal tiger. These species are considered "charismatic" because of their wide appeal. But many of the world's creatures that are disappearing are the small and seemingly unimportant parts of the

Lake Erie Water Snake

ecosystem, like a rare water snake or small beetles. Why care about them? Conservationists suggest several reasons for concern about the loss of species. For people like Kristen Stanford, protection of species, even the small ones, is worth the cold, the bitten hands, and the wet feet that come with being "the snake lady."

Sources: Water Snake, Lake Erie. (2001). Ohio Public Library Information Network. http://www.oplin.org/snake/fact%20pages/water_snake_lake_erie/water_snake_lake_erie.html. March 6, 2012.

Michael Scott, The Plain Dealer. "Lake Erie water snakes are making a comeback." Published Sunday, June 08, 2008, http://blog.cleveland.com/metro/2008/06/snakes.html.

into decline even though they are quite common. Species such as the passenger pigeon, once the most common bird in North America, can leave a huge ecological gap when they decline or disappear. Those species least likely to be harmed by human actions include widely distributed species with small size, rapid reproduction, short generation time, low parental care of offspring, and an ability to migrate (characteristics of *r*-strategists). Such species (roaches, houseflies, and others) are most likely to become pest species. Thus, the overarching effect of human disturbance of the environment is not only to decrease species that we may like, but also to increase a number that will become major pests.

Moving Forward

What will happen as rare or unknown species go extinct because of human activities? Some people will mourn their passing. We do not really know, however, what we are losing when species become extinct. One thing is certain: The natural world is less beautiful and less interesting as a result. We might be inclined to feel overwhelmed by these numbers and the significant decline in species and in abundances of organisms. But there are glimmers of hope. Sometimes species we thought were extinct are found not to be. Two of these are the Beck's petrel, not seen for 80 years before being found by an ornithologist in 2008, and the pygmy tarsier, not seen since 1921 and thought extinct but found on the Indonesian island of Sulawesi in 2008. Sometimes new populations of very rare species are discovered, as happened in the case of the highly threatened greater bamboo lemur. A new population of this rare species was found in 2007, around 400 kilometers (240 mi) from the only previously known population. As we saw in Stewardship, "Lake Erie's Island Snake Lady," sometimes the hard work of scientists and conservation volunteers pays off in the recovery of a rare and declining species such as the modest water snake. While success in protecting species begins with the courage and determination of individuals, conservation requires the coordinated efforts over regional, national, and international scales, involving the work of both scientists and policy makers.

Sometimes new protections emerge from a change in policy. Ironically, the conservation of birds was enhanced in the EU when concern over avian flu made it possible to pass regulations limiting the import of wild birds. Sometimes scientific accomplishments make conservation doable. For example, 2008 saw the first live rhinoceros birth from frozen semen, and black-footed ferrets, an extremely rare weasel-like animal, have been born from sperm stored from fathers who had died eight years before (**Fig. 6–14**). These breakthroughs in captive breeding may save species. Once in a while, conservationists catch a break, as they did in 2008, when a rare Vietnamese turtle, one of the last four of its species in the world, was swept from a lake by a flood and caught by a fisherman who was going to sell the reptile to a restaurant for soup. Conservationists were able to purchase the 68-kilogram (150-lb) turtle and return it to the lake. In the next section, we will see more of the efforts scientists and others are putting into saving wild species.

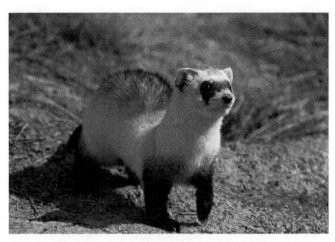

Figure 6–14 Captive breeding with new techniques. Captive breeders are now able to use frozen semen to produce black-footed ferrets, an extremely rare animal.

6.3 Saving Wild Species

If wild species and biodiversity as a whole have so much value and if they are in such decline, there must be efforts in the works to solve the problem. Indeed, there are. Those efforts involve basic science, individuals, corporations, public policy, and decisions at the local, national, and international levels (Table 6–3). Scientists are on the front lines of biodiversity protection, as they often have a better knowledge of what is out there in the world and whether or not it is declining. However, scientists cannot stop biodiversity loss by themselves. That requires laws, and it demands enforcement of those laws. Protection of biodiversity also requires stepping back to look at the big picture, seeing how people relate to the rest of the natural world, and examining how we can do so in more sustainable ways.

The Science of Conservation

The scientific projects that have been used to save the Lake Erie water snake, rhinos, and black-footed ferrets are just a few of many research activities in conservation biology, the branch of science that is most focused on the protection of populations and species. Conservation biologists use techniques like captive breeding, telemetry (transmitting data through remote communication), and tracking devices in order to learn more about the natural history of particular species and protect those that are vanishing. Scientists monitor species to see which are threatened with extinction and which are invasive and need control. They study the relationships between species and between biodiversity as a whole and ecosystem functions.

There is another critical element in the science of protecting species—**taxonomy**. Taxonomy is the cataloging of species and the naming of new ones. It allows us to understand what species are out there and to identify those in the most trouble. Right now, the field of taxonomy is suffering from a lack of experts, and this lack is harming biodiversity conservation. By 2018, there may be no specialists in fungi

TABLE 6-3 Actions Taken to Protect Species by Individuals and Different Groups

Group	Type of action	Example
Individual	Support policy	Vote to support biodiversity
	Smart consumerism	Purchase sustainable materials, use fewer resources
	Citizen science	Great Sunflower Project
Business	Sustainable practices	Coffee plantations with plants for birds
	Smart investment	Go into green technologies and businesses
Nonprofit	Land conservation	Protection of marine reserves/wildlife
	Captive breeding	Zoo programs
	Education	Environmental education
	Sustainable development	Working with local groups for conservation goals
Science	Basic research in natural history, taxonomy, captive breeding techniques	Rhino breeding
	Develop wildlife forensics	Scottish Wildlife Forensics labs
	Monitor species	IUCN Red List
	Control invasive species, and better understand other causes of species decline	Study effects of house cats or cell phone towers on birds
Government	Make sound policies for local and national needs	Lacy Act, Marine Mammal Act, Endangered Species Act
	Develop international treaties	CITES, Convention on Biodiversity

in the United Kingdom, despite the fact that fungi provide medicines, can be major crop pests, and are important parts of soil health.[12] Because most people cannot even identify the species we are dealing with, it is difficult to promote solutions. The loss of expertise as taxonomists retire and the pressure from international treaties to protect species may require increased funding to train new taxonomists.

Individuals and Corporations

Individuals can directly support conservation by being careful in their consumption of resources, use of chemicals, driving habits, and other personal choices. However, many of the actions individuals take are through support of nonprofits, pushing for policy actions, and pushing corporations to work in more-biodiversity-friendly ways. For example, consumers are insisting on more organic foods and certification of wild-caught fish or forest products as sustainable (some of these approaches are discussed in Chapter 7). Individuals can act as "citizen scientists" and take part in massive information-gathering efforts such as the Great Sunflower project, which monitors pollinators (Fig. 6–15), the Firefly Project (which tracks firefly abundance), the annual Audubon Society Christmas Bird count (in which volunteers count birds), Project Budburst (a project that tracks when plants change seasonally), and others.

Consumers also encourage businesses to care about species. Many businesses are beginning to realize that biodiversity loss could harm their profits. Biodiversity-friendly investing is on the rise as well. A survey in 2009 of global CEOs found that 27% expressed concern about the impacts of biodiversity loss on their business prospects.

Nonprofit Efforts

One way individuals contribute to conservation of biodiversity is through the funding of nonprofit organizations such as the World Wildlife Fund, Audubon Society, and many others. With some fundraising campaigns, people are able to "sponsor" individual whales, tigers, polar bears, and other creatures considered "charismatic"—that is, widely appealing. The efforts to protect these species, which often require

Figure 6–15 Citizen science. The Great Sunflower Project is one of many that links a network of amateur scientists to collect data on species. In this case, they study pollinators, which are in decline.

[12] S. Connor. "Fungi scientists are endangered species: Budget cuts threaten research into basics that propagate life on Earth," *The Independent* (November 2008).

large areas of habitat, protect other species as well. Land conservation is used to protect multiple species at the same time (discussed in more detail in Chapter 7). The oldest regional land conservancy in the United States is the Trustees of Reservations in Massachusetts.

Zoos have a special role in biodiversity conservation. Not everyone believes it is a good thing for animals to be kept in zoos, away from their natural habitat. However, in many cases, zoos have a two-fold role in protecting species. First, they actively educate the public so people care about species protection. Second, many are involved in research and in captive breeding programs. For some species, the breeding done at zoos and other captive breeding facilities is the difference between survival and extinction. Botanical gardens can have the same role for plants. Of course, breeding many species solely in captivity is not a sustainable long-term solution for species loss, but it may bridge the gap while humans figure out how to live more sustainably.

Governments: Local, State, and National Policies

Public policies, and the agencies that make and support them, are necessary for the protection of species. Governments from local to international are involved in monitoring, conserving, and protecting biodiversity. If we want to save wild species, we first need to ask who owns wildlife. In the United States, property owners do not own the wildlife living on their lands; wildlife resources are public resources, protected under the Public Trust Doctrine. The government holds these resources in trust for all its people and is obliged to provide protection for these resources. In the United States, this protective role is usually exercised by state fisheries and wildlife agencies. Sometimes the law mandates federal jurisdiction, as in the case of endangered species. Game animals were some of the first animals people recognized as having the potential to be overharvested; consequently, they are a group that receives special oversight, even if they are not currently rare.

Game Animals in the United States. Game animals are those animals traditionally hunted for sport, meat, or pelts. In the early days of the United States, there were no restrictions on hunting, and a number of species were hunted to extinction (the great auk, heath hen, and passenger pigeon) or near extinction (the bison and wild turkey). As game animals became scarce in the face of unrestrained hunting, regulations were enacted. State governments, backed up by the federal government, enacted laws establishing hunting seasons and bag limits and hired wardens to enforce the laws. Some species were given complete protection in order to allow their populations to build up to numbers that would once again allow hunting. The wild turkey, for example, was hunted to the brink of extinction. It made a slow comeback by the 1930s as a result of hunting restrictions and returned strongly after reintroduction into areas it had once inhabited. The turkey is now found in 49 states. Unfortunately, the turkey was also introduced to western states, where it

was not native, and it is now a pest in those areas. Ideally, in the future it would be protected in states where it is native and removed from states where it is invasive.

Hunting and Conservation. Using hunting and trapping fees as a source of revenue, state wildlife managers enhance the habitats that support important game species. In spite of what seems on the surface to be destruction of wildlife, hunting has many positive aspects. Besides the fees hunters pay, many hunters belong to organizations dedicated to the game they are interested in hunting. Organizations such as Ducks Unlimited raise funds that are used for the restoration and maintenance of natural ecosystems vital to the game they are interested in hunting.

Defenders of hunting and trapping argue that their prey are often animals that lack natural predators and would increase to the point of destroying their own habitat, something that frequently happens in the United States with larger animals such as deer and elk. For example, there are so many deer in Pennsylvania that, in 2004, they were estimated to be at three times the natural carrying capacity. The deer eat crops, damage cars in collisions, and seriously harm forest understories through extensive browsing. It might seem like hunting is the answer, but sometimes it is not that simple. Despite high deer numbers, some hunters have actually lobbied the state to take action to *increase* the deer herd. Why? These hunters are hunting in the northern and western part of the state, where deer populations were once heavy. Unfortunately, the deer have left these forests and have moved to the southern and eastern parts of the state, where they eat agricultural crops and browse in suburban developments. They wreak economic damage but are very difficult to hunt. Thus, the perception of hunters is that deer populations are declining, while the perception of many other people (including wildlife managers) is that there are too many deer for ecosystems to support.

Bring Back the Predators? Many members of the non-hunting public object to the killing of wildlife, and some groups, such as the Humane Society of the United States and People for the Ethical Treatment of Animals (PETA), actively campaign to limit or end hunting and trapping. Some practices that are regarded as especially cruel, such as the use of leghold steel traps, have been banned in several states as a result of ballot initiatives. Even people who are not opposed to hunting may feel that encouraging hunting because of a lack of other predators may not be getting at the fundamental problems with species loss. They argue for the return of predators such as grizzly bears, mountain lions, and wolves in order to restore more natural checks and balances to ecosystems. Because humans do not always get along well with top predators, such reintroductions are unlikely to occur on a large scale (Fig. 6–16).

Too Many Animals. Because wild animals are in the public trust, their numbers are managed by government agencies. Now that many populations are increasing, the government sometimes has to limit them. Many nuisance animals are thriving in highly urbanized areas, creating various health

Figure 6–16 **Wild cougar.** As humans encroach on wild habitat, animals come into human areas. This cougar was on a suburban roof in California. It was shot with a tranquilizer. Returning big predators to ecosystems is not likely to happen in human-inhabited areas.

hazards. Opossums, skunks, and deer are attracted to urban areas by opportunities for food; unsecured garbage cans and pet food left outside will ensure visits from raccoons. In 2010, the Centers for Disease Control and Prevention reported 6,153 cases of rabid animals in the United States, 60% of which were raccoons and skunks.[13]

One highly controversial effort to control unwanted animals is carried out by an agency of the U.S. Department of Agriculture. **Wildlife Services** responds to requests from livestock owners, farmers, homeowners, and others to remove nuisance animals and birds. "Removal" virtually always means killing, and Wildlife Services routinely uses poisons, traps, and other devices to kill around 2.5 million animals yearly. Of these, most are native species such as raccoons or skunks, but others, such as wild hogs and starlings, are exotic invasive species. Wildlife Services plays the important role of keeping both invasive species and native species from overtaking human areas and limiting negative human–wildlife interactions.

Protecting Endangered Species

In colonial days, huge flocks of snowy egrets inhabited the coastal wetlands and marshes of the southeastern United States. In the 1800s, when fashion dictated fancy hats adorned with feathers, egrets and other birds were hunted for their plumage. By the late 1800s, egrets were almost extinct. In 1886, the newly formed National Audubon Society began a press campaign to shame "feather wearers" and end the practice. The campaign caught on, and gradually attitudes changed; new laws followed. Government policies that protect animals from overharvesting are essential to keep species from the brink of extinction. Even when cultural standards change due to the efforts of individual groups (such as the National Audubon Society), laws and policy measures must

follow to ensure that endangered populations remain protected. Since the 1800s, several important laws have been passed to protect a wide variety of species.

Lacey Act. Florida and Texas were the first states to pass laws protecting plumed birds. Then, in 1900, Congress passed the **Lacey Act**, forbidding interstate commerce in illegally killed wildlife—and therefore making it more difficult for hunters to sell their kill. Since then, numerous wildlife refuges have been established to protect the egrets' breeding and migratory habitats. With millions of people visiting these refuges and seeing the birds in their natural locales, attitudes have changed significantly. Today, the thought of hunting these birds would be abhorrent to most of us, even if official protection were removed. Thus protected, egret populations were able to recover substantially. In the meantime, the Lacey Act and its amendments have become the most important piece of legislation protecting any wildlife from illegal killing or smuggling. Under the act, the U.S. Fish and Wildlife Service (USFWS) can bring federal charges against anyone violating a number of wildlife laws. In 2007, the Combat Illegal Logging Act of 2007 (S. 1930) was proposed to expand the Lacey Act to cover rare timber and timber products. It is still waiting to move forward.[14]

For examples of the work of the U.S. Fish and Wildlife Service: In 2007, special agents worked on more than 12,177 violations of the Lacey Act and other wildlife-related laws. Their efforts resulted in fines of more than $14 million and a total of 31 years of jail time for those convicted. In one case, owners of an animal park in South Dakota were caught trafficking bear gall bladders and buying and selling threatened grizzly bears; in another, a Utah man was fined for having 106 illegally caught bobcat skins that he had intended to sell

[13]J. D. Blanton, et al. *Rabies Surveillance in the United States During 2010.* Available at http://avmajournals.avma.org/doi/pdf/10.2460/javma.239.6.773.

[14]USFWS Actions. *US FWS Office of Law Enforcement.* Annual Report FY 2007 (2008). Available at http://www.fws.gov/le/aboutle/annual.htm.

in Europe (where their value was $38,000). In 2009, agents helped catch a man bringing endangered fish into the United States from Indonesia in a suitcase. In 2011, a Washington State couple was prosecuted for sale of bald and golden eagle body parts from at least 45 birds. As wildlife smuggling increases and budgets tighten, USFWS agents work harder to catch people harming the rarest species.

Endangered Species Act. Congress took another major step when it passed a series of acts to protect endangered species. The most comprehensive and recent of these acts is the **Endangered Species Act** of 1973 (reauthorized in 1988). Recall that an endangered species is a species that has been reduced to the point where it is in imminent danger of becoming extinct if protection is not provided (**Fig. 6–17**).

(a) Male Pine Barrens Tree Frog

(b) Silversword

(c) Red-cockaded Woodpecker

(d) Karner Blue Butterfly

(e) Swamp Pink

(f) Whooping Cranes

(g) Devil's Hole Pupfish

(h) White Oryx

(i) Manatee

Figure 6–17 Endangered species. Shown are some examples of endangered species—species whose populations in nature have dropped so low that they are in imminent danger of becoming extinct unless protection is provided.

Genetically distinct populations (subspecies) such as the Florida panther and the peninsular bighorn sheep may also be protected. Further, the act provides for the protection of threatened species, which are judged to be in jeopardy but not on the brink of extinction. When a species is officially recognized as being either endangered or threatened, the law specifies substantial fines for killing, trapping, uprooting (in the case of plants), modifying significant habitat of, or engaging in commerce in the species or its parts. The legislation forbidding commerce includes wildlife threatened with extinction anywhere in the world.

The Endangered Species Act is administered by the U.S. Fish and Wildlife Service for terrestrial and freshwater species (and a few marine mammals) and by the National Oceanic and Atmospheric Administration (NOAA) Fisheries Service for marine and anadromous species (those that migrate into freshwater). There are three crucial elements in the process of designating a species as endangered or threatened:

1. **Listing.** Species may be listed by the appropriate agency or by petition from individuals, groups, or state agencies.

Listing must be based on the best available information and must not take into consideration any economic impact the listing might have. Current listed species are summarized in Table 6–4.

2. **Critical Habitat.** When a species is listed, the agency must also designate as *critical habitat* the areas where the species is currently found or where it could likely spread as it recovers. A 1995 Supreme Court decision made it clear that federal authority to conserve critical habitats extended to privately held lands.

3. **Recovery Plans.** The agency is required to develop recovery plans that are designed to allow listed species to survive and thrive.

As Table 6–4 indicates, as of November 2011, 1,990 U.S. species were currently listed for protection under the act; recovery plans are in place for 1,138 of them. In addition, 251 candidate species are waiting to be listed.

Alternatives and Roadblocks. The Endangered Species Act was scheduled for reauthorization in 1992, but because of political battles, it has been operating on year-to-year

TABLE 6-4 Federal Listings of Threatened and Endangered U.S. Plant and Animal Species, 2011

Summary of Listed Species, Listed Populations,[a] and Recovery Plans[b] as of November 19, 2011

	United States			Foreign			Total Listings (U.S. and Foreign)	U.S. Listings with Active Recovery Plans[c]
	Endangered	Threatened	Total Listings	Endangered	Threatened	Total Listings		
Mammals	70	14	84	256	20	276	360	60
Birds	76	16	92	204	14	218	310	85
Reptiles	13	24	37	66	16	82	119	37
Amphibians	15	10	25	8	1	9	34	17
Fishes	77	68	145	11	1	12	157	101
Clams	64	8	72	2	0	2	74	70
Snails	25	12	37	1	0	1	38	29
Insects	51	10	61	4	0	4	65	40
Arachnids	12	0	12	0	0	0	12	12
Crustaceans	19	3	22	0	0	0	22	18
Corals	0	2	2	0	0	0	2	0
Animal Subtotal	422	167	589	552	44	604	1,193	469
Flowering Plants	613	147	760	1	0	1	761	638
Conifers and Cycads	2	1	3	0	2	2	5	3
Ferns and Allies	27	2	29	0	0	0	29	26
Lichens	2	0	2	0	0	0	2	2
Plant Subtotal	644	150	794	1	2	3	797	669
Grand Total	**1,066**	**317**	**1,383**	**553**	**54**	**607**	**1990**	**1,138**

Source: Department of the Interior, U.S. Fish and Wildlife Service, Division of Endangered Species, November 19, 2011.

[a]A listing has an E or a T in the "status" column of the tables in 50 C.F.R. §17.11(h) or 50 C.F.R. §17.12(h) (the "List of Endangered and Threatened Wildlife and Plants").

[b]Sixteen animal species (11 in the United States and 5 in foreign countries) are counted more than once in the above table, primarily because these animals have distinct population segments (each with its own individual listing status).

[c]Recovery plans pertain only to U.S. species.

SOUND SCIENCE
Using DNA to Catch Wildlife Criminals

Scotland: A group of men stand around, holding shovels, nets, and the leashes of dogs wearing radio collars. A local police officer stops them, wondering what they are up to. They claim to be hunting rabbits, but the police think otherwise. In other years, there might not be anything for the police to do, but now, it is easier to gather evidence. The police swab the mouths of the dogs, and their suspicions are confirmed when the gathered specimens are found to have traces of fox DNA.

Sound like an odd episode of *CSI: Wildlife*? You are right! But in this real-life drama, Scotland's own Wildlife DNA Forensic Unit came to the rescue to give the police the data they needed to apprehend criminals. The illegal fox hunters pleaded guilty, and the work of the first dedicated wildlife DNA forensic testing facility in Europe was showcased.

New technologies can often help in crimes against wildlife, much as it is widely used to solve crimes against humans. In Italy, scientists were able to show that the blood on a knife owned by a suspected poacher had come from a specific poached wild boar. Scientists at the Center for Conservation Biology at the University of Washington have worked to find the origin of contraband ivory shipped from Africa to Singapore. Were the elephants slaughtered for their tusks all from one place or scattered throughout Africa? They compared DNA from the ivory with DNA patterns found in elephant dung collected all over the African continent. By doing so, they were better able to identify where the poaching had occurred. In this instance, they found that the origin of the tusks was a small area centered in Zambia. The group's efforts could be increased to stop poaching. They were able to do the same with a second shipment of contraband ivory, detected in a shipping container in Malaysia. In this case, the elephants came from another region. Knowing how wildlife traffickers are attacking rare species is important to their protection.

Wildlife forensics is increasing as wildlife trafficking increases. Some people believe that the solution is not to ban traffic in rare species outright, but to "farm" them so that limited legal amounts could be harvested. This is a controversial approach, however. Regardless of how we try to protect them, crimes against wild species populations occur, and when they do, it is helpful to have cutting-edge science and technology to unravel the secrets.

Source: http://conservationbiology.net/research-programs/tracking-poached-ivory-2/

---

budget extensions. It has been a political lightning rod since its enactment. Opposition to the act comes from development, timber, recreational, and mineral interests as well as other lobby groups. Organizations such as the American Land Rights Association and the American Forest Resource Council continually lobby for weakening or abolishing the Endangered Species Act because they believe it limits their property rights to log, build buildings, and carry out other activities. In 2005, then-congressman Richard Pombo, who once chaired the House Resources Committee, sponsored H.R. 3824, the Threatened and Endangered Species Recovery Act (TESRA). TESRA had significant limitations from a scientific standpoint. The objections of scientists to TESRA were so strong that six scientific societies signed a joint statement outlining their concerns in 2006.[15] TESRA passed the House in the 109th Congress but failed to make it through the Senate and was not reintroduced subsequently.

Conflicting Values. Some critics claim that the Endangered Species Act has been a failure because only 23 of the 1,900 listed species have recovered and been taken off the list and 25 others downlisted from endangered to threatened (2011). In response, proponents state that the two main causes of extinction—habitat loss and invasive species—are on the increase. Furthermore, species are listed only when they have already reached dangerously low populations, which means that they almost certainly would have gone extinct without the protection. If success were measured by the number of species that have stabilized or increased their populations, then the act might be judged a success, as some 41% of listed species have responded this way after being listed.

Other critics of the Endangered Species Act believe that it does not go far enough. A major shortcoming is that protection is not provided until a species is officially listed as endangered or threatened and a recovery plan is established. For half of the protected vertebrate species, fewer than 1,000 individuals remained in each population at the time of listing; for half of the listed plant species, fewer than 120 individuals remained. Currently, the list's backlog includes some 253 "candidate species," all of which are acknowledged to be in need of listing. In the first 20 years following the passage of the Endangered Species Act, 114 U.S. species went extinct (or "missing," which means that, despite at least 10 years of survey, they haven't been seen). The majority of these never made it to the list and became extinct during a delay in listing procedures.

Another contentious issue is the establishment of critical habitat. Opponents believe that the critical habitat designation puts unwanted burdens on property owners and assert that the critical habitat findings have little merit in conserving species. TESRA, for example, would have completely eliminated critical habitat protections and replaced them with a statement that recovery plans must identify areas of "special value" to the protection of the species. However, nothing in this designation is intended to be mandatory. Critics of TESRA answered that critical habitat works; species with critical habitat have been twice as likely to be on the road to recovery as those without it. In fact, current efforts are

---

[15]*Scientific Societies' Statement on the Endangered Species Act* (February 27, 2006). Available at http://www.conbio.org/Sections/NAmerica/ScientificSocieties OnUSESA.pdf.

to protect the critical habitat of multiple species at once, an ecosystem approach.

Improving Legislation. In March 2006, a letter signed by almost 6,000 scientists from around the country was delivered to the U.S. Senate, urging them to pass legislation that maintains and strengthens the provisions and funding of the Endangered Species Act and to reject proposals that would weaken the act.

In the final analysis, the Endangered Species Act is a formal recognition of the importance of preserving wild species, regardless of whether they are economically important. Species listed as endangered or threatened have legal rights to protection under the law. The act is something of a last resort for wild species, but it embodies an encouraging attitude toward nature that has now become public policy. Some changes may make the act function better. These might include tax breaks as incentives to landowners caring for endangered species or other measures to lift the burden of critical habitat designations. In 2007, a bipartisan group of 17 senators introduced another bill—the Endangered Species Recovery Act (ESRA) of 2007 (S.700)—to suggest just that. The reauthorization of a strong Endangered Species Act, possibly with changes to better protect whole ecosystems, will be a major signal of our continuing commitment to consider the value of wild species on grounds other than economic or political.

Seeing Success

Efforts to protect species—such as the Lacey Act, the Marine Mammals Protection Act, the Endangered Species Act, and many other laws designed to keep our biotic heritage from going extinct—have resulted in some successes. The Lake Erie water snake is one such example. Another example of a species restored to many former areas of its range because of these protection and recovery efforts is the gray wolf. Other species have also benefited significantly from these laws.

Birds of Prey. One of the species recently removed from the Endangered Species List because its numbers have recovered significantly is the American bald eagle, the U.S. national symbol (Fig. 6–18). The peregrine falcon, another previously endangered species, has also been removed for the same reason. Both are large raptors—predatory birds at the top of the food chain. Both the bald eagle and the peregrine falcon were driven to extremely low numbers because of the use of DDT as a pesticide from the 1940s through the 1960s. Carried up to these predators through the food chain, DDT caused a serious thinning of the birds' eggshells that led to nesting failures in the two species and in numerous other predatory birds (see Chapter 1). DDT use was banned in both the United States and Canada in the early 1970s, and the stage was set for the birds to recover. On August 20, 1999, the peregrine falcon was delisted, and on June 28, 2007, the Interior Department took the American bald eagle off the Endangered Species List. Both raptors will still be protected by the Migratory Bird Treaty Act, and the eagle will be protected by the Bald and Golden Eagle Protection Act.

Figure 6–18 The American bald eagle. The Endangered Species Act worked well in bringing this magnificent national symbol to the point where it was dropped from the list.

Fly Away Home. A few species have gained exceptional public attention, and heroic efforts have been mounted to save them. Efforts to save the whooping crane, for example, include virtually full-time monitoring and protection of the single remaining flock, which for years numbered only in the teens. The historic migratory wild flock is increasing steadily and reached a population of 279 individuals in the spring of 2011 from a low of 14 cranes in 1939. This flock migrates from their wintering grounds on the Texas Gulf Coast to Wood Buffalo National Park in Canada. Nonmigratory flocks have been reintroduced in central Florida and Louisiana. Some 30 birds now make up these flocks. A spectacular effort has established a new migratory flock of 105 cranes that summer in Wisconsin and migrate to Florida. This flock was first "taught" its migratory path by following researchers in ultralight aircraft (Fig. 6–19). Although each of these flocks is extremely vulnerable to environmental changes, whooping cranes have suffered setbacks before, and conservationists remain hopeful.

Whooping cranes are one of the examples of successful conservation, and, although they still need help, their numbers are clearly increasing. Conservationists treasure these examples in a time when so many species are in decline. It is important to know that the work you do can make a difference. Another source of encouragement for people interested in saving wild species are the so-called "Lazarus species"—species that were thought extinct and later found to still have some members alive. The Bermuda petrel is one such species. Not seen since 1620, it was thought extinct for 330 years until 1951, when 18 nesting pairs were found on a remote island. The Takahe, a flightless bird of New Zealand, is another example. The last four known specimens were taken in 1898. In 1948, it was rediscovered. Both birds are endangered today, but not extinct. These stories of hope help motivate people in the hard work of protecting species.

Figure 6–19 Whooping cranes and pilot. A pilot in an ultralight aircraft leads a flock of whooping cranes in their migration from Wisconsin to Florida.

6.4 Protecting Biodiversity Internationally

Serious efforts are being made to preserve biodiversity around the world, especially in the tropics, where so much of the world's biodiversity exists. These protective efforts require an immense amount of coordination among local, state, and federal authorities. The National Biological Information Infrastructure is a collaborative program that makes protecting species easier for agencies in the United States, but the United States also has to coordinate with the rest of the world. These partnerships not only create treaties, but also monitor species, share scientific advances, and find solutions to the needs of people who are clashing with wild species.

International Developments

There are numerous international developments for the protection of species. Some, like the International Union for Conservation of Nature (IUCN, formerly called the World Conservation Union), are organizations that monitor the successes and failures of our conservation efforts. Others are organizations that help coordinate scientists or policy makers around the globe. For example, the Invasive Species Specialist Group (ISSG) is a part of the Species Survival Commission of IUCN. The ISSG is made up of invited world experts who act as advisors and maintain a global invasive species database. The policy and treaty makers have to hammer out documents like the Convention on Biological Diversity. Finally, there has to be funding for species protection, some of which is provided by the Critical Ecosystem Partnership Fund and other foundations.

The Red List. The IUCN maintains a "Red List" of threatened species.[16] Similar to the U.S. Endangered Species List,

the Red List uses a set of criteria to evaluate the risk of extinction for thousands of species throughout the world. The list is updated frequently, and there were 18,678 species of plants and animals on it in 2011. Once published in book form, the Red List is now available in searchable electronic format on the Internet. Each species on the list is given its proper classification, and its distribution, documentation, habitat, ecology, conservation measures, and data sources are described.

The IUCN is not actively engaged in preserving endangered species in the field, but its findings are often the basis of conservation activities throughout the world, and it provides crucial leadership to the world community on issues involving biodiversity. One of its efforts was to help establish the Trade Records Analysis for Flora and Fauna in International Commerce (TRAFFIC) network, which monitors wildlife trade and helps to implement the decisions and provisions of the Convention on International Trade in Endangered Species of Wild Fauna and Flora (CITES).

CITES. Endangered species outside the United States are only tangentially addressed by the Endangered Species Act. However, under the leadership of the United States, CITES was established in the early 1970s. CITES is not specifically a device to protect rare species—instead, it is an international agreement (signed by 169 nation-states) that focuses on trade in wildlife and wildlife parts. The treaty recognizes three levels of vulnerability of species—the highest being species threatened with extinction—and covers 5,000 animals and 28,000 plants, fungi, and other species. Restrictive trade permits and agreements between exporting and importing countries are applied to those species, sometimes resulting in a complete ban on trade if the nations agree. Every two or three years, the signatory countries meet at a Conference of the Parties. The latest such conference was held in 2011 in Bergen, Norway.

Perhaps the best-known act of CITES was to ban the international trade in ivory in 1989 in order to stop the rapid decline of the African elephant (from 2.5 million animals in 1950 to about 609,000 in 1989 and only around 470,000 in 2008). Recently, several countries have applied to CITES to resume ivory sales and conduct a limited harvest of elephants; permission was given for sales of stocks of ivory at several conferences, and each time poaching of elephants resumed. Unfortunately, legal sales of ivory from the few stable populations may make poaching in other populations worse. In 2006, 3.9 tons of ivory shipped from Cameroon and seized in Hong Kong were shown (via DNA testing) to have come from elephants in Gabon (see Sound Science, "Using DNA to Catch Wildlife Criminals"). Any plan to protect African elephants needs to enable people in Africa to manage wildlife without overexploitation, persuade others to stop using ivory, and use science to stop ivory crime. These changes require a world outcry against ivory collection and an expanded effort to stop ivory crime to save the African elephant from extinction.

---

[16]http://www.iucnredlist.org/

Convention on Biological Diversity. Although CITES provides some protection for species that might be involved in international trade, it is inadequate to address broader issues pertaining to the loss of biodiversity. With the support of the United Nations Environment Programme (UNEP), an ad hoc (formed for this purpose) working group proposed an international treaty that would move to conserve biological diversity worldwide. After several years of negotiation, the Convention on Biological Diversity was drafted and became one of the pillars of the 1992 Earth Summit in Rio de Janeiro. The Biodiversity Treaty, as the convention is called, was ratified in December 1993 and is now in force. One hundred ninety-two states and the European Union are treaty members. As originally organized, the treaty addresses three complementary objectives: (1) the conservation of biodiversity, (2) the sustainable use of biodiversity services, and (3) the equitable sharing of the use of genetic resources found in a country. The treaty establishes a secretariat and designates the Conference of the Parties (the treaty members) as the governing body. Ten conferences have been held, the latest in Nagoya, Aichi Prefecture, Japan, in October 2010. At that meeting, delegates adopted a Revised and Updated Strategic Plan, including Aichi Biodiversity Targets for the period 2011–2020, designated as the UN Decade of Biodiversity. After the joint international meeting, individual countries agreed to form national biodiversity strategies and action plans within two years. National reports on those strategies and plans are due by 2014.

Some examples of the Aichi Biodiversity Targets are:

- At least halve and, where feasible, bring close to zero the rate of loss of natural habitats, including forests

- Establish a conservation target of 17% of terrestrial and inland water areas and 10% of marine and coastal areas

- Restore at least 15% of degraded areas through conservation and restoration activities

- Make special efforts to reduce the pressures faced by coral reefs

The secretariat of the Convention on Biological Diversity and the UNEP jointly published the report *Global Biodiversity Outlook 1, 2, and 3* in 2001, 2006, and 2010, respectively. *Outlook 3* lays out issues for biodiversity in the 21st century and analyzes why some of the goals for 2010 were not met. The bottom line: Although the targets laid out in the *Strategic Plan* are achievable and the tools for achieving them are largely in place, it will take an unprecedented and costly effort to reach success, and more people need to become convinced of the immediacy of the problems associated with biodiversity loss. The loss of biodiversity is continuing at all levels. Deforestation continues; population trends of key land, freshwater, and marine species all show declines; and more species are threatened with extinction. One positive note is that the area of protected spaces is increasing.

Even though President Clinton signed the Convention on Biological Diversity in 1993, lobbying by a number of key organizations—especially those concerned about property rights—prevented ratification of the treaty by the U.S. Senate, leaving U.S. involvement in a state of limbo. However, many of the provisions of the treaty are being carried out by different U.S. agencies. The National Biological Service, for example, is working on several of the treaty's provisions. The United States continues to send delegations to the Conference of the Parties and participates in other related meetings, such as those dealing with genetically modified organisms.

Critical Ecosystem Partnership Fund. The Critical Ecosystem Partnership Fund emerged in August 2000. Jointly sponsored by the World Bank, Conservation International, the government of Japan, the MacArthur Foundation, and the Global Environment Facility, the fund provides grants to NGOs and community-based groups for conservation activities in biodiversity "hot spots"—34 regions, making up just 2.3% of Earth's land surface (Fig. 6–20), in which 75% of the most threatened mammals, birds, and amphibians are located. By 2011, the fund had already provided $137 million in grants to some 1,627 partners to work on preserving biodiversity in the hot spots.

Stewardship Concerns

What we do about wild species and biodiversity reflects on our wisdom and our values. Wisdom dictates that we take steps to protect the biological wealth that sustains so many of our needs and economic activities. Our values come from our view of species and their instrumental and intrinsic worth. Our values also reflect what we think about the importance of justice—whether we believe, for example, that the people who most benefit economically from the use of an ecosystem should be the same people who bear the risks of its decline, or whether we value maintaining choices and options for future generations.

Wisdom. The scientific team that put together the UN Global Biodiversity Assessment focused on four themes in its recommendations:

1. **Reforming policies that often lead to declines in biodiversity.** Many governments (including that of the United States) subsidize the exploitation of natural resources and agricultural activities that consume natural habitats.

2. **Addressing the needs of people who live adjacent to or in high-biodiversity areas or whose livelihood is derived from exploiting wild species.** Although protecting biodiversity benefits entire societies, the people who are closest to the protected areas are key to the success of efforts to maintain sustainability of natural resources. These people must be given ownership rights or at least communal-use rights to natural resources, and they must be involved in the protection and management of wildlife resources.

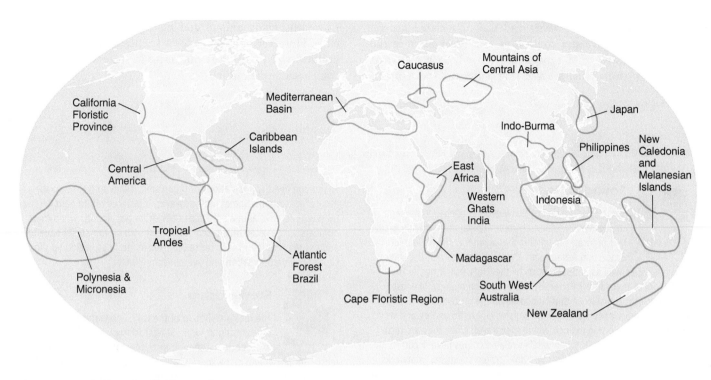

Figure 6–20 Biodiversity "hot spots." These regions are considered the "emergency rooms" of planetary biodiversity and represent most of the hot spots being funded by the Critical Ecosystem Partnership Fund. (*Source:* Redrawn from various sources.)

3. **Practicing conservation at the landscape level.** Too often, we tend to believe that a given refuge or park will protect the biodiversity of a region, when, in reality, many wild species require larger contiguous habitats or a variety of habitats. For example, to address the needs of migratory birds, summer and winter ranges and flyways between them must be considered.

4. **Promoting more research on biodiversity.** Far too little is known about how to manage diverse ecosystems and landscapes, and much remains to be learned about the species within the boundaries of different countries. Toward that end, a new field called biodiversity informatics has been established. Its goal is to put taxonomic data and other information on species online.[17] Species 2000, a program with the "objective of enumerating all known species of organisms on Earth," is one such effort.[18] Another is the Global Biodiversity Information Facility, whose express purpose "is to make the world's biodiversity data freely and universally available."[19]

Values. Our values also are demonstrated by our approach to wild species. Is the natural world simply grist for our increasing consumption, or is nature something to be managed sustainably and in a stewardly fashion and then passed on to our children and their children? Because we live together in society, we must be prepared to persuade others in our belief that wild species should be conserved. Our own consumption patterns—and our actions as citizens—can help, but coordination with nonprofit, scientific, business, and government agencies is necessary to slow species loss.

At the start of the chapter, we learned about breeding reserves for river dolphins in Bangladesh, developed through the efforts of conservation biologists. The success of other conservation efforts shows us that we can indeed stem the tide of species declines with hard work. Further strategies to address the loss of biodiversity must focus on preserving the natural ecosystems that sustain wild species. Ecosystems are discussed in detail later, including how we depend on them, what we are doing to them, and what we must do to resist the forces that seem to be leading to a future in which all that is left of wild nature is what we have managed to protect in parks, preserves, and zoos (Chapter 7).

Thomas Jefferson once said, "For if one link in nature's chain might be lost, another might be lost, until the whole of things will vanish by piecemeal."[20] As this quote

[17]F. A. Bisby. "The Quiet Revolution: Biodiversity Informatics and the Internet," *Science*, 89, 5488 (2000): pp. 2309–2312.
[18]Goddard Space Flight Center, An Online Catalogue of the World's Known Species. http://gcmd.nasa.gov/records/Species2000-99.html.
[19]Global Biodiversity Information Facility. http://www.gbif.org/informatics/infrastructure/.

[20] Jefferson, Thomas. Memoir on the Discovery of Certain Bones of a Quadruped of the Clawed King in the Western Parts of Virginia. *Transactions of the American Philosophical Society.* 1799. Vol. A, pp. 246–260.

suggests, loss of wild species and their associated genetic and ecosystem diversity could lead to a breakdown in the natural functioning of ecosystems. Indeed, as we look at the world around us, we see that Jefferson was correct.

Currently, many animal and plant populations are in decline. However, efforts made in science and policy and the political will of all of us can result in successes such as the comeback of the puffin.

REVISITING THE THEMES

Sound Science

Sometimes we do not know enough science to manage species well. Fortunately, many universities provide excellent programs in wildlife management. The Millennium Ecosystem Assessment and the Heinz State of the Nation's Ecosystems, as well as annual reports by the IUCN, pull together the solid work of thousands of scientists. Conservation biology, like restoration ecology, is a science that is focused on the protection of living things. The work of conservation biologists helps us to understand why some species are going extinct, where they travel, when they are recuperating, and sometimes when wildlife-related crimes have occurred. Sometimes scientists work together with "citizen scientists," networks of observers, to get more information. Other times they use cutting-edge technology such as DNA analysis to catch criminals. Furthermore, the science of taxonomy is foundational to the protection of species, and making sure we have scientists ready to study has to be part of the solution to biodiversity decline.

Sustainability

Because ecosystem capital is of such high value to human enterprises, the pathway to a sustainable future depends on protecting the wild species that make ecosystems work. Such protection is afforded by local and federal policies and international treaties. Sustainability is enhanced when we take steps to encourage healthy populations of organisms; if they thrive, so do their natural ecosystems. Sometimes, however, it is necessary to hunt or otherwise remove animals (such as deer) from populations when their numbers increase too much. Long-term plans for sustainability have to address the root issues that cause biodiversity declines, including those caused by overpopulation and overconsumption.

Stewardship

The reestablishment of the Lake Erie water snake is good stewardship at work. Stewardship places a high value on wild species. Although instrumental value is sufficient reason for preserving many species, perceiving intrinsic value might be the nearest to a pure stewardship ethic because it works out primarily for the sake of the species. Although some people dislike snakes, their protection is important for ecosystems. Other species, such as river dolphins, are easy to like, and people rally behind them for their protection, although they live in heavily populated areas.

The protection of biodiversity is tied to the ways people value wild species. These values can include instrumental or utilitarian values as well as intrinsic values. Wild species and their genes represent biological wealth, providing the basis for the goods and services coming from natural ecosystems and sustaining human life and economies. Species can also be thought of as a genetic bank, capable of being drawn on when new traits are needed. Losing biodiversity eventually leads to a biologically impoverished future.

REVIEW QUESTIONS

1. Define *biological wealth* and apply the concept to the human use of that wealth.

2. Compare instrumental value and intrinsic value as they relate to determining the worth of natural species. Where does Leopold's idea of the land ethic fit into these two categories?

3. What are the four categories into which the human value of natural species can be divided? Give examples of each one.

4. What means are used to protect game species, and what are some problems emerging from the adaptations of many game species to the humanized environment?

5. What is the Lacey Act, why was it needed, and how is it used to protect wild species?

6. How does the Endangered Species Act preserve threatened and endangered species in the United States? Give some examples of how the act has been implemented.

7. What is one example of an endangered species that has benefited from protection under the Endangered Species Act?

8. What is biodiversity? What do scientists need to know to calculate it for a habitat?

9. What do the letters in the acronym HIPPO stand for? What is an example of each?

10. Give several examples of ways habitat change can either harm species or aid them.

11. What are IUCN, CITES, and the Convention on Biological Diversity? How do their roles differ?

12. What are the Aichi Biodiversity Targets?

THINKING ENVIRONMENTALLY

1. Some people argue that each individual animal has an intrinsic right to survival. Should this right extend to plants and microorganisms? What about the *Anopheles* mosquito, which transmits malaria, or tigers that sometimes kill people in India? What about the bacteria that cause typhoid fever? Defend your position.

2. Choose an endangered or threatened animal or plant species, and use the Internet to research what is currently being done to preserve it. What dangers is your chosen species subject to?

3. The Endangered Species Act is the most important legislation in the United States for the protection of species. How-ever, there are critics who think it is too strict and those who think it is not strict enough. Investigate one example of the application of the law—for example, to gray wolves—and decide what you think ought to be done.

4. Log onto Conservation International's biodiversity hot spots Web page and research one of the 34 hot spots. What is being done to protect biodiversity in this location?

MAKING A DIFFERENCE

1. Instead of devoting your whole yard to grass, convert some of your yard to native plants. The National Wildlife Federation has a great deal of information on turning your backyard into wildlife habitat and even a certification program. They can be found on the Web.

2. Support groups that conserve and protect wildlife through the political process. Groups like the Center for Biological Diversity and others will alert members when there are political actions that they can support.

3. Consider volunteering or interning for a program that conserves wildlife. The Audubon Society has volunteer opportunities, as do many other wildlife conservation groups. These opportunities are found on the Internet.

4. Be careful about purchasing products that might come from a wild population. For example, it is better to buy pets bred in captivity rather than wild-caught pets.

MasteringEnvironmentalScience®

Go to **www.masteringenvironmentalscience.com** for practice quizzes, Pearson eText, videos, current events, and more.

CHAPTER 7

The Value, Use, and Restoration of Ecosystems

Caribbean Reef. Diver in the Caribbean passes a large Nassau grouper. Such fish are in decline.

BRIGHT SUN FILTERS through shallow water to reveal the colors of a tropical reef. Fish flit by branching arms of a coral. A parrotfish grazes a piece of seaweed, and a lobster hides at the base of a craggy rock. As the sun warms the clear water, divers swim by. An endangered Nassau grouper floats in an eddy, eyeing a smaller fish. A non-native lionfish snaps out, catching prey. It's another day in a tropical paradise. Suddenly, a SCUBA diver snatches the venomous lionfish and heads for the surface with the catch.

Today is the Lionfish Derby, held in the Florida Keys and run by the Reef Environmental Education Foundation (REEF). In the Derby, teams compete for cash and prizes to capture these invasive fish and remove them from this critical habitat. Lionfish lack predators in the Caribbean and eat the young of other fish. Researchers will use data from the captured fish to better understand their biology and ecology, and the capture removes some of the invaders from a habitat that is important to many other species. In 2011, the Florida Keys Lionfish Derby teams netted more than 1,500 fish.

CITIZEN SCIENTISTS. On a similar day elsewhere in the Caribbean, SCUBA divers move methodically through the water, recording the fish they see. They note the condition of coral reefs and record the presence of fish species, both herbivorous and carnivorous. This is also a REEF initiative: the Volunteer Survey Project. The SCUBA divers, trained volunteers in a network of "citizen scientists," will submit the information they collect, to be used by scientists who track what is happening with coral reef fish. Using these data, scientists have already been able to figure out a few things: Fish are declining, which affects the health of the coral reef. As herbivorous fish decline, algae and water plants can grow over the corals. Some of these produce toxic chemicals and kill the coral. As carnivorous fish decline, coral-eating sea stars are free to take over. The invasive lionfish can oust other native reef fish. Researcher Christopher Stallings of the Florida State University Coastal and Marine Lab is one of the scientists working with REEF. His work with the large database on fish in the Caribbean showed that some large-bodied fish like the Nassau grouper have completely disappeared in some highly populated areas.[1]

CRITICAL ECOSYSTEMS. Around the world, coral reefs are critical ecosystems. They act as nurseries for marine fish and as an early warning system for habitat degradation. Because they need clean, clear water and grow relatively slowly, corals show us when marine systems are in decline. Physical breakage, pollution,

heat, and invasive species combine to kill off these colonial animals and their algal symbionts. A coral reef is a good example of an ecosystem that provides humans with goods and services and that needs monitoring, protection, and sometimes restoration. The dive teams competing in the Lionfish Derby and the SCUBA divers recording species while they dive are ways that ordinary people can be involved in the care of an ecosystem.

One key to saving wild species is to preserve their habitats—the ecosystems in which they are found (Chapter 6). Populations of wild species continue to decline, however, because ecosystems are in decline throughout the world. In addition to the loss of species, the natural goods and services that ecosystems provide are also being degraded or lost. It is not only the natural world, but also human well-being that is threatened in the face of this unsustainable decline of ecosystems.

The focus in this chapter is particularly on the natural ecosystems that directly sustain human life and economy. We will pay special attention to those ecosystems that are in the deepest trouble. These ecosystems, the species in them, and the goods and services they generate are identified as **ecosystem capital**, a major component of the natural capital wealth of nations (Chapters 1, 2).

---

[1]C. Stallings. "Fishery-Independent Data Reveal Negative Effect of Human Population Density on Caribbean Predatory Fish Communities," *PLoS ONE* 4(5) (2009): [e5333].

7.1 Ecosystem Capital

Earth consists of ecosystems that vary greatly in their species makeup but that exhibit common functions, such as energy flow and the cycling of matter. The major types of terrestrial and aquatic ecosystems—the biomes—reflect the response of plants, animals, and microbes to different climatic conditions. Earth's land area can be divided into five broad categories for the purposes of this chapter (Table 7–1): forests and woodlands, grasslands and savannas, croplands, **wetlands**,

TABLE 7–1 Ecosystems on Earth's Surface

Ecosystem	Area (million km²)	Area (million mi²)	Percentage of Total Land Area
Forests and woodlands	47.3	18.2	31.7
Grasslands and savannas	30.2	11.6	20.2
Croplands	16.1	6.2	10.7
Wetlands	5.2	2.0	3.5
Desert lands and tundra	51.0	19.6	34.0
Total land area	**149.8**	**57.6**	**100.0**
Coastal ocean and bays	21.8	8.4	
Coral reefs	0.52	0.2	
Open ocean	426.4	164.0	
Total ocean area	**448.7**	**172.6**	

and **deserts** and **tundra**. The oceanic ecosystems can be categorized as coastal ocean and bays, coral reefs, and open ocean. These eight terrestrial and aquatic systems provide all of our food; much of our fuel; wood for lumber and paper; fibers—leather, furs, and raw materials for fabrics; oils and alcohols; and much more. The world economy and human well-being directly depend on the exploitation of the **natural goods** (referred to in Table 1–1 by the Millennium Ecosystem Assessment team as *provisioning services*) that can be extracted from ecosystems.

Ecosystems also perform a number of other valuable natural services, including *regulating* and *cultural services*, as they process energy and circulate matter in the normal course of their functioning (Table 1–1). Regulating services are benefits derived from regulation of ecosystem processes, such as flood control or climate moderation. Cultural services comprise nonmaterial benefits people gain from ecosystems, including spiritual enrichment, knowledge, and aesthetic enjoyment. Some of the services are general and pertain to essentially all ecosystems, whereas others are more specific. Finally, ecosystems provide services that maintain themselves: photosynthesis, for example. These are called *supporting services*.

Table 7–2 shows combinations of services provided to societies by a spectrum of ecosystems (a listing of ecosystem services can be found in Table 5–3). In their normal functioning, all natural and altered ecosystems perform some or all of these natural services, year after year. A team of natural scientists and economists calculated the total value of a year's global ecosystem goods and services to be $41 trillion (Chapter 5), and we receive them free of charge.

TABLE 7–2 Services from Various Types of Ecosystems

	Mountain and Polar	Forest and Woodlands	Inland Rivers and Other Wetlands	Drylands	Cultivated	Urban Parks and Gardens	Coastal	Island	Marine
Air quality regulation						√			
Biofuels					√				
Carbon sequestration		√							
Climate regulation (local and wide spread)	√	√		√		√	√		√
Cultural heritage					√	√	√		
Disease regulation and medicines		√	√		√				
Dyes					√				
Education					√				
Erosion control									
Fiber	√			√	√		√		
Flood regulation		√	√				√		
Food	√	√	√	√	√		√	√	√
Fresh and drinking water	√	√	√		√			√	
Fuelwood and timber		√		√	√		√		
Nutrient cycling			√		√		√		√
Pest regulation					√				
Pollution regulation			√						
Recreation, ecotourism, and aesthetic values	√	√	√	√	√	√	√	√	√
Sediment retention and transport			√						
Waste processing							√		
Water regulation						√			

Source: Millennium Ecosystem Assessment. "Living Beyond Our Means: Natural Assets and Human Well-Being" (Statement of the Millennium Ecosystem Assessment Board, 2005).

Figure 7–1 Shrimp aquaculture farms in Thailand. Carved out of mangrove forest, these shrimp farms provide only a fraction of the value of the services performed by the intact mangroves.

To illustrate the value of an ecosystem, consider a mangrove wetland in South Asia that is converted to a shrimp farm (Fig. 7–1), a common conversion. Studies of shrimp aquaculture (cultivating aquatic organisms like fish and shellfish under controlled conditions) in Thailand show that the economic value of the shrimp was $3,375 per acre over five years, following which the site is abandoned as yields decline sharply. Left intact, the mangroves provide services not fully captured in the marketplace: storm protection for coastline communities, forest products from mangrove harvest, and spawning ground for local fisheries. These services have a sustained estimated value of $14,450 per acre. In addition, there are net social costs of the shrimp farm in the form of pollution and land degradation that require expensive restoration, calculated at $2,200 per acre. Thus, the net income from the shrimp farming, when social costs are subtracted, is lowered to $1,175, which is only 8% of the value of services provided by the intact mangrove wetland.[2]

The benefit is local, short term, and specific to the shrimp farmer, who is likely to be from outside the community, while the loss of services is more regional, long term, and diffuse to all those living near the coast. Fortunately, shrimp farming in mangrove areas has been largely stopped because the farms do not do well long term and construction costs are high. But mangrove loss from conversion to rice agriculture, fuel, wood pulp, and other uses has continued. Many areas of Southeast Asia hit by the 2004 tsunami had been deprived of their protective mangrove forests and were more heavily damaged than those with intact mangroves. Mangroves are also efficient at taking up carbon dioxide and are home to globally threatened species. Removal of mangroves for aquaculture often ignores other benefits and costs.

Ecosystems as Natural Resources

If the natural services performed by ecosystems are so valuable, why are we still draining wetlands and removing forests? The answer is clear: a natural area will receive protection only if the value a society assigns to services provided in its natural state is higher than the value the society assigns to converting it to a more direct human use.

Natural ecosystems and the biota in them are commonly referred to as **natural resources**. As resources, they are expected to produce something of value, and the most commonly understood value is economic value. By referring to natural systems as resources, we are deliberately placing them in an economic setting, and it becomes easy to lose sight of their ecological value. Instead of natural resources, we use the concept of *ecosystem capital* in order to avoid making this mistake.

Valuing. Markets provide the mechanism for assessing economic value, but do poorly at placing monetary values on ecosystem services. People and institutions may express their preferences for different ecosystem services via the market, an instrumental value (Chapter 6). Instrumental valuation works fairly well for the provisioning services provided by ecosystems (goods such as timber, fish, and crops). However, many of the regulating and cultural services (and supporting services) provided by natural ecosystems—the more ecological values—are far more difficult to put prices on. These services are **public goods** (something that is not used up as people use it, and which can't be effectively limited, in order to charge money; for example, breathing air) not usually provided by markets, but contributing greatly to people's well-being. In fact, they are absolutely essential.

Regulating and cultural services provide benefits that are experienced over a large area, and their losses are also experienced regionally, rather than just locally. Large forested areas can modify the climate in a region and absorb and hold water in the hydrologic cycle. A small forest can be cut and the timber sold, with no noticeable impact on the weather, but with a definite economic value in a market setting, providing income to the owners. If the larger area is also cut, it will have both an immediate economic benefit and a long-term loss in regulating and supporting services. Thus, it will have an impact on people's well-being in the formerly forested area and well beyond, as short-term profits are made at the long-term environmental expense of many. When the benefits and losses in such conversions are reasonably evaluated economically, losses generally outweigh benefits (Chapter 4).

Private Versus Public Lands. Some natural ecosystems are maintained in a natural or seminatural state because that is how they provide the greatest economic (direct-use) value for their owners. For example, most of the state of Maine is owned by private corporations that exploit the forests for lumber and paper manufacturing. However, if Maine experienced a population explosion and corporations could sell their land to developers for more money than could be gained from harvesting timber, forested lands would quickly become house lots. Similar conversions can be pictured: tropical

[2]Elizabeth McLeod and Rodney V. Salm. *Managing Mangroves for Resilience to Climate Change*. IUCN Science Group Working Paper Series No. 2. 2006.

forests to grasslands for grazing, agricultural fields to sub-urbs, and wetlands to vacation developments.

Some natural ecosystems either are publicly owned (state and federal lands) or cannot be owned at all (ocean ecosystems). These ecosystems are still considered natural resources and may be subject to economically motivated exploitation. Sustainable exploitation of such systems will maintain the natural services they perform. Fortunately, ecosystems can not only sustain continued exploitation, but can also be restored from destructive uses that have degraded them and removed their natural biota.

Domesticated Nature. Whether private or public, human domination of the landscape is pervasive, and ecosystems have been converted or domesticated in vast areas of the planet. What we call natural may be only an illusion, because humankind has so converted and domesticated natural systems that it is difficult to find areas of the world unaffected by human impact. Even where systems appear natural, it is likely that humans have killed larger animals, suppressed wildfires, controlled rivers, introduced exotic species, and harvested wood. Elsewhere, we have converted grasslands and forests to grazing lands and crop cultivation, so that almost 50% of the land surface is now used in the production of crops and animal products and over half of the forests have been lost in the process. To be sure, domesticated ecosystems still provide provisioning and regulating and cultural services, and may do so sustainably, but they do so at our consent and largely for our benefit.

Future Pressures. As the human population continues to rise, pressures on ecosystems to provide resources will increase: more food, more wood, more water, and more fisheries products will be needed. Maintaining sustainable exploitation of ecosystem capital will become more difficult, in view of the already intense pressure being put on those ecosystems. The main objective of the thorough work of the Millennium Ecosystem Assessment was to evaluate the health of the services that people derive from the natural world. The assessment team found that 15 of the 24 services they evaluated were in decline worldwide, five were in a stable state, and four were increasing at the expense of other services (Chapter 1). The governing board of the assessment was so concerned about these findings that it published a separate document for a "nonspecialist" readership—*Living Beyond Our Means: Natural Assets and Human Well-Being.* This brief report begins: "At the heart of this assessment is a stark warning. Human activity is putting such strain on the natural functions of Earth that the ability of the planet's ecosystems to sustain future generations can no longer be taken for granted. . . . This assessment shows that healthy ecosystems are central to the aspirations of humankind."

7.2 Consumption and Production

An ecosystem's remarkable natural capacity to regenerate makes it (and its biota) a **renewable resource**. In other words, an ecosystem has the capacity to replenish itself despite

certain quantities of organisms being taken from it, and this renewal can go on indefinitely—it is sustainable. Recall that every species has the biotic potential to increase its numbers and that, in a balanced population, the excess numbers fall prey to parasites, predators, and other factors of environmental resistance (Chapter 5). It is difficult to find fault with activities that effectively put some of this excess population to human use. The trouble occurs when users (hunters, fishers, loggers, whalers) take more than the excess and deplete the breeding population.

Conservation Versus Preservation

Conservation of natural biotas and ecosystems does not imply *no* use by humans whatsoever, although this may sometimes be temporarily expedient in a management program to allow a certain species to recover its numbers. Rather, the aim of conservation is to *manage or regulate use* so that it does not exceed the capacity of the species or system to renew itself. Conservation is capable of being carried out sustainably, and when sustainability is adopted as a principle, conservation has a well-defined goal.

Preservation is often confused with conservation. The objective of the preservation of species and ecosystems is to ensure their continuity, regardless of their potential utility. Effective preservation often precludes making use of the species or ecosystems in question. For example, it is impossible to maintain old-growth (virgin) forests and at the same time harvest the trees. Thus, a second-growth forest can be conserved (trees can be cut, but at a rate that allows the forest to recover), but an old-growth forest must be preserved (it must not be cut down at all).

There are times when conservation and preservation come into conflict. The Muriqui monkey of Brazil was once thought to require virgin forests, leading to a concern for protecting such forests for the sake of the species (Fig. 7–2). Recent research has shown, however, that the monkeys actually do better in second-growth forests, which support

Figure 7–2 **Muriqui monkey.** Protection of this species of monkey in Brazil involves allowing some cutting of the forest in order to provide second-growth forests.

Figure 7–3 **Consumptive use.** Hunters in Papua, New Guinea bring home a captured wild pig. Wild game is an important food source for millions in many parts of the world.

a greater range of vegetation on which the monkeys feed. Thus, *conservation* of the forests is essential for *preservation* of this New World monkey, a seriously endangered species.

Patterns of Human Use of Natural Ecosystems

Before examining the specific biomes and ecosystems that are under the highest pressure from human use, we need to study a few general patterns of such use to understand what is happening in these natural systems and why it is happening.

Consumptive Use. People in more-rural areas make use of natural lands or aquatic systems that are in close proximity to them. When people harvest natural resources in order to provide for their needs for food, shelter, tools, fuel, and clothing, they are engaged in **consumptive use.** This kind of exploitation usually does not appear in the calculations of the market economy of a country. People may barter or sell such goods in exchange for other goods or services in local markets, but most consumptive use involves family members engaged in hunting and gathering to meet their own needs. Thus, people hunt for game (Fig. 7–3) and fish and gather fruits and nuts in order to meet their food needs; or they collect natural products like firewood, as well as wood or palm leaves to construct shelters or to use as traditional medicines. This "wild income," as it has been called, is highly important to the poor; some 90% of the 1.2 billion poorest people depend on forests for some of their income.

Wild game, or "bush meat," is harvested in many parts of Africa and provides a large proportion of the protein needs of people. In Congo, for example, bush meat may account for as much as 75% of a person's protein intake. The estimated take in the Congo basin alone is somewhere around 1 million metric tons annually. Without access to

these resources, people's living standard would decline and their very existence could be threatened. Unfortunately, this is a largely unregulated practice and often involves poaching in wildlife parks. According to the Convention on International Trade in Endangered Species (CITES), this practice has contributed to the decline of 30 endangered species. Making matters worse, commercial hunters have recently turned what was once a matter of local people using local wildlife for food into an unsustainable industry that supplies cities with tons of "fashionable" meat. For example, primate meat (e.g., chimpanzee) has been found in markets in New York, London, Paris, Brussels, and others.

Dependence on consumptive use is most commonly associated with the developing world but also exists in the more rural areas of the developed world, where people depend on wood for fuel or wild game for food. Their well-being would be diminished if they were denied access to these "free" resources.

Productive Use. In contrast to consumptive use, **productive use** is the exploitation of ecosystem resources for economic gain, as when products like timber and fish are harvested and sold for national or international markets (Fig. 7–4). Productive use is an enormously important source of revenue and employment for people in every country. More than 1.2 billion hectares of forests are managed for wood production. Nearly half of the wood removed, however, is used for fuel, so a great deal of the value of forests occurs on the consumptive, noneconomic side. Planted forests are on the increase, shifting timber harvest from natural to planted forests and making conservation of some natural forests easier. The global fisheries catch in 2008, which reached 90 million metric tons (83 million tons), was valued at $93.9 billion. Another productive

Figure 7–4 **Productive use.** Loggers load poplar logs to be transported to a lumber mill, where they will be made into waferboard for the building industry.

SUSTAINABILITY How Much for That Irrigation Water?

The dry bed of the Santa Cruz River in Arizona lies 20 feet below the bank sides, filled with water only in large floods, but it wasn't always so. In the late 1880s, a local farmer dug deep ditches and tapped into the underground water, moving below the shallow river bed. Fierce storms sent raging torrents through the channels, eroding the river bed, stranding farm fields above the precious water. The dry deep river of today and the increased cost of irrigation result from human actions of the past.

For years, humans have used the natural world as a place to obtain goods and services, often without paying for them. Humans are checking out at the global grocery store, with a basket of things that come from ecosystems: wood products, fish, fibers, chemicals, metals, water. How much is that flood control or clean air worth? How much is the irrigation from a river worth? To estimate the "value" of goods and services—things like photosynthesis, water cycling, and absorption of carbon dioxide—we need to know how ecosystems work and how our activities affect the rest of the system. That is part of what scientists do. We also have to determine how much the price of our activities and things we produce reflects the effect of our actions on ecosystems. This is done primarily by economists. Policy makers help figure out how we can act together to change the way things are done (Chapter 2), in order to incorporate the real-world cost of ecosystem capital into our human decisions.

How do natural and social scientists determine the value of ecosystems? Some valuation is dependent on what stakeholders think. Researchers doing a study on the Santa Cruz River asked participants, "Why do people think rivers are important? What do they value about rivers?" Respondents valued water quality, presence (in a river where stretches sometimes dried up altogether), lush vegetation, and habitat for birds and fish. They also valued human connections to the river, use by others downstream, and recharge of underground water and other ecosystem services. The people around the Santa Cruz River want the river to have a role in their daily lives and desire its health. Of course, putting economic value only on the ecosystem services people recognize, value, and are willing to pay for is a faulty approach, as we often do not know all the important features of ecosystems. However, it is a beginning and often provides useful information to policy makers.

How Much Is the Flood Control Worth? This picture of the Santa Cruz River shows the pressures rivers face—drying, erosion and invasive species.

Sources: B. Fisher et al. "Ecosystem Services and Economic Theory: Integration for Policy-Relevant Research." *Ecological Applications,* 18(8) (2008): 2050–2067.

P. L. Ringold, J. Boyd, D. Landers, and M. Weber. Report from the Workshop on Indicators of Final Ecosystem Services for Streams. 56p. EPA/600/R-09/137. July 2009.

M. Weber et al. Why are rivers Important? Ecosystem Service Definition via Qualitative Research: A Southwestern Pilot Study. Oral Presentation. December 9, 2010. http://conference.ifas.ufl.edu/aces10/Presentations/Thursday/C/AM/Yes/0845%20MattWeber.pdf.

use is the collection of wild species of plants and animals for cultivation or domestication. The wild species may provide the initial breeding stock for commercial plantations or ranches, or they may be used as sources of genes to be introduced into existing crop plants or animals to improve their resistance or to add other desirable genetic traits. Finally, wild species continue to provide sources of new medicines (Chapter 6).

Tenure. Consumptive and productive uses of natural ecosystem resources are the consequence of the rights of **tenure,** or property rights, over the land and water holding those resources. Four kinds of tenure are recognized: (1) *private ownership,* which restricts access to natural resources; (2) *communal ownership,* which permits use of natural resources by members of the community; (3) *state ownership* of natural resources, which implies regulated use; and (4) *open access,* where natural resources can be used by anyone. In all of these arrangements—private, communal, state, and open access—there is the potential either for sustainable use of the resources or for unsustainable use leading to the loss of the resources and the services provided by the natural ecosystem being exploited. As a result, the perspective of stewardship is vital. Do the resource managers and harvesters see themselves as caretakers, as well as exploiters, of the natural resource? Are public policies that encourage stewardship and sustainability in place? Is the local or national government presence weak or corrupt? Are sound scientific principles employed in management strategies? Keep these questions in mind as we next examine two patterns that are commonly seen when people exploit natural resources.

Maximum Sustainable Yield. The central question in managing a renewable natural resource is this: How much continual use can be sustained without undercutting the capacity of the species or system to renew itself? A scientific model employed to describe this amount of use is the maximum sustainable yield (MSY): the highest possible rate of use that the system can match with its own rate of replacement or maintenance. Besides pertaining to the harvesting of natural biota, the concept of MSY can apply to the maintenance of parks, air quality, water quality and quantity, and soils—indeed, the entire biosphere. *Use* can refer to the cutting of timber, hunting, fishing, park visitations, the discharge of pollutants into air or water, and so on. Natural systems can withstand a certain amount of use (or abuse, in terms of pollution) and still remain viable. However, a point exists at which increasing use begins to destroy the system's regenerative capacity. Just short of that point is the MSY.

Optimal Population. An important consideration in understanding how the MSY works is the **carrying capacity** of the ecosystem—the maximum population the ecosystem can support on a sustainable basis. If a population is well below the carrying capacity of the ecosystem (Fig. 7–5a), then allowing that population to grow will increase the number of reproductive individuals and thus the yield that can be harvested. However, as the population approaches the carrying capacity of the ecosystem, new individuals must compete with older individuals for food and living space. As a result, recruitment (survival of new individuals in the population) may fall drastically (Fig. 7–5b). When a population is at or near the ecosystem's carrying capacity, production—and hence sustainable yield—can be increased by thinning the population so that competition is reduced and optimal growth and reproductive rates are achieved. Thus, the MSY cannot be obtained with a population that is at the carrying capacity. Theoretically, the **optimal population** for harvesting the MSY is just halfway to the carrying capacity.

The practical use of this model is complicated by the fact that the carrying capacity—and, therefore, the optimal population—is variable. Carrying capacity may vary from year to year as the weather fluctuates. Replacement of harvested individuals may also vary from year to year, because some years are particularly favorable to reproduction and recruitment, while others are not. Human impacts, such as pollution and other alterations of habitats, adversely affect reproductive rates, recruitment, carrying capacity, and, consequently, sustainable yields. For these reasons alone, managing natural populations to achieve the MSY is fraught with difficulties. Furthermore, accurate estimates of the size of the population and the recruitment rate must be made continually, and these data are hard to come by for many species.

Precautionary Principle. The conventional approach has been to use the estimated MSY to set a fixed quota—in fishery management, the **total allowable catch (TAC)**. If the data on population and recruitment are inaccurate, it is easy to overestimate the TAC, especially when there are pressures from fishers (and the politicians who represent them) to maintain a high harvest quota. In the face of such uncertainties, and also in response to repeated cases of overuse and depletion of resources, resource managers have been turning to the **precautionary principle**. That is, where there is uncertainty, resource managers must favor the protection of the living resource. Thus, the exploitation limits must be set well enough below the MSY to allow for uncertainties. Those using the resource ordinarily want to push the limits higher, however, so the result is frequent conflicts between users and managers. These conflicts are addressed in greater detail when the problems of fisheries are discussed later in this section.

Using the Commons. Where a resource is owned by many people in common or by no one (open access), it is known as a common-pool resource, or **commons**. Strictly speaking, a commons refers to a system with open access where use by one does not subtract from use by others; for example, knowledge is a commons. Examples of natural common-pool

Figure 7–5 Maximum sustainable yield. The maximum sustainable yield occurs when the population is at the optimal level (meaning the rate of increase in population is at a maximum). (a) The logistic curve of population size in relation to carrying capacity. (b) Recruitment plotted against population size, showing the effects of competition and decreased population levels.

(a) (b)

resources include federal grasslands, on which private ranchers graze their livestock; coastal and open-ocean fisheries used by commercial fishers; groundwater drawn for private estates and farms; nationally owned woodlands and forests harvested for fuel in the developing countries; and the atmosphere, which is polluted by private industry and everyone who drives motor vehicles.

The exploitation of such common-pool resources presents some serious problems and can lead to the eventual ruin of the resource—a phenomenon called the "tragedy of the commons," taken from the title of a 1968 essay by the late biologist Garrett Hardin.[3] Sustainability implies that common-pool resources will be maintained so as to continue to yield benefits not just for the present, but also for future users.

Tragedy of the Commons. As described by Hardin, the original "commons" were pastures around villages in England. These pastures were provided free by the king to anyone who wished to graze cattle. Herders were quick to realize that whoever grazed the most cattle stood to benefit the most. Even if they realized that a particular commons was being overgrazed, those who withdrew their cattle simply sacrificed personal profits, while others went on using that commons. One herder's loss became another's gain, and the commons was overgrazed in any case. Consequently, herders would add to their herds until the commons was totally destroyed. The lesson of this story is that where there is no management of the commons, the pursuit of individuals' own interests will lead to a tragedy for all.

Hardin's essay applies to a limited, but significant, set of problems that arise where there is open access to a common-pool resource, but where there is no regulating authority (or there is one, but it is ineffective) and no functioning community. Exploitation of the resource then becomes a free-for-all in which profit is the only motive. Coastal and offshore fisheries have consistently demonstrated the reality of the tragedy of the commons, with stocks of desirable fish declining all over the world. The tragedy can be avoided only by limiting freedom of access.

Limiting Freedom. One arrangement that can mitigate the tragedy is private ownership. When a renewable natural resource is privately owned, access to it is restricted and, in theory, it will be exploited in a manner that guarantees a continuing harvest for its owner(s). This theory does not hold, however, when an owner maximizes immediate profit and then moves on. Modern corporations lend themselves to this strategy: For example, corporate raiders can take over a natural resource—say, a timber company and its holdings—and clear-cut the forest in order to pay off debts incurred in the process of the takeover. Many owners, though, will be in for the long run and manage the resources more responsibly because it is in their best interests to do so.

Where private ownership is unworkable or lacking, the alternative is to regulate access to the commons. Regulation should allow for (1) protection, so that the benefits derived from the commons can be sustained; (2) fairness in access rights; and (3) mutual consent of the regulated. Such regulation can be the responsibility of the state, but it does not have to be. In fact, the most sustainable approach to maintaining the commons may be local community control, wherein the power to manage the commons resides with those who directly benefit most from its use and there are strong social ties and customs that can function well over time to protect the commons. By contrast, in many situations, state control of a commons has accelerated its ruin and has led to an associated social breakdown and the impoverishment of people.

Maine Lobsters. The lobster is a tasty crustacean found in the colder marine waters of the Northern Hemisphere, especially where there are shallow-water rocky subtidal seascapes interspersed with sandy patches. The state of Maine is famous for its lobsters, and management of the lobster fishery—a common-pool resource—has evolved into a workable combination of state and local regulation. The state has established conservation laws that protect juvenile and breeding female lobsters and limit the number of lobster traps (Fig. 7–6). The lobster fishers, however, have developed a second set of local rules that determine who can fish a given harbor and coastline area. It is an informal system, but it works because the fishers are part of a functioning community where they know each other and are monitoring each other's harvesting. The result is a successful outcome where the state's lobster fishery is thriving even though the number of fishers has more than doubled since 1973.

Public Policies. In sum, to achieve the objectives of conservation when harvesting living resources, it is important to consider both the concept and limitations of the MSY and the social and economic factors causing overuse and degradation that diminish the sustainable yield. After reviewing these factors, public policies can be established and enforced that protect natural resources effectively. Some principles that should be embodied in these policies are presented in Table 7–3. When policies based on principles like these are in place, it is possible for people to continue to put natural resources to sustainable consumptive and productive uses. The vast harvest taken from the natural world each year is proof that sustainable use not only is possible, but also actually occurs with many resources and in many locations around the world.

In some situations, however, exploitation and degradation have gone too far, and the resilience of an ecosystem has been overcome. In those cases, natural services and uses can be restored only if the habitats are deliberately restored as well. In recent years, the need for the restoration of damaged ecosystems has become clear, and a new subdiscipline with that objective—called **restoration ecology**—has been developed. This is discussed in Section 7.4.

The next section discusses a number of still-functioning biomes and ecosystems that are in trouble because of their great economic importance.

---

[3]Garrett Hardin. "The Tragedy of the Commons," *Science* 162 (1968): 1243–1247.

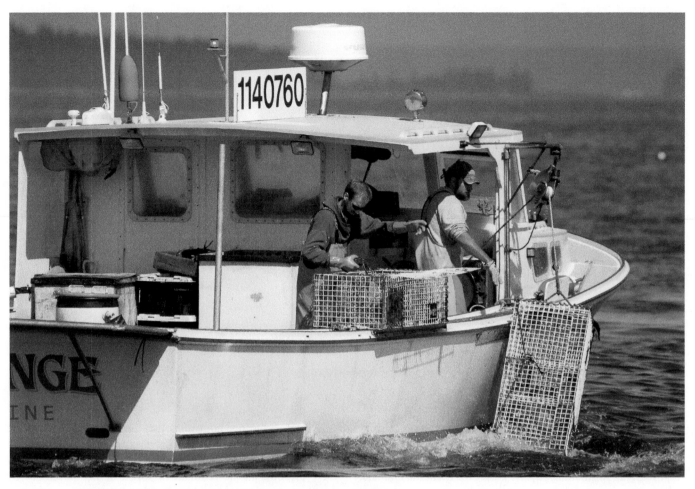

Figure 7–6 **Exploiting a commons.** Lobster boat unloading a lobster pot in Maine waters.

TABLE 7–3 Principles That Should Be Incorporated into Public Policies to Protect Natural Resources
1. Natural resources cannot be treated as open-access commons. Habitats and species should be held by private, communal, or state entities that are responsible for their exploitation and sustainability.
2. Scientific research should be employed to assess the health of the resource and to set sustainable limits on its use.
3. To accommodate uncertainty, the precautionary principle should be used in setting limits for exploitation.
4. Regulations should be enforced; the resource must be protected from poaching.
5. Economic incentives that encourage the violation of regulations should be eliminated.
6. Subsidies that encourage exploitation of the resource should be removed.
7. All stakeholders should be involved in resource-related decisions; those living close to the resource should share in profits from its use.
8. Security of tenure is crucial for poor people who depend on the resource for their well-being.

7.3 Biomes and Ecosystems Under Pressure

Although human activities affect virtually all biomes and ecosystems, some are under more pressure than others. This section begins with a look at the forest biomes, the most important of all biomes in terms of their economic significance and potential for active human management.

Forest Ecosystems

Forests are the normal ecosystems in regions with year-round rainfall that is adequate to sustain tree growth. Forests are also the most productive systems the land can support, and they are self-sustaining. Forests and woodlands (ecosystems with mixed trees and grasses) perform a number of vital natural services. Among other things, they conserve biodiversity,

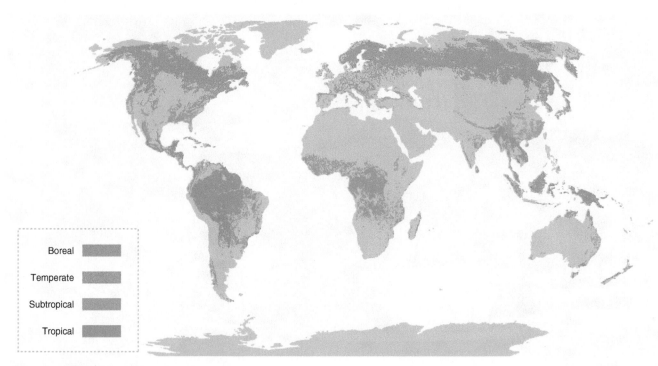

Figure 7–7 World forest biomes. The FAO *Global Forest Resources Assessment 2000* produced this map showing the locations of the major world forests.

moderate regional climates, prevent erosion, store carbon and nutrients, and provide recreational opportunities. They provide a number of vital goods, too, such as lumber (the raw material for making paper), fodder for domestic animals, fibers, gums, latex, fruit, berries, nuts, and fuel for cooking and heating. In fact, forests provide fuel, food, medicine, and income for more than 1.6 billion people, mostly in the developing countries. In spite of this value, the major threat to the world's forests is not simply their exploitation, but rather their total destruction.

Forest Resources Assessments. The UN's Food and Agricultural Organization (FAO) conducts periodic assessments of forest resources and compares the data with previous information in order to evaluate trends in forested areas. Figure 7–7 shows the locations of the four major world forest biomes. The FAO produced the *Global Forest Resources Assessment 2010*. The most recent FAO forestry report was titled *State of the World Forests 2011*. Forest ecosystems are tracked by other groups as well, such as NASA's earth observatory. Major findings by those assessing forests are as follows:

1. In 2005, the world's forest cover was 3.95 billion hectares (9.8 billion acres), or 30% of total land area. The FAO defines "forests" as lands where trees are the dominant life form and produce a canopy greater than 10% cover. An additional 1.4 billion hectares (3.5 billion acres) are classified as "other wooded land," sometimes referred to as "woodlands," where the tree cover is less than 10% or the trees and/or shrubs are species that do not grow to a height above 5 meters. Forests account for 50% of plant productivity.

2. Deforestation continues to occur, primarily in the developing countries. Forest cover in the developed countries has remained stable. The FAO defines **deforestation** as the removal of forest and replacement by another land use. Thus, logging per se does not count as deforestation if the forests are allowed to regenerate. The current global rate of net deforestation is estimated at 7.3 million hectares (18 million acres) per year, some 18% better than in the 1990s. The annual net changes in forest area in major world regions are shown in Figure 7–8.

3. Throughout the world, the most important forest product is wood for industrial use; half of forest lands are designated for "production," where the wood is harvested for pulp (paper source), lumber, and fuelwood. Close to 1.2 billion hectares (2.9 billion acres), about 30% of the world's forests, are managed for production of forest products, including wood.

4. Worldwide, 13.5% of forests are in legally established protected areas. This proportion represents an increase, a recognition by many countries of the important non-timber services of forests. China in particular has increased forests in order to slow the spread of deserts and soil loss (Chapter 14).

5. The role of forests in climate change was formally acknowledged in November 2001 at a meeting of the signers of the Kyoto Protocol in Marrakech, Morocco. The outcome of this accord is a much more thorough inventory of the role of forests as carbon stores, sources of carbon emissions, and carbon sinks. Some estimates are that 45% of the carbon stored on land is in forests—

CHANGE IN FOREST AREA BY REGION, 1990–2010

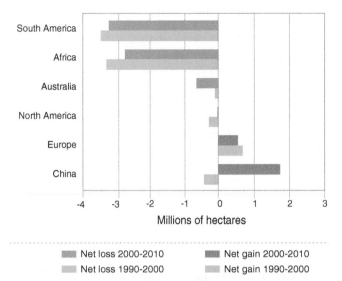

Net loss 2000-2010 ■ Net gain 2000-2010
Net loss 1990-2000 ■ Net gain 1990-2000

Figure 7–8 Net changes in forest area. The annual net change of forests from 2000 to 2010 in the different regions of the world. Virtually all of the losses occurred in tropical forests of South America and Africa.

(*Source:* Food and Agriculture Organization [FAO] of the United Nations, Global Forest Resources Assessment 2010, p. xvi.)

as much as 289 gigatonnes (GT). However, reduction in forest area caused this number to drop about 0.5 GT per year between 2005 and 2010.

6. Insect pests, disease, invasive species, and fires affect global forests significantly. In the United States and Canada, the mountain pine beetle has killed more than 11 million acres of forest since the 1990s.

7. Government spending on forestry is not replaced. On average, governments spend about $7.50 (managing timber and building and maintaining logging roads) and collect about $4.50 per hectare. Those that spend less also receive less. Overall, governments "generally spend more on forestry than they collect in revenue."[4] About 80% of the world's forests are publically owned, some managed locally and others by central national governments.

Forests as Obstacles. Even though the current rate of deforestation is lower than in the 1990s, it is still a major cause for concern. Why are forests being cleared when they could be managed for wood production on a sustainable basis? Even though forests are highly productive systems, it has always been difficult for humans to exploit them for food. Most deforestation is used to convert forests into pastures and agricultural land. Unlike forests, grasslands have short food chains in which herbaceous growth supports large herbivores that can yield meat and other animal products. Alternatively, forests can be replaced by cultivated plants that are used directly for food. Thus, forests have always been an

obstacle to conventional animal husbandry and agriculture. Indeed, the first task the early European colonists faced when they came to the Western Hemisphere was to clear the forests so they could raise crops. Once the forests were cleared, continual grazing or plowing effectively prevented the trees from regrowing.

Consequences. Clearing a forest has the following immediate consequences for the land and its people:

- Overall productivity of the area is reduced.
- Standing stock of nutrients and biomass, once stored in the trees and leaf litter, is enormously reduced.
- Biodiversity is greatly diminished.
- Soil is more prone to erosion and drying.
- The hydrologic cycle is changed as water drains off the land instead of being released by transpiration through the leaves of trees or percolating into groundwater.
- A major carbon dioxide sink (removal of CO_2 from the air) is lost.
- Land no longer yields forest products.
- People who depend on harvesting forest products lose their livelihood.

The trade-off, of course, if you cut down a forest, is that now the land will yield crops or support livestock, more people may be fed, and (usually) more profit will accrue to the owners, but sometimes those effects do not last. If forests are not cleared and converted to other uses, they could be managed to yield a harvest of wood for fuel, paper, and building materials indefinitely. Approximately 3 billion cubic meters (3.7 billion yd³) of wood are harvested annually from the world's forests for fuel, wood, and paper (Fig. 7–9). It is unreasonable to expect the countries of the world—especially the developing countries—to forgo making use of their forests. However, forest-management practices vary greatly in their impact on the forest itself and on surrounding ecosystems.

Figure 7–9 Logging operations. A forest in New Guinea is logged for its tropical wood.

[4]FAO. Global Forest Resources Assessments, Key Findings 2010, p. 9. http://www.pefc.org/images/stories/documents/external/KeyFindings-en.pdf.

Types of Forest Management. The practice of forest management, usually with the objective of producing a specific crop (hardwood, pulp, softwood, wood chips, etc.), is called **silviculture**. Several practices are employed, with quite different impacts on the total forest ecosystem involved. Because trees take from 25 to 100 years to mature to harvestable size, the normal process of management is a rotation, which is a cycle of decisions about a particular stand of trees from its early growth to the point of harvest. Two options are open to the forester: even-aged management and uneven-aged management. With even-aged management, trees of a fairly uniform age are managed until the point of harvest, cut down, and then replanted, with the objective of continuing the cycle in a dependable sequence.

Clear-Cutting. Typically, fast-growing, but economically valuable, trees are favored for even-aged management. (Others are culled from the stand.) In the Pacific Northwest, Douglas fir is frequently managed this way. Harvesting is often accomplished by **clear-cutting**—removing an entire stand at one time. This management strategy has been severely criticized because it creates a fragmented landscape with serious impacts on biodiversity and adjacent ecosystems; also, a clear-cut leaves an ugly, unnatural-looking site for many years. Large timber companies often employ the practice because it is efficient at the time of harvest and it does not involve much active management and planning.

Other Methods. Uneven-aged management of a stand of trees can result in a more diverse forest and lends itself to different harvesting strategies. For example, in **selective cutting**, some mature trees are removed in small groups or singly, leaving behind a forest that continues to maintain a diversity of biota and normal ecosystem functions. Replanting is usually unnecessary, as the remaining trees provide seeds. Another strategy is **shelter-wood cutting**, which involves cutting the mature trees in groups over a period of, say, 10 or 20 years, such that at any time there are enough trees both to provide seeds and to give shelter to growing seedlings. Like selective cutting, this method takes more active management and skill, but unlike clear-cutting, it leaves a functional ecosystem standing. In effect, it should lead to a sustainable forest, an objective that the entire wood and paper industry is currently focusing on—at least in principle.

Sustainable Forestry. In forestry, sustainability must be carefully defined. A common objective of forestry management is **sustained yield**, which means that the production of wood is the primary goal and the forest is managed to harvest wood continuously without being destroyed. It is similar in concept to MSY in that its objective is to maximize harvest rates, but it ignores the ecosystem properties of forests. **Sustainable forest management**, by contrast, was defined at the United Nations Conference on Environment and Development (UNCED) of 1992: *Forests are to be managed as ecosystems, with the objectives of maintaining the biodiversity and integrity of the ecosystem, but also to meet the social, economic, cultural and spiritual needs of present and future generations.* This sentiment has been expanded into a list of principles for sustainable forestry.

Tropical Forests. Because of their continued deforestation, tropical forests are of great concern. They are the habitat for millions of plant and animal species and a storehouse of biodiversity. These forests are also crucial in maintaining Earth's climate, serving as a major sink for carbon and restraining the buildup of global carbon dioxide. Nevertheless, tropical forests continue to be removed at a rapid rate. Between 1960 and 1990, 20% of the tropical forests (over 445 million hectares, or 1.1 billion acres)—equivalent to two-fifths of the land area of the United States—were converted to other uses. According to the FAO, in 2010 the annual global deforestation rate was about 13 million hectares (32 million acres), down from about 16 million hectares per year in the 1990s. Most of this loss occurred in the tropical forests (Fig. 7–10).

Reasons for Removal. Deforestation is caused by a number of factors, all of which come down to the fact that the countries involved are in need of greater economic development and have rapid population growth. The FAO concluded that the current major cause of deforestation is conversion to pastures and agriculture. Many governments in the developing world are promoting deforestation by encouraging the colonization of forested lands. Indonesia, for example, has embarked on a program of resettlement and intends to convert 20% of its remaining forests to agricultural production. The clearing of forests for subsistence agriculture is especially intense in Africa, where population growth is unrelenting. In Brazil's Amazon basin, commercial ranches, home to some 74 million cattle, are replacing rain forests, enabling Brazil to dominate the beef export market. The Brazilian government has introduced antideforestation measures, which had some success in reducing the Amazon deforestation for several years (2004–2007), but recent satellite-based reports indicate that the rate is rising again.

New Trends. Left to grow, the forests of the developing world are an important resource that can generate much-needed revenue. Developing countries account for 26% of the international trade in forest products. Often,

DESIGNATED FUNCTIONS OF FORESTS, 2010

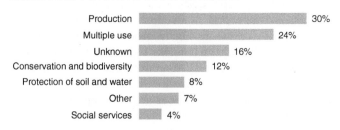

Production	30%
Multiple use	24%
Unknown	16%
Conservation and biodiversity	12%
Protection of soil and water	8%
Other	7%
Social services	4%

Figure 7–10 Designated uses of forests. Worldwide, forests have different ecosystem services for which they are managed.

(*Source:* Food and Agriculture Organization (FAO) of the United Nations, Global Forest Resources Assessment 2010, pg. xxvi.)

concessions are sold to multinational logging companies, which reap high profits by exploiting the economic desperation of the developing countries and harvest the timber with little regard for regenerating the forest. Chinese and other Asian companies are logging millions of acres of tropical forest in smaller countries like Belize, Suriname, and Papua New Guinea, where regulation is weak and corruption is strong. More important is the consumptive use of forests by millions of people living in the forests or on their edges. Owning few private possessions and often little land, they absolutely depend on foraging in and extracting goods from the forests.

There are encouraging trends in forest management in the developing world—trends that indicate that those in power are paying more attention to the needs of indigenous people and the importance of forest goods and services (other than just wood). These actions include practicing sustainable forest management, designating forest areas for conservation, establishing more-sustainable plantations of trees for wood or other products (cacao, rubber, etc.) (Fig. 7–11), and setting aside extractive reserves (areas for nonwood products) that yield nontimber goods. Some 3.6 million hectares (9 million acres) of the Brazilian Amazon have been set aside as extractive reserves.

Another trend is the preservation of forests as part of a national heritage and putting them to use as tourist attractions. This practice can often generate much more income than logging can. Putting forests under the control of indigenous villagers is an important part of forest protection in many parts of the world. The villagers can then collectively use the forest products in traditional ways. Given tenure over the land, the villagers tend to exercise stewardship over their forests in a way that is sustainable. Where this practice has been implemented, the forests have fared better than where they have been placed under state control.

Certification. The **Forest Stewardship Council** was the result of a recent initiative directed toward the certification of wood products. This alliance of nongovernmental organizations (including the World Wide Fund for Nature and National Wildlife Federation, industry representatives, and forest scientists) has developed into a major international organization with the mission of promoting sustainable—or, as they call it, "responsible"—forestry by certifying forest products for the consumer market. By 2009, more than 110 million hectares (242 million acres) in 81 countries had been certified. Certification makes it possible for consumers to choose wood products that have been harvested sustainably.

Ocean Ecosystems

Covering 75% of Earth's surface, the oceans and coastal ecosystems provide priceless goods and services that enable commerce and enhance human well-being. As vast as the oceans are, human activities have impacted them, often severely. A team of British, Canadian, and American scientists recently constructed a global map that pictures the severity of the effects of such human impacts as commercial shipping, resource extraction, nutrient runoff from land, fishing, species invasion, and greenhouse gas emissions (Fig. 7–12). The team's work provides a first attempt at documenting the human impacts throughout the oceans and is expected to stimulate strategies for minimizing the ecological impact of human activities in locations where that impact is especially severe. One of those activities is commercial fishing.

Marine Fisheries. Fisheries provide employment for at least 200 million people and account for more than 15% of the total human consumption of protein. The term *fishery* refers either to a limited aquatic area or to a group of fish or shellfish species being exploited. For years, the oceans beyond a 12-mile limit were considered international commons. By the end of the 1960s, however, numerous regions of the sea were being seriously depleted of many species by overfishing on the part of international fleets equipped with factory ships and modern fish-finding technology. In the mid-1970s, as a result of agreements forged at a series of UN Conferences on the Law of the Sea, nations extended their limits of jurisdiction to 200 miles offshore. The United States accomplished this with the Magnuson Act of 1976. Since many prime fishing grounds are located between 12 and 200 miles from shore, this action effectively removed most fisheries from the international commons and placed them under the authority of particular nations. As a result,

Figure 7–11 Plantation forest. A rubber tree plantation in Vietnam.

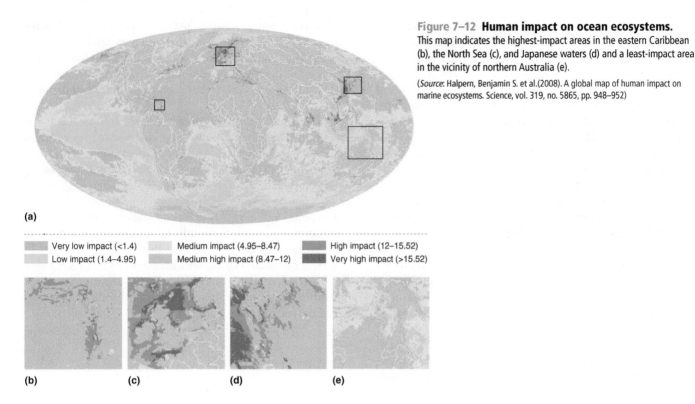

(a)

Legend		
▨ Very low impact (<1.4)	▨ Medium impact (4.95–8.47)	▨ High impact (12–15.52)
▨ Low impact (1.4–4.95)	▨ Medium high impact (8.47–12)	▨ Very high impact (>15.52)

(b)   **(c)**   **(d)**   **(e)**

Figure 7–12 Human impact on ocean ecosystems.
This map indicates the highest-impact areas in the eastern Caribbean (b), the North Sea (c), and Japanese waters (d) and a least-impact area in the vicinity of northern Australia (e).

(*Source:* Halpern, Benjamin S. et al.(2008). A global map of human impact on marine ecosystems. Science, vol. 319, no. 5865, pp. 948–952)

some fishing areas recovered, while nationally based fishing fleets expanded to exploit the fisheries.

The Catch. The total recorded harvest from marine fisheries and fish farming is reported annually by the FAO. The harvest has increased remarkably since 1950, when it was just 20 million metric tons (**Fig. 7–13**). By 2009, it had reached almost 145 million metric tons. Aquaculture accounted for 55.1 million metric tons, or 38% of world fish supplies that year. The trends in the figure show that the "capture" fisheries leveled off in the 1990s and the continued rise in fish production is due to aquaculture. Of the total of 145 million metric tons, 90 million metric tons were the freshwater and marine fisheries catch, to which should be added approximately 7 million tons of bycatch (fish caught and discarded).

One of the effects of this increase in fishing effort is the removal of large fish. Because large and slow-growing fish take longer to replace, ocean fish are changing—to smaller individuals and those that reproduce more rapidly. As fishers capture too many of one species, they move on to the next. First, they overfish the top predators—such as tuna, marlin, and swordfish—then those smaller and lower on the food chain. This process of moving from species to species as each type is depleted is known as "fishing down the food chain." It means that commercial fishing has made long-lasting changes to basic ecological processes in marine ecosystems.

Aquaculture. Modern aquaculture, the farming of aquatic organisms, includes species ranging from seaweed to bivalve mollusks to freshwater and marine fish and has increased dramatically in the past 20 years (see Fig. 7–13). This production is offsetting the plateau in the wild capture fisheries, but coastal aquaculture is not without its problems and critics. For example, shrimp farming in many tropical areas has been criticized for destroying mangrove habitats, accelerating the decline of fisheries for some species that depend on the mangroves for a part of their life cycle. Another concern is that farming carnivorous species such as shrimp and salmon requires food—often in the form of fishmeal from marine organisms caught in the wild. More than 37% of the capture fisheries are species like whiting, herring, and anchovy that are reduced to fish products to

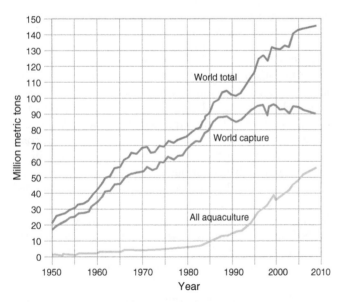

Figure 7–13 The global fish harvest. The global fish catch plus aquaculture equals the world total. Note how aquaculture is providing all of the increase since 1995. Shown are data for 1950–2008.

(*Source:* Data from FAO. 2010. The State of the World's Fisheries and Aquaculture.)

SOUND SCIENCE

Restoration Science: Learning How to Restore

A group of people walk across the flat landscape, bent over, moving slowly from side to side. From a distance their motion looks odd. Up close, you can see they are throwing something on the ground from containers in their hands. They look like ancient farmers, in a planting ritual going back millennia, but they are not. They are ecologists and volunteers restoring an abandoned farm to a native prairie. The seeds they cast are from native grasses like big blue stem and plants like wild lupine, purple coneflower, and Black-eyed Susan.

Volunteers have painstakingly picked the seeds over a period of months, and now, the soil plowed and ready, the seeds are being planted. Later, when both native plants and non-native agricultural weeds have grown, the team will reconvene to burn the field, giving the native, fire-adapted plants an edge and clearing out the weeds. Right now it is planting time. For this moment to happen, a lot of other things had to be done first. Seeds were collected some months ago. Some species needed to be chilled for weeks to stimulate growth. Some were scratched (or "scarified"), others soaked and exposed to fungi that would help them grow.

Humans are doing the work that a healthy soil would do in a natural setting.

In order to find the most effective ways to restore an ecosystem such as an abandoned farm, old mining area, or former construction site, scientists first must do extensive research. Much of this research owes a debt of gratitude to the restoration pioneers at the Curtis prairie (Madison, Wisconsin), the oldest ecologically restored prairie in the world. Scientists at the University of Wisconsin-Madison have been experimenting with restorations for 75 years, coming up with many of the techniques and scientific advances that are used in other places.

Even so, scientists will agree that restoration will not bring back the system that was degraded. Usually, what is restored differs significantly from the original. Prevention is a better approach, and restoration should be used when other approaches have failed.

Restoration Ecology. Prairie seeds collected for restoring prairie habitat.

Sources: R. H. Hilderbrand, A. C. Watts, and A. M. Randle. "The Myths of Restoration Ecology." *Ecology and Society*, 10(1) (2005): 19. http://www.ecologyandsociety.org/vol10/iss1/art19/.

M. P. Zedler, B. Herrick, and J. Zedler, 2008. Curtis Prairie: 75-Year-Old Restoration Research Site. http://botany.wisc.edu/zedler/images/Leaflet_16.pdf.

feed farm-raised fish and animals. Salmon and shrimp aquaculture farms consume several times as much fish protein as they actually produce.

Spread of diseases from farmed to wild populations and pollution of waters by fish farms' nutrients are other concerns that accompany aquaculture. The result in many cases is conflict among the various users, and the long-term outlook for coastal aquaculture is that nearshore waters are becoming less and less available for farming.

One approach is open-ocean aquaculture, which is the farming of coastal species in ocean waters several kilometers from the shoreline. This is a new practice in North America, and even in Europe and other areas where it has been long practiced, total production levels are far lower than they could be. Open-ocean waters are relatively clean. High water quality is important for aquaculture, but it is especially critical for species such as bivalve mollusks, which concentrate pathogens and other pollutants that can be passed on to human consumers. Also, new satellite-based remote-sensing efforts are revealing previously unknown nutrient-rich upwelling zones. In some areas in the Gulf of Maine, for example, phytoplankton concentrations can exceed the levels thought to occur only in enriched estuarine waters. This means that open-ocean waters may be able to support a high productivity of farmed species such as the blue mussel. Mussels and other bivalve mollusks are herbivorous animals, feeding lower on the food web. A long-term sustainable approach to aquaculture would see more use of herbivorous species, reducing the impact on the wild fish stocks.

The Limits. The world fish catch may appear stable, but many species and areas are overfished. The FAO has concluded that 52% of fish stocks are fully exploited (at their maximum sustainable yield), 16% are overexploited and will likely decline further, and 8% are depleted and are much less productive than they once were. Much of the catch (one-third) is of such low commercial value that it is used only for fishmeal and oil production. Aquaculture is growing in developing countries, helping to alleviate poverty and improve the well-being of rural people.

The FAO has also concluded that the capture fisheries are at their upper limit, as indicated by the long-term catch data. Fisheries scientists reason that if overexploited and depleted fisheries were restored, the catch could increase by at least 10 million metric tons. That could happen, however, only if fishing for many species was temporarily eliminated or greatly reduced and the fisheries were managed on a more sustainable basis. At the 2002 Johannesburg World Summit,

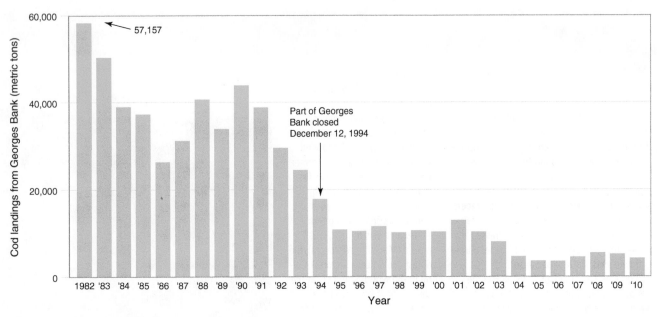

Figure 7–14 Fishery in distress. Data showing cod landings from Georges Bank, 1982–2010. (*Source:* NOAA, 2011.)

delegates agreed (one of the few agreements to come out of the meeting) to restore depleted global fisheries to achieve an MSY "on an urgent basis" by 2015 and to establish a network of protected marine areas by 2012. Recent studies have shown that marine reserves provide sheltered nurseries for surrounding areas and can supply world-record-size fish to adjacent fisheries.

Georges Bank. Events on Georges Bank, New England's richest fishing ground, illustrate well the fisheries' problems. Cod, haddock, and flounder (called groundfish because they feed on or near the bottom and are caught by bottom trawling) were the mainstay of the fishing industry for centuries. In the early 1960s, these species accounted for two-thirds of the fish population on the bank. After 1976, fishing on Georges Bank doubled in intensity, resulting in a decline in the desirable species and a rise in the so-called rough species—dogfish (sharks) and skates. As the rough species increased their numbers, fishers focused their attention on them, even though they were less valuable. Predictably, dogfish and skate populations have also been overfished and are now subject to regulation.

Management Councils. The prized species declined on Georges Bank because the fishery was poorly managed. The Magnuson Act established eight regional management councils made up of government officials and industry representatives. The councils are responsible for creating management plans for their regions, while the National Marine Fisheries Service (NMFS) provides advice and scientifically based information on assessing stocks. The NMFS also has the authority to reject elements of the plans submitted to it by the councils. The New England Fishery Management Council (NEFMC) began its task by setting TAC quotas, but fishers claimed that the TACs were set too low and successfully argued for an indirect approach that employed mesh

with openings of a size that allowed smaller fish to escape. In less than 10 years, the number of boats fishing Georges Bank doubled, with disastrous results, as indicated by the cod-landing data (Fig. 7–14).

The NEFMC discarded the mesh-size approach and initiated a number of regulations designed to take some pressure off the Georges Bank cod. Vessels were restricted in the days they could spend at sea, areas of the bank were closed to fishing, and target TACs were set at levels designed to reduce the harvest. In addition, the NMFS has been buying back fishing permits and paying fishers to scrap their boats. In spite of these measures, cod landing consistently exceeded the TAC for years, by 150–200%, until 2004–2005, when the stock had plummeted to its lowest level ever and restrictions finally led to a much-reduced harvest. Recently, the New England ground fishery (with the blessing of the NEFMC) began to operate a community-based quota system; this has been so successful that 17 additional groups of eastern fishers have petitioned to start similar systems.

Other Cod Fisheries. The Grand Banks off the coast of Newfoundland were once the richest fishing grounds in the world. The cod, however, were decimated by Canadian fishers, who were encouraged by their government to exploit the fishery and were given little warning of its imminent collapse. By 1991, the cod population had dropped to one-hundredth of its former size. In 1992, the fishery was closed, costing the jobs of 35,000 fishers. So far, the cod population has not rebounded, and cod are at their lowest levels in a century. Across the water, Europe's cod fishery is experiencing the same decline: The North Sea's cod stocks are now only 15% of what they were in the 1970s. Proposals to reduce harvests have met with fierce resistance from the European Union fishing nations, who argue that the reductions would destroy them.

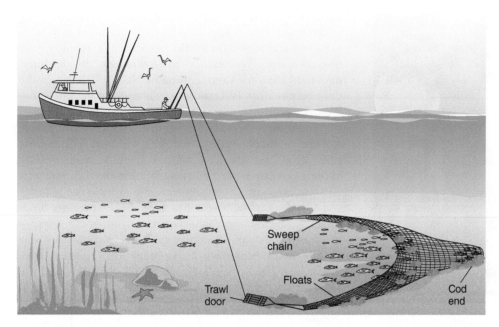

Figure 7–15 Bottom trawling. Because of the way the ocean bottom is degraded, this method, used to harvest groundfish, has been compared to clear-cutting forests. The steel trawl doors weigh up to 5 tons, and the distance between the doors is as much as 200 feet.

Sweep chain

Floats

Trawl door

Cod end

The basic problem of the fisheries is that there are too many boats—rigged with high technology that gives the fish little chance to escape—chasing too few fish. Equipped with sophisticated electronic equipment that can find fish in the depths and with trawlers with 200-foot-wide openings that scoop up everything on and close to the bottom, the fishing industry has become too efficient (Fig. 7–15). A better system of management is needed and the size of the fishing fleet must be reduced, so that the remaining fishers are better able to make a living without overfishing. One system, called **catch shares,** effectively gives fishers the equivalent of property rights in the fishery. The rights are transferable and allow the fishers to determine how and when they will harvest their catch. Coupled with accurate population assessments by fishery scientists, the catch shares system has produced an economically stable and environmentally sustainable Pacific halibut fishery, and there is no reason that it should not be applied to fisheries everywhere.

Fisheries Law Reauthorized. In December 2006, Congress passed the second reauthorization of the Magnuson Act, with strong bipartisan support: the **Magnuson-Stevens Fishery Conservation and Management Reauthorization Act.** In the new legislation, the structure of the regional councils is retained, but they are required to set catch limits based on sound scientific advice from the council's Scientific and Statistical Committee (SSC). The annual catch limits are to be set below the maximum sustainable yield, and the councils are to employ precautionary principles in setting those limits. The law also requires councils to end overfishing within two years after a species is judged to be overfished (it used to be 10 years!). As with the previous version of the act, depleted fish stocks must be rebuilt and maintained at biologically sustainable levels. The law also requires steps to be taken to assess and minimize bycatch. Limited access programs may be developed along the lines of the catch shares system. Clear accountability measures are required to ensure that the councils

and their scientists follow the mandates of the new law. Some fisheries scientists were disappointed that the new law does not require an ecosystem-based approach to fisheries management, instead maintaining the existing species-by-species approach. It does, however, strengthen the role of the SSCs, which improves the science-based approach to fisheries management.

Marine Reserves. Marine Protected Areas (MPAs) are areas of the coasts and sometimes open oceans that have been closed to all commercial fishing and mineral mining. They often allow less-harmful use like small-scale fishing, tourism, and recreational boating, although some MPAs prohibit all such activities. The number of MPAs is growing, now numbering more than 4,000 of varying sizes. More than 18% of coral reefs are covered by MPAs, but not all of these are rigorously managed. The benefits of MPAs are well known and include basic protection of these vital ecosystems, increased tourism, and the spillover of fish and larvae from the MPA to surrounding fisheries. The most direct path to the restoration of a fishery or a damaged habitat is likely to be the creation of a marine reserve. In 2009, President George W. Bush established three huge MPAs in waters surrounding several South Pacific islands, totaling 505,000 square kilometers (195,000 mi^2) in size.

International Whaling. Another fishery of great concern to the international community is the great whale. Whales, found in the open ocean and in coastal waters, were heavily depleted by overexploitation until the late 1980s. Whales once were harvested for their oil but are now prized for their meat, considered a delicacy in Japan and a few other countries. In 1974, the International Whaling Commission (IWC), an organization of nations with whaling interests, decided to regulate whaling according to the principle of maximum sustainable yield. Whenever a species of whale dropped below the optimal population for such a yield, the

Figure 7–16 Current whaling operation. Butchers slice into a Baird's beaked whale at a pier-side slaughterhouse in Wada, Japan.

IWC instituted a ban on hunting that species in order to allow the population to recover. At that time, three species (the right whale, bowhead whale, and blue whale) were at very low levels and were immediately protected. Because of difficulties in obtaining reliable data on and enforcing catch limits, the IWC took more-drastic action and placed a moratorium on the harvesting of all whales beginning in 1986. The moratorium has never been lifted; however, some limited whaling by Japan, Iceland, and Norway continues, as does harvesting by indigenous people in Alaska, the Russian Federation, and Greenland (Fig. 7–16).

Table 7–4 lists the status of 13 whale species or populations that are of commercial interest. Estimates of the numbers remaining range from 100 Northwest Pacific gray whales to up to 2 million sperm whales. Their main threat today is entanglement with fishing gear and collisions with ships. Although reliable data are still hard to acquire, many of the whale species appear to be recovering. The bowhead, gray, and southern right whales, for example, recently were upgraded from "vulnerable" to "lower risk" by the International Union for Conservation of Nature (IUCN). In the time between the IWC moratorium and the present, however, the basis of the ethical controversy over whaling has shifted from conservation to animal rights. Many people worldwide simply believe that it is wrong to kill and eat such large and unique mammals. People from whaling nations counter with the argument that their culture eats whales, just as other cultures eat cows or turkeys.

Whale Stakes. There has been heavy pressure from three members of the IWC—Japan, Iceland, and Norway—to reopen whaling. The interests of these countries focus on the small minke whale, although the Japanese have begun taking the much larger fin whales. In 1993, Norway resumed whaling for minkes, citing the country's right to refuse to accept specific IWC rulings. Norway based its decision on information submitted by the Scientific Committee of the IWC, which judged the minke population to be numerous enough to absorb a sustainable exploitation. Currently, Norway takes up to 650 and Japan more than 1,000 minke whales per year, the Norwegians for human consumption and the Japanese for "scientific purposes." It is no secret that the Japanese "scientific" harvest ends up in commercial markets; the Japanese people, however, are losing their taste for whale meat, and much of it ends up as pet food or in school dinners.

The IWC is right in the middle of this controversy. At its annual meetings, prowhaling members push for a resumption of whaling with quotas, and antiwhaling countries oppose any such resumption. The 2007 meeting of the IWC reaffirmed the moratorium on commercial whaling, and subsequent meetings have not changed that.

One contentious issue, however, is the claim that Japan and Iceland kill whales under permits given for scientific purposes but really use the law as a loophole to get around the moratorium on commercial whaling.

TABLE 7–4 Remaining Numbers of Large Whales

Endangered	Vulnerable	Lower Risk or Insufficient Data
Blue whale (3,000–5,000)	Sperm whale (1 million–2 million)	Minke whale (935,000)
North Atlantic right whale (300–350)		Bryde's whale (40,000–80,000)
North Pacific right whale (under 1,000)		Bowhead whale (11,750)
Fin whale (50,000–90,000)		Southern right whale (7,500)
Sei whale (50,000)		Humpback whale (63,600)
Northwest Pacific gray whale (100)		Gray whale (26,300)

Sources: WWF, IUCN *Red Data List* (2008), and International Whaling Commission.

Figure 7–17 **Whale watching.** A group of humpback whales entertains boatloads of whale watchers on Stellwagen Bank just north of Provincetown, Cape Cod. Whale watching has replaced whaling in New England waters that were once famous as whaling centers.

Whale Watching. Whale watching has become an important tourist enterprise in coastal areas (Fig. 7–17). For example, Stellwagen Bank, within easy reach of boats from Boston, Cape Ann, and Cape Cod, Massachusetts, has become the center of a whale-watching industry estimated to be worth more than $30 million annually in New England alone. Whale watching now flourishes in 87 countries and generates more than $1 billion in business annually.

Besides having aesthetic and entertainment value, whale watching is of scientific value. Whale-watching tour boats usually carry along a biologist who identifies the whale species and interprets the experience for the visitors. Unfortunately, whales can be spooked by boats following too closely. In 2011, a U.S. researcher was charged with bringing boats too close and feeding whales, an activity that could teach whales to come too close to boats and lead to their injury.

Coral Reefs. In a band from 30° north to 30° south of the equator, coral reefs (such as the Caribbean reefs discussed at the chapter's start) occupy shallow coastal areas and form atolls, or islands, in the ocean. Coral reefs are among the most diverse and biologically productive ecosystems in the world. The reef-building coral animals live in a symbiotic relationship with photosynthetic algae called **zooxanthellae** and, therefore, are found only in water shallower than 75 meters (245 ft). The corals build and protect the land shoreward of the reefs and attract tourists, who enjoy the warm, shallow waters. In addition, because the reefs attract a great variety of fish and shellfish, they are important sources of food and trade for local people, generating an estimated $30 billion per year in tourism and fishing revenues. In recent years, coral reefs have been the subject of concern because they have shown signs of deterioration in areas close to human population centers. The year 1998 was a watershed: Before then, an estimated 11% of coral reefs had been destroyed by human activities. Since

then, the percentage of destroyed reefs has increased to 20%. The threats are both global and local.

Extensive **coral bleaching** (wherein the coral animals expel their symbiotic algae and become white in appearance) severely damaged an estimated 16% of the world's reefs (Fig. 7–18) during the record-high sea surface temperatures accompanying the 1997–1998 El Niño. Some coral bleaching is an annual phenomenon related to the normal high temperatures and light intensities of summer, but the events of 1998 were unprecedented in scope. Studies have shown that increased sea surface temperatures can bring on 100% bleaching; indeed, 2010 brought the highest global water temperatures on record, and the second worst coral bleaching event since we have kept records. Corals are resilient, recovering from bleaching if sea surface temperatures decline in a short time, and some species are more tolerant of bleaching than others. Repeated bleaching, however, weakens the corals and eventually kills them. Many had been recovering from 1998 temperatures more than a decade later, when new record temperatures set them back.

The other global threat—one that is more long-term—is **ocean acidification**. As the surface oceans take up increasing amounts of the CO_2 pumped into the atmosphere by humans, seawater becomes more acid and the carbonate ion concentration is reduced. This in turn makes it more difficult for coral animals to build their calcium carbonate skeletons. Scientists point out that persistent high summer temperatures and the gradual acidification of the oceans could permanently wipe out coral reefs over vast areas of the shallow tropical oceans—an enormous loss of biodiversity and economic value.

Islanders and coastal people in the tropics often scour the reefs for fish, shellfish, and other edible sea life. Some exploitation of the reefs, however, is driven by the lucrative trade in tropical fish for food and the pet trade. Local residents sometimes use dynamite and cyanide to flush the fish out of hiding in the coral, a practice that is not only destructive to the coral, but also dangerous to the perpetrators.

Figure 7–18 **Bleached coral.** This coral in the Red Sea shows the effects of excessively warm temperature.

"Fishing" with cyanide is a growing (illegal) practice that has been encouraged by exporters in the Indo-Pacific region.

One solution to this destructive trade is to foster effective, sustainable management of the coral reef resources. Ideally, such management would be community based so that local people benefit from the exploitation. Another solution is to incorporate coral reefs in Marine Protected Areas (MPAs). A recent study found that 980 MPAs are already providing 19% of the world's coral reefs with some level of protection. Again, effective management and enforcement are essential, and even this is not always effective.

Mangroves. Often, just inland of coral reefs is a fringe of mangrove trees. These trees have the unique ability to take root and grow in shallow marine sediments. There they protect the coasts from damage due to storms and erosion and form a rich refuge and nursery for many marine fish. Despite these benefits, mangroves are under assault from coastal development, logging, and shrimp aquaculture. Between 1983 and the present, half of the world's 45 million acres (18 million ha) of mangroves were cut down, with percentages ranging from 40% (in Cameroon and Indonesia, for example) to nearly 80% (in Bangladesh and the Philippines, for instance). The massive removal of mangroves has brought on the destabilization of entire coastal areas, causing erosion, the siltation of sea grasses and coral reefs, and the ruin of local fisheries. Developing nations that once considered the mangroves to be useless swampland are now beginning to recognize the natural services they perform. Local and international pressure to stop the destruction of mangroves is growing. (Mangroves are highlighted in the section in this chapter on forests as well.)

We have investigated how the management (or lack thereof) of natural resources has affected several ecosystems around the world, focusing on forests and ocean systems. We could, however, have looked at freshwater ecosystems such as lakes and rivers, grasslands, or mountain areas. In each case, we could have looked at the use of natural capital from those ecosystems and whether humans are using the ecosystem goods and services in a sustainable way. In the next section, we will focus on the connection between public policy and natural resource management as it is reflected in public and private lands in the United States and at ways to restore degraded ecosystems.

7.4 Protection and Restoration

The time has passed when the loss of ecosystems could be excused on the grounds that there are suitable substitute habitats just over the hill. With the rising human population, industrial expansion, and pressure to convert natural resources to economic gain, there will always be reasons to exploit natural ecosystems. The last resort for many species and ecosystems is protection by law in the form of national parks, wildlife refuges, and reserves. The World Database on Protected Areas (WDPA) recognizes 106,900 "protected areas,"

sites whose management is aimed at "achieving specific conservation objectives," according to the Convention on Biological Diversity. These sites, representing 13% of Earth's land area, cover a spectrum of protection from strict nature preserves to managed resource use. However, establishment of a protected area is not always followed by effective management and control over misuse.

Public and Private Lands in the United States

In March 2009, the Omnibus Public Lands Management Act was signed into law by President Obama. This sweeping legislation protected an additional 2.1 million acres of wilderness, increased the wild and scenic river system by 50%, established new national parks and monuments, and provided for a new federal land system, the National Landscape Conservation System. The United States is unique among the countries of the world in having set aside a major proportion of its landmass for public ownership. Nearly 40% of the country's land is publicly owned and is managed by state and federal agencies for a variety of purposes, excluding development. The distribution of federal lands, shown in **Figure 7–19**, is greatly skewed toward the western states, a consequence of historical settlement and land distribution policies. Nonetheless, although most of the East and Midwest are in private hands, forests and other natural ecosystems still function all across these regions.

Wilderness. Land given the greatest protection (preservation) is designated as **wilderness**. Authorized by the Wilderness Act of 1964, this classification includes 109 million acres in more than 700 locations—more than 4% of the land area of the United States. The act provides for the permanent protection of these undeveloped and unexploited areas so that natural ecological processes can operate freely. Permanent structures, roads, motor vehicles and other mechanized transport are prohibited. Timber harvesting is excluded. Some livestock grazing and mineral development are allowed where such use existed previously; hiking and other similar activities are also allowed. Areas in any of the federally owned lands can be designated as wilderness; the Bureau of Land Management, National Park Service, Forest Service, and Fish and Wildlife Service all manage wilderness lands.

National Parks and National Wildlife Refuges. The **national parks**, administered by the National Park Service, and the **national wildlife refuges**, administered by the Fish and Wildlife Service, provide the next level of protection to 84 million and 96 million acres, respectively. Here the intent is to protect areas of great scenic or unique ecological significance, protect important wildlife species, and provide public access for recreation and other uses. The dual goals of protecting and providing public access often conflict with each other, because the parks and refuges are extremely popular, drawing so many visitors (more than 310 million visits a year) that protection can be threatened

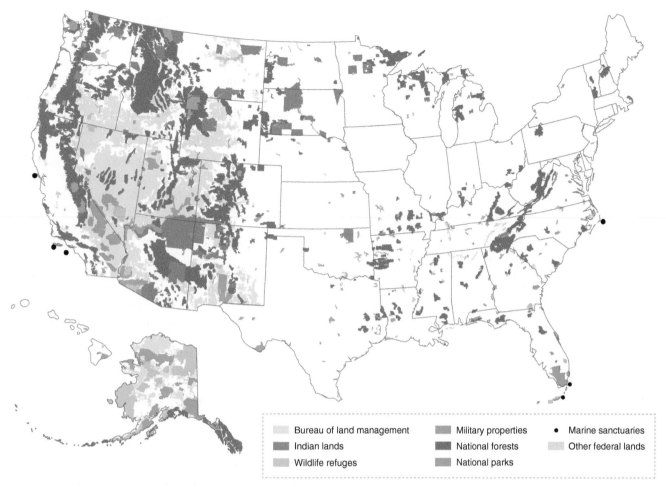

Figure 7–19 Distribution of federal lands in the United States. Because the East and Midwest were settled first, federally owned lands are concentrated in the West and Alaska.

(*Source:* Council on Environmental Quality, *Environmental Trends,* 1989.)

by those who want to see and experience the natural sites. At a number of the most popular parks, auto traffic has been replaced by shuttle vehicles because of the problems of parking and habitat destruction accompanying the use of motor vehicles within the parks. All of the federal agencies involved are trying to cope with the rising tide of recreational vehicles like snowmobiles and off-road vehicles used on most federal lands. The Blue Ribbon Coalition, a lobbying group representing owners and manufacturers of off-road vehicles, fiercely defends keeping federal lands accessible to these vehicles.

Increasingly, agencies, environmental groups, and private individuals are working together to manage natural sites as part of larger ecosystems. For example, the Greater Yellowstone Coalition has been formed to conserve the larger ecosystem that surrounds Yellowstone National Park (Fig. 7–20). Yellowstone and Grand Teton National Parks form the core of the ecosystem, to which seven national forests, three wildlife refuges, and private lands are added to form the greater ecosystem of 18 million acres. The coalition acts to restrain forces threatening the ecosystem. Thus, it has challenged the Forest Service's logging activities, addressed residential sprawl and road building on the private lands, acted to protect crucial grizzly bear habitat, and curtailed

the senseless shooting of bison that wander off the national parklands in search of winter grazing.

This cooperative approach is important for the continued maintenance of biodiversity because so much of the nation's natural lands remain outside of protected areas. Cooperation may also help restrict development up to the borders of the parks and refuges, keeping them from becoming fairly small natural islands in a sea of developed landscape.

National Forests. Forests in the United States represent an enormously important natural resource, providing habitat for countless wild species as well as supplying natural services and products. These forests range over 740 million acres, of which about two-thirds are managed for commercial timber harvest. Almost three-fourths of the managed commercial forestland is in the East and privately owned; the remainder is mainly in the West and is administered by a number of government agencies, primarily the Forest Service and the Bureau of Land Management.

In the United States, although we have cut all but 5% of the forests that were here when the colonists first arrived, second-growth forests have regenerated wherever forestlands have been protected from conversion to croplands or house

Figure 7–20 **Greater Yellowstone ecosystem.** Yellowstone National Park is the center of a much larger ecosystem, which has received attention from the Greater Yellowstone Coalition.

lots. There are more trees in the United States today than there were in 1920. In the East, some second-growth forests have aged to the point where they look almost as they did before their first cutting, except for the absence of the American chestnut and elm. Now scientists are trying to breed disease-resistant American chestnuts and elms.

The Forest Service is responsible for managing 193 million acres of national forests. The Bureau of Land Management oversees 258 million acres that are a great mixture of prairies, deserts, forests, mountains, wetlands, and tundra. Most federal timber production comes from the national forest lands.

Multiple Use. The Forest Service's management principle in the 1950s and 1960s was multiple use, which allowed for a combination of extracting resources (grazing, logging, and mining), using the forest for recreation, and protecting watersheds and wildlife. Although the intent was to achieve a balance among these uses, multiple use actually emphasized the extractive uses; that is, it was output oriented and served to justify the ongoing exploitation of public lands by private interest groups (ranchers, miners, and especially the timber industry).

New Forestry. A forest-management strategy called **new forestry** was introduced in the late 1980s. This practice is directed more toward protecting the ecological health and diversity of forests than toward producing a maximum harvest of logs. New forestry involves cutting trees less frequently (at 350-year intervals instead of every 60 to 80 years), leaving wider buffer zones along streams to reduce erosion and protect fish habitats, leaving dead logs and debris in the forests to replenish the soil, and protecting broad landscapes—up to 1 million acres—across private and public boundaries, while involving private landowners in management decisions. The Forest Service began adopting some of these management principles in the early 1990s, and they formed the core of what is now the official management paradigm of the Forest Service: ecosystem management.

To harvest timber, government foresters select tracts of forest they judge ready for harvesting and then lease the tracts to private companies, which log and sell the timber. The timber harvest from national forests has been a controversial issue. Historic data on timber sales (Fig. 7–21) reflect major shifts in logging. Note the rapid rise following World War II to satisfy the housing boom that was under way at the time, the drop reflecting rising environmental concern in the 1970s, increased logging during the Reagan-Bush years, and a steep drop with the Clinton administration as a result of renewed environmental concern. According to a recent Forest Service analysis, growth of forests has exceeded harvests for

Figure 7–21 **National forest timber sales.** Timber sales over the years reflect changes in resource needs and political philosophy.

(*Source:* US Forest Service FY 1905–2011 National Summary Cut and Sold Data and Graph. Available from http://www.fs.fed.us/forestmanagement/documents/sold-harvest/documents/1905-2011_Natl_Summary_Graph.pdf. May 1, 2012.)

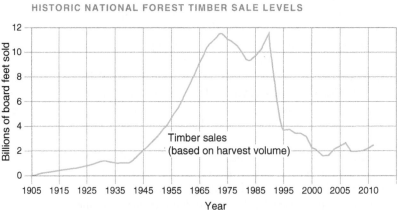

HISTORIC NATIONAL FOREST TIMBER SALE LEVELS

several decades in both national and private forests, indicating that the forests are being managed sustainably.

The Roadless Controversy. The Clinton administration's Forest Service chief, Mike Dombeck, embraced the ecosystem management paradigm, and one of his first acts was to initiate a moratorium on building new logging roads, which became the Roadless Area Conservation Rule. The Forest Service had been criticized for its road building because the existing roads had contributed to the destruction of forests and streams. The timber industry and many members of Congress from states with national forests objected to the moratorium. They believed that it would halt timber harvests and prevent access by off-road vehicles in roadless areas (they were right!). Some 58 million acres of forestland were affected by the moratorium. The Bush administration, unhappy with the roadless rule, replaced the road ban with a ruling in 2005 that allows governors to ask the secretary of agriculture to open lands to roads and development. In 2006, this ruling was canceled by a federal district court order to reinstate the roadless rule. Another district court tossed out the roadless rule in 2008, creating conflicting court decisions and initiating a lengthy appeal process. Under President Barack Obama, a 2011 decision made the roadless rule the law of the land, although there have already been court challenges. Currently, this rule continues to protect 58 million acres of forests.

Fires. The years 2006 and 2007 set new records for forest fires, with 9.9 million acres burning the former year (a record) and 9.3 million acres the latter. With a decade of drought in the western states (2011 was one of the worst on record for Texas) and serious drought in the South, it is no surprise that forest fires have become more extensive. Many scientists believe that this drought pattern is a consequence of the buildup of greenhouse gases and their impacts on climate. A hot debate has focused on why so much forest land bears what is called "fuel loads"—meaning dead trees and dense understories of trees and other vegetation—and what to do about it. Most observers believe that a combination of fire suppression and common logging practices are responsible for the high fuel loads. Ecologists remind us that wildfires can also be seen as natural disturbances, rather than ecological disasters—a confirmation of the dynamic nonequilibrium nature of ecosystems (Chapter 5).

Salvage logging, one response to fires, involves harvesting timber from recent burns (fires often consume only the outer branches of trees). The Forest Service authorizes sales of timber on recently burned national forest lands but is required to follow conservation safeguards mandated by the National Environmental Policy Act and the Endangered Species Act. This takes time, but in recent years, this kind of logging has been profitable to private operators in national forests. A 2006 study of postwildfire logging in an Oregon forest showed, however, that salvage logging not only added to the continued fire risk (loggers left branches and brush behind), but also actually killed up to three-fourths of the seedlings that had regenerated on the burned land.[5] Many scientists believe that the best approach to regenerating a forest is to do nothing; removing the dead trees kills seedlings, disturbs the soil, removes nesting sites for wildlife, and reduces nutrients and shade needed for new trees to grow.

Protecting Nonfederal Lands. In 2008, voters across the nation approved $7.3 billion in spending for the preservation of open space and for parks. California and Florida, in particular, spent $700 million together. Pennsylvania commissioned a report on public lands and parks in 2008 and discovered that in Philadelphia alone the parks provided millions of dollars in revenue, cost savings, and taxes—a total (estimated $1.1 billion) about ten times the amount the city spends on parks each year.

Land Trusts. Often, landowners and townspeople want to protect natural areas from development but are wary of turning the land over to a government authority. One creative option is the **private land trust,** a nonprofit organization that will accept either outright gifts of land or **easements**—arrangements in which the landowner gives up development rights into the future but retains ownership of the parcel. The land trust may also purchase land to protect it from development. The land trust movement is growing considerably: There were 429 land trusts in the United States in 1980 and more than 1,723 in 2010, as reported by the Land Trust Alliance, an umbrella organization in Washington, DC, serving local and regional trusts. These trusts protect almost 47 million acres of land. The Nature Conservancy, a national and international land trust, also protects 102 million acres in other countries.

Land trusts are proving to be a vital link in the preservation of ecosystems. In 1999, alarmed about signs of development in their region, 30 residents of Grand Lake Stream in northeastern Maine (pop. 150) met to share their concerns. Out of that meeting grew the Downeast Lakes Land Trust, which, over time, has carried out a $30 million conservation effort that has protected 342,000 acres of woodlands, 60 lakes, and 1,500 miles of riverfront. Members are currently in a campaign to raise funds for another 21,000 acres. These lands connected several other conservation holdings in eastern Maine and New Brunswick, and the result (to the surprise of the original 30 residents) is that more than 1 million contiguous acres are protected against development. The Downeast Land Trust is busy now constructing hiking trails and canoe-access campsites so that the public will be able to enjoy hiking, canoeing, and fishing in the conserved landscape.

Ecosystem Restoration

A great increase in restoration activity has occurred during the past 30 years, spurred on by federal and state programs and the growing science of restoration ecology. The intent of ecosystem restoration is to repair the damage to specific lands and waters so that normal ecosystem integrity,

---

[5]D. C. Donato, J. B. Fontaine, J. L. Campbell, W. D. Robinson, J. B. Kauffman, and B. E. Law. "Post-Wildfire Logging Hinders Regeneration and Increases Fire Risk," *Science* 311 (January 20, 2006): 352.

resilience, and productivity return. It has become a worldwide, $70 billion industry. Because of the complexity of natural ecosystems, however, the practical task of restoration is often difficult. Frequently, soils have been disturbed, pollutants have accumulated, important species have disappeared, and other—often exotic—species have achieved dominance.

For these reasons, a thorough knowledge of ecosystem and species ecology is essential to the success of restoration efforts. The ecological problems that can be mended by restoration include those resulting from soil erosion, surface strip mining, draining of wetlands, hurricane damage, agricultural use, deforestation, overgrazing, desertification, and the eutrophication of lakes. Every case is different. Some cases involve working with several different ecological problems at the same time, such as the huge restoration project under way in the (formerly) vast Everglades of southern Florida.

Everglades Restoration. A much-publicized plan to restore the Everglades received congressional approval in 2000. The plan, the **Comprehensive Everglades Restoration Plan (CERP)**, is expected to take 36 years and almost $11 billion to complete **(Fig. 7–22)**. The federal government promised to provide half of the funds, and state, tribal, and local agencies the other half. CERP is managed by the U.S. Army Corps of Engineers, the federal agency that was actually responsible for creating much of the system of water control that made the restoration necessary.

The Everglades is a network of wetland landscapes that once occupied the southern half of Florida. Now reduced to half its original size through development and wetlands draining, it is still an amazing and unique ecosystem, harboring a great diversity of species and many endangered and threatened species. It is home to 16 wildlife refuges and four national parks, the crown jewel being Everglades National Park.

Because Florida is so flat, the general topography promoted a slow movement of water south from Lake Okeechobee by way of a 40-mile-wide, 100-mile-long shallow "river of grass" ending in Florida Bay. Floridians brought the water flow under human control with a system of 1,000 miles of canals, 720 miles of levees, and hundreds of water control structures (locks, dams, and spillways), bounded on the east by a string of cities and their suburbs. In its center, 550,000 acres of croplands were created, which form a lucrative sugarcane industry. Now, water shortages in the winter leave too little for the natural systems, and in the summer rainy season, too much water is diverted to the Everglades. The water quality, once pristine, is now degraded because of nutrients (especially phosphorus) from agricultural runoff.

Water Release. A broader restoration program was originally begun in 1996, coordinated by the South Florida Ecosystem Restoration Task Force. The total task force project is expected to cost close to $15 billion. The plan calls for removing 240 miles of levees and canals and creating a system of reservoirs and underground wells to capture water for release during the dry season. The new flowage is designed to restore the river of grass, thereby restoring the 2.4 million acres of Everglades—not to the original state, but at least to a healthy system that promotes the second goal of the task force. If CERP does its job, close to 2 billion gallons of water that flow out of the Everglades each day will be redirected to flow southward. The plan calls for 80% of this water to feed the Everglades and 20% to feed the thirst of South Florida's cities and farms.

Funding. One of the most difficult parts of any restoration is funding. A major step in the restoration of the Florida Everglades project was announced in 2008, when U.S. Sugar agreed to sell its land and facilities to the state of Florida for $1.7 billion. This sale involved 187,000 acres of land to the south and east of Lake Okeechobee and could recreate wetlands to store up to 1.2 cubic kilometers (0.28 cubic miles) of water that otherwise would need to be pumped into reservoirs and underground wells during the summer. Currently, the excess water is pumped eastward and westward out to sea, disturbing the salinity and nutrient regimes in the receiving estuaries. The water stored in the new wetlands would then be free to flow south into the Everglades during the dry season, once the path to the Everglades is made clear by other planned projects. Unfortunately, this planned sale has been scaled way back because of Florida's financial uncertainties, a result of the recent national recession. The new proposal would invest $530 million for 72,500 acres of land south of Lake Okeechobee and leave open future options for the state to buy more land.

There is no blueprint for a project like the Everglades restoration. The long time frame, the need for a continued infusion of federal and state money, and the great difficulties that will arise in carrying out the restoration guarantee that the project will attract skepticism as well as effusive praise. It will be in the news for a long time.

Pending Restorations. As the values of natural ecosystems become more recognized, efforts to restore damaged or lost ones will become increasingly important. Many other large systems, such as the California Bay Delta, Chesapeake Bay, Platte River basin, and Upper Mississippi River system, have suffered from human abuse and ignorance and are now the focus of restoration projects. The Mississippi delta, battered by Hurricanes Katrina and Rita in 2005, is in need of a huge effort to restore the damaged wetlands and barrier islands. Restoration is under way at many sites that are ecological gems, including the Galápagos Islands, under siege from many exotic species; the Illinois River, confined by levees; the Brazilian Atlantic forest, severely deforested; and Tampa Bay, affected by its urban surroundings.

Final Thoughts

Ecosystems everywhere are being exploited for human needs and profit. In addition to all the examples discussed in this chapter, other areas that are in trouble include overgrazed rangelands, and rivers that are overdrawn for irrigation water. The purpose of this chapter has been to highlight some of the most critical problems and to indicate steps being taken to correct them. It is certain that greater pressures will be put on natural ecosystems as the human population

◆ Surface Water Storage Reservoirs
181,300 acres of above and in-ground reservoirs are planned to store millions of gallons of water.

● Aquifer Storage and Recovery
More than 300 underground water storage wells are proposed to store up to 1.6 billion gallons of treated water a day in confined aquifers.

◐ Stormwater Treatment Areas
35,600 acres of manmade wetlands will be constructed to remove pollutants and other harmful contaminants from water before it is discharged to the Everglades.

■ Wastewater Reuse
Two advanced treatment plants are proposed to recycle more than 220 million gallons of wastewater a day, adding a new source of high quality water for the southern Everglades.

★ Seepage Management
Barriers are proposed to be built to stop the rapid underground seepage of water out of the Everglades, which today results in the loss of millions of gallons of water each year.

▲ Removing Barriers to Sheetflow
More than 240 miles of canals and levees may be removed to restore the historic overland sheetflow through the Everglades wetlands. Sections of Tamiami Trail will be elevated to handle increased water flows contributed by CERP project features.

✦ Operational Changes
Changes will be made in the regional water management system to benefit Lake Okeechobee, the Everglades, and the coastal estuaries.

Figure 7–22 The Everglades restoration plan. The goal of this plan is to restore historical water flow patterns so that ecological restoration can occur. The seven major features of the plan are described at the left of the map. The lower three maps illustrate the historical, current, and future water flow through southern Florida.
(*Source:* Comprehensive Everglades Restoration Plan, www.evergladesplan.org.)

continues to rise. These pressures must be met with increasingly effective protective measures if we want to continue to enjoy the goods and services provided by ecosystems. The problems are most difficult in the developing world, where poverty forces people to take from nature in order to survive. If natural areas are to be preserved, the needs of people must be met in ways that do not involve destroying ecosystems. People must be provided with alternatives to overexploita-

tion, a situation requiring both wise leadership and effective international aid.

In April 2000, when he was UN Secretary-General, Kofi Annan included in his millennium report to the General Assembly a stern warning that far too little concern was being given to the sustainability of our planet: "If I could sum it up in one sentence, I should say that we are plundering our children's heritage to pay for our present unsustainable practices. . . . We must preserve our forests, fisheries, and the diversity of living species, all of which are close to collapsing under the pressure of human consumption and destruction. . . . in short," Annan stated, "we need a new ethic of stewardship." Indeed, under UN sponsorship, the Billion Tree Campaign, begun in 2006, overran its goal in 18 months and has now become the Seven Billion Tree Campaign. From individuals to heads of states, people in 155 countries are planting trees, acting in stewardship concern for the climate and for peoples' needs.

REVISITING THE THEMES

Sound Science

Calculating a total allowable catch (TAC) requires solid scientific data on fish populations and an understanding of the MSY model. These limits are difficult, if not impossible, to accomplish for mobile creatures such as fish and whales. Fisheries scientists are constantly challenged to assess fish stocks accurately, and their recommendations can often be trumped by political and economic decisions, as is well illustrated in the plight of the New England fisheries. Ensuring sustainable harvests in forests requires thorough scientific assessments of tree growth and a balancing of the needs of ecosystems with those of the harvesters. The restoration of ecosystems requires a great deal of sound science in the form of species and ecosystem ecology. It also requires the ability to make midcourse corrections, which projects like the Everglades restoration will require in the future. Scientists at the Curtic prairie set the stage for the discipline of restoration ecology. Scientists today use not only experiments, but also data collected by citizen scientists to test hypotheses, as the example of the REEF data collection showed.

Sustainability

The protection of forests, reefs, and other ecosystems requires intelligent policies and practices. Often this requires coordination, as an unregulated commons almost always tends to overuse. This is why we have the International Whaling Commission, for example. Unfortunately, there are many cases of unsustainable use: the taking of "bush meat" by commercial hunters, the cyanide poisoning of coral reefs, the exploitation of a commons where there is open access to all, and the deforestation in tropical rain forests, to name a few. The principle of sustainability is built into the model of the maximum sustainable yield, but for fisheries it turns out

to be harder to accomplish in practice than in theory. For this reason, it is wise to use the precautionary principle in attempting to set such a threshold for a resource. Sustainable forestry, however, is not so difficult, as long as it is focused on managing the forests as functioning ecosystems and as long as biodiversity is respected. Where resources are being exploited in much of the developing world, sustainability is unworkable without taking into account the needs of local people and involving them in management decisions. Incorporating ecosystem services into our calculations will make protection of ecosystems more economically viable. Such an approach requires a knowledge of the value of ecosystem capital.

Stewardship

Stewardship care of ecosystems means consciously managing them so as to benefit both present and future generations. Sustainable consumptive and productive use of ecosystem resources involves tenurial rights over them; exercising these rights should be a matter of stewardship embodied in rules and policies. Table 7–3 presents a set of principles that promote such stewardship. When forests and fisheries are under the control of the people who most directly depend on their use, stewardship can flourish. Management of the fisheries exhibits both good and poor stewardship in different regions: Compare the Pacific Northwest and Georges Bank fisheries. Individuals can show stewardship by acting as citizen scientists or informed consumers or helping nonprofits such as land trusts.

Finally, it is heartening to see the former UN secretary-general endorsing a stewardship ethic as an important step in preserving the natural resources that are under tremendous pressure from present generations. The Seven Billion Tree Campaign is a tangible demonstration of that ethic.

REVIEW QUESTIONS

1. How did individuals act to help scientists in the Caribbean Sea?

2. What are some goods and services provided by natural ecosystems?

3. Compare the concept of ecosystem capital with that of natural resources. What do the two reveal about values?

4. Compare and contrast the terms *conservation* and *preservation*.

5. Differentiate between consumptive use and productive use. Give examples of each.

6. What does maximum sustainable yield mean? What factors complicate its application?

7. What is the tragedy of the commons? Give an example of a common-pool resource, and describe ways of protecting such resources.

8. When are restoration efforts needed? Describe efforts under way to restore the Everglades.

9. Describe some of the findings of the most recent FAO Global Forest Resources Assessments. What are the key elements of sustainable forest management?

10. What is deforestation, and what factors are primarily responsible for deforestation of the tropics?

11. What is the global pattern of exploitation of fisheries? Compare the yield of the capture fisheries with that of aquaculture.

12. Compare the objectives of the original Magnuson Act with those of the 2006 Magnuson-Stevens Fishery Conservation and Management Reauthorization Act.

13. What is the current status of the large whales? Discuss the controversy over continued whaling by some countries.

14. How are coral reefs and mangroves being threatened, and how is this destruction linked to other environmental problems?

15. Compare the different levels of protection versus use for the different categories of federal lands in the United States.

16. Describe the progression of the management of our national forests during the past half century. What are current issues, and how are they being resolved?

17. How do land trusts work, and what roles do they play in preserving natural lands?

THINKING ENVIRONMENTALLY

1. It is an accepted fact that both consumptive use and productive use of natural ecosystems are necessary for high-level human development. To what degree should consumptive use hold priority over productive use? Think about more than one resource (lumber, bush meat, etc.).

2. Consider the problem presented by Hardin of open access to the commons without regulation. To what degree should the freedom of the use of these areas be limited by the authorities? Make use of Table 7–3 when you defend your position.

3. Consider the benefits and problems associated with coastal and open-ocean aquaculture. Is aquaculture a useful practice overall? Justify your answer.

4. Kofi Annan stated that we are in need of a "new ethic of stewardship." What principles should this new ethic be built on?

MAKING A DIFFERENCE

1. To determine the impact you have on the ecosystems around you, calculate your ecological footprint (several sites on the Internet can help with this). What can you do to lower your ecological footprint?

2. Consider Michael Pollan's work *The Omnivore's Dilemma*. The book deals with America's eating habits, government regulations regarding food production, farming techniques, and similar topics. Decide which eating habits are ecologically sustainable and which are not. Go to the Internet and search for sites that offer ecosystem-friendly recipes.

3. By transporting firewood from its native area, you may run the risk of spreading diseases and alien insect species that can damage trees and overrun whole areas of forest. You can

avoid this by using firewood harvested locally or, if you need to carry firewood a distance, by finding wood marked with a U.S. Department of Agriculture (USDA) tag confirming that the logs are safe to move.

4. Organize a volunteer tree-planting group. You can purchase young trees at a nursery, college agricultural department, or city government. To raise money for a large project, try to find individual or corporate sponsors.

5. When you visit parks and other natural areas, stay on the designated trails. Avoid making new trails that might lead to erosion, and never disturb nesting birds and wild animals raising their young.

MasteringEnvironmentalScience®

Go to **www.masteringenvironmentalscience.com** for practice quizzes, Pearson eText, videos, current events, and more.

PART THREE

The Human Population and Essential Resources

TWO THOUSAND ELEVEN WAS A NEWSWORTHY YEAR. The Occupy Wall Street protests in America, the Arab Spring uprisings in the Middle East, and the financial difficulties in the Eurozone were events that captured the world's attention and will affect us for years to come. The world also celebrated another milestone in 2011 when the United Nations Population Division estimated that on October 31 global human population reached 7 billion. On that day, in various places around the globe, babies were celebrated as the "seven billionth." Celebrations began in the Philippines, where tiny Danica May Camacho was born in Manila's Jose Fabella Memorial Hospital. Of course, naming one particular infant the 7 billionth is purely symbolic. Estimating the day on which human population will reach a specific number is impossible. We cannot count people accurately enough or frequently enough to know such a thing precisely. But we do know that human populations are continuing to rise. Like Danica May, each new person needs shelter, food, education, and, eventually, a job. We need to find ways to accommodate the population at the same time as it is increasing rapidly. Global population is projected to reach more than 10 billion by the year 2100. Virtually all of the increase will be in middle- and low-income countries, which are already densely populated and straining to meet the needs of their people for food, water, health care, shelter, and employment.

YET IN RECENT DECADES, a population decline has begun to occur in some industrialized countries. Populations are aging in these countries, bringing serious social, economic, and political consequences such as a shrinking workforce, a rising retiree population, escalating health care costs, and increasing "replacement migration" of workers from developing countries.

YOU WILL LEARN HOW human populations are similar to and different from populations of other species (Chapter 8). We will see how historic changes in technology have affected our population growth and how that growth can affect the rest of the world. We will also look at the demographic transition, which has brought an end to population growth in much of the industrialized world. Next, we will discuss what needs to be done to bring the developing countries through the demographic transition and look at efforts being made to change consumption and population patterns (Chapter 9). Finally, we will look at the critical resources humans need, how we manage and use these resources, and their relationship to a growing population (Chapters 10–13). It is necessary to look at population and consumption concerns in tandem with resource use and pollution because population growth and its twin, consumption, affect every environmental issue.

Running out of water. These villagers in the dry southwest of China are lined up to get water. Parts of China are in the midst of the worst drought in 60 years, an event that is making China's water problems worse.

Water: Hydrologic Cycle and Human Use

CHINA HAS A WATER PROBLEM. The growing population requires more and more to grow food and sustain cities, and yet much of the country is dry. The wetter southeast is crowded with people, while the drier southwest is experiencing the worst drought in 60 years. In the center of the country lies the central plateau, an area of intense agricultural production; in the north and northwest is the extremely dry Gobi desert, which is creeping south and east yearly. Ten provinces of China are so water-poor that they fall beneath the World Bank's definition of water poverty: 1,000 m^3 of water per year per person. The karst, or limestone regions, of the south offer a unique problem. Precipitation, while not scarce, rapidly percolates through porous rock to travel in vast underground rivers, inaccessible to most rural residents of the area. Such underground river water is undrinkable because of all of the surface pollutants that percolate down it to the water table.

DAM BUILDING. China's explosive economic growth has fueled a rising middle class that wants a more diverse diet, but such foods are energy and water intensive. China's need for power has triggered a dam-building spree. The central plateau, home of the richest agriculture, is experiencing crop loss from too much groundwater removal. Unfortunately, pumping the 100 km^3 per

LEARNING OBJECTIVES

1. **Water, a Vital Resource:** Explain the unique properties that make water so vital, the differences in water availability in different societies, and conflicts over availability of clean water.

2. **Hydrologic Cycle, and Human Impacts:** Explain the movement of water through the hydrologic cycle and human impacts on the cycle.

3. **Human Controlled Flooding and Drought:** Describe the ways humans try to provide clean freshwater and some of their outcomes.

4. **Water Stewardship, Economics, and Policy:** Describe options for meeting rising demands for water, new innovations in water science and technology, and public policies for water in a water-scarce world.

year that China uses to irrigate requires a great deal of energy as well. Vice President Xi Jinping visited the United States in 2012 to discuss, among other things, dropping trade barriers to some U.S. agricultural products. While China is already a big importer of U.S. products, growing more water-intensive crops elsewhere will save water in China, making the trade represent not only needed food but saved water.

LONG-DISTANCE TRANSPORT. In addition to building dams, the Chinese government is working on moving water long distances. One such undertaking is the South-to-North Water Diversion Project (SNWT), a 50-year venture (two parts are scheduled to be delivering water by 2014) with an estimated cost of $64 billion that will bring water to the arid north. An eastern route will carry water from the Yangtze River 1,152 km (716 mi) to Tianjin, through a series of canals, reservoirs tunnels, and natural rivers, and a central route will carry water 1,264 km (785 mi) from the south of Beijing. Together they should carry 28 km^3 (6.7 mi^3) of water per year.

China is a microcosm of the world. All over, we are trying to balance needs for energy, agriculture, drinking water, and biodiversity. As we welcome new people into our crowded global community, finding clean, safe water for all will be one of our top priorities.

Chapter 10, the first of four chapters on essential resources, focuses on water. The concepts here will be strongly intertwined with those we have already seen in chapters on population and development and with later chapters on soil, food production, and climate change.

10.1 Water: A Vital Resource

Water is absolutely fundamental to life as we know it. Happily, Earth is virtually flooded with water. A total volume of some 1.4 billion cubic kilometers (325 million mi^3) of water covers 75% of Earth's surface. About 97.5% of this volume is the saltwater of the oceans and seas. The remaining 2.5% is **freshwater**—water with a salt content of less than 0.1% (1,000 ppm). This is the water on which most terrestrial biota, ecosystems, and humans depend. Of the 2.5%, though, two-thirds is bound up in the polar ice caps and glaciers. Thus, only 0.77% of all water is found in lakes, wetlands, rivers, groundwater, biota, soil, and the atmosphere (**Fig. 10–1**). Nevertheless, evaporation from the oceans combines with precipitation to resupply that small percentage continually through the solar-powered hydrologic cycle, described in detail in Section 10.2. Thus, freshwater is a continually renewable resource.

Streams, rivers, ponds, lakes, swamps, estuaries, groundwater, bays, oceans, and the atmosphere all contain water, and they all represent ecosystem capital—goods and services vital to human interests (see Table 5–2 for the array of aquatic ecosystems and their characteristics). They provide drinking water, water for industries, and water to irrigate crops. Bodies of water furnish energy through hydroelectric power and control flooding by absorbing excess water. They provide transportation, recreation, waste processing, and habitats for aquatic plants and animals. Freshwater is a vital resource for all land ecosystems, modulating the climate through evaporation and essential global warming (when water is in the atmosphere as water vapor). During the past two centuries, many of these uses (and some threats to them) have led us to construct a huge infrastructure designed to bring water under control. We have built dams, canals, reservoirs, aqueducts, sewer systems, treatment plants, water towers, elaborate pipelines, irrigation systems, and desalination plants. As a result, waterborne diseases have been brought under control in the developed countries, vast cities thrive in deserts, irrigation makes it possible to grow 40% of the world's food, and one-fifth of all electricity is generated through hydropower. These great benefits are especially available to people in the developed countries (**Fig. 10–2a**).

In the developing world (Fig. 10–2b), by contrast, 1.1 billion people still lack access to safe drinking water, 2.6 billion do not have access to adequate sanitation services, and more than 1.8 million deaths each year are traced to waterborne diseases (mostly in children under five). All too often in these countries, water is costly or inaccessible to the poorest in society, while the wealthy have it piped into their homes. In addition, because of the infrastructure that is used to control water, whole seas are being lost, rivers are running dry, millions of people have been displaced to make room for reservoirs, groundwater aquifers are being pumped down, and disputes over water have raised tensions from local to international levels. Freshwater is a limiting resource in many parts of the world and is certain to become even more so as the 21st century unfolds.

Feeding a growing world population will challenge our water management infrastructure, especially as cities and industries compete with agriculture for scarce water resources. The growing impact of climate change on the hydrologic cycle is in turn worsening the problems brought on by droughts and floods. Rainfall variability can reduce the economic growth of nations as floods devastate some croplands and droughts dry them up in other parts of the world. Even in the United States, effects from climate change will vary. A 2011 report from the Department of the Interior suggested that one of the biggest impacts will be to lower the summer availability of water in already dry areas of the Southwest.[1]

There are two ways to consider water issues. The focus in this chapter is on *quantity*—that is, on the global water cycle and how it works, on the technologies we use to control water and manage its use, and on public policies we have put in place to govern our different uses of water. Later we

Figure 10–1 Earth's water. The Earth has an abundance of water, but terrestrial ecosystems, humans, and agriculture depend on accessible freshwater, which constitutes only 0.77% of the total.

---

[1]Alexander, P. et al., Reclamation, SECURE Water Act Section 9503(c), Reclamation Climate Change and Water, Report to Congress 2011, U.S. Department of the Interior, Denver, CO.

(a)   (b)

Figure 10–2 Differences in availability. Human conditions range from (a) being able to luxuriate in water to (b) having to walk long distances and pull from deep pumps to obtain enough simply to survive. In many cases, however, the abundance of water is illusory because water supplies are being overdrawn.

will focus on water *quality*—that is, on water pollution and its consequences, on sewage-treatment technologies, and on public policies for dealing with water pollution issues (Chapter 20). Water—so vital to life—moves through the land, oceans, and atmosphere in a cycle.

10.2 Hydrologic Cycle: Natural Cycle, Human Impacts

Earth's water cycle, also called the **hydrologic cycle,** is represented in **Figure 10–3.** The basic cycle consists of water rising to the atmosphere through **evaporation** (movement of water molecules from the surface of the liquid to a gas state) and **transpiration** (the loss of water vapor as it moves from the soil through green plants and exits through leaf pores) and returning to the land and oceans through **condensation** (formation of liquid water from a gas state) and **precipitation** (release of water from clouds in form of rain, sleet, snow, or hail). Modern references to the hydrologic cycle distinguish between **green water** and **blue water**. Green water is water in vapor form, while blue water is liquid water wherever it occurs. Green water and blue water are vitally linked in the hydrologic cycle. Terms commonly used to describe water are listed and defined in Table 10–1 on page 243.

Evaporation, Condensation, and Purification

Recall that a weak attraction known as hydrogen bonding tends to hold water molecules (H_2O) together (Chapter 3). Below 32°F (0°C), the kinetic energy of the molecules is so low that the hydrogen bonding is strong enough to hold the molecules in place with respect to one another, and the result is

ice. At temperatures above freezing but below boiling (212°F or 100°C), the kinetic energy of the molecules is such that hydrogen bonds keep breaking and re-forming with different molecules. The result is *liquid water.* As the water molecules absorb energy from sunlight or an artificial source, the kinetic energy they gain may be enough to allow them to break away from other water molecules entirely and enter the atmosphere. This process is known as evaporation, and the result is **water vapor**—water molecules in the gaseous state.

You will learn later that water vapor is a powerful greenhouse gas (Chapter 18). It contributes about two-thirds of the total warming from all greenhouse gases. The amount of water vapor in the air is the **humidity**. Humidity is generally measured as **relative humidity**, the amount of water vapor as a percentage of what the air can hold *at a particular temperature.* For example, a relative humidity of 60% means that the air contains 60% of the maximum amount of water vapor it could hold at that particular temperature. The amount of water vapor air can hold changes with the temperature. When warm, moist air is cooled, its relative humidity rises until it reaches 100%, and further cooling causes the excess water vapor to condense back to liquid water because the air can no longer hold as much water vapor (**Fig. 10–4**).

Condensation is the opposite of evaporation. It occurs when water molecules rejoin by hydrogen bonding to form liquid water. If the droplets form in the atmosphere, the result is fog and clouds (fog is just a very low cloud). If the droplets form on the cool surfaces of vegetation, the result is dew. Condensation is greatly facilitated by the presence of **aerosols** in the atmosphere. Aerosols are microscopic liquid or solid particles (like hair spray) originating from land and water surfaces. They provide sites that attract water vapor

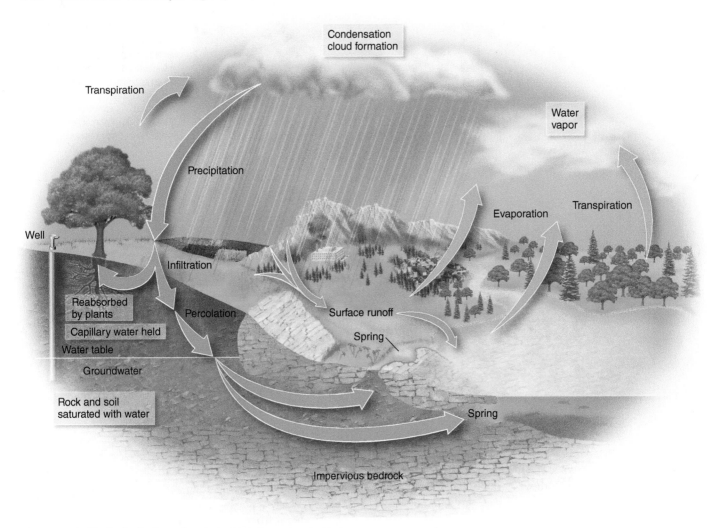

Figure 10–3 The hydrologic cycle. The Earth's freshwater is replenished as water vapor enters the atmosphere by evaporation and transpiration from vegetation, leaving salts and other impurities behind. As precipitation hits the ground, three additional pathways are possible: surface runoff, infiltration, and reabsorption by plants. Green arrows depict green water, present as vapor in the atmosphere; blue arrows show liquid water.

Figure 10–4 Condensation. The amount of water vapor that air can hold changes with the temperature. The red line follows an air mass that starts with 40% relative humidity (RH) at 30°C and is cooled. When the mass of air cools to 17°C, it has reached 100% RH, and condensation begins, forming clouds. If we started with a higher RH, clouds would form sooner when the air is cooled. Further cooling and condensation result in precipitation.

and promote the formation of droplets of moisture. Aerosols may originate naturally, from sources such as volcanoes, wind-stirred dust and soil, and sea salts. Anthropogenic sources—sulfates, carbon, and dust—contribute almost as much as natural sources (more in some locations) and can have a significant impact on regional and global climates.

Purification occurs when water is separated from the solutes and particles it contains. The processes of evaporation and condensation purify water naturally. When water in an ocean or a lake evaporates, only the water molecules leave the surface; the dissolved salts and other solids remain behind in solution. When the water vapor condenses again, it is thus purified water—except for the pollutants and other aerosols it may pick up from the air. The water in the atmosphere turns over every 10 days, so water is constantly being purified. (The most chemically pure water for use in laboratories is obtained by distillation, a process of boiling water and condensing the vapor.)

Thus, evaporation and condensation are the source of all natural freshwater on Earth. Freshwater that falls on the land as precipitation gradually makes its way through aquifers, streams, rivers, and lakes to the oceans (blue water flow). In the process, it carries along salts from the land,

TABLE 10–1 Terms Commonly Used to Describe Water

Term	Definition
Water quantity	The amount of water available to meet demands.
Water quality	The degree to which water is pure enough to fulfill the requirements of various uses.
Freshwater	Water having a salt concentration below 0.1%. As a result of purification by evaporation, all forms of precipitation are freshwater, as are lakes, rivers, groundwater, and other bodies of water that have a throughflow of water from precipitation.
Saltwater	Water that contains at least 3% salt (30 parts salt per 1,000 parts water), typical of oceans and seas.
Brackish water	A mixture of freshwater and saltwater, typically found where rivers enter the ocean.
Hard water	Water that contains minerals, especially calcium or magnesium, that cause soap to precipitate, producing a scum, curd, or scale in boilers.
Soft water	Water that is relatively free of minerals.
Polluted water	Water that contains one or more impurities, making it unsuitable for a desired use.
Purified water	Water that has had pollutants removed or is rendered harmless.
Storm water	Water from precipitation that runs off of land surfaces in surges.
Green water	Water in vapor form originating from water bodies, the soil, and organisms—the source of water for precipitation.
Blue water	Precipitation, renewable surface water runoff, and groundwater recharge—the focus of management and the main source of water for human withdrawals and natural ecosystems.

which eventually accumulate in the oceans. Salts also accumulate in inland seas or lakes, such as the Great Salt Lake in Utah. The salinization of irrigated croplands is a noteworthy human-made example of this process (Chapter 11). Most of the freshwater from precipitation, however, is returned directly to the atmosphere by evaporation and transpiration.

Precipitation

Warm air rises from Earth's surface because it is less dense than the cooler air above. As the warm air encounters the lower atmospheric pressure at increasing altitudes, it gradually cools as it expands—a process known as **adiabatic cooling**. When the relative humidity reaches 100% and cooling continues, condensation occurs and clouds form. As condensation intensifies, water droplets become large enough to fall as precipitation. **Adiabatic warming**, by contrast, occurs as cold air descends and is compressed by the higher air pressure in the lower atmosphere.

Precipitation on Earth ranges from near zero in some areas to more than 2.5 meters (100 in.) per year in others (**Figure 10–5** shows the pattern over land). The distribution

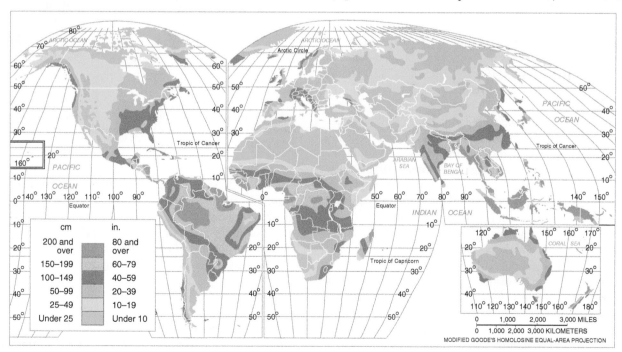

Figure 10–5 **Global precipitation.** Note the high rainfall in equatorial regions and the regions of low rainfall to the north and south. (*Source:* Robert W. Christopherson, *Elemental Geosystems,* 7th ed., Pearson Education, Upper Saddle River, NJ.)

depends on patterns of rising and falling air currents. As air rises, it cools, condensation occurs, and precipitation results. As air descends, it tends to become warmer, causing evaporation to increase and dryness to result. A rain-causing event that you see in almost every television weather report is the movement of a cold front. As the cold front moves into an area, the warm, moist air already there is forced upward because the cold air of the advancing front is denser. The rising warm air cools, causing condensation and precipitation along the leading edge of the cold front.

Two factors—global convection currents and rain shadow—may cause more or less continuously rising or falling air currents over particular regions, with major effects on precipitation.

Convection Currents. At the equator, the rays of the sun are nearly perpendicular to the Earth's surface; at the poles, light rays come at an angle through the atmosphere. That difference causes the surface of the Earth to be hotter in some places than others and drives great air movements, called "global convection currents." As the air at the equator is heated, it expands, rises, and cools; condensation and precipitation occur. The constant intense heat in these equatorial areas ensures that this process is repeated often, thus causing high rainfall, which, along with continuous warmth, supports tropical rain forests.

Rising air over the equator is just half of the convection current, however. The air, now dry, must come down again. Pushed from beneath by more rising air, it literally "spills over" to the north and south of the equator and descends over subtropical regions (25° to 35° north and south of the equator), resulting in subtropical deserts. The Sahara of northern Africa and the Kalahari of southern Africa are prime examples. The two halves of the system composed of the rising and falling air make up a **Hadley cell** (Fig. 10–6a and b). Because of Earth's rotation, winds are deflected from the strictly vertical and horizontal paths indicated by a Hadley cell and tend to flow in easterly and westerly directions—the **trade winds** (Fig. 10–6c), which blow almost continuously from the same direction.

Rain Shadow. When moisture-laden trade winds encounter mountain ranges, the air is deflected upward, causing cooling and high precipitation on the windward side of the range. As the air crosses the range and descends on the other side, it becomes warmer and increases its capacity to pick up moisture. Hence, deserts occur on the leeward (downwind) sides of mountain ranges. The dry region downwind of a mountain range is referred to as a **rain shadow** (Fig. 10–7). The severest deserts in the world are caused by the rain-shadow effect. For example, the westerly trade winds, full of moisture from the Pacific Ocean, strike the Sierra Nevada Mountains in California. As the winds rise over the mountains, large amounts of water precipitate out, supporting the lush forests on the western slopes. Immediately east of the southern Sierra Nevada, however, lies Death Valley, one of the driest regions of North America. Likewise, the Gobi desert in China is in the rain shadow of the Himalayas.

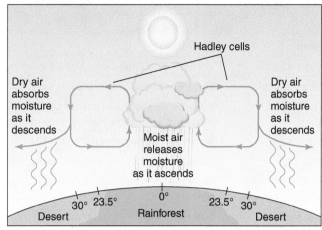

(a) Hadley cells at the equator

(b) Global air flow patterns

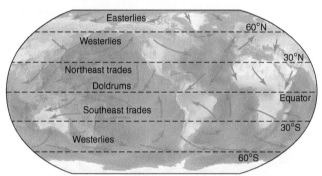

(c) Global trade winds

Figure 10–6 **Global air circulation.** (a) The two Hadley cells at the equator. (b) The six Hadley cells on either side of the equator, indicating general vertical airflow patterns. (c) Global trade-wind patterns, formed as a result of Earth's rotation.

Figure 10–5 shows general precipitation patterns for the land; the general atmospheric circulation (Fig. 10–6) and the effects of mountain ranges (Fig. 10–7) combine to give great variation in the precipitation reaching the land. The distribution of precipitation in turn largely determines the biomes and ecosystems found in a given region (Chapter 5).

Groundwater

As precipitation hits the ground, it may either soak into the ground (**infiltration**) or run off the surface. The amount that soaks in compared with the amount that runs off is called the **infiltration-runoff ratio**.

Figure 10–7 Rain shadow. Moisture-laden air in a trade wind cools as it rises over a mountain range, resulting in high precipitation on the windward slopes. Desert conditions result on the leeward side as the descending air warms and tends to evaporate water from the soil.

Runoff flows over the surface of the ground into streams and rivers, which make their way to the ocean or to inland seas. All the land area that contributes water to a particular stream or river is referred to as the **watershed** for that stream or river. All ponds, lakes, streams, rivers, and other waters on the surface of Earth are called **surface waters**.

Water that infiltrates has two alternatives (Fig. 10–3). The water may be held in the soil in an amount that depends on the water-holding capacity of the soil. This water, called **capillary water**, returns to the atmosphere either by evaporation from the soil or by transpiration through plants (a green water flow). The combination of evaporation and transpiration is referred to as **evapotranspiration**.

The second alternative is **percolation** (a blue water flow). Infiltrating water that is not held in the soil is called **gravitational water** because it trickles, or percolates, down through pores or cracks under the pull of gravity. Sooner or later, however, gravitational water encounters an impervious layer of rock or dense clay. It accumulates there, completely filling all the spaces above the impervious layer. This accumulated water is called **groundwater**, and its upper surface is the **water table** (Fig. 10–3). Gravitational water becomes groundwater when it reaches the water table in the same way that rainwater is called lake water once it hits the surface of a lake. Wells must be dug to depths below the water table. Groundwater, which is free to move, then seeps into the well and fills it to the level of the water table.

Recharge. Groundwater will seep laterally as it seeks its lowest level. Where a highway has been cut through rock layers, you can frequently observe groundwater seeping out. Layers of porous material through which groundwater moves are called **aquifers**. It is often difficult to determine the location of an aquifer. Many times these layers of porous rock are found between layers of impervious material, and the entire formation may be folded or fractured in various ways. Thus,

groundwater in aquifers may be found at various depths between layers of impervious rock. Also, the **recharge area**— the area where water enters an aquifer—may be many miles away from where the water leaves the aquifer. Underground aquifers hold some 99% of all *liquid* freshwater; the rest is in lakes, wetlands, and rivers.

Underground Purification. As water percolates through the soil, debris and bacteria from the surface are generally filtered out. However, water may dissolve and leach out certain minerals. Underground caverns, for example, are the result of the gradual leaching away of limestone (calcium carbonate). In most natural situations, the minerals that leach into groundwater are harmless. Indeed, calcium from limestone is considered beneficial to health. Thus, groundwater is generally high-quality freshwater that is safe for drinking. A few exceptions occur when the groundwater leaches minerals containing sulfide, arsenic, or other poisonous elements that make the water unsafe to drink.

Drawn by gravity, groundwater may move through aquifers until it finds some opening to the surface. These natural exits may be **seeps** or **springs**. In a seep, water flows out over a relatively wide area; in a spring, water exits the ground as a significant flow from a relatively small opening. As seeps and springs feed streams, lakes, and rivers, groundwater joins and becomes part of surface water. A spring will flow, however, only if it is *lower* than the water table. Whenever the water table drops below the level of the spring, the spring will dry up. Groundwater movement actually constitutes one of the loops in the hydrologic cycle.

Loops, Pools, and Fluxes in the Cycle

The hydrologic cycle consists of four physical processes: evaporation, condensation, precipitation, and gravitational flow. There are three principal loops in the cycle: (1) In the evapotranspiration loop (consisting of green water), the water evaporates and is returned by precipitation. On land, this water—the main source for natural ecosystems and rain-fed agriculture—is held as capillary water and then returns to the atmosphere by way of evapotranspiration. (2) In the surface runoff loop (containing blue water), the water runs across the ground surface and becomes part of the surface water system. (3) In the groundwater loop (also containing blue water), the water infiltrates, percolates down to join the groundwater, and then moves through aquifers, finally exiting through seeps, springs, or wells, where it rejoins the surface water. The surface runoff and groundwater loops are the usual focus for human water resource management.

In the hydrologic cycle, there are substantial exchanges of water among the land, the atmosphere, and the oceans; such exchanges are the cycle's fluxes. **Figure 10–8** shows estimates of these fluxes and of the sinks that hold water globally. About 97% of the Earth's water is in the oceans. Each year a volume of water evaporates off of the ocean surface that would cover it to 100 cm deep, about 425,000 cubic kilometers. Additional water evaporates from land and ice. All together the hydrologic cycle annually moves the equivalent of 25 times the water in the Great Lakes. Absent from Figure 10–8, however, are the human impacts on the cycle, which are large and growing.

Human Impacts on the Hydrologic Cycle

A large share of the environmental problems we face today stem from direct or indirect impacts on the water cycle. These impacts can be classified into four categories: (1) changes to Earth's surface, (2) changes to Earth's climate, (3) atmospheric pollution, and (4) withdrawals (or diversions) for human use.

Changes to the Surface of Earth. Imagine a temperate forest, its trees rooted in thick soil, drawing water from below, sending water up and out leaves, each tree stopping raindrops in a storm, letting them run down the trunk. The soil and leaf litter slow the water, letting it soak in. Then imagine cutting down the trees. What would happen? Put up a

Figure 10–8 Yearly water balance in the hydrologic cycle. The data show (1) the contribution of water from the oceans to the land via evaporation and then precipitation, (2) the movement of water from the land to the oceans via runoff and groundwater seepage, and (3) the net balance of water movement between terrestrial and oceanic regions of Earth. Values are in cubic kilometers per year. (*Source:* Figure 4.2 from *Earth Science*, 8th ed., by Edward Tarbuck and Frederick K. Lutgens, copyright © 1997 by the authors, reprinted by permission of Pearson Education, Inc., Upper Saddle River, NJ; revised with data from *GEO Yearbook 2003*, United Nations Environment Programme.)

TABLE 10–2 U.S. Demands on Freshwater

Use	Gallons (Liters) Used per Person per Day
Consumptive	
Irrigation and other agricultural use	485 (1,835)
Nonconsumptive	
Electric power production	477 (1,805)
Industrial use	72 (273)
Public supply and self-supply	164 (621)

Source: S. S. Hutson, N. L. Barber, J. F. Kenny, K. S. Linsey, D. S. Lumia, and M. A. Maupin, *Estimated Use of Water in the United States in 2000* (Circular 1268) (Reston, Va.: U.S. Geological Survey, 2004).

parking lot, a strip mall, a highway. Soon, the very processes that make up the water cycle will be altered. Alterations to the land surface stem primarily from removing vegetation, putting down impervious surfaces, and degrading wetlands.

Loss of Vegetation. In most natural ecosystems, precipitation is intercepted by vegetation and infiltrates into porous topsoil. From there, water provides the lifeblood of natural and human-created ecosystems. As forests are cleared or land is overgrazed and plants are not there to intercept rainfall, the pathway of the water cycle is shifted from infiltration and groundwater recharge to runoff, and the water runs into streams or rivers almost immediately. This causes floods, surface erosion, sediment, and other pollutants. Increased runoff means less infiltration and, therefore, less evapotranspiration and groundwater recharge. Lowered evapotranspiration means less moisture for local rainfall. Groundwater may be insufficient to keep springs flowing during dry periods. Dry, barren, and lifeless streambeds are typical of deforested regions—a tragedy for both the ecosystems and the humans who are dependent on the flow.

Taming Rivers and Wetlands. Wetlands function to store and release water in a manner similar to the way the groundwater reservoir does, only on a shorter time scale. Therefore, the destruction of wetlands has the same impact as deforestation: Flooding is increased, droughts are also increased, and waterways are polluted. In the Midwest, many fields have been provided with underground drainage pipes (tiles) to move water more quickly so the fields can be planted. This action lowers the water table, and the result is predictable: Rainwater is moved more quickly from the land to the rivers to the ocean. Channelizing rivers (by straightening them) has much the same effect (Chapter 7).

Building Impervious Surface. Roads, buildings, parking lots, and other structures actually cover the soil, so even a slow steady rain cannot infiltrate.[2] In some places,

impervious surface can cover 90% of the area. The lower 48 states have more than 43,000 square miles of impervious surface, about the size of Ohio (Figure 10–9).

Dams. One of the chief ways people try to lower flood risk is by building dams. Dams store water and have the opposite effect from many of the other land changes: They slow the movement of water to the ocean. However, because they are not wetlands, they often do not result in increased groundwater recharge. In dry areas, the pooling of water in reservoirs can leave water exposed to evaporation. Ironically, evaporative loss of water can cause regional water loss even when the object of the reservoir building was water provision during drought. Dams also cause some serious ecological problems. The Three Gorges Dam on the Yangtze River is a good example.

Flooding on the Yangtze River took more than 300,000 lives in the 20th century. This fact, combined with a need for power, prompted the building of one of the most spectacular dams in the world, the Three Gorges Dam. Completed in 2006, it is the largest hydroelectric project in the world (in terms of its maximum capacity), holding back 1.4 trillion cubic feet of water and generating as much as 84.7 billion kilowatt-hours of electricity annually, as much as the energy produced by burning 50 million tons of coal. The power generated raised the proportion of China's electricity generated from renewable sources from 7% to 15%. It will, for a time, bring much of the major flood potential of the Yangtze under control.

However, the dam has come with a high price. More than 1.3 million people have been displaced and relocated, and another 3 million to 4 million people will be relocated in coming years to make way for the 600-kilometer-long (410-mile long) reservoir. As the reservoir fills, lowering the Yangtze River flow by 50%, saltwater has crept upriver at the mouth of the river, ships have been stranded, pollutants have accumulated, and many fish populations have been reduced due to interference with breeding cycles. In spite

Figure 10–9 Impervious surface.
Impervious surface such as seen on roofs, roads and parking lots, decreases the amount of water that can go into the soil and recharge groundwater and increases the amount of water and the speed with which water runs off surfaces.

---

[2]Schueler, Thomas R. "The Importance of Imperviousness." Reprinted in *The Practice of Watershed Protection.* 2000. Center for Watershed Protection, Ellicott City, MD.

of the many drawbacks, Chinese officials continue with the project.

Moving Water to the Ocean. Overall, almost all human actions on land surface move water more quickly from rain to the ocean and lessen the amount going into groundwater. These actions contribute to both floods and droughts and increase erosion (Chapter 11). Floods are one of the most costly problems with the water cycle and have always been common. In many parts of the world, however, the frequency and severity of flooding are increasing—not because precipitation is greater, but because land use has changed, as we have described. Deforestation, cultivation, impervious surfaces, wetland loss, and other changes have increased, causing erosion and reducing infiltration. A recent study of floods in 56 developing countries has confirmed the "sponge" effect of forests, concluding that continued loss of forests will lead to greater loss of lives and economies for the developing countries where floods are frequent. For example, extreme flooding in Bangladesh (a very flat country only a few feet above sea level) is now more common because the Himalayan foothills in India and Nepal have been deforested. Due to sediment deposited from upriver erosion, the Ganges River basin has risen 5–7 meters (15–22 ft) in recent years. Floods are also increasing as a result of climate change, discussed shortly. **Figure 10–10** shows the impacts of flood waters in flooding that occurred in 2010 in Pakistan.

Solutions to water problems caused by land use changes include changes in requirements for new construction. One change in land use planning has been the requirement in many places to build flood retention ponds near new construction. These areas do not function as wetland habitat very well and often have pollutants and generalist weedy species. However, they do stop floods and allow infiltration. The protection of wetlands and river vegetation has been important to slowing run-off. Another solution is to grow more vegetation in cities. Urban gardening, rooftop gardens, and the planning of parks can increase soil infiltration in some cases and can also lower heat. There is also a move to go to new types of surfaces, especially for driveways, that are more environmentally friendly. These solutions will be discussed under sustainable cities as well (Chapter 23).

Climate Change. There is now unmistakable evidence that Earth's climate is warming because of the rise in greenhouse gases, and as this occurs, the water cycle is being altered (Chapter 18). A warmer climate means more evaporation from land surfaces, plants, and water bodies because evaporation increases with temperature. A wetter atmosphere means more and, frequently, heavier precipitation and more flood events. In effect, global warming is believed to be speeding up the hydrologic cycle. Already, the United States and Canada have experienced a 5–10% increase in precipitation over the past century. Regional and local changes are difficult to project; different computer models predict different outcomes for a given region. However, global climate models project a radically changing hydrological world as the 21st century unfolds (Chapter 18). The climatologists calculate that a warmer climate will likely generate more hurricanes and more droughts; extended droughts in the western United States are likely to occur more frequently. They also calculate that many of the currently water-stressed areas like East Africa and the Sahel region will get less water, which will bring large agricultural losses (Chapter 12).

Climate change has two other key impacts on water bodies. First, warm water has a greater volume. Warming the oceans contributes to sea level rise. Second is the movement of water from ice (the cryosphere) to liquid water. Glaciers and polar ice melt, and that water makes its way to the ocean. Both thermal expansion and melting ice contribute to the sea level rise that is already apparent. Melting ice adds freshwater, which is lighter than saltwater and does not mix well. The influx of great volumes of freshwater may affect ocean currents (see Sound Science, "What's New in the Water Cycle?"). Models suggest that oceans will rise about 2 to 3 feet (0.8 to 1 m) by 2100. While that does not sound like much, more than 630 million people live in low elevation areas, less than 10 meters above sea level. You can imagine that many will have to move and others will experience flooding.

Atmospheric Particles. Tiny atmospheric particles (aerosols) form nuclei that enable water to condense into droplets. The more such particles there are, the greater is the tendency for clouds to form. Anthropogenic aerosols are on the increase, primarily in the form of sulfates (from sulfur dioxide in coal), carbon (as soot), and dust. They form a brownish haze that is associated with industrial areas, tropical burning, and dust storms. Their impact on cloud formation is substantial, and where these aerosols occur, solar radiation to Earth's surface is reduced (so they have a cooling effect).

Their most significant impact, however, is on the hydrologic cycle. Because aerosols promote the formation of smaller-than-normal droplets in the clouds, aerosols actually *suppress* rainfall where they occur in abundance, even though they encourage cloud formation. As they do so, the

Figure 10–10 Flooding in Pakistan. The 2010 floods in Pakistan broke records and walls. Twenty million people were displaced.

SOUND SCIENCE

What's New in the Water Cycle?

The water cycle is pretty straightforward on a first approximation. Every fourth grader has studied at least the basics. But scientists still find more to study. The cutting edge in the study of hydrologic cycle science is in trying to figure out what will cause changes in the future, especially how the global water cycle will be affected by human actions.

Peter Wadhams, a professor of oceanographic physics at the University of Cambridge, England, wanted to know more about the ocean and climate change. One big question he was interested in is how the ocean responds to changes in the water cycle as ocean temperatures rise. There are large currents (thermohaline currents) in the water that move vast quantities of water around, in a slow-moving "ocean conveyor." Wind and tides provide the energy for these currents. The speed, volume, and direction of currents can be affected by climate change because of two principles: cold water is denser than warm, and freshwater is less dense than saltwater. When deep water rises, it brings nutrients toward the surface; as surface water sinks, it brings oxygen down. Waters warmed in the tropics redistribute heat to the cold poles.

These currents help warm Europe and the east coast of North America. But there may be changes in the future. As glacial melt water and rain run-off from Siberia increase in the Arctic, cold freshwater forms a layer on top of the saltwater there. Enough freshwater might change the ocean conveyor, some scientists have hypothesized. In 2005, Wadhams and his colleagues investigated the cold dense waters of the Greenland Sea where columns of very dense

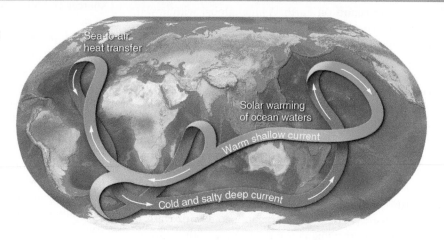

Sea-to-air heat transfer

Solar warming of ocean waters

Warm shallow current

Cold and salty deep current

water form. These "chimneys" (which can be 100 km in diameter and which last for months) carry water down more than 2400 m towards the sea floor, contributing to the movement of masses of cold water in the deep ocean. But instead of the dozen gigantic rivers of water flowing downward that they had found other times, they found only two. Does this mean the deep ocean currents will slow? Is the change long term? Right now, Wadhams and others aren't sure what will happen. Some scientists say any shift in the thermohaline circulation is likely to occur slowly; others think a slowing of the conveyor could occur more abruptly.

The Greenland Sea isn't the only place marine currents are studied. In 2012, scientists from the University of Washington, including graduate student Sarah Purkey, explored the deepest, coldest waters on Earth—off of Antarctica. They found that those waters,

dubbed the Antarctic Bottom Water, have declined in volume by 60% (losing an equivalent of 50 times the flow of the Mississippi River) over the past several decades. The deep ocean is becoming less cold and dense, and scientists expect this to change the way the oceans work. Even though the basic hydrologic cycle is well known, the details of how it works and what changes we might expect in a changing environment are still part of today's science. Wadhams, Purkey and all of their colleagues are on the cutting edge of sound science.

Sources: Wunsch, C. (2002). "What is the thermohaline circulation?" *Science* 298(5596): 1179–1181. doi:10.1126/science.1079329. PMID 12424356.
Wadhams, P. (2004). "Convective chimneys in the Greenland Sea: A review of recent observations." *Oceanography and Marine Biology* 42, 1–27
Purkey, S. G., & Johnson, G. C. "Global contraction of Antarctic Bottom Water between the 1980s and 2000s.". *Journal of Climate*, 2012

atmospheric cleansing that would normally clear the aerosols is suppressed, and they remain in the atmosphere longer than usual. With suppressed rainfall comes drier conditions, so more dust and smoke (and more aerosols) are the result. Ironically, this type of air pollution works just opposite to the impact of the greenhouse gases on climate and the hydrologic cycle. Again, there are significant differences; the aerosol impact is more local, whereas the impact of greenhouse gases on climate and the hydrologic cycle is more global. In addition, the greenhouse gases are gradually accumulating in the atmosphere, while the aerosols have a lifetime measured in days.

Withdrawal for Human Use. Finally, there are many problems related to the fourth impact, diversion and

withdrawals of water for human use (as we make use of surface waters and groundwater). We will discuss these impacts next, as we look at how humans try to have enough clean freshwater—and not too much.

10.3 Water: Getting Enough, Controlling Excess

Meeting water needs is a primary goal in our rapidly crowding world. We are seeing both stresses and successes. Between 1990 and 2012, 2 billion people were given access to clean drinking water, an achievement that met the Millennium Development Goal for water. However, water needs are very serious in many countries (Fig. 10–11).

According to the Millennium Ecosystem Assessment, human use now appropriates about 3,600 cubic kilometers of water per year, which represents 27% of the accessible freshwater runoff on Earth. Annual global withdrawal is expected to rise by about 10% every decade. While the human population tripled in the 20th century, use of water increased sixfold, much of that increase to enable water intensive higher-yielding agriculture.

The U.S. Geological Service periodically prepares estimates of major uses of freshwater in the United States (Table 10–2). It is significant that Americans use less water now than they did in 1980, even with population increases (Fig. 10–12). Most of the water used in homes and industries is for washing and flushing away unwanted materials, and the water used in electric power production is for taking away waste heat. These are **nonconsumptive water uses** because the water, though now contaminated with wastes, remains available to humans for the same or other uses if its quality is adequate or if it can be treated to remove undesirable materials. In contrast, irrigation is a **consumptive water use** because the applied water does not return to the local water resource. It can only percolate into the ground or return to the atmosphere through evapotranspiration. In either case, the water does reenter the overall water cycle but is gone from human control.

Worldwide, the largest use of water is for irrigation (70%), second is for industry (20%), and third is for direct human use (10%) (Fig. 10–13). These percentages vary greatly from one region to another, depending on natural precipitation and the degree to which the region is developed (Fig. 10–10). Most increases in withdrawal are due to increases in irrigated lands. In the United States, irrigation accounts for 65% of freshwater consumption.

Sources

About 20% of domestic water comes from groundwater sources and 80% from surface waters (rivers, lakes, reservoirs) in the United States. Before municipal water supplies were developed, people drew their water from whatever source they could: wells, rivers, lakes, or rainwater. This approach is still used in rural areas in the developing countries. Women in many of these countries walk long distances each day to fetch water. Because surface waters and shallow wells often receive runoff, they frequently are polluted with various wastes, including animal excrement and human sewage likely to contain pathogens (disease-causing organisms). In fact, an estimated 90% of wastewater in developing countries is released to surface waters without any treatment. Yet, unsafe as it is, this polluted water is the only water available for an estimated 1.1 billion people in less developed countries (Fig. 10–14 on page 252). It is commonly consumed without purification, but not without consequences: According to the UN World Health Organization, contaminated water is responsible for the deaths of more than 1.6 million people in developing countries each year, 90% of whom are children. Increasing water sanitation is part of the Millennium Development Goals.

Technologies. In the industrialized countries, the collection, treatment, and distribution of water are highly developed. Larger municipalities rely primarily on surface-water sources, while smaller water systems tend to use groundwater. In the former, dams are built across rivers to create reservoirs, which hold water in times of excess flow and can be drawn down at times of lower flow. In addition, dams and reservoirs may offer power generation, recreation, and flood control. Reservoirs created by dams on rivers are also major sources of water for irrigation. In this case, no treatment is required. However, water for

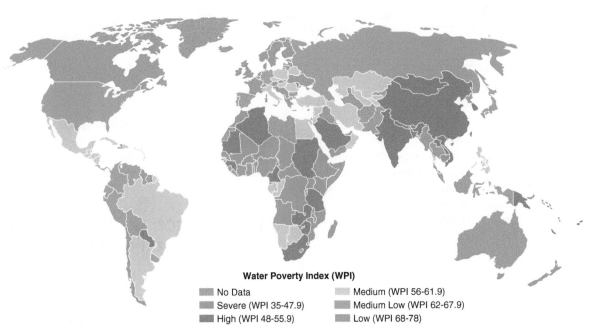

Water Poverty Index (WPI)

- No Data
- Severe (WPI 35-47.9)
- High (WPI 48-55.9)
- Medium (WPI 56-61.9)
- Medium Low (WPI 62-67.9)
- Low (WPI 68-78)

Figure 10–11 Water Poverty Index. Patterns of water availability across the Earth involve not only precipitation but also human population uses.

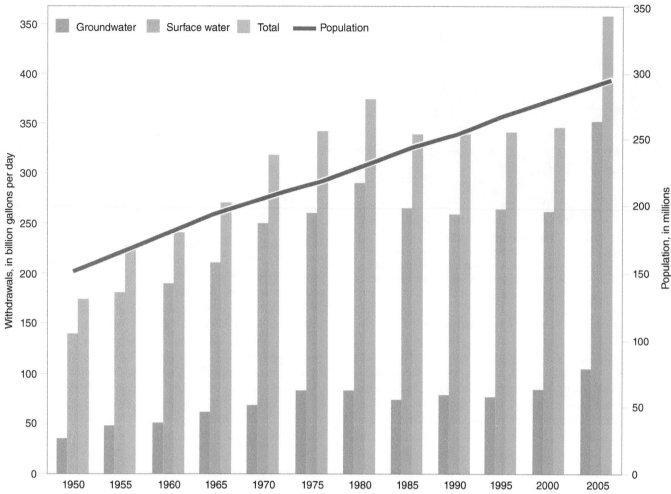

Figure 10–12 **U.S. trends in population and freshwater withdrawals.** Since 1980, Americans have been using less water, even though the population has increased substantially. (*Source:* S. S. Hutson, N. L. Barber, J. F. Kenny, K. S. Linsey, D. S. Lumia, and M. A. Maupin, *Estimated Use of Water in the United States in 2000* (Circular 1268) (Reston, VA: U.S. Geological Survey, 2004).)

municipal use is piped from the reservoir to a treatment plant, where it is treated to kill pathogens and remove undesirable materials, as shown in **Figure 10–15.** After treatment, the water is distributed through the water system to homes, schools, and industries. Wastewater, collected by the sewage system, is carried to a sewage-treatment plant, where it is treated before being

discharged into a natural waterway (Chapter 20). Often, wastewater is discharged into the same river from which it was withdrawn, but farther downstream.

Whenever possible, both water and sewage systems are laid out so that gravity maintains the flow through the system. This arrangement minimizes pumping costs and

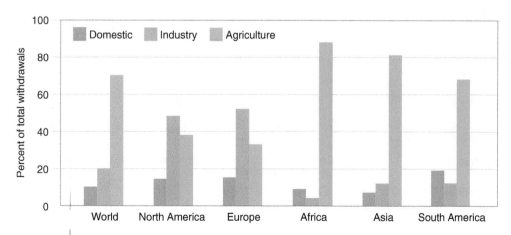

Figure 10–13 **Regional usage of water.** The percentage used in each category varies with the climate and relative development of the region. A less developed region with a dry climate (e.g., Africa) uses most of its water for irrigation, whereas an industrialized region (e.g., Europe) requires the largest percentage for industry.

Figure 10–14 Water in the developing world. In many villages and cities of the developing world, people withdraw water from rivers, streams, and ponds. These sources are often contaminated with pathogens and other pollutants. This Kenyan man is collecting water from a river used by people and animals.

increases reliability. On major rivers, such as the Mississippi, water is reused many times. Each city along the river takes water, treats it, uses it, treats it again, and then returns it to the river. In developing nations, the wastewater frequently is discharged with minimal or no treatment. Thus, as the water moves downstream, each city has a higher load of pollutants to contend with than the previous city had, and ecosystems at the end of the line may be severely affected by the

pollution. Pollutants include industrial wastes as well as pollutants from households because industries and residences generally utilize the same water and sewer systems.

Smaller public drinking-water systems frequently rely on groundwater, which often may be used with minimal treatment because it has already been purified by percolation through soil. More than 1.5 billion people around the world rely on groundwater for their domestic use. Both surface water and groundwater are replenished through the water cycle (Fig. 10–3). Therefore, in theory at least, these two sources of water represent a sustainable or renewable (self-replenishing) resource, but they are not inexhaustible. Over the past 50 years, groundwater use has outpaced the rate of aquifer recharge in many areas of the world.

Is Bottled Water the Answer? One-half of Americans buy bottled water, which is sometimes seen as a solution to limited water availability, particularly after disasters. Sales of bottled water were $34 billion (about 50 billion bottles) in 2008 in the United States alone. Unfortunately, use of bottled water has a number of negative environmental effects. First, the bottling can occur on a large scale in areas where locals also want to use the water. Does a company have the right to pump out millions of gallons of water from an aquifer? This has been disputed. For example, after many years in the courts, in 2009, Michigan Citizens for Water Conservation won a lawsuit to keep Nestlé Waters North America, Inc., from pumping 400 gallons of water a minute from a

(a) Water is often taken from a river or reservoir, piped to the treatment plant, treated, used, then returned to the source.

(b) At the treatment plant, water is treated to kill pathogens and remove undesirable material.

Figure 10–15 Municipal water use and treatment. The stages of water treatment are outlined in the figure. Water is taken from a river or reservoir, piped to a treatment plant, treated with chemicals, filtered, adjusted for pH, and stored before being used.

groundwater supply in Michigan. The proposed pumping was drying a local stream. Nestlé was allowed to pump, but at a reduced rate. Bottled water also requires a great deal of energy, for the making of plastic bottles and the transportation of the product. Overall, bottled water may be good for emergencies but is not a good solution for a lack of drinking water generally.

Surface Waters

Surface waters are diverted for use, slowed and held in dams, and moved along swiftly by levees, impervious surfaces, channelized rivers, and devegetation. Of these effects, the use of dams is the most prominent for keeping and using surface water.

Dams and the Environment. To trap and control flowing rivers, more than 48,000 large dams (more than 50 feet high) have been built around the world. Dams together have a storage capacity around 6,000 km³, serving 30–40% of the world's irrigated land and providing 19% of the world's total electricity supply. Of the 42,600 cubic kilometers of annual runoff in the hydrologic cycle, only 31% is accessible for withdrawal because many rivers are in remote locations and much of the remaining water is required for navigation, flood control, and the generation of hydroelectric power. Sixty-five percent of ocean bound freshwater is stopped by dams at some point. The large dams have an enormous direct social impact, leading to the displacement of an estimated 40 million to 80 million people worldwide (primarily in China and India) and preventing access by local people to the goods and services of the now-buried ecosystems.

Dam Impacts. The United States is home to some 75,000 dams at least 6 feet in height and an estimated 2 million

smaller structures (**Fig. 10–16**). These have been built to run mills (now an obsolete usage), control floods, generate electric power, and provide water for municipal and agricultural use. These dams have enormous ecological impacts. When a river is dammed, valuable freshwater habitats, such as waterfalls, rapids, and prime fish runs, are lost. When the river's flow is diverted to cities or croplands, the waterway below the diversion is deprived of that much water.

The impact on fish and other aquatic organisms is obvious, but the ecological ramifications go far beyond the river. Wildlife that depends on the water or on food chains involving aquatic organisms is also adversely affected. Wetlands dry up, resulting in frequent die-offs of waterfowl and other wildlife that depended on those habitats. Fish such as salmon, which swim from the ocean far upriver to spawn, are seriously affected by the reduced water level and have problems getting around the dam, even one equipped with fish ladders (a stepwise series of pools on the side of the dam, where the water flows in small falls that fish can negotiate). If the fish do get upriver, the hatchlings have similar problems getting back to the ocean. On the Columbia and Snake rivers, juvenile salmon suffer 95% mortality in their journey to the sea as a result of negotiating the dams and reservoirs that block their way.

Glen Canyon Dam is an example of a large dam with significant environmental effects. On the Columbia River, the dam provides hydropower and created the second largest artificial lake in America: Lake Powell. An environmental impact study in the late 1980s and early 1990s concluded that the operation of the Glen Canyon Dam on the Colorado River had seriously damaged the downstream ecology of the Colorado River and its recreational resources (hiking, river rafting). In response, Congress passed the Grand Canyon Protection Act in 1992, which required a process of "adaptive management" that would adjust

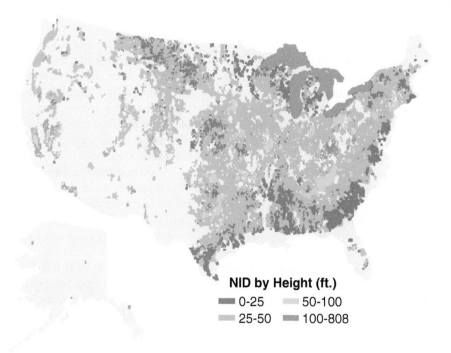

NID by Height (ft.)
- 0-25
- 25-50
- 50-100
- 100-808

Figure 10–16 **Number of dams in the United States.** Each point represents a dam; the colors tell the height. (Source National Inventory of Dams Map)

Figure 10–17 Removal of a dam. The 2011 removal of the Conditt Dam on the White Salmon River in Washington state cleared the way for salmon to spawn upstream.

water-release rates in a manner designed to enhance the ecological and recreational values of the river. This rule has helped balance the needs of different stakeholders.

Dams Gone. Increasingly, people are recognizing the costs of dams and finding them to be unacceptable. Removing a dam is not easy, however. Legal complexities abound where long-existing uses of a dam (to control floods or to provide irrigation water or lake-like still water for recreation) conflict with the expected advantages of removal (to reestablish historic fisheries such as salmon and steelhead runs or to restore the river for recreational and aesthetic use). Practical problems also exist. However, more than 714 dams have already been removed. **Figure 10–17** shows the successful removal of a dam on the White Salmon River.

Diversion of Surface Water. In addition to dams, humans move freshwater through diversion projects to take water to places where it is scarce. One example is the diversion project in China mentioned at the beginning of the chapter. When water is moved from one watershed to another, it is called an interbasin water transfer. The largest diversion project ever proposed for North America was the North American Water and Power Alliance (NAWAPA) XXI project. Designed in the 1950s, the ambitious project was proposed to bring water from Alaska, down through Canada, and into the dry Midwest and western states through 369 separate construction projects. As proposed, it would double the water available to the lower 48 states. Public sentiment in Canada has run against the project, and it has been shelved. China has discovered already, though, that large water diversion projects can bring unexpected environmental costs including water pollution or the effects of water loss in the original rivers and lakes.

Impacts on Estuaries. When river waters are diverted on their way to the sea, serious impacts are seen in **estuaries**—bays and rivers in which freshwater mixes with seawater. Estuaries are among the most productive ecosystems on Earth; they are rich breeding grounds for many species of fish, shellfish, and waterfowl. As a river's flow is diverted (say, to irrigate fields), less freshwater enters and flushes the estuary. Consequently, the salt concentration increases, profoundly affecting the estuary's ecology. This is exactly what is happening in San Francisco Bay. More than 60% of the freshwater that once flowed from rivers into the bay has been diverted for irrigation in the Central Valley (2.5 million acres irrigated) and for municipal use in southern California (25 million people served). In dry years (which are becoming more common), the farms and municipalities remove a third of the water that would normally flow through the delta into San Francisco Bay. Without the freshwater flows, saltwater from the Pacific has intruded into the bay, with devastating consequences. Chinook salmon runs have almost disappeared. Sturgeon, Dungeness crab, and striped bass populations are greatly reduced. Exotic species of plants and invertebrates have replaced many native species, and the tidal wetlands have been reduced to only 8% of their former extent.

Upriver from the bay, more than a thousand miles of levees protect farmlands that have sunk 20 feet or more below sea level due to compacting. If the levees collapsed during an earthquake, massive amounts of saltwater would be sucked upriver and would shut down the huge pumps that divert freshwater to the cities and farms. Given these major problems, the CALFED Bay-Delta Program was established, according to its mission statement, to "develop and implement a long-term comprehensive plan that will restore ecological health and improve water management for beneficial uses of the Bay-Delta System." However, this is not working, as major stakeholders (farmers, government agencies, environmental groups) have not been able to agree on changes to the delta recommended by scientists.

(a)

(b)

(c)

Figure 10–18 **Exploitation of an aquifer.** (a) Pumping up water from the Ogallala aquifer has made this arid region of the United States into some of the most productive farmland in the country. (b) Water is applied by means of center-pivot irrigation, in which the water is pumped from a central well to a self-powered boom that rotates around the well, spraying water as it goes. (c) An aerial photograph shows the extent of center-pivot irrigation throughout the region. Groundwater depletion will bring an end to this kind of farming.

The problem is not limited to the United States. The southeastern end of the Mediterranean Sea was formerly flushed by water from the Nile River. Because this water is now held back and diverted for irrigation by the Aswan High Dam in Egypt, that part of the Mediterranean is suffering severe ecological consequences (such as severe coastal erosion) as sediments normally flowing out to the coast are kept behind the dam.

Groundwater

Groundwater is the large unseen storage of water that accumulated slowly in porous rock over millennia. As mentioned before, some 99% of all liquid freshwater is in underground aquifers. Of this groundwater, more than three-fourths has a recharge rate of centuries or more. Such groundwater is considered "nonrenewable." Because groundwater supplies are vital for domestic use and especially for agriculture, they are a resource that requires management.

Groundwater Levels. The agriculture of the midwestern United States makes the country the breadbasket for the world. Water to support that agriculture is mined from deep underground. Within the seven-state High Plains region of the

United States, the Ogallala aquifer supplies irrigation water to 4.2 million hectares (10.4 million acres), one-fifth of the irrigated land in the nation (Fig. 10–18). This aquifer is probably the largest in the world, but it is mostly "fossil water," recharged during the last ice age. The recent withdrawal rate has been about 28 billion cubic meters (23 million acre-ft) per year, two orders of magnitude higher than the recharge rate. Water tables have dropped 30–60 meters (100–200 ft) and continue to drop at the rate of 6 feet per year. Irrigated farming has already come to a halt in some sections, and it is predicted that over the next 20 years another 1.2 million hectares (3 million acres) in this region will be abandoned or converted to dryland farming (ranching and the production of forage crops) because of water depletion.

Renewable groundwater is replenished by the percolation of precipitation water, so it is vulnerable to variations in precipitation. In tapping groundwater, we are tapping large, but not unlimited, natural reservoirs, contained within specific aquifer systems. Its sustainability ultimately depends on balancing withdrawals with rates of recharge. For most of the groundwater in arid regions, there is essentially no recharge. The resource must be considered nonrenewable. Like oil, it can be removed, but any water removed today will be unavailable for the future. Groundwater depletion has several undesirable consequences.

Falling Water Tables. The simplest indication that groundwater withdrawals are exceeding recharge is a falling water table, a situation that is common throughout the world. Because irrigation consumes far and away the largest amount of freshwater, depleting water resources will ultimately have its most significant impact on crop production. Although running out of water is the obvious eventual conclusion of overdrawing groundwater, falling water tables can bring on other problems.

Diminishing Surface Water. Surface waters are affected by falling water tables. In various wetlands, for instance, the water table is essentially at or slightly above the ground surface. When water tables drop, these wetlands dry up, with the ecological results described earlier. Further, as water tables drop, springs and seeps dry up as well, diminishing even streams and rivers to the point of dryness. Thus, excessive groundwater removal creates the same results as the diversion of surface water.

Land Subsidence. Over the ages, groundwater has leached cavities in the ground. Where these spaces are filled with water, the water helps support the overlying rock and soil. As the water table drops, however, this support is lost. Then there may be a gradual settling of the land, a phenomenon known as **land subsidence**. The rate of sinking may be 10–15 centimeters (6–12 in.) per year. In some areas of the San Joaquin Valley in California, land has settled as much as 9 meters (29 ft) because of groundwater removal. Land subsidence causes building foundations, roadways, and water and sewer lines to crack. In coastal areas, subsidence causes flooding unless levees are built for protection. For example, where a 10,000-square-kilometer (4,000-mi^2) area in the Houston–Galveston Bay region of Texas is gradually sinking because of groundwater removal, coastal properties are being abandoned as they are gradually being inundated by the sea. Land subsidence is also a serious problem in many other places throughout the world. When it happens in cities, underground pipes break, causing leaks and wastage of domestic water. Sewage pipes can also fracture, contaminating the groundwater aquifer. Subsidence is a serious problem in many cities in developing countries, where the public water supply is not dependable.

Another kind of land subsidence, a **sinkhole**, may develop suddenly and dramatically (**Fig. 10–19**). A sinkhole results when an underground cavern, drained of its supporting groundwater, suddenly collapses. Sinkholes may be 300 feet (91 m) across and as deep as 150 feet. The problem of sinkholes is particularly severe in the southeastern United States, where groundwater has leached numerous passageways and caverns through ancient beds of underlying limestone. An estimated 4,000 sinkholes have formed in Alabama alone, some of which have "consumed" buildings, livestock, and sections of highways.

Saltwater Intrusion. Another problem resulting from dropping water tables is **saltwater intrusion**. In coastal

Figure 10–19 Sinkhole. The removal of groundwater may drain an underground cavern until the roof, no longer supported by water pressure, collapses. The result is the sudden development of a sinkhole, such as this one, which appeared in Plant City, Florida, on May 29, 2000.

regions, springs of outflowing groundwater may lie under the ocean. As long as a high water table maintains a sufficient head of pressure in the aquifer, freshwater will flow into the ocean. Thus, wells near the ocean yield freshwater (**Fig. 10–20a**). However, lowering the water table or removing groundwater at a rapid rate may reduce the pressure in the aquifer, permitting saltwater to flow back into the aquifer and hence into wells (**Fig. 10–20b**). Saltwater intrusion is a serious problem in many European countries along the Mediterranean coast.

10.4 Water Stewardship: Supply and Public Policy

The hydrologic cycle is entirely adequate to meet human needs for freshwater because it processes several times as much water as we require today. However, the water is often not distributed where it is most needed, and the result is a persistent scarcity of water in many parts of the world. In the developing countries, there is still a deficit of infrastructure, such as wells, water-treatment systems, and (sometimes) large dams, for capturing and distributing safe drinking water. Despite the growing negative impacts of overdrawing water resources, expanding populations create an ever-increasing demand for additional water for agriculture, industry, and municipal use. Water for food dominates the current water demand, estimated at 6,800 cubic kilometers per year. Of this, some 5,000 cubic kilometers are used as green water flow in the world's rain-fed agriculture and 1,800 cubic kilometers as blue water flow in the form of irrigation water withdrawn from rivers, lakes, and groundwater. It is estimated that 4,500 cubic kilometers (of the total 6,800 km^3) are attributed to the developing countries to fulfill current food needs.

If we assume that virtually all of the future population increase will be in the developing countries, then so also will be the increased need for food.

Figure 10–20 **Saltwater intrusion.** (a) Where aquifers open into the ocean, freshwater is maintained in the aquifer by the pressure of freshwater inland. (b) Excessive removal of water may reduce the pressure so that saltwater moves into the aquifer.

(a)

(b)

What are the possibilities for meeting existing needs and growing demands in a sustainable way? Planners call for a **Blue Revolution,** a radical change in the way we use water. There are only about five options: (1) capture more of the runoff water, (2) gain better access to existing groundwater aquifers, (3) desalt seawater, (4) conserve present supplies by using less water, and (5) make food production more efficient. Making matters more difficult, there is no single U.S. agency responsible for forming public policy on such water supply issues.

Capturing Runoff

While individuals may put out rain barrels to capture runoff from roofs and villages may use cisterns to catch rainwater, dams are the best example of surface water capture and are widely used. China is the best example of both the pros and cons of dam building, which we have already discussed. In an effort to provide hydropower while cutting greenhouse gas emissions, China has committed to an aggressive program of dam building. New dam projects threaten China's remaining biodiversity. In the United States, protection has been accorded to some rivers with the passage of the Wild and Scenic Rivers Act of 1968, which keeps rivers designated as "wild

and scenic" from being dammed or affected by other harmful operations. There are 252 designated wild and scenic rivers in the United States. Some 12,600 miles of rivers have been protected. The numerous large and small dams across the country have affected some 600,000 miles of our rivers, by comparison. Those rivers designated as wild and scenic are in many ways equivalent to national parks.[3]

Tapping More Groundwater

Already, more than 2 billion people depend on groundwater supplies. In many areas, groundwater use exceeds aquifer recharge, leading to shortages as the water table drops below pump levels. Groundwater depletion is considered the single greatest threat to irrigated agriculture, and it is happening in many parts of the world. India, China, West Asia, countries of the former Soviet Union, the western United States, and the Arabian Peninsula are all experiencing declining water tables. Calculations by the International Water Management Institute suggest that an expansion of

---

[3]Wild and Scenic Rivers: Leading the Charge to Protect the Nation's Last, Best Rivers. American Rivers. http://www.americanrivers.org/our-work/protecting-rivers/wild-and-scenic/ Sept 2012.

irrigation on the order of 20% might be possible, but this will not meet the food needs in the developing countries by 2030.[4]

Exploiting renewable groundwater will continue to be an option, but it is unlikely to provide great increases in water supply because these same sustainable supplies, recharged by annual precipitation, are being increasingly polluted. Agricultural chemicals such as fertilizers and pesticides, animal wastes, and industrial chemicals readily enter groundwater, making groundwater pollution as much of a threat to domestic water use as depletion. For example, some 60,000 square kilometers of aquifers in western and central Europe will likely be contaminated with pesticides and fertilizers within the next 50 years. Also, India and Bangladesh are plagued with arsenic-contaminated groundwater, which has extracted a heavy toll in sickness and death for millions in those countries.

Desalting Seawater

The world's oceans are an inexhaustible source of water, not only because they are vast, but also because any water removed from them will ultimately flow back in. Not many plants can be grown in full seawater, however, and although researchers are developing salt-tolerant plants via genetic modification, we are not there yet. Thus, with increasing water shortages and most of the world's population living near coasts, there is a growing trend toward **desalination** (desalting) of seawater for domestic use. More than 15,000 desalination plants have been installed in some 120 countries, especially in the Middle East. Many Australian cities, such as Perth, also rely on desalination. Perth relies on water from the Indian Ocean, desalinized in a plant powered by wind turbines.

Two technologies—microfiltration (reverse osmosis, or RO) and distillation—are commonly used for desalination. Smaller desalination plants generally employ microfiltration, in which great pressure forces seawater through a reverse osmosis membrane filter fine enough to remove the salt. Larger facilities, particularly those that can draw from a source of waste heat (for example, from electrical power plants), generally use distillation (evaporation and condensation of vapor). Efficiency is gained by using the heat given off by condensing water to heat the incoming water. Even where waste heat is used, however, the costs of building and maintaining the plant, which is subject to corrosion from seawater, are considerable. Costs can be two to four times what most city dwellers in the United States currently pay, but it is still not a high price to pay for drinking water in areas of the world that are prone to drought and is much cheaper than bottled water.

In January 2008, the Tampa Bay seawater desalination plant was completed, signaling a new day for desalination (Fig. 10–21). The plant is the country's first ever built to serve as a primary water source. The plant uses salty cooling water

Figure 10–21 Desalination plant. The Israel Ashkelon Seawater desalination plant is the largest reverse osmosis desalinization plant in the world, producing 330,000 m3/d of drinking water.

from a power plant and reverse osmosis to produce 25 million gallons of drinking water per day (MGD), providing Pasco County, Pinellas County, St. Petersburg, and other cities with some 10% of their drinking water. The Tampa Bay region has experienced chronic water shortages and is exploiting an opportunity that has attracted worldwide attention. The water is expected to cost Tampa Bay Water $2.49 per 1,000 gallons wholesale over 30 years—more than the $1 per 1,000 gallons for existing groundwater sources, but still a reasonable cost.

Although the higher cost might cause some people to cut back on watering lawns and to implement other conservation measures, most people in the United States could afford desalinized water without unduly altering their lifestyles. For irrigating croplands, however, the higher cost of desalinized seawater would probably be prohibitive, except possibly for high-value cash crops like greenhouse flowers or vegetables.

The world's largest RO desalination plant employs a unique energy recovery device (a rotary displacement pump) that is helping greatly to make desalination affordable. It was built at Hadara, between Tel Aviv and Haifa in Israel, and will produce 72 MGD, with a potential expansion to 94 MGD. The largest distillation plant is the Jebel Ali desalination plant in the United Arab Emirates, producing 215 MGD, or 2,500 gallons per second.

Using Less Water

A developing-nation family living where water must be carried several miles from a well finds that one gallon per person per day is sufficient to provide for all of its essential needs, including cooking and washing. Yet, a typical household in the United States consumes an average of 380 liters (100 gal) per person per day. If all indirect uses are added (especially irrigation), this figure increases to 4,900 liters (1,300 gal) per person per day. Similarly, a peasant farmer may irrigate by carefully ladling water onto each plant with a dipper, while typical modern irrigation floods the whole field. The way water resource planners think is beginning

[4]M. Falkenmark and J. Rockström, "The New Blue and Green Water Paradigm: Breaking Ground for Water Resources Planning and Management," *Journal of Water Resources Planning and Management* 132 (May/June 2006): pg 131

to change, however: Instead of asking how much water we "need" and where can we get it, people are now asking how much water is available and how can we best use it. The good news is that the U.S. rate of water use per capita has actually begun to drop, which can be attributed to some well-needed water conservation strategies already put in place. Some specific measures that are being implemented to reduce water withdrawals are described in the next several subsections.

Agriculture. Agriculture is far and away the largest consumer of freshwater—some 40% of the world's food is grown in irrigated soils, which produce 100–400% higher yields than traditional farming. Most present-day irrigation wastes huge amounts of water, and in fact, half of it never yields any food. Where irrigation water is applied by traditional flood or center-pivot systems, 30–50% is lost to evaporation, percolation, or runoff. Several strategies have been employed recently to cut down on this waste. One is the surge flow method, in which computers control the periodic release of water, in contrast to the continuous-flood method. Surge flow can cut water use in half.

Drip, Drip. Another water-saving method is the drip irrigation system, a network of plastic pipes with pinholes that literally drip water at the base of each plant (Fig. 10–22). Although such systems are costly, they waste much less water. Also, they have the added benefit of retarding salinization (see Chapter 11). Studies have shown that drip irrigation can reduce water use 30–70%, while actually increasing crop yields, compared with traditional flooding methods. Although drip irrigation is spreading worldwide, especially in arid lands such as Israel and Australia, 97% of the irrigation in the United States, and 99% throughout the world, is still done by traditional flood or center-pivot methods.

The reason that so few farms have changed over to drip irrigation systems is that it costs about $1,000 per acre to install them. In comparison, water for irrigation is heavily subsidized by the government, so farmers pay next to nothing for it. Therefore, it makes financial sense to use the cheapest system for distributing water, even if it is wasteful. Calculations of construction costs and energy subsidies to provide irrigation water to farmers indicate an annual subsidy of $4.4 billion for the 11 million acres of irrigated land in the western United States, an average of $400 an acre. Governments collect an average of 10% or less of the actual cost in water fees charged to farmers. Reducing this subsidy would greatly encourage water conservation through the use of more efficient irrigation technologies.

Treadle Pumps. In the developing countries, irrigation often bypasses the rural poor, who are at the greatest risk for hunger and malnutrition. Affordable irrigation technologies can be remarkably successful, as in Bangladesh, where low-cost treadle pumps (Fig. 10–23) enable farmers to irrigate their rice paddies and vegetable fields at a cost of less than $35 a system. The pump is worked with the feet like a step exercise machine, is locally manufactured, and has been adopted by millions. The irrigation it affords makes it possible for farmers to irrigate small plots during

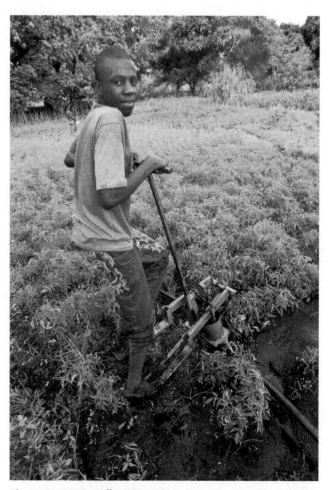

Figure 10–23 Treadle pump. This treadle pump in Zambia is operated like a step exercise machine. Millions of these pumps now allow rural farmers to raise crops during dry seasons.

Figure 10–22 Drip irrigation. Irrigation consumes the most water. Drip irrigation offers a conservative method of applying water.

STEWARDSHIP

The Energy/Water/Food Trade: Waste One, Waste Them All

Ever stand in a public restroom and see someone run the sink water and not turn it off? What about seeing someone leave their car idling? Or throwing food in the trash? Drive you crazy? It should! Because the way the world is intertwined, if you waste one (energy, water, or food), you waste the others or at least waste the opportunity to obtain them. It works this way:

It takes energy to get clean freshwater, especially if you live in a dry area or a place with water pollution. The water might have to be cleaned or moved long distances. Bottled water is even more energy intensive. For example, in California, the California State Water Project is the largest single user of energy in the state. One of its activities is moving water over the Tehachapi Mountains, which requires as much energy as a third of the household energy use in the region. Wasting water means you waste the energy it took to get it, clean it, and heat it, too. Because we need to be efficient with energy so we can avoid greater harm to the environment, water waste isn't just about the water—it hurts the whole system.

It takes water to get energy. This is true when water is used in cooling (nuclear plants), in coal mining, and in coal power plants. The newest way of getting natural gas, called hydraulic fracturing, uses enormous amounts of water. There are more than 35,000 wells fractured in the United States each year, using an estimated 70 billion to 140 billion gallons of water. When the water is used, it is mixed with toxic chemicals and injected deep into the Earth, rather than returned to the regional water cycle. The use of water for fracking, as this process is called, directly competes with other uses of water such as agriculture and has been the source of lawsuits in dry states such as Wyoming and Montana.

Another example is biofuels. Crops used for biofuels such as ethanol are usually raised using

land and water that could have been used for food crops. Their use to fuel vehicles drove up the cost of basic food staples in 2007, contributing to the world food crisis (Chapter 12). Wasting energy might mean we have to obtain more energy and use more water, making it harder to produce adequate food.

We use water and energy to grow, store, and move food. Wasting food means that water and energy cannot be used for something else. It takes 1,300 liters of water to produce a kilogram of wheat, 3,000 liters for a kilogram of eggs, and 15,500 liters for a kilogram of beef. It also takes energy to store food and a great deal to transport it. The average American foodstuff travels 1,500 miles. As much as 40% of the energy used in food production is in the manufacture of pesticides and fertilizers (Chapters 12 and 13). But much of the recent increase in food energy cost is due to increased processing and packaging, such as for single-serving foods.

Food is often wasted. A Food and Agriculture Organization (FAO)–commissioned study found that 1.3 billion tons, roughly a third, of the food we produce for human consumption is wasted each year. This is the equivalent of half of the world cereals crop. Some food waste is lost at harvest or in storage or processing. Some is in stores and at consumers' tables. Any way you work it, if we can save food, we can feed more people and use less water and energy.

Sources: NRDC. (2004). "Energy Down the Drain: The Hidden Costs of California's Water Supply." http://www.nrdc.org/water/conservation/edrain/edrain.pdf; EPA. (2011). Draft Plan to Study the Potential Impacts of Hydraulic Fracturing on Drinking Water Resources. Report Number: EPA/600/D-11/001

Chapagain, A. K., Hoekstra, A. Y. (2004). "Water Footprints of Nations." *Value of Water Research Report Series* (UNESCO-IHE) 6; Jenny Gustavsson, Christel Cederberg, Ulf Sonesson, Robert van Otterdijk, and Alexandre Meybeck. (2011). *Global Food Losses and Food Waste,* FAO.

dry seasons from groundwater lying just a few feet below the surface. More than 1.5 million treadle pumps have been sold in Bangladesh alone, increasing the productivity of more than 600,000 acres of farmland there. The pumps are now also in use in India, Nepal, Myanmar, Cambodia, Zambia, Kenya, and South Africa.

Enhance Soil Water Retention. We have already addressed the need and options for improvement in irrigation technology. However, most of the agriculture

in developing countries is rain-fed, depending on green water flow from soil and resulting in evapotranspiration. Further, most of the soils are dryland soils, receiving only 10 to 30 inches of rainfall per year (Chapter 11). Crops raised on these soils are characteristically low in yield. Storing the seasonal rainfall with "check dams" (small rock or raised soil dams across seasonal water courses) increases yields. These dams recharge aquifers, restrain soil erosion, and provide for some irrigation water. Another strategy is to enhance rainfall retention, maintain soil fertility, and restrain soil erosion through conservation tillage, where crop residues are left in place and new crops are planted with little or no tilling.

Municipal Systems. The 100 gallons of water each person consumes per day in modern homes are used mostly for washing and removing wastes—that is, for flushing toilets (3–5 gallons per flush), taking showers (2–3 gallons per minute), doing laundry (20–30 gallons per wash), and so on. Watering lawns, filling swimming pools, and other indirect consumption only adds to this use.

Water conservation has long been promoted as a "save the environment" measure, though without much effect. Now, numerous cities are facing the stark reality that it will be extremely expensive—and in many cases, impossible—to increase supplies by the traditional means of building more reservoirs or drilling more wells. The only practical alternative, they are discovering, is to take real steps toward reducing water consumption and waste. A considerable number of cities have programs whereby leaky faucets will be repaired and low-flow showerheads and water-displacement devices in toilets will be installed free of charge.

Lawns. Grass is the most heavily irrigated crop. Cities in Arizona are paying homeowners to replace their lawns with **xeriscaping**—landscaping with desert species that require no additional watering—and the business is thriving. Many cities and towns ban certain uses of water when droughts reduce the available supply.

A Flush World. In 1997, the last phase of a regulation authorized by the 1992 National Energy Act took effect, and it became illegal to sell 6-gallon commodes. In their place is the wonder of the flush world: the 1.6-gallon toilet. Newer versions use even less water than the first, less effective low-flow toilets; the newest work perfectly well and save 10 gallons or more a day per person. In fact, the newest models are dual flush, with options for a 1.28-gallon (solids) or 0.8-gallon (liquids) flush. The 50 million low-flow toilets now in place in the United States save an estimated 600 million gallons of water a day. Los Angeles is offering the low-flow toilets free as part of its efforts to restore Mono Lake, which had lost a great deal of water. In 2011, the City of San Francisco found the downside of low-flow toilets: While the city had saved 20 million gallons of water a year (just from toilets!), the low-flow toilets weren't pushing the sewage through the pipes as quickly as before. To solve the problem, city engineers are planning to kill bacteria with chemicals, though other solutions have been pointed out.

Gray Water. It seems wasteful to raise all domestic water to drinking-water standards and then use most of it to water lawns and flush toilets. Increasingly, gray water recycling systems are being adopted in some water-short areas. **Gray water**, the slightly dirtied water from sinks, showers, bathtubs, and laundry tubs, is collected in a holding tank and used for such things as flushing toilets, watering lawns, and washing cars. Going further, a number of cities are using treated wastewater (sewage water) for irrigating golf courses and landscapes, both to conserve water and to abate the pollution of receiving waters (see Chapter 20). Residents of California use more than 160 billion gallons of treated wastewater for such purposes, and in Israel, 70% of treated wastewater is reused for irrigation of nonfood crops. If the idea of reusing sewage water turns you off, recall that *all* water is recycled by nature. There is hardly a molecule of water you drink that has not moved through organisms—including humans—numerous times. A number of communities are already treating their wastewater so thoroughly that its quality exceeds what many cities take in from lakes and rivers.

Virtual Water. Another option for reducing water loss in water-stressed regions is to import food or goods that require a great deal of water, to ship *virtual water*, as it is called. Many arid countries avoid using their own water supplies by importing farm products from regions that have excess freshwater. Indeed, an estimated 800 cubic kilometers of virtual water are traded yearly in the form of foodstuffs. However, many of the arid countries are also economically poor and have a limited ability to purchase great quantities of food. Furthermore, shipping takes energy, and as we have seen, wasting energy is eventually bad for water, too.

One thing consumers can do is purchase products that have a low "water footprint." Production of meat, for example, almost always requires a great deal more water, but locally grown vegetables, whole foods you cook yourself, and whole grains require less. Packaging and things transported across the world represent greater water inputs. Individuals can figure out their own water footprint by looking on the Web for one of several ways to calculate it.

Public-Policy Challenges

The hydrologic cycle provides a finite flow of water through each region of Earth. When humans come on the scene, this flow of water is inevitably divided between the needs of the existing natural ecosystems and the agricultural, industrial, and domestic needs of humans, with the latter usually being met first. In fact, recent calculations indicate that humans now use 26% of total terrestrial evapotranspiration and 54% of accessible precipitation runoff. We are major players in the water cycle, and as we have seen, many facets of our water use are unsustainable. It takes public policy to strike a sustainable balance between competing water needs, and this is often sadly lacking.

Conflict. Maintaining a supply of safe drinking water for people is a high-priority issue. In addition, water for irrigation is vital to food production across much of the world. Often, these two demands come into conflict, generating what have been referred to as "water wars." One example was in Cochabamba, Bolivia, when the World Bank refused to renew loans unless the country opened

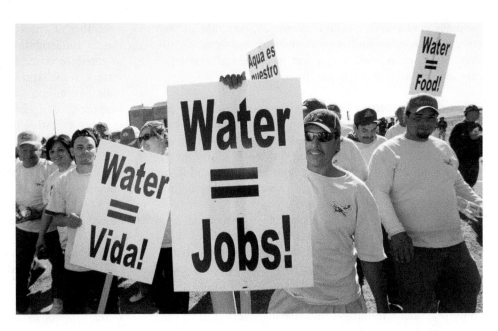

Figure 10–24 Water wars. Tensions mount over water rights in a world with increasing numbers of people trying to use the same resource. Here farmers protest lack of water in Gustine, California in 2009. National and international policies can ease these tensions.

water resources to foreign privatization. Investors were supposed to put money into providing clean drinking water, but some locals found they lost access to water and rates skyrocketed. This led to protests and the government eventually had to change plans. **Figure 10–24** depicts protesters in California after a federal judge ordered that less water could be pumped from the Sacramento Delta, where endangered fish live. This ruling pitted environmentalists against farmers and urban residents in a state with continual water stress.

National Water Policy. Many countries have addressed their water resources and water needs with a national policy; not so the United States. The Clean Water Act and subsequent amendments authorize the U.S. Environmental Protection Agency (EPA) to develop programs and rules to carry out its mandate for oversight of the nation's water quality (considered in Chapter 20). The EPA, however, does not deal with water quantity. There is no federal agency to provide similar oversight for the water quantity issues discussed in this chapter.

Peter Gleick, a leading expert on global freshwater resources, addresses this public-policy need,[5] pointing out that most water policy decisions in the United States are made at local and regional levels. National policies, however, are needed to guide these lower-level decisions and also to deal with interstate issues and federally managed resources. The last time a water policy report was issued was in 1950, when President Harry S Truman established a water resources policy commission and the commission gave its report. This commission needs to be revived or a new one needs to be established, and in either case,

it must be given a mandate to collect data on water resources and problems and issue recommendations on how the federal government could facilitate water stewardship in the 21st century.

Key Issues. Any water resources policy commission needs to address several key ideas. Two of these are increasing efficiency and stopping subsidies. In the United States, scarcity and rising costs have led to significant gains in efficiency. As a result, water withdrawals peaked in the early 1980s and have leveled off since then (Fig. 10–9). This change has been attributed to steps taken in all three sectors (domestic, industry, and irrigation) to reduce water losses. The United States still has a high per capita water use compared with the rest of the world. Also, water subsidies need to be reduced or eliminated. Policy makers have persistently subsidized water resources, especially for agricultural use, and the result has been enormous waste and inefficiencies. This undervaluing of the resource harms ecosystem services. In addition, polluters must be charged according to their effluents. When municipalities, farmers, and industries are allowed to pollute waterways without any accountability, the result is that everyone downstream is forced to pay more to clean up the water and aquatic ecosystems are degraded accordingly. Various approaches are possible, such as permit fees, "green taxes," direct charges, and market-based trading (see Chapter 20). In the 2012 Water for Food conference in Lincoln, Nebraska, one of the major messages was that there is no one-size-fits-all policy for protecting water supplies.

Public policy needs to focus on the watershed level as well. Watershed management must be integrated into the pricing of water. Watersheds hold the key to water purity, aquifer recharge, and water storage, as well as the maintenance of natural wetland and riparian habitats that are vital to many plants and animals. The City of New York

---

[5]Peter H. Gleick, "Global Water: Threats and Challenges Facing the United States," *Environment* 43 (March 2001): 18–26.

found out that every dollar it invested in watershed management paid off handsomely, saving as much as $200 for new treatment facilities. One part of managing watersheds is to regulate dam operations so that river flow is maintained in a way that simulates natural flow regimes. When this happens, rivers below dams can sustain recreational fisheries and other uses, and the natural biota flourishes.

Finally, the United States must respond to the global water crisis with adequate levels of international development aid. Achieving the Millennium Development Goal of reducing by half the 1.1 billion people without access to safe drinking water will save millions of lives and billions of dollars annually.

International Action. On the international front, the World Commission on Water for the 21st Century sponsors the World Water Forum, which convened for the sixth time in March 2012. The findings of the forum relate directly to solving the great water-related needs of Earth, especially in the developing countries. With a large proportion of the developing world already experiencing shortages of clean water or water for agriculture, the population increases and pressure to develop these countries' resources that are certain to come in the next few decades will undoubtedly subject hundreds of millions to increased water stress. The problem is not that the Earth contains too little freshwater; rather, it is that we have not yet learned to manage the water that our planet provides. To quote the World Water Council's *World Water Vision* report, "There is a water crisis, but it is a crisis of management. We have threatened our water resources with bad institutions, bad governance, bad incentives, and bad allocations of resources. In all this, we have a choice. We can continue with business as usual, and widen and deepen the crisis tomorrow. Or we can launch a movement to move from vision to action—by making water everybody's business."[6]

---

[6]*World Water Vision: Making Water Everybody's Business.* World Water Council, 2000.

REVISITING THE THEMES

Sound Science

What is known about the hydrologic cycle is the result of sound scientific research—research that is needed to make progress in managing water resources. Work performed under the Millennium Ecosystem Assessment has given us a better understanding of such matters as groundwater recharge, essential river flows, and the interactions between different land uses and water resources. The techniques of water treatment have been fine-tuned by scientific work as well as the development of reverse osmosis for desalination. Sound science is being used to figure out current questions. One we do not yet have an answer to is what is likely to happen with oceanic thermohaline circulation.

Sustainability

The opening story showed how unsustainable China's water use is. Still, the hydrologic cycle is a remarkable global system that renews water and does so sustainably. Groundwater—especially the fraction that is nonrenewable because it was formed centuries ago—is being used in an unsustainable manner. The consequences are immediate: Water tables disappear into the depths of the Earth, farms dry up because there is no water, and land subsidence ruins properties and groundwater storage itself. Conserving water through xeriscaping, low-flush toilets, gray water use, and more efficient food production and consumption is a sustainable path.

Stewardship

Exchanges among land, water, and atmosphere represent a cyclical system that has worked well for eons and that can continue to supply all our needs into the future—if we manage water wisely. However, we are changing the cycle in ways that reflect a lack of wisdom and a lack of resolve to meet people's needs in a just way. One way to remedy this is to look at water, energy, and food as interrelated. Increased inefficiency and lower waste are necessary in all three areas if we are to provide water and food for more people. Stewardship of water resources means that we consider the needs of the natural ecosystems—and especially endangered species—when we make policy decisions. It means that we address the wastefulness that characterizes so much of our water use. It means in particular that we show concern and help the millions who lack adequate clean water and are suffering because of it. Some examples of good stewardship are the Glen Canyon Dam operation, the removal of outdated dams to restore river flow, the use of treadle pumps in many developing countries, and xeriscaping. In the United States, developing a national water policy would be a huge step in stewardship management.

REVIEW QUESTIONS

1. What are the lessons to be learned from China's water hardships?

2. Give examples of the infrastructure that has been fashioned to manage water resources. What are the challenges related to developing countries?

3. What are the two processes that result in natural water purification? State the difference between them. Distinguish between green water and blue water.

4. Describe how a Hadley cell works, and explain how Earth's rotation creates the trade winds.

5. Why do different regions receive different amounts of precipitation?

6. Define *precipitation, infiltration, runoff, capillary water, transpiration, evapotranspiration, percolation, gravitational water, groundwater, water table, aquifer, recharge area, seep,* and *spring.*

7. Use the terms defined in Question 6 to give a full description of the hydrologic cycle, including each of its three loops—namely, the evapotranspiration, surface runoff, and groundwater loops. What is the water quality (purity) at different points in the cycle? Explain the reasons for the differences.

8. How does changing Earth's surface (for example, by deforestation) change the pathway of water? How does it affect streams and rivers? Humans? Natural ecology?

9. Explain how climate change and atmospheric pollution can affect the hydrologic cycle.

10. What are the three major uses of water? What are the major sources of water to match these uses?

11. How do dams facilitate the control of surface waters? What kinds of impacts do they have?

12. Distinguish between renewable and nonrenewable groundwater resources. What are the consequences of overdrawing these two kinds of groundwater?

13. What are the five options for meeting existing water scarcity needs and growing demands?

14. Describe how water demands might be reduced in agriculture, industry, and households.

15. What is the status of water policy in the United States? Cite some key issues that should be addressed by any new initiatives to establish a national water policy.

THINKING ENVIRONMENTALLY

1. Imagine that you are a water molecule, and describe your travels through the many places you have been and might go in the future as you make your way around the hydrologic cycle time after time. Include travels through organisms.

2. Suppose some commercial interests want to create a large new development on what are presently wetlands. Describe a debate between those representing the commercial interests and those representing environmentalists who are concerned about the environmental and economic costs of development. Work toward negotiating a consensus.

3. Describe how many of your everyday activities, including your demands for food and other materials, add pollution to the water cycle or alter it in other ways. How can you be more stewardly with your water consumption?

4. An increasing number of people are moving to the arid southwestern United States, even though water supplies are already being overdrawn. If you were the governor of one of the states in this region, what policies would you advocate to address this situation?

5. Suppose some commercial interests want to develop a golf course on what is presently forested land next to a reservoir used for city water. Describe the impacts this development might have on water quality in the reservoir.

MAKING A DIFFERENCE

1. Since 1992, showerheads and faucets have been required to use no more than 2.5 gallons of water per minute. If you have older plumbing, it's possible that you may not meet these standards. Equipment such as aerating showerheads can help you reduce your water use (and your water bill) without decreasing effectiveness too much.

2. Consider taking a "navy" shower (so-called because ships at sea must conserve water): Wet down, then turn the shower off, then soap down, and then rinse down. You will save both water and energy this way.

3. Americans drink billions of single-use water bottles per year. In addition to the carbon miles it takes to ship these products, most Americans simply throw the recyclable containers away. A much more sustainable method of drinking is simply to fill reusable bottles with filtered tap water.

4. Old water heaters are most likely running at less than 50% efficiency. If this is the case for you, you can replace your water heater with a newer model or simply use a tankless heater, which heats water only when you need it.

5. A dishwasher can save more than 5,000 gallons of water per year as well as hundreds of hours of your time. Scraping your dishes first, running the washer only for full loads, and using the energy-saver settings can reduce water and energy usage even more.

MasteringEnvironmentalScience®

Go to **www.masteringenvironmentalscience.com** for practice quizzes, Pearson eText, videos, current events, and more.

CHAPTER 11

Soil: The Foundation for Land Ecosystems

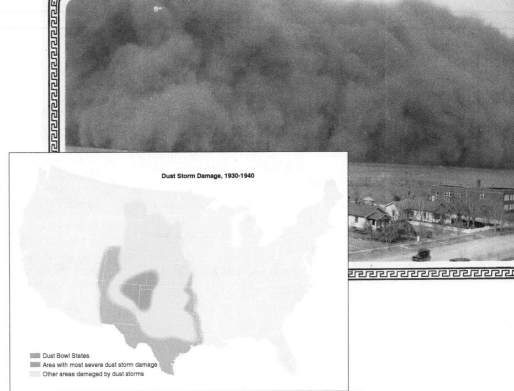

Dust Storm Damage, 1930-1940

- Dust Bowl States
- Area with most severe dust storm damage
- Other areas damaged by dust storms

The Dust Bowl. The Dust Bowl era in the 1930s was a time of drought and wind erosion that devastated farming in the American Midwest. This wall of dust approached Rolla, Kansas on April 14, 1935.

> "The nation that destroys its soil, destroys itself."
> —*Franklin D. Roosevelt*[1]

A CHURNING WALL OF SOIL, two miles high, bore across the plains. People caught outside fled for buildings, cloths held to their faces. Some faced with the blinding swirl lost their way and died, suffocated by dust. Dust was everywhere, driven by the howling winds: blinding, choking, filling cracks and windows. People wept, prayed, cried, despaired; the Apocalypse had come. The day was Black Sunday, April 14, 1935. The dust storm was the worst of the "black blizzards" in the tragic period we call the American Dust Bowl. The almost-decade-long period of drought and dry storms was arguably the longest and worst environmental disaster in US history. The storms carried tons of soil across seven states and left devastation in their wake. Some people fled the dust states or died, while others stayed and survived, only to find themselves coughing and sickly when storm after storm filled the air with dust, victims of a disorder called "dust pneumonia."

THE DUST BOWL BEGINS. A drought beginning in 1931 precipitated the disaster. By 1934, it was profound: More than 75% of the country was in drought, and 27 states were severely affected. Although drought was the trigger, human policies and practices made the Dust Bowl worse. Rising wheat and cotton prices encouraged people to plant more and more land, even in areas more suited to ranging animals. During wet years, crops were

LEARNING OBJECTIVES

1. **Soil and Plants:** Describe the basic parts of soil, soil communities, and soil profiles.

2. **Soil Degradation:** Explain how soils are degraded by several effects, including overcultivation, overgrazing, deforestation, mining, and killing soil biota.

3. **Soil Conservation:** Describe soil conservation requires action at two levels, from individual landholders and through public policy.

[1]Letter, February 26, 1937, to state governors. Available from http://www.presidency.ucsb.edu/ws/?pid=15373

bountiful, but plowing broke through the tough roots of prairie plants that held soil together, broke open the ground, and laid the dirt open to be borne about by the winds. Lack of trees or other windbreaks allowed soil to move freely. By 1935, estimates were that 850 million tons of topsoil had been blown off of the southern plains in that year alone. By the end of the Dust Bowl, many areas had lost 75% of their topsoil, once some of the richest soil in the world.

The Homestead Act of 1862, which enabled settlers to claim land and settle it, played a role in the disaster. By encouraging hundreds of thousands of small farms (160 to 320 acres) to be established between 1880 and 1920, the act ensured that too much land was cultivated in some areas of the country. Small farm owners were unlikely to let land lie fallow, diversify into pasture, plant crops with strips of vegetation in between, or farm less intensively. These homesteads were more vulnerable to financial ruin during drought. Homesteaders fled the southern plains in the largest migration in American history, described by John Steinbeck in his novel *The Grapes of Wrath*.

A dust storm on June 5, 2011 that hit Phoenix, Arizona, gave only the tiniest glimpse of such storms to modern Americans. The storm hit a peak height of at least 5000 to 6000 ft (1500 to 1800 m). The front edge was almost 100 mi (160 km) long (Fig. 11–1). As was the case in the '30s, an ongoing drought in Arizona in 2011 was a contributing factor to the severity of the storm. But such storms are rare now, in part because of better soil protection practices and the movement from more intensive cultivation of marginal lands. Around the world however, loss of soil continues to plague farmland and contribute to poor crops, water pollution, and the spread of deserts.

PAST NEGLECT. Ninety percent of the world's food comes from land-based agricultural systems, and the percentage is growing as the ocean's fish and natural ecosystems are increasingly being depleted. Protecting and nurturing agricultural soils, which are the cornerstone of food production, must be a central feature of sustainability. Yet it is a feature that has been overlooked repeatedly in the past. The Dust Bowl is not the only time such land degradation has occurred. The fall of the ancient Greek, Roman, and Mayan empires was more the result of a decline in agricultural productivity due to soil erosion than of outside forces.

Figure 11–1 A dust storm in Phoenix, Arizona. A 2011 dust storm in Phoenix showed just a tiny picture of what the 1930s dust bowl was like.

As the world's population grows past 7 billion, croplands and grazing lands are being increasingly pressed to yield more crops. A landmark 1991 Global Assessment of Soil Degradation (GLASOD) study reported that 15% of Earth's land was degraded, mostly due to soil erosion. Yet a new study by the Land Degradation Assessment in Drylands (LADA) found that **land degradation** is worse than that.[2] More than 20% of cultivated areas, 30% of forests, and 10% of grasslands were degraded between 1981 and 2003. Some 2 billion people depend directly on the land undergoing degradation. Throughout the world, soils have been (and continue to be) degraded by erosion, the buildup of salts, and other problems that can only undermine future productivity. Farm soils are not the only concern. Mining affects soils, as does deforestation. Both contribute to water and soil pollution as well as loss of ecosystem services from the ecosystems that were displaced.

Our objective in this chapter is to develop an understanding of the attributes of soil required to support good plant growth, of how these attributes may deteriorate under various practices, and of what is necessary to maintain a productive soil. We will then look at what is being done nationally and internationally to rescue this essential resource and to establish practices that are sustainable.

[2]Bai, Z. G. et al. (2008). Global Assessment of Land Degradation and Improvement 1: Identification by Remote Sensing. Report 2008/01, FAO/ISRIC—Rome/ Wageningen.

11.1 Soil and Plants

Soil can be defined as solid material of geological and biological origin that is changed by chemical, biological, and physical processes, giving it the ability to support plant growth.

A rich soil is much more than the dirt you might get out of any hole in the ground. Indeed, agriculturists cringe when anyone refers to soil as "dirt." The quality of soil can make the difference between harvesting an abundant crop and abandoning a field to weeds. You have already learned that various detritus feeders and decomposers feed on organic debris in an ecosystem (Chapter 4). Nutrients from the detritus are released into the soil and absorbed by producers, thus recycling the nutrients. In short, productive topsoil involves dynamic interactions among organisms, detritus, and mineral particles of soil (Fig. 11–2).

Soil Characteristics

Most soils are hundreds or thousands of years old and change very slowly. Soil science is cross-disciplinary and is at the heart of agricultural and forestry practice. Many years of the study of soils have resulted in a system of classification of soil profiles and soil structure and a taxonomy of soil types from all over the world—as well as a large body of scientific literature investigating relevant topics. This section presents just enough of this information to enable you to open the door to soil science; you may even be motivated to follow up on your own in this fascinating field.

Soil Texture. The mineral material of soil, or **parent material**, has its origin in the geological history of an area. Parent material can be rock or sediments deposited by wind, water, or ice. Sooner or later parent material is broken down by natural **weathering** (gradual physical and chemical breakdown) to the point where often it is impossible to tell just what kind of rock the soil came from. As rock weathers, it breaks down into smaller and smaller fragments—stones and smaller "soil separates." These are classified as sand, silt, and clay. **Sand** is made up of particles from 2.0 to 0.063 millimeters in size, **silt** particles range from 0.063 to 0.004 millimeters, and **clay** is anything finer than 0.004 millimeters (Fig. 11–3). Particles larger than sand are called gravel, cobbles, or boulders, depending on their size. You can see the individual rock particles in sand, and you may be familiar with the finer particles called silt, but you would need a good microscope to see clay particles.

Proportions. The sand, silt, and clay particles constitute the mineral portion of soil. **Soil texture** refers to the relative proportions of each type of particle in a given soil. If one predominates, soil is said to be sandy, silty, or clayey. A proportion that is commonly found in soil consists of roughly 40% sand, 40% silt, and 20% clay. A soil with these proportions is called a **loam**. You can determine the texture of a given soil by shaking a small amount of it with water in a large test tube to separate the particles and then allowing them to settle. Because particles settle according to their

Figure 11–2 Topsoil formation. Soil production involves a dynamic interaction among mineral particles, detritus, and members of the detritus food web.

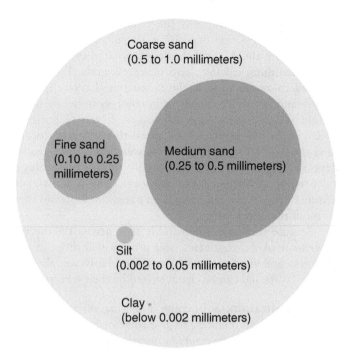

Figure 11–3 The relative sizes of soil particles. Clay particles are too small to see with the naked eye, while silt particles are slightly larger. Sand particles vary from small (but still larger than silt) to large. Gravel and boulders are larger still.

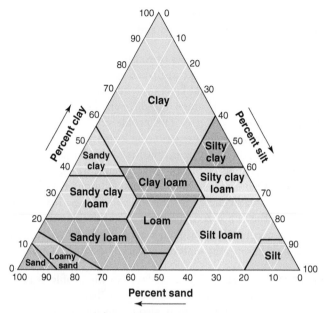

Figure 11–4 The soil texture triangle. Relative proportions of sand, clay, and silt are represented on each axis. Major classes of soil are indicated on the triangle. For clay, read across horizontally; for silt, read diagonally downward toward the left from the right axis; for sand, read diagonally upward to the left from the bottom axis. The texture content of any soil should total 100% if the triangle is read properly.

weight, sand particles settle first, silt second, and clay last. (More precise measurements require a laboratory analysis.) Soil scientists classify soil texture with the aid of a triangle that shows the relative proportions of sand, silt, and clay in a given soil (Fig. 11–4).

Properties. Soil scientists often ask questions about how the components of soil determine its properties. Three basic considerations determine how several important properties of soil are influenced by texture:

1. Larger particles have larger spaces separating them than smaller particles have. (Visualize the difference between packing softballs and packing golf balls in containers of the same size.)

2. Smaller particles have more surface area relative to their volume than larger particles have. (Visualize cutting

a block in half again and again. Each time you cut it, you create two new surfaces, but the total volume of the block remains the same.)

3. Nutrient ions and water molecules tend to cling to surfaces. (When you drain a nongreasy surface, it remains wet.)

These properties of matter profoundly affect such soil properties as infiltration, nutrient- and water-holding capacities, and aeration (Table 11–1). Note how soil properties correspond to particle size (sand, silt, and clay) in the table.

Soil texture also affects **workability**—the ease with which a soil can be cultivated. Workability has a tremendous impact on agriculture. Clayey soils are very difficult to work with because even modest changes in moisture content can turn them from too sticky and muddy to too hard and even bricklike.

TABLE 11–1	Relationship Between Soil Texture and Soil Properties				
Soil Texture	Water Infiltration	Water-Holding Capacity	Nutrient-Holding Capacity	Aeration	Workability
Sand	Good	Poor	Poor	Good	Good
Silt	Medium	Medium	Medium	Medium	Medium
Clay	Poor	Good	Good	Poor	Poor
Loam	Medium	Medium	Medium	Medium	Medium

Sandy soils are very easy to work because they become neither muddy when wet nor hard and bricklike when dry.

Soil Profiles. The processes of soil formation create a vertical gradient of layers that are often (but not always) quite distinct. These horizontal layers are known as **soil horizons**, and a vertical slice through the different horizons is called the **soil profile** (Fig. 11–5). The profile reveals a great deal about the factors that interact in the formation of a soil. The topmost layer, the O horizon, consists of dead organic matter (detritus) deposited by plants: leaves, stems, fruits, and seeds. Thus, the O horizon is high in organic content and is the primary source of energy for the soil community. Toward the bottom of the O horizon, the processes of decomposition are well advanced, and the original materials may be unrecognizable. At this point, the material is dark and is called **humus**.

Subsurface Layers. The next layer in the profile is the A horizon, a mixture of mineral soil from below and humus from above. The A horizon is also called **topsoil**. Fine roots from the overlying vegetation permeate this layer. The A horizon is usually dark because of the humus that is present and may be shallow or thick, depending on the overlying ecosystem. Vital to plant growth, topsoil grows at the rate of an inch or two every hundred years. In many soils, the next layer is the E horizon, where E stands for **eluviation**—the process of **leaching** (dissolving away) many minerals due to the downward movement of water. This layer is usually paler in color than the two layers above it.

O Horizon: Humus. (surface litter, decomposing plant matter)

A Horizon: Topsoil. (mixed humus and leached mineral soil)

E Horizon: Zone of leaching. (less humus, minerals resistant to leaching)

B Horizon: Subsoil. (accumulation of leached minerals like iron and aluminum oxides)

C Horizon: Weathered parent material. (partly broken-down minerals)

Figure 11–5 Soil profile. Major horizons from the surface to the parent material in an idealized soil profile.

Below the E horizon is the B horizon. This layer is characterized by the deposition of minerals that have leached from the A and E horizons, so it is often high in iron, aluminum, calcium, and other minerals. Frequently referred to as the **subsoil**, the B horizon is typically high in clay and is reddish or yellow in color from the oxidized metals present. Below the B horizon is the C horizon, which is the parent mineral material that originally occupied the site. This layer represents weathered rock, glacial deposits, or volcanic ash and usually reveals the geological process that created the landscape. The C horizon is affected little by the biological and chemical processes that go on in the upper layers.

Because there are innumerable soils across the diverse landscapes of the continents, soil profiles will differ in the thickness and the content of the layers. However, all soils exist in layers and can be characterized by their texture.

Soil Classification. Soils come in a wide variety of vertical structures and textures. To give some order to this diversity, soil scientists have created a taxonomy, or classification system, of soils. It works much like the biological taxonomy with which you may be familiar (see Chapter 6). The most inclusive group in the taxonomy is the **soil order**. If you are classifying a soil, you find the order first and then work your way downward through the taxonomic categories (*suborders, groups, subgroups, families*) until you come to the soil *class* that best corresponds to the soil in question. There are literally hundreds of soil classes. **Figure 11–6** displays the worldwide distribution of the 12 major orders. Following are the characteristics of the four major soil orders that are most important for agriculture, animal husbandry, and forestry and a fifth soil type that is particularly important to environmental health.

Mollisols. Mollisols are fertile, dark soils found in temperate grassland biomes. They are the world's best agricultural soils and are encountered in the Midwestern United States; across temperate Ukraine, Russia, and Mongolia; and in the pampas (a broad region of grassy plains) in Argentina. They have a deep A horizon and are rich in humus and minerals; precipitation is insufficient to leach the minerals downward into the E horizon.

Oxisols. These are soils of the tropical and subtropical rain forests. They have a layer of iron and aluminum oxides in the B horizon and have little O horizon, due to the rapid decomposition of plant matter. Most of the minerals are in the living plant matter, so oxisols provide limited fertility for agriculture. If the forests are cut (as in "slash-and-burn" agriculture, a common practice in the tropics), a few years of crop growth can be obtained, but in time, the intense rainfall leaches the minerals downward, forming an impervious hardpan that resists further cultivation.

Alfisols. Alfisols are widespread, moderately weathered forest soils. Although not deep, they have well-developed O, A, E, and B horizons. Alfisols are typical of the moist, temperate forest biome and are suitable for agriculture if they are supplemented with organic matter or mineral fertilizers to maintain soil fertility.

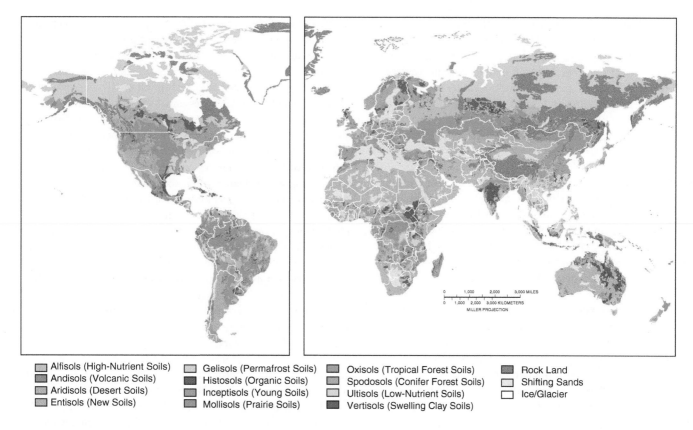

Alfisols (High-Nutrient Soils)
Andisols (Volcanic Soils)
Aridisols (Desert Soils)
Entisols (New Soils)

Gelisols (Permafrost Soils)
Histosols (Organic Soils)
Inceptisols (Young Soils)
Mollisols (Prairie Soils)

Oxisols (Tropical Forest Soils)
Spodosols (Conifer Forest Soils)
Ultisols (Low-Nutrient Soils)
Vertisols (Swelling Clay Soils)

Rock Land
Shifting Sands
Ice/Glacier

Figure 11–6 Global map of soil orders. The map shows the worldwide distribution of the 12 soil orders.
(*Source:* After the U.S. Department of Agriculture's Natural Resources Conservation Services, World Soil Resources staff.)

Aridisols. These are the very widespread soils of **dry-lands** and deserts (drylands are arid, semiarid, and seasonally dry areas). The paucity of vegetation and precipitation leaves aridisols relatively unstructured vertically. They are thin and light colored and, in some regions, may support enough vegetation for rangeland animal husbandry. Irrigation used on these soils usually leads to salinization, as high evaporation rates draw salts to surface horizons, where they accumulate to toxic levels.

The descriptions of these four classes of soil demonstrate that different soils vary.

Another Type of Soil: Hydric. Another soil type that is particularly important, although not necessarily good for agriculture, is **hydric soils**. These soils indicate a wetland or aquatic site. Hydric soils are not a soil class on their own, but are members of a number of other classes. Hydric soils are used in delineating the boundaries of wetlands, in order to get permits for construction, and to protect wetlands and water bodies from the negative impacts of development. The soil order histosols includes several types of hydric soils. They contain a buildup of undecayed vegetation called **peat** and hence are called peatlands. Peat contains a great deal of energy and can be dried and burned. Vast areas of northern zones are hydric soils, including soil order gelisols, that are permanently frozen at some depth, a condition called permafrost. One of the concerns about climate change is that in a warmer world, permafrost areas will thaw and greater rates of decay will occur. This would act as positive feedback, putting more greenhouse gases released from decaying peat into the atmosphere (Chapter 18).

Soil Constraints. Soil scientists study more than soil classification. They often research the relationship of soil to plants it supports. Such scientists speak of "soil constraints," meaning the various characteristics of soils that limit primary productivity, especially in agriculture and forestry. These constraints include poor soil drainage (hydromorphy), low ability to retain nutrients, high levels of aluminum, low levels of phosphorous, soil cracking (from certain types of clays), the presence of soluble salts (salinity and sodicity), shallowness, and high erosion likelihood. Let's look at the characteristics that enable soils to support plant growth, especially agricultural crops.

Soil and Plant Growth

For their best growth, plants need a root environment that supplies optimal amounts of mineral nutrients, water, and air (oxygen). The pH (relative acidity) and salinity (salt concentration) of soil are also critically important. **Soil fertility**—soil's ability to support plant growth—often refers to the presence of proper amounts of nutrients, but it also includes soil's ability to meet all the other needs of plants. Farmers speak of a given soil's ability to support plant growth as the **tilth** of soil.

Mineral Nutrients and Nutrient-Holding Capacity.
Mineral nutrients—phosphate (PO_4^{3-}) potassium (K^+), calcium (Ca^{2+}), and other ions—are present in various rocks, along with non-nutrient elements. Minerals initially become available to roots through the weathering of rock. Weathering, however, is much too slow to support normal plant growth. The nutrients that support plant growth in natural ecosystems are supplied mostly through the breakdown and release (recycling) of nutrients from detritus.

Leaching. Nutrients may literally be washed from soil as water moves through it, a process called **leaching**. Leaching not only lessens soil fertility but also contributes to pollution when materials removed from soil enter waterways. Consequently, soil's capacity to bind and hold nutrient ions until they are absorbed by roots is important. This property is referred to as the soil's **nutrient-holding capacity**.

Fertilizer. In agricultural systems, there is an unavoidable removal of nutrients from soil with each crop because nutrients absorbed by plants are contained in the harvested material. Therefore, agricultural systems require inputs of nutrients to replace those removed with the harvest. Nutrients are replenished with applications of **fertilizer**—material that contains one or more necessary nutrients. Fertilizer may be organic or inorganic. Organic fertilizer includes plant or animal wastes or both; manure and compost (rotted organic material) are two examples. Organic fertilizer also includes leguminous fallow crops (alfalfa, clover) or food crops (lentils, peas), which fix atmospheric nitrogen. Inorganic fertilizers are chemical formulations of required nutrients, without any organic matter included. Inorganic fertilizers are much more prone to leaching than organic fertilizers.

Water and Water-Holding Capacity. As with nutrients, the supply of water in soil is crucial to plant growth. Water is constantly being absorbed by the roots of plants, passing up through the plant and exiting as water vapor through microscopic pores in the leaves—a process called **transpiration**. The pores, called *stomata* (singular, *stoma*), are essential to permit the entry of carbon dioxide and the exit of oxygen in photosynthesis; however, the plant's loss of water via transpiration through the stomata is dramatic. A field of corn, for example, transpires an equivalent of a field-sized layer of water 43 centimeters (17 in.) deep in a single growing season. Plants with inadequate water may wilt (close their stomata to save water and fold up) and eventually die.

Water is resupplied to soil naturally by rainfall or artificially by irrigation. Three attributes of soil are significant in this respect. First is soil's ability to allow water to infiltrate or soak in. If water runs off the ground surface, it won't be useful to the plants. Worse, it may cause erosion, which is discussed shortly.

Second is soil's ability to hold water after it infiltrates, a property called **water-holding capacity**. Poor water-holding capacity implies that most of the infiltrating water percolates on down below the reach of roots—not very far in the case of seedlings and small plants—again becoming useless. What is desired is a good water-holding capacity—the ability to hold a large amount of water like a sponge—providing a reservoir from which plants can draw between rains. Sandy soils are notorious for their poor water-holding capacity, whereas clayey and silty soils are good at holding water.

The third critical attribute of soil is its ability to minimize **evaporative water loss**. This kind of evaporation depletes soil's water reservoir without serving the needs of plants. The O horizon functions well to reduce evaporative water loss by covering soil. These aspects of soil-water relationship are summarized in **Figure 11–7**.

Figure 11–7 Plant-soil-water relationships. When water evaporates from the leaves of a plant, a vacuum is created that pulls the water up through the plant tissues. The roots draw water from soil to replenish the evaporated water. The sun's energy drives transpiration via the initial evaporation process. Water lost from the plant by transpiration must be replaced from a reservoir of water held in soil. In addition to the amount and frequency of precipitation, the size of this reservoir depends on soil's ability to allow water to infiltrate, to hold water, and to minimize direct evaporation.

Aeration. Novice gardeners commonly kill plants by over-watering, or "drowning," them. Roots need to "breathe." Basically, they need a constant supply of oxygen for energy via metabolism. Land plants depend on soil being loose and porous enough to allow the diffusion of oxygen into, and carbon dioxide out of, the soil, a property called soil **aeration.** Overwatering fills the air spaces in soil, preventing adequate aeration. Plants that live in very wet soil have special adaptations to get oxygen. **Compaction,** or packing of soil, which occurs with excessive foot or vehicular traffic, also lowers soil air content. Compaction also reduces infiltration and increases runoff. Again, soil texture strongly influences this property, as indicated in Table 11–1.

Relative Acidity (pH). The term **pH** refers to the acidity or alkalinity of any solution. A solution that is neither acidic nor alkaline is said to be neutral and has a pH of 7. The pH scale, which runs from 1 to 14, is discussed more fully later (Chapter 19). For now, it is important to know that different plants are adapted to different pH ranges. Most plants do best with a pH near neutral, but many plant species are specialized for distinctly acidic or alkaline soils (blueberries, for example, are notorious acid lovers).

Salt and Water Uptake. A buildup of salts in soil makes it impossible for the roots of a plant to take in water. Indeed, if salt levels in soil get high enough, water can be drawn *out* of the plant (by osmosis), resulting in dehydration and death. Only plants with special adaptations can survive saline soils, and to date, none of those are crop plants. The importance of the problem is explained in Section 11.2, when we discuss how irrigation may lead to the accumulation of salts in soil (salinization).

Soil and Carbon Storage. Soils hold carbon from dead organisms. Sometimes this matter decays rapidly and sometimes slowly, but scientists estimate that soils hold as much as three times the amount of carbon held in the atmosphere and living plants. Right now, scientists are keenly interested in knowing what drives the rate of organic matter decay in soils. It used to be thought that temperature was the main driving factor, but a study in 2011 suggested that soil factors such as moisture, physical separation of particles, and placement of roots may play a role.[3] Microbial communities also play a role. This information may be used to make more accurate predictions of the carbon cycle. Charcoal (burned wood) is an organic material that decays very slowly. Some researchers have suggested burying charcoal ("biochar") as a way of sequestering carbon in soil, after discovering that Amazonian indigenous peoples had used charcoal in fields. The newest research, however, suggests that biochar may be less effective than first hoped. Either way, soils with organic matter that decays slowly have higher fertility.

The Soil Community

As we've seen, to support desired plant growth, soil must (1) have a good supply of nutrients and good nutrient-holding capacity; (2) allow infiltration, have good water-holding capacity, and resist evaporative water loss; (3) have a porous structure that permits good aeration; (4) have a pH near neutral; and (5) have low salt content. Moreover, these attributes must be sustained. How does a soil provide and sustain such attributes? Which is the best soil?

Recall the principle of limiting factors: The poorest attribute is the limiting factor (Chapter 3). The poor water-holding capacity of sandy soil, for example, may preclude agriculture altogether because soil dries out so quickly. The inability of clay soils to allow water infiltration or aeration prevents these from being good soils. As Table 11–1 indicates, the best soil textures are silts and loams because limiting factors are moderated in these two types of soil. Even though silts and loams are rated only "medium" for use in agriculture, their soil texture limitations are greatly improved by the organic parts of the soil ecosystem—the detritus and soil organisms.

Organisms and Organic Matter in Soil. The dead leaves, roots, and other detritus accumulated on and in soil support a complex food web, including numerous species of bacteria, fungi, protozoans, mites, insects, millipedes, spiders, centipedes, earthworms, snails, slugs, moles, and other burrowing animals (Fig. 11–8). The most numerous and important organisms are the smallest—the bacteria; literally millions of bacteria can be seen and counted in a gram of soil.

Humus. As all these organisms feed, the bulk of the detritus is consumed through cell respiration. Carbon dioxide, water, and mineral nutrients are released as by-products (see Chapter 4). However, each organism leaves a certain portion undigested; that is, a portion resists breakdown by the organism's digestive enzymes. This residue of partly decomposed organic matter is humus, found in high concentrations at the bottom of the O horizon. A familiar example is the black or dark brown spongy material remaining in a dead log after the center has rotted out. **Composting** is the process of fostering the decay of organic wastes under more or less controlled conditions, and the resulting compost is essentially humus. Humus is good for plant growth because it has an extraordinary capacity for holding both water and nutrients—as much as 100 times greater than the capacity of clay, on the basis of weight.

Soil Structure and Topsoil. As animals feed on detritus on or in soil, they often ingest mineral soil particles as well. For example, it is estimated that as much as 37 tons per hectare (15 tons per acre) of soil pass through earthworms each year in the course of their feeding. As the mineral particles go through the worm's gut, they actually become "glued" together by the indigestible humus compounds. Thus, earthworm excrements—or castings, as they are called—are relatively stable clumps of inorganic particles plus humus. The burrowing activity of organisms keeps the clumps loose. This loose, clumpy characteristic is a desirable **soil structure**

[3]Schmidt, Michael W. I. et al. (2011). Persistence of soil organic matter as an ecosystem property. *Nature*, 478(7367), 49.

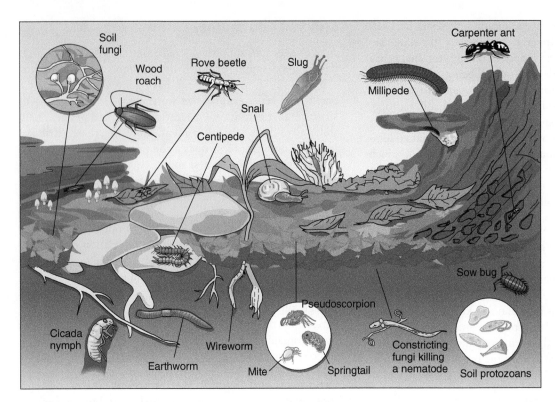

Figure 11–8 Soil as a detritus-based ecosystem. A host of organisms, major examples of which are shown here, feed on detritus and burrow through soil, forming a humus-rich topsoil with a loose, clumpy structure.

(Fig. 11–9). Whereas soil texture describes the size of soil particles, soil structure refers to their arrangement. A loose soil structure is ideal for infiltration, aeration, and workability. The clumpy, loose, humus-rich soil that is best for supporting plant growth is topsoil, represented in a soil profile as the A horizon (see Figure 11–5).

If plants are grown on adjacent plots, one of which has had all its topsoil removed, the results are striking: The yield from plants grown on subsoil is only 10% to 15% of that from plants grown on topsoil. In other words, a loss of all the topsoil would result in an 85% to 90% decline in productivity. The development of topsoil from subsoil or parent material is a process that takes hundreds of years or more.

Figure 11–10 shows a site where the topsoil was removed 50 years ago to provide fill for a highway. Although a lichen cover and some stunted trees have developed on the exposed gravel, there is still no topsoil there.

Interactions. There are some important interactions between plants and soil biota. A highly significant one is the symbiotic relationship between the roots of some plants and certain fungi called **mycorrhizae**. Drawing some nourishment from the roots, mycorrhizae penetrate the detritus, absorb nutrients, and transfer them directly to the plant **(Fig. 11–11)**. Thus, there is no loss of nutrients to leaching. Another important relationship is that of certain bacteria that add nitrogen to soil (Chapter 3).

Figure 11–9 Humus and the development of soil structure. On the left is a humus-poor sample of loam. Note that it is a relatively uniform, dense "clod." On the right is a sample of the same loam, but rich in humus. Note that it has a very loose structure, composed of numerous aggregates of various sizes.

Figure 11–10 The results of removing topsoil. This "soil" is nothing but gravel with topsoil removed. After 50 years, only lichens and a few stunted trees have developed. The white object is a ballpoint pen.

Figure 11–11 Mycorrhizae. Symbiotic fungi connect to the roots of plants; they help get nutrients and increase root absorption, while getting protection and food. Here you can see a canning electron micrograph of the small fungal hyphae entering the plant root hair. Mycorrizae can be purchased as a soil additive and increase crop yields for gardeners.

Not all soil organisms are beneficial to plants, however. For example, nematodes, small worms that feed on living roots, are highly destructive to some agricultural crops. In a flourishing soil ecosystem, however, nematode populations may be controlled by other soil organisms.

Soil Enrichment or Mineralization. You can now see how the aboveground and soil portions of an ecosystem support each other. The bulk of the detritus, which supports soil organisms, is from green-plant producers, so green plants support soil organisms. In turn, by feeding on detritus, soil organisms create the chemical and physical soil environment that is most beneficial to plant growth.

Green plants protect soil and, consequently, themselves in two other important ways: The cover of living plants and detritus (1) protects soil from erosion and (2) reduces evaporative water loss. Thus, it is desirable to maintain an organic mulch around any garden vegetables that do not maintain a complete cover themselves.

Unfortunately, the mutually supportive relationship between plants and soil can be broken all too easily. The maintenance of topsoil depends on additions of detritus in sufficient quantity to balance losses. Without continual additions of detritus, soil organisms will starve, and their benefit in keeping soil loose and nutrient rich will be lost. Additional consequences can occur as well. Although resistant to digestion by soil organisms, humus does decompose at the rate of about 2% to 5% of its volume per year. As soil's humus content declines, the clumpy aggregate structure created by soil particles glued together with the humus breaks down. Water- and nutrient-holding capacities, infiltration, and aeration decline as well. This loss of humus and the consequent collapse of topsoil are referred to as the **mineralization** of soil because what is left is just the gritty mineral content—sand, silt, and clay.

Thus, topsoil is the result of a dynamic balance between detritus additions and humus-forming processes, on the one hand, and the breakdown and loss of detritus and humus (Fig. 11–12) on the other. Soil deteriorates or is revitalized through loss or additions of organic matter.

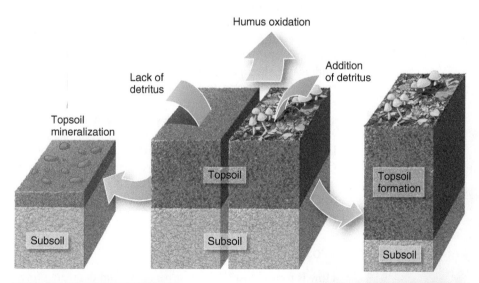

Figure 11–12 The importance of humus to topsoil. Topsoil is the result of a balance between detritus additions and humus-forming processes as well as their breakdown and loss. If additions of detritus are insufficient, soil will gradually deteriorate.

Humus oxidation

Lack of detritus

Addition of detritus

Topsoil mineralization

Topsoil

Topsoil formation

Subsoil

Subsoil

Subsoil

Loss of humus results in topsoil mineralization and consequent loss of:
• Water-holding capacity
• Nutrient-holding capacity
• Water infiltration
• Aeration

Gain of humus results in topsoil formation and consequent gain in:
• Water-holding capacity
• Nutrient-holding capacity
• Water infiltration
• Aeration

11.2 Soil Degradation

In natural ecosystems, there is always a turnover of plant material, so new detritus is continuously supplied. However, when humans come on the scene and cut forests, graze livestock, or grow crops, the soil is at the mercy of our management or mismanagement. When key soil attributes required for plant growth or for other ecosystem services deteriorate over time, the soil is considered degraded. Before we were able to ask how serious this problem was, we needed some way to track and assess soil changes (Figure 11.13). This has now been done on a global scale, though it was very difficult.

The GLASOD report on degraded land quoted earlier (15% degraded) was for a long time the only truly global assessment. The data for the report came from questionnaires sent to soil experts around the world. Very little of the information was validated by collecting data on actual soil conditions or information on crop productivity. The authors actually pointed this out in the report. Long before GLASOD, however, scientists had been trying to gather soil data. The ISRIC World Soil Information (once the International Soil Research Information Centre) was started in 1966 as an offshoot of a World Soil Museum created in 1961 and housed in the Netherlands. All over the world, regional governments were collecting data on land, land use, agriculture, and soils, but it was often in different formats and scales or with different vocabulary. Standardizing information from around the world and providing data to researchers has been part of the job of the ISRIC World Soil Information organization.

The GLASOD map was a huge undertaking, but it was not as accurate as we needed. For example, 75% of the soils in Burkina Faso, one of the poorest and most densely populated countries in the dryland region of West Africa, were considered degraded. However, agricultural yields for virtually all crops have increased in the past 40 years, dur-

ing which time the population more than doubled. Eventually, the GLASOD data were considered suspect and out of date.

GLASOD was followed by a project launched by the Food and Agricultural Organization of the United Nations (FAO), called the Land Degradation Assessment in Drylands (LADA). Land degradation is defined as a reduction in the capacity of land to perform ecosystem functions and services that support society and development. This project used satellite remote-sensing techniques to produce an overall view of soil quality, called the Global Assessment of Land Degradation and Improvement (GLADA).[4] The GLADA assessment employed data from a 23-year time series by National Oceanic and Atmospheric Administration (NOAA) satellites and precipitation data from more than 9,300 land stations. One analysis combined plant productivity with rain-use efficiency to produce a map of regions that are worsening, calling them "hot spots," and regions that are showing improving trends, calling them "bright spots."

Updating Soil Science

GLADA was updated in 2010. The update used new techniques to estimate aboveground plant biomass from satellite images. Satellites can measure light variations, which can be used to calculate measures of greenness. Greenness is then used as an index of aboveground biomass, which in turn is used to assess land degradation because degraded land produces less vegetation. But even undergraded lands in some biomes do not produce a lot of vegetation, so the program actually measures changes—is the ability of the land to produce vegetation declining over time? In times of drought or at certain times of year, one would expect vegetation to decline anyway, so the program must account for seasons and the effect of droughts to measure whether the land is degraded for any length of time. This is an area where scientific ability to accurately model what is happening is both rapidly improving and crucial. One of the findings of the updated GLADA study was that land degradation is changing in China differently than people expected. Land degradation is most conspicuous in the humid south and east, where urban development is more intense, rather than the dry north and west, because of aggressive land protection and reforestation efforts in the north by the Chinese government. Other researchers have tried to estimate the effect of soil degradation on China's crop yields (Fig. 11–14). One of the most critical land degradations is erosion, discussed next.

Erosion

How is topsoil lost? The most pervasive and damaging force is **erosion**, the process of soil and humus particles being picked up and carried away by water or wind. Erosion

Figure 11–13 Soil research. Researchers such as the one shown here measure soil radiation. They study soil in the hopes of protecting and enhancing productivity.

[4]Bai, Z. G., Jong, R. de, & van Lynden, G. W. J. (2010). An Update of GLADA—Global Assessment of Land Degradation and Improvement. ISRIC report 2010/08, ISRIC—World Soil Information, Wageningen.

Figure 11–14 Soil degradation and crops in China. Across China, soil degradation is affecting croplands, especially in the south and east, even though the north and west are where desertification occurs. (Source: Liming Ye and Eric Van Ranst. (2009). Production scenarios and the effect of soil degradation on long-term food security in China. *Global Environmental Change, 19*(4), 464–481.)

follows any time soil is bared and exposed to the elements. The removal may be slow and subtle, as when soil is gradually blown away by wind, or it may be dramatic, as when gullies are washed out in a single storm.

In most natural terrestrial ecosystems, a vegetative cover protects against erosion. Falling raindrops are intercepted by the vegetation, and the water infiltrates gently into the loose topsoil without disturbing its structure. With good infiltration, runoff is minimal. Runoff that does occur is slowed as the water moves through the vegetative or litter mat. Similarly, vegetation slows the velocity of wind and holds soil particles.

Splash, Sheet, and Gully Erosion. When soil is left bare and unprotected, however, it is easily eroded. **Splash erosion** occurs in storms as the impact of falling raindrops breaks up the clumpy structure of the topsoil. The dislodged particles wash into spaces between other aggregates, clogging pores and thereby decreasing infiltration and aeration. The decreased infiltration results in more water running off, carrying away the fine particles from the surface, a phenomenon called **sheet erosion**. As further runoff occurs, the water

converges into rivulets and streams, which have greater volume, velocity, and energy and hence greater capacity to pick up and remove soil. The result is the erosion into gullies, or **gully erosion** (Fig. 11–15). This process of erosion can become a cycle that perpetuates.

Desert Pavement and Cryptogamic Crusts. Wind and water erosion both involve the differential removal of soil particles. The lighter particles of humus and clay are the first to be carried away, while rocks, stones, and coarse sand remain behind. Consequently, as erosion removes the finer materials, the remaining soil becomes progressively coarser—sandy, stony, and finally, rocky. Such coarse soils frequently reflect past or ongoing erosion. Did you ever wonder why deserts are full of sand? The sand is what remains after the finer, lighter clay and silt particles have blown away. However, in some deserts, the removal of fine material by wind has left a thin surface layer of stones and gravel called a **desert pavement**, which protects the underlying soil against further erosion (Fig. 11–16). Damaging this surface layer with vehicular or pedestrian traffic allows another episode of erosion to commence.

Figure 11–15 Erosion. Severe erosion due to poor farming practices near Bosencheve, Mexico.

(a)

(b)

Figure 11–16 Formation of desert pavement. (a) As wind erosion removes the finer particles, the larger grains and stones are concentrated on the surface. (b) The result is desert pavement, which protects the underlying soil from further erosion. The Sinai Desert has a mixture of desert pavement, rock and tracks from vehicles, which break up the desert pavement and initiate further erosion.

Water erosion can cause other changes in soil composition. Often, when rainfall clogs soils, the soils harden when they dry. Following this, the soil may be colonized by different kinds of primitive plants (algae, lichens, and mosses) called cryptogams. Their growth and colonization create a crust on the soil, called a **cryptogamic crust.** Such crusts have a positive ecological impact; they can stabilize soil, slow erosion, and add nutrients through nitrogen fixation. However, they can also inhibit water infiltration and seed generation. They are readily broken up by livestock trampling or human

intrusion, and if the soil below is loosened, it can again be subject to wind and water erosion. Accordingly, let us now take a closer look at the practices that lead to erosion, one of the major elements of land degradation.

Causing and Correcting Erosion

Three major practices that expose soil to erosion and lead to soil degradation are overcultivation, overgrazing, and deforestation, all of which are a consequence of unsustainable management practices. All of these are practices with impacts that can be reversed, as we will see.

Overcultivation.

Traditionally, the first step in growing crops has been plowing to control weeds. The drawback is that the soil is then exposed to wind and water erosion. Further, soil may remain bare for a considerable time after planting and again after harvest. Plowing is frequently considered necessary to loosen soil to improve aeration and infiltration through it, yet all too often the effect is just the reverse. Splash erosion destroys soil's aggregate structure and seals the surface, so that aeration and infiltration are decreased. The weight of tractors used in plowing adds to the compaction of soil. In addition, plowing accelerates evaporative water loss.

Despite the harmful impacts inherent in cultivation, systems of crop rotation—a cash crop such as corn every third year, with hay and clover (which fixes nitrogen as well as adding organic matter) in between—have proved sustainable. If farmers abandon rotation, degradation and erosion exceed regenerative processes, and the result is a decline in the quality of soil. This is the essence of overcultivation.

No-Till. A technique that permits continuous cropping, yet minimizes soil erosion, is **no-till agriculture**, which is now routinely practiced in areas of the United States. According to this technique, the field is first sprayed with herbicide to kill weeds, and then a planting apparatus is pulled behind a tractor to accomplish several operations at once. A steel disk cuts a furrow through the mulch of dead weeds, drops seed and fertilizer into the furrow, and then closes it (Fig. 11–17). At harvest, the process is repeated, and the waste from the previous crop becomes the detritus and mulch cover for the next. Thus, the soil is never left exposed, erosion and evaporative water loss are reduced, and there is enough detritus, including roots from the previous crop, to maintain the topsoil. Of course, this requires the use of herbicides, which have their own problems and may increase the effects of pests that remain in crop residues from one season to another (Chapter 13).

Figure 11–17 Apparatus for no-till planting. This no till planter is planting corn over stubble with minimal disturbance to the protective vegetation layer on the surface of the soil. The apparatus creates furrows with cutting discs, applies herbicide and fertilizer, drops in seeds, and closes the furrows.

A variation on this theme is **low-till farming**, which is catching on in Asia. For example, to plant wheat after a rice crop has been harvested, only one pass over a field is made—to plant seed and spread fertilizer. Previously, farmers would plow 6 to 12 times to break up the muddy soil and dry it out for the wheat, and then they would irrigate the land.

Fertilizer. Another aspect of overcultivation involves the use of inorganic versus organic fertilizer. There is no question that optimal amounts of required nutrients can be efficiently provided by the suitable application of inorganic chemical fertilizer. The failing of chemical fertilizer is its lack of organic matter to support soil organisms and build soil structure. Under intensive cultivation—one or more cash crops every year—nutrient content may be kept high with inorganic fertilizer, but mineralization, and thus soil degradation, proceeds in any case. Then, with the soil's loss of nutrient-holding capacity, applied inorganic fertilizer is prone to simply leach into waterways, causing pollution.

This is not to say that chemical fertilizers do not have a valuable place in agriculture—after all, the exclusive use of organic material may not provide enough of certain nutrients to support optimal plant growth. What is required is for growers to understand the different roles played by organic material and inorganic nutrients and then to use each as necessary.

Natural Resources Conservation Service. Regardless of cropping procedures and the use of fertilizer, a number of other techniques are widely employed to reduce erosion. Among the most conspicuous are **contour farming** (plowing and cultivating at right angles to contour slopes) and **shelterbelts** (protective belts of trees and shrubs alongside plowed fields) (Fig. 11–18). The U.S. **Natural Resources Conservation Service (NRCS)**, formerly the Soil Conservation Service, was established in response to the Dust Bowl tragedy of the early 1930s. Through a nationwide network of regional offices, the NRCS provides information to farmers or other interested persons regarding soil and water conservation practices. (Federal extension service offices will test soil samples, provide an analysis thereof, and make recommendations.) The NRCS performs an inventory of erosion losses in the United States (the Natural Resources Inventory, last conducted in 2007). Estimates indicate that soil erosion on croplands has lessened in recent years, from 2.1 billion tons in 1992 to 1.7 billion tons in 2007. This decrease is likely a consequence of improved conservation practices, such as windbreaks, grassed waterways, and field border strips of perennial vegetation to filter runoff.

Overgrazing.

Grasslands that receive too little rainfall to support cultivated crops or are too steep for cropping have traditionally been used for grazing livestock. In fact, some 65% of dryland areas are rangelands. Unfortunately, such lands are too often overgrazed. As grass production fails to keep up with consumption, erosion follows and the land becomes barren.

Overgrazing is not a new problem. In the United States in the 1800s, the American buffalo (bison) was slaughtered to starve out Native Americans and allow for stocking the

(a)

(b)

Figure 11–18 Contour farming and shelterbelts. (a) Cultivation up and down a slope encourages water to run down furrows and may lead to severe erosion. The problem is reduced by plowing and cultivating along the contours at a right angle to the slope. In this photograph, strip cropping is also being utilized: The light green bands are one type of crop, the dark bands another. (b) Shelterbelts—belts of trees around farm fields—break the wind and protect soil from erosion, seen in New Zealand.

rangelands with cattle. Cattle overgrazing became rampant, leading to erosion and encroachment by hardy desert plants such as sagebrush, mesquite, and juniper, which are not palatable to cattle. Western rangelands now produce less than 50% of the livestock forage they produced before the advent of commercial grazing. Yet overstocking and the federal subsidizing of ranching means that in 2005 the grazing program on federal public lands cost $144 million and brought in only $21 million to the federal government. The Obama administration has proposed a grazing fee increase.

The broader ecological impact of overgrazing should not go unnoticed, either. The National Public Lands Grazing Campaign documents the many harmful effects of livestock grazing on public lands. Livestock compete with native animals for forage, reducing the latter's numbers substantially (about one-third of the endangered species in the United States are in jeopardy because of overgrazing or other practices associated with raising cattle, such as predator-control programs and the suppression of fire). Particularly hard hit

are wooded zones along streams and rivers, zones that are trampled by cattle seeking water. The resulting water pollution by sediments and cattle waste is high on the list of factors making fish species the fastest-disappearing wildlife group in the United States. A study of rangeland management concluded that (1) desertification affects some 85% of North America's drylands and (2) the most widespread cause of rangeland desertification is livestock grazing.[5]

Public Lands. In many cases, overgrazing occurs because rangelands are public lands not owned by the people who own the animals. Where this is the case, herders who choose to have fewer livestock on the range sacrifice income, while others continue to overgraze the range. This problem, known as the "tragedy of the commons," was discussed earlier (Chapter 7).

In a variation of the tragedy of the commons, the U.S. Bureau of Land Management (BLM) and the Forest Service lease grazing rights for 2 million square kilometers of federal (i.e., taxpayer-owned) lands. The income to the government is less than private land owners would be paid for grazing rights, though ranchers have to do more on federal lands, such as provide water and fences and get permits. Altogether it pays the government far less than the costs of administration: The grazing program loses money, and the 2012 grazing fee ($1.35 per cow and calf per month) is less than a tenth of what grazing fees are on private lands. A worse problem is the ecological cost exacted by livestock to watersheds, streams, wildlife, and endangered species, considered to be as high as $500 million. Attempts in Congress and the Department of the Interior (which houses the BLM) to raise grazing fees are consistently met with opposition from western congressmen, who threaten to cut the BLM budget.

One solution lies in better management. Restoration of rangelands could benefit both wildlife and cattle production. The NRCS has a program (the **Conservation Stewardship Program**) that provides information and support to enable ranchers who own their lands to burn unwanted woody plants, reseed the land with perennial grass varieties that hold water, and manage cattle so that herds are moved to a new location before overgrazing occurs. One solution gaining favor among ranchers and environmental groups is for the government to buy up some of the 26,000 existing grazing permits and "retire" rangelands. The ranchers would be offered a generous payment for the permits they hold, and the land would be used for wildlife, recreation, and watershed protection.

Deforestation. Forest ecosystems are extremely efficient systems both for holding and recycling nutrients and for absorbing and holding water because they maintain and protect a very porous, humus-rich topsoil. Investigators at Hubbard Brook Forest in New Hampshire found that converting a hillside from forest to grass doubled the amount of runoff

[5]Government Accountability Office. Livestock Grazing: Federal Expenditures and Receipts Vary, Depending on the Agency and the Purpose of the Fee Charged (September 30, 2005).

and increased the leaching of nutrients many-fold. Much worse is what occurs if the forest is simply cut and soil is left exposed. The topsoil becomes saturated with water and slides off the slope in a muddy mass into waterways, leaving barren subsoil that continues to erode. Forests continue to be cleared at an alarming rate (Chapter 7). The problem is particularly acute when tropical rain forests are cut. Tropical soils (oxisols) are notoriously lacking in nutrients from leaching by rainwater. When the forests are cleared, the thin layer of humus with nutrients readily washes away. Only the nutrient-poor subsoil is left.

The Other End of the Erosion Problem. Water that is unable to infiltrate flows over the surface immediately into streams and rivers, overfilling them and causing flooding. Eroding soil, called **sediment**, is carried into streams and rivers, clogging channels and intensifying flooding, filling reservoirs, killing fish, and generally damaging the ecosystems of streams, rivers, bays, and estuaries. Excess sediments and nutrients resulting from erosion are recognized as the greatest pollution problem of surface waters in many regions of the world. Meanwhile, groundwater resources are also depleted because the rainfall runs off rather than recharging groundwater. This is another example of the tight connection between water availability and quality and the health of soils.

Drylands and Desertification

Recall that clay and humus are the most important components of soil for both nutrient- and water-holding capacity. As clay and humus are removed, nutrients are removed as well because they are bound to those particles. The loss of water-holding capacity is even more serious, however. Regions that have sparse rainfall or long dry seasons support grasses, scrub trees, or crops only insofar as soils have good water-holding and nutrient-holding capacity. As these soil properties are diminished by the erosion of topsoil, such areas become deserts, both ecologically and from the standpoint of agricultural production. Indeed, the term **desertification** is used to denote this process. Note that desertification doesn't mean advancing deserts; rather, the term refers to a permanent reduction in the productivity of arid, semiarid, and seasonally dry areas (traditionally called drylands). It is a process of land degradation with a number of possible causes, including extended droughts, overgrazing, erosion, deforestation, and overcultivation.

Dryland ecosystems cover 41% of Earth's ice-free land area. They are defined by precipitation, not temperature. Beyond the relatively uninhabited deserts, much of the land receives only 25 to 75 centimeters (10 to 30 in.) of rainfall a year, a minimal amount to support rangeland or non-irrigated cropland (Fig. 11–19). Droughts are common features of the climate in drylands. When the rainfall returns, however, vegetation often returns. Despite this, according to the Millennium Ecosystem Assessment, 10–20% of these lands suffer from some form of land degradation. These drylands, occupying some 6 billion hectares, are home to more than 2 billion people and are found on every continent except

Figure 11–19 Drylands cultivation. Farmers till soil in Jinan, China, planting a crop in the semi-desert soil in anticipation of some rainfall.

Antarctica. Since these dryland areas are commonly inhabited by some of the poorest people on Earth, promoting sustainable land management is essential for improving standards of living and meeting the Millennium Development Goals (MDGs) successfully.

Recognizing the severity of this problem, the United Nations established the Convention to Combat Desertification (UNCCD), which was signed and officially ratified by more than 100 nations in 1996. Regular conferences of the parties and other UNCCD meetings have been concerned with such issues as the funding of projects to reverse land degradation, "bottom-up" programs that enable local communities to help themselves, the gathering and dissemination of traditional knowledge on effective drylands agricultural practices, and the development of a 10-year strategic plan. Affected countries have also been developing National Action Programs. One alliance, TerrAfrica, was formed in 2005 by several UN agencies and African countries to fight land degradation in sub-Saharan Africa. The alliance is designed to coordinate efforts toward arresting land degradation and promoting sustainable land management. For example, the government of Madagascar has been working on sustainable land management with several TerrAfrica partners, combating land degradation in its upland watersheds and southern arid lands. Even though variations in climate often play a role in the processes of desertification, it is human impacts that pose the greatest threat to the health of dryland ecosystems. This highlights yet again the connection between soil, water, and human actions.

Water and Soil: Irrigation, Salinization, and Leaching

How we use water has a huge effect on soil health, especially in agricultural systems. Nowhere is this more clear than with irrigation—supplying water to croplands by artificial means.

Figure 11–20 Flood irrigation. The traditional method of irrigation is to flood furrows between rows with water from an irrigation canal. This method is extremely wasteful because most water evaporates or percolates beyond the root zone or because the water table rises to waterlog soil and prevent the crop from growing.

Figure 11–21 Salinization. Millions of acres of irrigated land are now worthless because of the accumulation of salts left behind as water evaporates.

Irrigation has dramatically increased crop production in regions that typically receive low rainfall and is a major part of the Green Revolution (Chapters 8, 12). However, irrigation is also a major contributor to land degradation. Traditionally, water has been diverted from rivers through canals and flooded through furrows in fields, a technique known as **flood irrigation** (Fig. 11–20). **Center-pivot irrigation,** in which water is pumped from a central well through a gigantic sprinkler that slowly pivots itself around the well, has gained popularity as an irrigation method (see Figures 10–16b and c). In more recent years, the much more efficient **drip irrigation,** in which water is taken directly to plants through small tubes, is used at least on some crops.

In the United States, the Bureau of Reclamation is the major government agency involved with ongoing supplies of irrigation water to the western regions. More than 800 dams and reservoirs have been constructed by the bureau since its inception in 1902, and it now provides irrigation water for 4 million hectares (10 million acres) of farmland. Total irrigated land acreage in the United States is 22 million hectares (55 million acres), one-sixth of all cultivated cropland, according to the U.S. Department of Agriculture.

Worldwide, irrigated acreage has risen dramatically in the past few decades. The FAO estimates that total irrigated land now amounts to just more than 300 million hectares (741 million acres). New irrigation projects continue to be built, but the expansion in acreage is now being offset in large part by a negative trend: *salinization.*

Salinization. Salinization is the accumulation of salts in and on soil to the point where plant growth is suppressed (Fig. 11–21). Salinization occurs because even the freshest irrigation water contains at least 200 to 500 ppm (0.02% to 0.05%) dissolved salts. Adding water to dryland soils also dissolves the high concentrations of soluble minerals that are often present in those soils as salts when water evaporates. Because it happens in drylands and renders the land less productive or even useless, salinization is considered a form of desertification.

Worldwide, an estimated 1.5 million hectares (3.7 million acres) of agricultural land—or the equivalent of Connecticut and Rhode Island—is lost yearly to salinization and waterlogging. Pakistan alone has lost an estimated 6.3 million hectares (15.5 million acres) of farmland to salinization. In Mozambique, a promising irrigation project in the Limpopo Valley brought water to more than 33,000 hectares (81,500). Unfortunately by 2012, more than 10,000 of those hectares (25,000) were unusable because of salinization. Adding to the problems, water supplies in many places are fast being depleted by withdrawals for irrigation (Chapter 10).

Salinization can be avoided, and even reversed, if sufficient water is applied to leach the salts down through soil. Attention must be paid to where the salt-laden water goes. For example, the Kesterson National Wildlife Refuge in California was destroyed by pollution from irrigation drainage from selenium-enriched soils of the San Joaquin Valley. After receiving the salty drainage water for only three years, birds, fish, insects, and plants began to die off. The site was declared a toxic waste dump and has been drained and capped with soil. At least 14 other locations in the western United States have been identified as having the potential to accumulate toxic irrigation water, now known as the Kesterson Effect.

Leaching. In places that are heavily irrigated or have heavy rainfall, soils can lose nutrients to leaching. This is particularly true in tropical soils. Sometimes this is a problem because nutrients are leached out of soil, and sometimes it is a problem because toxins are released from being bound to soil particles. One good example of the latter results from a change in soil pH. Soil pH can change with acid rain, a byproduct of burning fossil fuels. As acid rain percolates through soil, it can change the amount of attraction between some chemicals and soil particles. This change can have two important effects. Nutrients such as calcium, magnesium, and potassium that are bound to clay and humus can be separated from soil particles more easily and can be leached out of soil by rain. Another effect is the mobilization of toxins.

Aluminum is usually held in soil in a nontoxic form: aluminum hydroxide. Acid rain breaks chemical bonds, releasing toxic aluminum ions from the insoluble aluminum hydroxide, a process that stunts the roots of plants, keeping them from absorbing nutrients.

Loss of Soil Biota

Soil health is largely regulated by microorganisms and detritus. Organic material holds water, binds mineral particles together, and slowly releases nutrients. Soil microbes help plants germinate, obtain nutrients, and perform other activities. Erosion, salinization, acid rain, and waterlogging can kill soil biota. Some other human activities we have not discussed can also lower soil fertility. One new effect on soil is that of nanoparticles. Nanoparticles are tiny and are used for a variety of purposes. For example, extremely small beads of silver are added to many products as an antimicrobial agent. You can buy "antimicrobial" socks and other products. Unfortunately, nanoparticles can have negative effects on water and soil. A study in the *Journal of Hazardous Materials* in 2011 showed that nanoparticles can kill beneficial soil bacteria and can keep plants from being able to take up nitrogen. However, the study looked at high concentrations of nanoparticles. It is unclear what their effects will be in soils generally. One of the problems with nanoparticles is that they became widely used before sufficient prior study on their environmental effects was completed.

Land Use Changes: Impacts of Mining

Agriculture is the human activity that probably affects soils the most. However, other activities damage soil as well. Just as in the water cycle, soils are affected by land use changes. Construction projects, for example, remove vegetation and topsoil and often lead to erosion. One of the most significant non-agricultural impacts on soil due to land use is the effect of mining.

The scene after a strip mining operation is completed is often similar to a moonscape—great piles of rocks with topsoil removed. In some parts of the United States, these areas are required to be restored, though restoration success varies. In the removed mountaintops of Appalachia, the plateaus left after coal mining are green but relatively unproductive (Chapter 14). The topsoil is gone, too poor to support crops or most trees, and the vegetation that is planted is usually the non-native *Lespedeza cuneata*.

Mining is big business around the world. In addition to coal, people mine gypsum, phosphates, salts, metals, and many other materials, even materials called rare earths that are used in making electronics. Mining removes vegetation and has huge impacts on water quality, human health, and soil erosion. Because of these connections, mining is of importance in our discussions on fossil fuels, water pollution, environmental health, and hazardous waste (Chapters 14, 20, 17, and 22). In 2008, the first International Conference on Mining Impacts on the Human and Natural Environments

was held in Florida. In 2012, conferences were held in Manila, Philippines (March), and Nevada City, Nevada (May), on the impacts of mining on the environment and the need for effective land restoration. Hopefully, this is a direction scientists will pursue.

11.3 Soil Conservation

There is broad consensus that soils are vital to human societies and that they should be preserved. This is encouraging, and so long as this consensus translates into action, we will be moving in the direction of sustainability. Because topsoils grow so slowly (an inch every hundred years at best), sustainability means doing all we can to reduce soil erosion and prevent degradation. However, we will also briefly discuss soil restoration, which can be done after degradation has occurred.

Soil conservation must be practiced at two levels. The most important is the level of the individual landholder. As the story of Gabino López demonstrates (see Sound Science, "Sustainable Agriculture Research with Farmer Experimenters"), those working on the land are best situated to put into practice the conservation strategies that not only enhance their soils, but also bring better harvests and improve their way of life. A great deal of traditional knowledge exists with landholders, who routinely practice soil conservation techniques. The increased production you will read about in Burkina Faso is a prime example. This is stewardship in action.

The second level is public policy. In particular, farm policies play a crucial role in determining how soils are conserved. Policies governing the grazing of public lands and forestry practices also lead to either good or poor stewardship of soils. The two levels must work in harmony to bring about effective, sustainable stewardship of soil resources. Let us examine briefly what is being done in these two areas, beginning with individual landholders.

Helping Individual Landholders

In the developing world as well as the developed world, it is the individual landholders, farmers, and herders who hold the key to sustainable soil stewardship. They must be convinced that what they do will work, that it is affordable, and that, in the long run, their own well-being will improve. It may require help in the way of microlending, sound advice (often best coming from their peers) or simply encouragement to experiment (Chapter 9).

Toward those ends, the UN Convention to Combat Desertification is a large step in the right direction. Other efforts include the new TerrAfrica Alliance and the Sustainable Agriculture and Rural Development Initiative (SARD) facilitated by the FAO. The latter is a kind of umbrella organization that coordinates efforts to reach small farmers with sound agricultural practices; SARD puts the efforts in the context of encouraging sustainable development and achieving the MDGs. An example is found in the Bobo Diaulasso region of

Thirty-five years ago, Gabino López attended classes on sustainable agriculture in San Martín Jilotepeque, Guatemala, and then returned to his village to apply what he had learned to his own small farm. He planted vegetation barriers along the contours of his land to stop erosion and applied cow manure to enrich the soil. His maize harvest increased from 0.8 to 1.3 tons/hectare (1,050 lb/acre). López's harvest jumped to 3.4 tons/hectare when he plowed under his crop residues, as opposed to when he burned them or rotated crops. Aware of his success, his friends asked him for advice, and before long, López became an international consultant in *ecological agriculture*, traveling from Mexico to Ecuador and even India. He and his fellow farmers employ a number of practices that follow the "five golden rules of the humid tropics": (1) keeping soil covered, (2) using minimal or even no tillage, (3) using mulch to provide nutrients for crops, (4) maximizing biomass production, and (5) maximizing biodiversity. As a result, the maize harvest has averaged 4.3 tons/hectare in a number of local villages.

López and his fellow farmers had to deal with both erratic rainfall and the possibility of mudslides. López worked with COSECHA, a Honduran nongovernmental organization (NGO) to connect farmers to research by involving them from the start as "farmer experimenters." To overcome the problem of irregular rainfall, the farmers tested a number of different contraptions for trapping and holding the water for small-scale irrigation. The farmers decided that 1- to 2-cubic-meter catchments were ideal and found many additional uses for the water. Water harvesting is joining green manures and natural pest control in the growing reach of agricultural development that involves villagers experimenting and teaching others what they learn.

Many Central American farmers have to work fields on hillsides, called steep lands. They are difficult to till with machinery, and mudslides are common. While much of the soil conservation work in the world is focused on drylands (lands where soil moisture is very low), steep lands offer their own problems. American researchers have worked with farmer experimenters in the Philippines, another area with steep land farming, to solve some of the unique problems such agriculture causes. In one study, experimenters used high-value crops that grow thickly as a type of hedge between

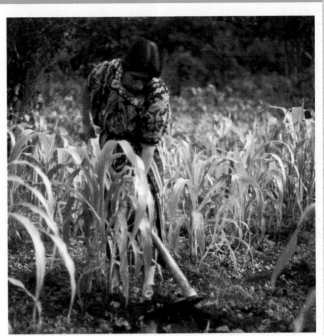

plots of other crops. They also changed when crops were planted in order to have plants that lowered erosion in the field during times when more erosion occurs. For example, corn and cabbage were grown during rainy months rather than tomato because soil loss was lessened. The participation of farmers in the research provided real-world data and made it easier to adopt better soil conservation practices.

Burkina Faso, a rural community in Africa's drylands. Here intensive farming, driven by population growth, has led to a loss of soil fertility and declining crop yields. An FAO project has stepped in to enable a group of farmers to organize and adopt a range of sustainable practices, such as mixing legume and cereal grain plots to preserve soil fertility, cultivating soybeans to diversify income sources, and producing forage to feed livestock during the extended dry season. FAO brought the landholders and other stakeholders together to consolidate these findings into a set of established practices that could be implemented in other similar situations.

The Keita Project. Preventing and reversing the degradation of dryland soils remains a key need for helping the more than 2 billion people who live in drylands, who are often among the poorest on Earth and subject to climatic variations that can destroy their livelihood and well-being. Niger is one of the hottest countries of the world, with much of its land in the Sahara Desert itself. Below the Sahara, Niger is part of the Sahel, an ecoclimatic belt that runs across Africa from the Atlantic Ocean to the Red Sea. It is a semiarid grassland, receiving 6–20 inches of rainfall a year, but often less in drought years. In 1982, the Italian government initiated a project in the Keita district of Niger, more than 4,000 square miles of plateaus, rocky slopes, and grasslands inhabited by 230,000 people. The project targeted the serious degradation brought on by overpopulation and the effects of soil and wind erosion. Some 41 dams were established to catch water from the monsoonal summer rains, more than 18 million trees were planted, and countless check dams were constructed to stop rainwater sheet erosion and provide soil and moisture for crops (see Chapter 10, p. 260). Most of the work was carried out by local people, especially women, who were paid with food. The antierosion land management scheme took many years, but it worked. The Keita district is now a flourishing environment for crops (Fig. 11–22), livestock, and people. Desertification has been halted. The people now have control over their plots of land, an important step toward long-term stewardship of local resources.

SUSTAINABILITY

New Ditches Save Soil

A hard rain pounds on a dusty farm field. Water races down a slope, running in rivulets through the rows, flowing over weeds at the field's edge, swelling the ditch that runs between it and the next field. In minutes the ditch is full, its banks covered with the rushing water. Thunder and lightning fill the sky overhead. The ditch's walls begin to crack, slumping into the torrent. Eddies of water carry brown soil away. The soil leaves the field to head downstream—to a river that does not need this sediment, to clog an estuary, to cover organisms, and to remove a valued resource from the farm that needs it.

Farm ditches are a valuable way to control the flow of water. They keep fields from lying sodden after long rains, but they can also be channels of erosion and can become eroded themselves in a thundering summer downpour. Researchers in Iowa are trying to design a new kind of ditch—one that is effective under normal conditions but can also keep down erosion in extreme storm events. They call this approach "two-stage ditch design." At the bottom of the

ditch is a typical narrow channel. Partway up the ditch are two broad vegetated areas (like benches) that lie on either side of the channel, enclosed by banks that go up to the level of the field. The vegetated flat areas are designed to slow water and stop sediment in the case of a storm event. The ditches do more than save farmer's soil. In rivers, they protect freshwater mussels from the effects of silt. Sediment can overload waterways and kill vulnerable organisms. Far away, less sediment and fewer nutrients will arrive to pollute the distant Gulf of Mexico, an indication of just how connected ecosystems are.

The two-stage ditch design was created by the Nature Conservancy and collaborating partners. General Mills, Cargill, and the Natural

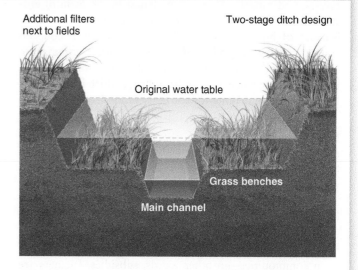

Resource Conservation Service provided funding. Other partners helped with testing, monitoring, and working with landowners. It has been used extensively in Ohio and other states. The two-stage drainage ditch is a good example of a low-tech solution to a common problem—one that will help limit erosion of valuable farm soil.

Two Chains of Events. Desertification has been happening in many places and, when made worse by climate change or extended drought, can lead to permanent degradation and to greater poverty and misery. The human factors responsible include population growth and immigration, unjust land tenure policies, and economic pressure to produce cash crops, all of which intensify the pressure on the land to increase its

ecosystem services. The productivity of the land declines as overgrazing and overcultivation lead to increased erosion. These results are only made worse in the face of extended drought and some impacts of climate change.

This series of events is not inevitable, however. In contrast, in places such as such as Burkina Faso and Niger, dryland dwellers take corrective measures, including better managing livestock and grazing, adopting soil and water conservation measures, and diversifying their income in ways that relieve pressure on the land. The result is a sustainable relationship with dryland ecosystems that results in improving human well-being. Some of the processes of desertification, although distressing, may be signs of the cyclical nature of dryland ecosystems; they simply mean that in time things are likely to change and that what seemed irreversible was in fact not.

Soil Restoration. Although prevention of soil degradation is the best policy, in some cases, soil restoration can be done. Addition of organic material and use of rooted plants to trap soils as well as introduction of soil biota are all components. Sometimes contaminants need to be removed as well. When this is done using organisms, it is called bioremediation. For example, in the case of petroleum contamination, soil microbes are used to break down the contaminant. In other cases, compost, manure, other plant products, and earthworms are added to enhance degraded soils.

Figure 11–22 Land in the Keita district of Niger. This district was the recipient of a remarkable land restoration effort headed by the government of Italy.

Public Policy and Soils

Despite the crucial importance of saving agricultural land, forests, and rangeland, soil degradation in the form of erosion, desertification, and salinization continues to occur because of human activities. The losses are on a collision course with sustainability. Who is responsible for making changes? At the first level, it is the individual landowner, but landowners are subject to public policies, which is the second level of decision making for soil conservation.

Subsidies. Farm policy in the United States was originally focused solely on increasing production. This goal has been achieved, as is demonstrated by continuing high yields and surpluses. The federal government supports U.S. agriculture through a number of programs; the farm lobby is a powerful one that has successfully maintained its support through the years. In more recent years, farm policy has emphasized maintaining farm income and support of farm commodities—in other words, subsidies. Farmers are guaranteed price levels for many products, including grains, cotton, sugar, peanuts, dairy products, and soybeans. This helps keep food prices from fluctuating year to year. In their book *Perverse Subsidies*, Norman Myers and Jennifer Kent[6] point out how subsidies are bad news for the economy and the environment. Myers and Kent argue that subsidies encourage excessive use of pesticides and fertilizers, reduce crop rotation by locking farmers into annual crop support subsidies, and promote the continued drawdown of groundwater aquifers through irrigation. Recall from Section 11.2 how similar subsidies to ranchers for grazing on federal lands have undercut the objectives of soil conservation for those lands.

Sustainable Agriculture. In comparison, the goals of sustainable agriculture are to (1) maintain a productive topsoil, (2) keep food safe and wholesome, (3) reduce the use of chemical fertilizers and pesticides, and last, but far from least, (4) keep farms economically viable. Professional agriculturists are becoming increasingly aware of the shortfalls of modern farming and are at work developing alternatives. Many options actually mimic practices of the past, such as contouring, crop rotation, terracing, the use of smaller equipment, and the application of a reduced amount of chemicals or no chemicals at all. In 1988, the U.S. Department of Agriculture started the Sustainable Agriculture Research and Education (SARE) program, which provides funding for investigating ways to accomplish all of the goals of sustainable agriculture just listed. The program has continued to receive funding of $5 million to $12 million annually, a small but encouraging amount earmarked for building and disseminating knowledge about sustainable agricultural systems.

Farm Legislation. The Federal Agricultural Improvement and Reform Act (FAIR) of 1996 attempted to bring needed reforms. Subsidies and controls over many farm commodities were reduced or eliminated, giving farmers greater flexibility in deciding what to plant, but also forcing them to rely more heavily on the market to guide their decisions. Unfortunately, declining commodity prices prompted yearly emergency farm aid packages, essentially maintaining the subsidies and controls targeted by FAIR.

The 2002 Farm Security and Rural Investment Act succeeded FAIR. It continued to subsidize a host of farm products, maintaining price supports and farm income for American farmers. The latest farm bill is the Farm Bill of 2012, which as of this writing is still under discussion. Before that, the Farm Bill of 2008 was passed by Congress over President George W. Bush's veto. The president objected to the continued high level of support to big farms, arguing that payment limitations and subsidies for crops were too high. Unfortunately, because of subsidies for corn ethanol production, the bill encouraged farmers to plow under remaining native grasslands. It does, however, continue a number of programs aimed at soil and wetland conservation.

Conservation Programs. In 1985, Congress passed the **Conservation Reserve Program (CRP)**, under whose authority highly erodible cropland could be established as a "conservation reserve" of forest and grass. Farmers are paid each year for land placed in the reserve.

Farm bills continue to set out conservation funding. Funding has been provided for two newer programs, the Wildlife Habitat Incentives Program (WHIP) and the Environmental Quality Incentives Program (EQIP), both of which encourage conservation-minded landowners to set aside portions of their land or address pollution problems. The 2002 farm bill initiated the Conservation Security Program (CSP), a voluntary program that encourages stewardship of private farmlands, forests, and watersheds by providing landowners incentives to conserve soil and water resources on their lands. This was renamed the Conservation Stewardship Program in the 2008 farm bill; more than $1 billion was provided for the new CSP. More than 12 million acres of farmlands may be enrolled each year. The 2012 farm bill is still in process at the time of this writing.

Public policies aside, farmers should have incentives to nurture the soil on lands under cultivation. The more farmers incorporate conservation practices in their operations, the more productive their farms will become in the long run. The same applies to those who care for livestock that graze open rangelands. Most observers agree that the most significant obstacle to establishing sustainable soil conservation is a lack of knowledge about what such conservation can do. In particular, this applies to the developing countries, where agricultural policies often are poorly developed and the majority of landholders have little access to agricultural extension services like those provided in the United States by the NRCS. In cases where they are provided with such services, as with Gabino López, they often accomplish surprising gains in agricultural production.

---

[6]Norman Myers and Jennifer Kent, *Perverse Subsidies: How Tax Dollars Can Undercut the Environment and the Economy* (Washington, D.C.: Island Press, 2001).

REVISITING THE THEMES

Sound Science

Soil science uses the principles of sound science to understand how soils are formed, how they are structured, and how they can be sustained. As with any science, however, it is possible to draw erroneous conclusions from the data, as seen with the GLASOD data on world soils and soil degradation and with the data on soil erosion in the United States. The truth is that more field measurements are desperately needed, and the UNCCD's Land Degradation Assessment in Drylands (LADA) is a big step in that direction. In the United States, soil erosion is measured with map reading and equations, and when some scientists actually measured erosion (see p. XXX), they found that the equation approach grossly overestimated erosion rates. Science can include farmers as scientists, giving data on soil use that might be hard to obtain otherwise.

Sustainability

Topsoils take hundreds of years to form and represent the most vital component of land ecosystems. Under most conditions, they are highly sustainable. Because of heavy human use for agriculture, grazing, and forestry and activities like urban expansion and mining, however, lands are being degraded, causing the productivity of those ecosystems to decline. In particular, the drylands have been recognized as extremely vulnerable, and the UNCCD has been helping farmers to adopt new approaches to farming. Programs like COSECHA and TerrAfrica are spreading the word on these new approaches as well as on many sound traditional approaches that are not widely known. The sustainable agriculture practices in Guatemala and around the world are a way to improve soil health. On the other hand, the fees charged for grazing livestock on public lands in the United States are woefully inadequate and promote poor and unsustainable use of public lands.

Stewardship

Those who work the land or graze their livestock are stewards of the soil. So are miners or anyone else using land. They are temporary tenants whose lives will be far shorter than the time it took to form the soil. Their stewardship can lead to sustainable soil health, or it can lead to further erosion and degradation of soil. A few short years of poor management can lead to the loss of hundreds of years' worth of topsoil. Soil is cared for at the local level. Soil stewardship takes place one field at a time, by the people who are most familiar with the land. In many countries, soil erosion is being reversed with practices like no-till agriculture and contour strip cropping. In the United States, the Conservation Stewardship Program encourages farmers to care for soils on their lands. This and other conservation programs under the U.S. Department of Agriculture have been adequately supported by the Food, Conservation, and Energy Act of 2008.

REVIEW QUESTIONS

1. Describe the events that led to the devastation of the Dust Bowl and what role human decision making played.

2. Name and describe the properties of the three main components of soil texture.

3. What are the different layers, or horizons, that compose a soil profile? What makes each one distinct from the others?

4. Name and describe four major soil orders listed in this chapter. Where are they mainly found? How do hydric soils relate to soil orders?

5. What are the main things that plant roots must obtain from soil? Name and describe a process (natural or unnatural) that can keep plants from obtaining the amounts of each of these things they need for survival.

6. Describe, in terms of both content and physical structure, the soil environment that will best fulfill the needs of plants.

7. State and define the relationships among humus, detritus, and soil organisms. Describe the role each of these factors plays in creating a soil favorable to plants.

8. What is meant by mineralization? What causes it? What are its consequences for soil?

9. What are some problems with the sweeping claims made about soil erosion and soil degradation? How have these claims been challenged?

10. What is the impact of water and wind on bare soil? Define and describe the process of erosion in detail.

11. What is meant by desertification? Describe how the process of erosion leads to a loss of water-holding capacity and, hence, to desertification.

12. What are drylands? Where are they found, and how important are they for human habitation and agriculture?

13. What are three major cultural practices that expose soil to the weather?

14. What is meant by salinization, and what are its consequences? How does salinization result from irrigation?

15. Explain how soil biota can be killed by human actions and some of the effects.

16. What are the two levels at which soil conservation must be practiced? Give an example of what is being done at each level.

THINKING ENVIRONMENTALLY

1. Why is soil considered to be a detritus-based ecosystem? Describe how the aboveground portion and the below-ground portion of an ecosystem act as two interrelated and interdependent communities.

2. Suppose you have uncovered an excellent new technique for keeping dryland soils moist and fertile. How would you get your message to the subsistence farmers?

3. Critique the following argument: Erosion is always with us; mountains are formed and then erode, and rivers erode canyons. You can't ever eliminate soil erosion, so it is foolish to ask people to do so.

4. The current system of management of grazing lands by the BLM is clearly unsustainable. What would you suggest in the way of public policy to make it sustainable?

MAKING A DIFFERENCE

1. To prevent soil erosion in your gardens, mulching twice a year can hold moisture in during the summertime and keep plants warmer during the winter. It also keeps rain from washing away your precious topsoil.

2. Don't use a leaf blower. It can erode topsoil more than even some of the most violent winds. It also burns fossil fuels.

3. Try mowing your fallen leaves to make shreds. Leave the shredded leaves in place and cover some with bark chips in garden beds to generate soil that is aerated, is rich with nutrients, and holds moisture better. Both of these practices combat erosion.

4. Composting is extremely sustainable and a very good method to practice. Two-thirds of solid waste is made up of purely organic material such as table scraps, trimmings from the yard, and paper products. Information on how to compost is available on the Internet. If you don't have enough space for traditional composting, you could try vermicomposting, which utilizes the surprising sustainable powers of worms. Many municipalities have yard waste composting as well.

5. When you use fertilizers, use organic products and ones labeled "slow-release" because "quick-release" fertilizer can be easily washed out and pollutes groundwater.

MasteringEnvironmentalScience®

Go to www.masteringenvironmentalscience.com for practice quizzes, Pearson eText, videos, current events, and more.

PART FOUR

Harnessing Energy for Human Societies

Power station in a major industrial area of Shanghai, China.

Ｈｏｗ ESSENTIAL ARE ENERGY SOURCES and services to human societies? Industrialized countries are so completely dependent on fossil fuels and nuclear energy that we cannot imagine an economy apart from these energy sources. Developing countries are following the same example, hoping to enhance the well-being of their people. They have a long way to go; more than 1.5 billion people lack access to electricity, and another billion have unreliable service. Our pursuit of energy sources and services exacts an underappreciated toll in human life and well-being. The processes of energy exploration, extraction, transportation and power generation carry risks that often result in accidental human deaths. Even greater fatalities and loss of health come from the air pollution that accompanies fossil fuel use. In terms of both accidents and pollution, fossil fuels are the most dangerous form of energy generation.

ＴＨＥＲＥ IS MORE BAD NEWS. A recent analysis of the world's oil reserves suggests that oil production may peak within the next decade and then begin a decline that will drive prices up to new heights. Will we invade wildlife refuges and fragile coastal waters to withdraw every last drop of oil from the ground? Looming in the background is the specter of global climate change and the struggle to deal with this threat, which is tied so thoroughly to the use of fossil fuels. Then there are the direct costs of energy and the drag placed on economic recovery and growth by rising fuel costs. It wasn't so long ago that gasoline was selling for less than $2 a gallon. Added to this are the hidden costs of subsidies paid to fossil fuel companies, estimated at $550 billion a year globally.

ＴＨＥＲＥ IS GOOD NEWS, TOO. Wind turbines are appearing all over the landscape on every continent. Solar panels adorn rooftops, and solar "farms" are harvesting the Sun's limitless energy. Biofuels like ethanol are powering millions of vehicles. Regulations are mandating major increases in vehicle fuel economy, and new standards are making energy use far more efficient. Renewable energy sources are on the move, already supplying 10% of electrical generation in the United States and 20% of the global electricity supply.

ＣＡＮ WE CHART a path to a secure energy future? One approach is "business as usual"—pump oil, drive gas-guzzling vehicles, gouge mountains for coal, and lace the countryside with natural-gas wells and pipelines—but there are severe consequences to this approach. An alternative—the sustainable and more secure future—is to focus our energy policy on greater energy efficiency and renewable energy. A 2011 *USA Today*/Gallup poll showed that 83% of Americans favored energy legislation that provides incentives for using alternative energy sources; it was at the top of a list of eight actions Congress could take. The challenge is there, and the choice is ours to make. Part Four describes what is going on in this important area.

CHAPTER 16
Renewable Energy

CHAPTER 16

Renewable Energy

Offshore wind power. The Middlegrunden wind farm, some 2 miles off Copenhagen, Denmark, consists of 20 turbines with a capacity of 40 MW. The wind farm produces about 4% of Copenhagen's power. A larger offshore wind farm for Nantucket Sound, off the southern Massachusetts coast, is soon to commence construction.

LEARNING OBJECTIVES

1. **Strategic Issues: Explain why it is essential to replace fossil fuels with renewable energy sources, and give some details of what has to be done.**

2. **Putting Solar Energy to Work: Recall how much solar energy reaches Earth, and discuss how this energy is being turned into hot water and electricity.**

3. **Indirect Solar Energy: Summarize what is being done to employ hydropower, wind power, and biomass energy to meet energy needs.**

4. **Renewable Energy for Transportation: Discuss how renewable energy is beginning to meet the need to replace oil for transportation, and assess the technologies involved.**

5. **Additional Renewable-Energy Options: Explore the potential for geothermal energy, tidal power, and wave power to meet current and future energy needs.**

6. **Policies for a Sustainable-Energy Future: Evaluate how our national energy policies encourage both renewable energy and energy conservation.**

CAPE WIND. Nantucket Sound, a shallow body of water south of Cape Cod, rarely sees a windless day. Indeed, coastal locations are well known for their constant and often cooling winds, attracting vacationers and year-round residents, who also enjoy the beaches and scenery. Summer populations in Massachusetts towns on Cape Cod swell to many times their winter numbers, putting stress on the area's energy infrastructure. So, in 2001, when Cape Wind Associates proposed an offshore wind farm in Nantucket Sound that could supply 75% of Cape Cod's electricity needs, the company expected a warm welcome. Not so. Instead, its proposal ignited a firestorm of controversy. The proposed wind farm would not be small. Some 130 turbines, each 417 feet tall, would be spread over 24 square miles of Nantucket Sound and generate 470 megawatts (MW) of power. Concerns ranged from "visual pollution" to threats to the area's tourism, navigation, fishing industry, and migrating birds. Organizations like the Alliance to Protect Nantucket Sound filed numerous lawsuits since Cape Wind first proposed the wind farm, and all were eventually dismissed. Proponents of the project, however, view these concerns as a classic case of NIMBY (not in my backyard) and point out that New England desperately needs the renewable energy of offshore winds. Opinion polls on and off Cape Cod strongly support the project. The Bureau of Ocean Energy Management (BOEM), which has authority over all offshore developments in federal waters, issued a favorable environmental impact statement, and Interior Secretary Ken Salazar signed a lease for Cape Wind to proceed. The Federal Aviation Administration recently declared the project free of interference with aeronautical operations, thus giving Cape Wind its final major permit.

During the time that Cape Wind has been trying to build the country's first offshore wind farm, nine European countries have been busy erecting 1,200 offshore turbines that have the capacity to generate some 3.2 gigawatts

Figure 16–1 Solar power bag. Konarka has developed a flexible, thin-film plastic PV system called Power Plastic that shows great promise for many solar applications.

Figure 16–2 Solar thermal power in Southern California. A solar-trough power plant. Sunlight striking the parabolic-shaped mirrors is reflected onto the central pipe, where it heats a fluid that is used in turn to boil water and drive turbogenerators.

(GW, = 1,000 megawatts) of electricity. More than 100 GW capacity is planned or under construction for offshore wind power in Europe alone. In the United States, offshore wind has gotten a boost from the Department of Interior, with its "Smart from the Start" accelerated leasing regulations and funding subsidies from the Department of Energy (DOE). This program focuses on the Atlantic Outer Continental Shelf, where 20 projects have already begun the planning and permitting process.[1] These would contribute hugely to the DOE's goal of achieving 20% of our electricity from wind energy by 2030.

Meanwhile, land-based wind turbines are sprouting up everywhere. In the hills east of San Francisco, regiments of wind turbines standing in rows up the slopes and over the crests of the hills are producing electrical power equivalent to that produced by a large coal-fired power plant. At the end of 2011, wind power capacity in the United States reached 47 GW, enough to power 13 million homes. Every year, installations of wind turbines set new records. Wind turbines are operating as well in India, Mexico, Argentina, New Zealand, and other countries around the world.

SOLAR NOW. Imagine you're in a strange environment, perhaps outdoors, out of range of any electrical outlets, and your iPad battery is running low. No problem. Just plug it in to your handy Eco Traveler Solar Power Bag and let its flexible solar panel charge up the device (Fig. 16–1). The bag works for GPS, cell phones, computers, any

number of small devices. The solar power is captured by a thin sheet of plastic polymer, called Power Plastic, made by Konarka, the company that developed the product. Power Plastic has been built into building curtain walls and the roofs of transit shelters in San Francisco and promises to appear in many more products. Power Plastic captures solar energy with an efficiency of 8.3%, which is not as efficient as silicon photovoltaic (PV) cells at 15–20%, but efficient enough considering its flexibility and adaptability.

Panels of traditional silicon-based PV cells are providing electricity in both developed and developing countries around the world. Throughout Israel and other countries in warm climates, it is now commonplace to have water heated by the Sun. Even in temperate climates, many people have discovered that proper building design, insulation, and simple solar collection devices can reduce energy bills by 75% or more. In the desert northeast of Los Angeles are "farms" with rows of trough-shaped mirrors tipped toward the Sun (Fig. 16–2). These reflectors are focusing the Sun's rays to boil water or synthetic oil and drive turbogenerators.

As these examples demonstrate, the use of energy from the Sun and wind has been making remarkable progress, to the point where renewable sources of energy are becoming cost competitive with traditional energy sources—and are far more practical in many situations. But can they replace fossil fuels as the foundational energy sources of modern societies? Given the unsustainability of our present course—due to the limited supplies of fossil fuels and their polluting impacts on global climate and the air we breathe—is it possible that renewable energy will gain the lion's share of energy in the future? Indeed, do we have any choice?

---

[1]U.S. Department of Energy. A National Offshore Wind Strategy: Creating an Off-shore Wind Energy Industry in the United States. U.S. Department of Energy and U.S. Department of the Interior. February, 2011. www1.eere.energy.gov/wind/pdfs/national_offshore_wind_strategy.pdf. August 3, 2012.

16.1 Strategic Issues

The objective of this chapter is to give you a greater understanding of the potential for capturing energy from sunlight, wind, biomass, flowing water, and other sources. In 2011,

renewable energy provided 9.4% of U.S. primary energy (Fig. 16–3) and 12.6% of electrical power generation; President Barak Obama has called for 80% of the nation's electricity to be generated from clean energy (non-fossil fuel) sources by 2035. Worldwide, renewable-energy supplies 16%

PERCENT OF U.S. ENERGY USE IN 2011

Biomass energy 48.3%
Hydropower 34.7%
Wind 12.8%
Geothermal 2.5%
Solar 1.7%

Total = 9.14 quadrillion btu units
(= 9.4% of U.S. energy use in 2011)

Figure 16–3 Renewable-energy use in the United States. A mix of sources of renewable energy provided 9.4% of the nation's energy used in 2011. (*Source:* Data from Department of Energy, Energy Information Agency, August, 2012.)

TABLE 16–1 Renewable Electric Power at End of 2011, GW Power Capacity

Technology	World Total	United States
Hydropower	970	79
Wind power	238	47
Biomass power	72	14
Solar PV	70	4
Geothermal power	11	3.1
Solar thermal power	1.8	0.5
Ocean (tidal) power	0.5	0
Total renewable power capacity	1,360	147

(*Source:* REN21. Global Status Report. 2012.)

of energy use and 20% of electricity supply (Table 16–1). The UN has targeted a reduction in fossil fuel energy of 80% by 2050, meaning that other sources would have to supply that much. These are ambitious and serious goals, and they raise some significant questions.

Why?

First, why should we want to replace fossil fuels with renewable sources in global energy use, in a matter of decades? The most salient reason is global climate change (see Chapter 18). It is the use of fossil fuels that has loaded the atmosphere with the greenhouse gas carbon dioxide (CO_2), raising the concentration of that one gas by more than 40% to its present concentration of 400 parts per million (ppm). As a result, global temperatures and sea level have already risen, with serious environmental consequences. If we were to continue to increase our use of fossil fuels at the present rate, atmospheric CO_2 would be over 600 ppm by midcentury and well over 1000 ppm by 2100, with global temperature and sea level increases that would be catastrophic. Most international agencies have agreed that to avoid catastrophic climate change it will be necessary to achieve a stable CO_2 level of 450 ppm by mid-century. This is why there is a call to reduce our use of fossil fuels by 80% before 2050.

There are other reasons. Oil and gas reserves will only last a matter of decades, so we are going to have to find new energy sources anyway, and in this century (Chapter 14). Also, there are 1.4 billion people who currently do not have access to electricity and many more whose access is intermittent at best. Renewable energy sources are well suited to supplying power in areas not served by a central electrical grid. And there is the matter of other pollutants, such as sulfur dioxide, mercury and nitrogen oxides, all of which are given off as we burn fossil fuels and all of which contribute significantly to poor health and fatalities.

Getting It Done

Second, is it even possible to accomplish a shift to renewables in so short a time span? Here we encounter some significant problems. Fossil fuels are great sources of concentrated energy, and we access them, distribute them, and employ them in a massive infrastructure. Our modern industrial so-

ciety "has been built around, by and for fossil fuels,"[2] as one commentator put it. It took 70 to 100 years to build the infrastructure of our fossil fuel economy, and we only have a few decades to rebuild much of this infrastructure around clean energy sources (by clean energy, Obama and others are including *nuclear power*, which does not generate CO_2). This is nothing short of a revolution, possibly on the order of the response of the United States to the onset of World War II, where factory after factory shifted its production from peacetime to wartime goods. Clearly, the manufacture of wind turbines, PV panels, transmission lines, concentrated solar power plants, electric vehicles, recharging stations, and so on would have to take place in a relatively short period of time, and this would require massive government support.

Another barrier to accomplishing this transition is the way in which government subsidies, at least in the United States, have strongly favored fossil fuels. For the years 2002–2010, government subsidies to fossil fuels were $98 billion versus $45 billion for renewables. Globally, subsidies encouraging fossil fuel consumption rose to $409 billion (versus $66 billion to renewables). This would have to change, and the fossil fuel, automotive, and utility industries pose an enormous obstacle to change, as they do everything they can to maintain their subsidies.

However, the global shift from fossil fuels to renewable or clean energy sources is starting to happen, so the question is, will it happen fast enough? There are some encouraging developments to suggest that it is possible, but much more has to be done:

• Venture capitalists are sinking a lot of money into green technologies; globally, a record $257 billion was invested in 2011 into wind farms, solar power, electric cars, and so on.

---

[2]Roberts, David. "Direct subsidies to fossil fuels are the tip of the (melting) iceberg." *Grist*, October 26, 2011.

- Thirty-nine states now have some form of a renewable portfolio standard (RPS) or alternative energy portfolio standard (AEPS), which requires electric utilities to generate a certain amount of electricity from sources other than fossil fuels; for example, California must generate 33% of its electricity from renewable sources by 2021.

- Natural gas is becoming more available and can fill a "bridge energy" role to substitute for coal (because coal generates twice as much CO_2 as natural gas per kW of electricity) and to work in tandem with renewable sources that are intermittent in their delivery, to smooth out gaps in electricity generation.

- It may be possible to continue to use coal *if*, and *only if*, the CO_2 generated in the coal power plant is captured from the waste stream and sequestered, known as carbon capture and sequestration (CCS). The technology is known, but the process adds a significant cost to the electricity generated.

- It is possible to hold greenhouse gas emissions to a limit of 450 ppm CO_2— if we stop building more fossil fuel infrastructure and allow the present infrastructure to live out normal lifespans. In other words, it is the future coal power plants and gasoline-powered automobile manufacturing plants that will commit the world to exceeding safe limits of greenhouse gas emissions.

We can now turn our attention to the different forms of renewable energy.

16.2 Putting Solar Energy to Work

Before turning our attention to the practical ways that solar energy is captured and used, let us consider some general concepts of solar energy.

Solar energy originates with thermonuclear fusion in the Sun. (Importantly, all the chemical and radioactive by-products of the reactions remain behind on the Sun.) The solar energy reaching Earth is radiant energy, entering at the top of the atmosphere at 1,366 watts per square meter, the **solar constant.** This energy ranges from ultraviolet light to visible light and infrared light (heat energy) (Fig. 16–4). About half of this energy actually makes it to Earth's surface, 30% is reflected, and 20% is absorbed by the atmosphere. Thus, full sunlight can deliver about 700 watts per square meter to Earth's surface when the Sun is directly overhead. At that rate, the Sun can deliver 700 MW of power (the output of a large power plant) to an area of 390 square miles (1,000 km²). The total amount of solar energy reaching Earth is vast—almost beyond belief. Just 40 minutes of sunlight striking the land surface of the United States yields the equivalent energy of a year's expenditure of fossil fuel. The Sun delivers 10,000 times the energy used by humans.

Moreover, using some of this solar energy will not change the basic energy balance of the biosphere. Solar energy absorbed by water or land surfaces is converted to heat energy and eventually lost to outer space. Even the fraction that is absorbed by vegetation and used in photosynthesis is ultimately given off again in the form of heat energy as various consumers break down food (Chapter 3). Similarly, if humans were to capture and obtain useful work from solar energy, it would still ultimately be converted to heat and lost in accordance with the Second Law of Thermodynamics (see Chapter 3). The overall energy balance would not change.

Although solar energy is an abundant source, it is also diffuse (widely scattered), varying with the season, latitude, and atmospheric conditions. The main problem with using solar energy is one of taking a diffuse and intermittent source and concentrating it into an amount and form, such as fuel or electricity, that can be used to provide heat and run vehicles,

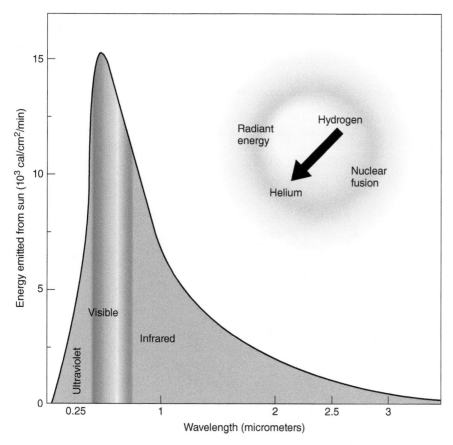

Figure 16–4 The solar-energy spectrum. Equal amounts of energy are found in the visible-light and the infrared regions of the spectrum. In the Sun, the nuclear fusion of hydrogen to form helium emits a spectrum of radiant energy that reaches Earth.

Figure 16–5 The principle of a flat-plate solar collector. As sunlight is absorbed by a black surface, it is converted to heat. A clear glass or plastic window over the surface allows the sunlight to enter the collector, which traps the heat. Air or water is heated as it passes over and through tubes embedded in the black surface.

appliances, and other machinery. These problems involve the *collection*, *conversion*, and *storage* of solar energy. Also, in the final analysis, overcoming such hurdles must be cost effective. In the sections that follow, you will see how we can overcome or, even better, sidestep these three problems in various ways to meet our energy needs in a cost-effective manner.

Solar Heating of Water

Solar hot-water heating is already popular in warm, sunny climates. A solar collector for heating water consists of a thin, broad box with a glass or clear plastic top and a black bottom in which water tubes are embedded (Fig. 16–5). Such collectors are called **flat-plate collectors.** Faced toward the Sun, the black bottom gets hot as it absorbs sunlight—similar to how black pavement heats up in sunlight—and the clear cover prevents the heat from escaping, as in a greenhouse. Water circulating through the tubes is heated and conveyed to a tank, where it is stored.

In an *active system*, the heated water is moved by means of a pump. In a *passive* solar water-heating system, the system must be mounted so that the collector is lower than the tank. Thus, heated water from the collector rises by natural convection into the tank, while cooler

water from the tank descends into the collector (Fig. 16–6). The tank will usually have a source of auxiliary heat (electric or gas) in order to get the temperature to a desired level or to provide heat when solar energy is insufficient.

In temperate climates, where water in the system might freeze, the system may be adapted to include a heat-exchange coil within the hot-water tank. Then antifreeze fluid is circulated between the collector and the tank. In the United States, approximately 2.5 million solar hot-water systems have been installed, but this is still only a small fraction of the total number of hot-water heaters. The reason is the initial cost, which is five to 10 times as much as gas or electric heaters. However, over time, the solar system costs less to operate than an electric or a gas system. In China, more than 18 million households are getting their hot water from solar thermal systems; China leads the world in this application of solar energy.

Solar Space Heating

The same concept for heating water with the Sun can be applied to heat spaces. Flat-plate collectors such as those used in water heating can be used for space heating. Indeed, the collectors for space heating may even be less expensive, homemade devices, because it is necessary only to have air circulate through the collector box. Again, efficiency is gained if the collectors are mounted, to allow natural convection to circulate the heated air into the space to be heated (Fig. 16–7).

Building = Collector. The greatest efficiency in solar space heating, however, is gained by designing a building to act as its own collector. The basic principle is to have windows facing the Sun. In the winter, because of the Sun's angle of incidence, sunlight can come in and heat the interior of the building (Fig. 16–8a). At night, insulated drapes or shades can be pulled down to trap the heat inside. The well-insulated

Figure 16–6 Solar water heaters. In nonfreezing climates, simple water-convection systems may suffice. In freezing climates, an antifreeze fluid is circulated. Solar heat is augmented by an auxiliary heat source in the hot-water tank.

Figure 16–7 Passive hot-air solar heating. Many homeowners could save on fuel bills by adding homemade solar collectors like the one shown here. Air heated in the collector moves into the room by passive convection.

Figure 16–8 Solar building siting.
In contrast to utilizing expensive and complex active solar systems, solar heating *can* be achieved by suitable architecture and orientation of the home at little or no additional cost. (a) The fundamental feature is large, Sun-facing windows that permit sunlight to enter during the winter months. Insulating drapes or shades are drawn to hold in the heat when the Sun is not shining. (b) Suitable overhangs, awnings, and deciduous plantings prevent excessive heating in the summer.

building, with appropriately made doors and windows, acts as its own best heat-storage unit. Beyond good insulation, other systems for storing heat, such as tanks of water or masses of rocks, have not proved to be cost effective. Excessive heat load in the summer can be avoided by using an awning or overhang to shield the window from the high summer Sun (Fig. 16–8b).

Along with design, positioning, and improved insulation, appropriate landscaping can contribute to the heating and cooling efficiency of both solar and nonsolar space-heating designs, thereby conserving energy. In particular, deciduous trees or vines on the sunny side of a building can block much of the excessive summer heat while letting the desired winter sunlight pass through. An evergreen hedge on the shady side can provide protection from the cold.

Energy Stars. In almost any climate, a well-designed passive solar-energy building can reduce energy bills substantially, with an added construction cost of only 5–10%. Because about 25% of our primary energy is used for space and water heating, proper solar design, broadly adopted, would create enormous savings on oil, natural gas, and electrical power. In 2001, the Environmental Protection Agency (EPA) extended its **Energy Star Program** to buildings and began awarding the Energy Star label to public and corporate edifices. Buildings awarded the label use at least 40% less energy than others in their class and must meet a number of other criteria to qualify. By 2012, more than 17,000 buildings had earned the label, representing more than 2.5 billion square feet of space—a major contribution to **energy conservation**.

A common criticism of solar heating is that a backup heating system is still required for periods of inclement weather. Good insulation is a major part of the answer to this criticism. People with well-insulated solar homes find that they have minimal need for backup heating.

When backup is needed, a woodstove or gas heater may be enough. In any case, the criticism concerning the need for backup heating misses the point: The objective of solar heating is to reduce our dependency on conventional fuels. Even if solar heating and improved insulation reduced the demand for conventional fuels by a mere 20%, that would still represent sustainable savings of 20% of the traditional fuel and its economic and environmental costs.

Solar Production of Electricity

Solar energy can also be used to produce electrical power, providing an alternative to coal and nuclear power. There are two distinct approaches: photovoltaic systems and concentrated solar power (CSP).

Photovoltaic Cells. A solar cell—more properly called a **photovoltaic, or PV, cell**—looks like a simple wafer of material with one wire attached to the top and one to the bottom (Fig. 16–9). As sunlight shines on the wafer, it puts out an amount of electrical current roughly equivalent to that emitted by a flashlight battery. Thus, PV cells collect light and convert it to electrical power in one step. The cells,

Figure 16–9 Photovoltaic cell. Converting light to electrical energy, this cell provides enough energy to run the small electric motor needed to turn the fan blades.

measuring about four inches square, produce about one watt of power. Some 40 such cells can be linked to form a module that generates enough energy to light a lightbulb. Varying amounts of power can be produced by wiring modules together in panels.

How They Work. The simple appearance of PV cells belies a highly sophisticated level of science and technology. Each cell consists of two very thin layers of semiconductor material separated by a junction layer. The lower layer has atoms with single electrons in their outer orbital that are easily lost. The upper layer has atoms lacking electrons in their outer orbital; these atoms readily gain electrons. The kinetic energy of light photons striking the two-layer "sandwich" dislodges electrons from the lower layer, creating a current that can flow through a motor or some other electrical device and back to the upper side. Thus, with no moving parts, solar cells convert light energy directly to electrical power, with an efficiency of 15–20%.

Because they have no moving parts, solar cells do not wear out. However, deterioration due to exposure to the weather limits their life span to about 30 years. The major material used in PV cells is silicon, one of the most abundant elements on Earth, so there is little danger that the production of PV cells will ever suffer because of limited resources. The cost of these cells lies mainly in their sophisticated design and construction.

Uses. PV cells are already in common use in pocket calculators, watches, and numerous toys. Panels of PV cells provide power for rural homes, irrigation pumps, traffic signals, radio transmitters, lighthouses, offshore oil-drilling platforms, Earth-orbiting satellites, and other installations that are distant from power lines. It is not hard to imagine a future in which every home and building has its own source of pollution-free, sustainable electrical power from an array of PV panels on the roof. Current installations in many countries and in some 43 states in the United States employ *net metering*, where the rooftop electrical output is subtracted from the customer's use of power from the power grid.

Cost. The cost of PV power (cents per kilowatt-hour) is the cost of the installed PV systems divided by the total amount of power they may be expected to produce over their lifetime (currently as low as 12 cents per kilowatt-hour). This cost is quite comparable to that of other power alternatives (8–16 cents per kilowatt-hour for residential electricity in the United States). The first PV cells had a cost factor several hundred times that of electricity from conventional power stations transmitted through the power grid, so those cells were used mainly in areas far from the grid. PV power had its first significant application in the 1950s, in the solar panels of space satellites. This application started the development cycle rolling. As more efficient cells and less expensive production techniques evolved, costs came down dramatically. In turn, applications, sales, and potential markets expanded, creating the incentive for further development. In response to this, it is the fastest-growing energy technology industry in the world. In 2011, the industry shipped solar panels with a total capacity of 24 GW; existing solar PV panels now have the capacity to turn sunlight into more than 70 GW of electricity (Fig. 16–10).

Inverters. The most complicated (and yet necessary) component of a PV system is the **inverter**. The inverter (Fig. 16–11) acts as an interface between the solar PV modules and the electric grid or batteries. It must change the incoming direct current (DC) from the PV modules to alternating

Figure 16–10 The market for PV panels. Global sales of PV panels have increased dramatically, exceeding 70,000 MW by 2011. More than three-fourths of the PV panels are connected to the electric grid. (*Source: Renewables 2012 Global Status Report.*)

Figure 16–12 **PV power plant.** The Copper Mountain Solar Facility in Nevada consists of 775,000 solar panels and has an installed capacity of 48 MW. It is the largest PV plant in the United States. The plant was built in 11 months at a cost of $141 million.

Figure 16–11 **PV system inverter.** Inverter (on right) and controllers for a PV system at Channel Islands National Park, California. The inverter is a device that connects the PV panels of a rooftop system to the electric grid or devices powered by PV electricity. It converts the direct current coming from PV panels to alternating current and also acts as a control for the system.

current (AC) compatible with the electricity coming from the grid and/or the devices that will be powered by the PV system. It must also act as a control, able to detect and respond to fluctuations in voltage or current on either DC or AC, and it must be robust enough to withstand the high temperatures of an attic (where rooftop PV systems are involved). An inverter for a rooftop system will cost several thousand dollars, but in most cases, these are also eligible for local and national subsidies. Like the cost of PV cells, the cost of inverters has also come down over time.

Utilities. The utility companies are moving toward large-scale PV installations. At the end of 2011, there were 40 plants worldwide with capacities greater than 20 MW, with 31 more planned or under construction. The largest one in the United States is the 48 MW Copper Mountain Solar Facility in Nevada (Fig. 16–12), providing electricity for 14,000 homes. The world's largest solar PV power plant is in Canada—the Sarnia PV Power Plant, with a 97 MW capacity. This record won't last long, as there are much

larger ones under construction. In some cases, PV is getting the nod over Concentrated Solar Power, or CSP, facilities (discussed later), because it can be added in smaller increments, allowing limited transmission lines to handle the voltages.

However, the most promising future for PV power is in the installation of PV panels on rooftops, where a huge amount of unused space is readily available. California's Edison International is busy installing 150 solar projects on warehouse and factory roofs; the company anticipates spending $875 million to provide 250 MW of electricity on commercial rooftops. For residential use, utilities in many states have established programs that provide incentives to customers to install 2- to 4-kilowatt (kW) PV systems on their roofs. A 2 kW system provides about half of the annual energy needs of a residence, and in case the homeowner is generating more than needed, the utility buys the excess electricity at the retail rate. Even though the rooftop systems represent a loss in power purchases, the utilities benefit because they avoid the need to build expensive new power plants. A federal investment tax credit of 30% of the system cost was enacted in the Emergency Economic Stabilization Act of 2008, providing incentives to homeowners to go solar. Sunny California experienced a 47% increase in rooftop solar in 2010 and passed the 1,000 MW (1 GW) mark in late 2011. The world leader in installed rooftop PV is Germany, with more than 12 GW installed capacity.

New PV Technologies. To compete with electricity from conventional sources, the cost of solar cells needs to be low. At least four new technologies may drive the cost even lower: (1) thin-film PV cells, in which cheap amorphous silicon or cadmium telluride is used instead of expensive silicon crystals, and the film can be applied as a coating on roofing tiles or glass; (2) a 3-D silicon solar cell that captures up to 25% of the incoming light energy; (3) glass coated with light-absorbing dyes that transmit energy to solar cells on the edge of the glass, while allowing much of the light to pass through to conventional solar panels; (4) the flexible plastic polymer cells illustrated in Figure 16–1. All of these techniques are either in production or close to it.

Concentrated Solar Power (CSP). If you have ever focused sunlight through a magnifying glass to burn a hole in a leaf, you have used CSP. Several technologies have been developed that convert solar energy into electricity by using reflectors (or concentrators) such as mirrors to focus concentrated sunlight onto a receiver that transfers the heat to a conventional turbogenerator. These devices work well only in regions with abundant sunlight and plenty of space, and they are producing power in the U.S. Southwest and in Spain. A major drawback to this technology is the need for a lot of water to cool the steam generated. Nevertheless, CSP is growing rapidly, now at 1.8 GW generating capacity globally, with a number of projects under construction. The two methods currently in the lead for CSP are the solar (or parabolic) trough and the power tower.

Solar Trough. One method that is proving to be cost effective is the **solar-trough** collector system, so named because the collectors are long, trough-shaped reflectors tilted toward the Sun (Fig. 16–2). The curvature of the trough is such that all of the sunlight hitting the collector is reflected onto a pipe running down the center of the system. Oil or some other heat-absorbing fluid circulating through the pipe is thus heated to very high temperatures. The heated fluid is passed through a heat exchanger to boil water and produce steam for driving a turbogenerator.

Nine solar-trough facilities in the Mojave Desert of California have been connected to the Southern California Edison utility grid since the early 1990s. Solar-trough is the most developed of CSP technologies, and most new CSP plants are solar-trough. Soon to be largest in the world, Solana, a new 250 MW solar trough plant, is under construction in the Arizona desert. One advantage of this technology is the capability of storing some of the thermal energy for release at night; the Solana plant will store energy for many hours.

Power Tower. A **power tower** is an array of Sun-tracking mirrors that focuses the sunlight falling on several acres of land onto a receiver mounted on a tower in the center of the area (Fig. 16–13). The receiver transfers the heat energy collected to a molten-salt liquid, which then flows either to a heat exchanger

to drive a conventional turbogenerator or to a tank at the bottom of the tower to store the heat for later use. Presently, the Sierra SunTower is the only power tower operating in the United States, generating 5 MW of electricity.

Spain has CSP projects under construction for some 1,300 MW, both solar-trough and power tower systems. A royal decree and government subsidies have paved the way for Spain to become a world leader in commercial CSP development (adding substantially to its rising investment in PV power plants).

The Future of Solar Energy

Solar electricity is growing at a phenomenal rate—the solar PV business is a $30 billion industry, and sales continue to grow exponentially (see Figure 16–10). The industry is hard-pressed to keep up with current demand. Solar energy does have certain disadvantages, however. First, the available technologies are still more expensive than conventional energy sources, though solar sources are getting close to parity with conventional ones. Second, solar energy works only during the day, so it requires a backup energy source, a storage battery, or thermal storage for nighttime power. Also, the climate is not sunny enough to use solar energy in the winter in many parts of the world. Against these drawbacks should be weighed the hidden costs that are not included in the cost of power from traditional sources: air pollution, strip mining, greenhouse gas emissions, and nuclear waste disposal, among others.

Matching Demand. The Sun provides power only during the day, but 70% of electrical demand occurs during daytime hours, when industries, offices, and stores are in operation. Thus, considerable savings still can be achieved by using solar panels just for daytime needs and continuing to rely on conventional sources at night. In particular, the demand for air-conditioning, which, after refrigeration, is the second largest power consumer, is well matched to energy from PV cells. In the long run, the nighttime load might be carried by forms of indirect solar energy, such as wind power and hydropower (discussed later in the chapter).

It is a fact that about 61% of our electrical power (54% worldwide) is currently generated by coal-burning and nuclear power plants (Chapter 14, Table 14–1). Therefore, the development of solar and wind electrical power can be seen as gradually reducing the need for coal and nuclear power. Unlike new nuclear or coal power plants, which take years to plan and build, solar or wind facilities can become operational within months of the decision to build them. The utility does not have to guess what power demands will be in 10 or 15 years. With solar or wind power, a utility can add capacity as it is needed, make relatively small investments at any given time, and have those investments start paying back almost immediately. Thus, this approach involves much less financial risk both for the utility and for its consumers.

One further advantage of solar and wind facilities is their relative invulnerability to terrorist attack compared with oil and gas pipelines and large power plants, especially

Figure 16–13 Sierra SunTower. Sun-tracking mirrors are used to focus a broad area of sunlight onto a molten-salt receiver mounted on the two towers. The hot salt is stored or pumped through a steam generator, which drives a conventional turbogenerator.

Transfer of Energy Technology to the Developing World

The nations of the industrialized Northern Hemisphere have achieved their level of development by using energy technologies based largely on fossil fuels (and, to a lesser extent, nuclear energy). These nations' development took place during a time when fossil fuels were inexpensive. Only as those fuels became more expensive did the nations of the North begin to get serious about technologies that would make energy use more efficient. The specter of global climate change has brought a new perspective to the need to wean the industrialized North away from fossil fuel energy in the 21st century.

The same traditional fossil fuel–based technologies have been adopted by the developing nations of the Southern Hemisphere, except that these nations are lagging behind in their ability to implement the technology on a large scale. As discussed earlier in the chapter, however, the fossil fuel–based energy pattern of the 20th century will have to be replaced largely with renewable-energy systems in the 21st century. We have only one or two generations remaining for the dominance of fossil fuel energy. If the United States and other developed nations are willing to play a significant role in helping the developing nations, it is questionable whether the same developmental path the North took should be promoted. Instead, there is the opportunity to engage in some "leapfrogging" technology transfer: The North can put its development dollars into such technologies as photovoltaics, wind turbines, and efficient public transport systems for the cities.

The solar route is especially attractive for many of the climates in the developing world, where an estimated 1.4 billion people lack electricity. For example, more than 200,000 PV systems installed in Kenya over a 20-year period now provide power to 5% of the rural Kenyan population. The systems, with costs ranging from $300 to $1,500, are successfully marketed to people with incomes averaging less than $100 per month. Only the solar panels are imported; local companies provide the batteries and other system components. People use the energy for lighting, television, and radio. Annual sales in Kenya exceed 30,000 systems, a sign that the technology is in great demand and is fostering appropriate development in the area. Credit and financing extended to both companies and users have been key to this success. Some of the financing originates with development agencies from the North, but the majority is Kenyan. Building the infrastructure to market and service the PV systems has also been an essential part of the success story, and that can be accomplished by a relatively small number of organizations and individuals. These solar home systems are being added in many other developing countries, especially China, Bangladesh, India, Mexico, and Morocco.

nuclear facilities. Further, renewables produce no hazardous wastes and are geographically dispersed.

Solar power has also proved suitable for meeting the needs of electrifying villages and towns in the developing world, where, because centralized power is unavailable, rural electrification projects based on PV cells are already beginning to spread throughout the land (see Sustainability, "Transfer of Energy Technology to the Developing World"). The cost of the alternative—putting roughly 1.4 billion people who are still without electricity on the **power grid** (and thus requiring central power plants, high-voltage transmission lines, poles, wires, and transformers)—is unimaginable.

Solar electric power has a bright future. Costs of solar PV systems are declining by about 5% per year, as efficiencies of PV cells improve and manufacturers achieve economies of scale with the rising demand. Homeowners are ready to spend $10,000 or more to install rooftop PV systems, especially when subsidies are now available from the federal government and many states. The technology is now mature, and many small installation companies are competing for home solar PV installations. Finally, the solar energy resource is huge in comparison with all of the finite fossil and nuclear fuel resources, which will last only a few generations at most. We need only exploit a small fraction of solar potential to meet all of our energy needs. Undoubtedly, the future planetary energy source is going to be solar-based.

Of course, solar power is only one of a number of renewable forms of energy. Some of these other sources are derived from solar energy and have been around for a long time.

16.3 Indirect Solar Energy

Water, fire, and wind have provided energy for humans throughout history. Dams, firewood, windmills, and sails represent indirect solar energy because energy from the Sun is the driving force behind each. (Recall in Chapter 10 how solar energy powers the hydrologic cycle of evaporation and precipitation and also drives the convection currents that produce the wind). What is the potential for expanding these options from the past into major sources of sustainable energy for the future?

Hydropower

Early in technological history, it was discovered that the force of falling water could be used to turn paddle wheels, which in turn would drive machinery to grind grain, saw logs into lumber, and run simple machines. The modern culmination of this use of waterpower, or hydropower, is huge hydroelectric dams, where water under high pressure flows through channels, driving turbogenerators (**Fig. 16–14**). The amount of power generated is proportional to both the height of the water behind the dam—that is what provides the pressure—and the volume of water that flows through (Chapter 10 describes the role played by dams in trapping and controlling rivers for flood control, irrigation, and hydropower).

About 7.9% of the electrical power generated in the United States currently comes from hydroelectric dams, most of it from about 300 large dams concentrated in the Northwest and Southeast. Worldwide, hydroelectric dams have a

Figure 16–14 Hoover Dam. About 7.9% of the electrical power used in the United States in 2011 came from large hydroelectric dams such as this one on the Colorado River in Nevada.

generating capacity of 970 GW, with more very large projects in the construction or planning stage. Hydropower generates 19% of electrical power throughout the world and is by far the most abundant form of renewable energy in use.

Trade-offs. Dams—in particular, the larger ones—are often controversial; they provide important benefits but also involve some serious consequences. The most obvious *advantages* are these:

- Hydropower eliminates the cost and environmental effects of fossil fuels and nuclear power. Hydroelectric plants have longer lives than fuel-fired ones; some plants have been in service for 100 years.

- The dams provide flood control on many rivers that have taken huge tolls in human lives, and they also provide irrigation water for agriculture. Some 40% of the world's food is generated from the irrigation facilitated by the reservoirs behind dams.

- Reservoirs behind the dams often provide recreational and tourist opportunities.

- Dams can be employed in **pumped-storage power plants**; during the night, when electricity demand is low, the dam's hydrogenerator pumps water up to an elevated reservoir through a tunnel. At times of high demand, the water is returned to the lower reservoir through the tunnel, where it spins turbines and generates electricity.

There are also some serious *disadvantages*, however:

- The reservoir created behind the dam inevitably drowns farmland or wildlife habitats and perhaps towns or

land of historical, archaeological, or cultural value. Glen Canyon Dam (on the border between Arizona and Utah), for example, drowned one of the world's most spectacular canyons.

- Dams and the large reservoirs created behind them often displace rural populations. In the past 50 years, some 40 million to 80 million people have been forced to move to accommodate the rising waters of reservoirs.

- Dams impede or prevent the migration of fish, even when fish ladders are provided. Federal surveys show that fish habitats are suffering in the majority of the nation's rivers because of damming.

- Because the flow of water is regulated according to the need for power, dams wreak havoc downstream. Water may go from near flood levels to virtual dryness and back to flood levels in a single day. Other ecological factors are also affected because sediments with nutrients settle in the reservoir, meaning that smaller-than-normal amounts reach the river's mouth.

More Dams? Even if such trade-offs were not enough, thoughts of greatly expanding waterpower in the United States are nullified by the fact that few sites conducive to large dams remain. Already, 75,000 dams six feet high or more dot U.S. rivers, with an estimated 2 million smaller structures. As a result, only 2% of the nation's rivers remain free flowing, and many of these are now protected by the Wild and Scenic Rivers Act of 1968, a law that effectively gives certain scenic rivers the status of national parks. The United States and most developed countries have already brought their hydropower to capacity, and the trend is in the direction of removing many of the dams that impede the natural flow of rivers.

Proposals for new dams outside of the United States are embroiled in controversy over whether the projected benefits justify the ecological and sociological trade-offs. For example, the 39-meter-high Nam Theun 2 Dam, a 1,075 MW project on a tributary of the Mekong River in Laos, is expected to help that country begin a process of economic development. The project received final approval in 2005 from the World Bank and Asian Development Bank for guarantees and loans, and construction was completed in 2010. The project has displaced 6,200 people and has inundated 175 square miles (450 km^2) of the Nakai Plateau. In addition, it is basically being built to sell power to Thailand (only 75 MW are to be channeled to Laos at first). International Rivers (IR) is monitoring implementation of the project. Charges and countercharges have flown back and forth between the World Bank and IR concerning the impacts of the dam, especially on downstream communities; it is likely too soon to issue a verdict on the dam's overall effects.

Another huge dam, completed in 2006, is the Three Gorges Dam on the Yangtze River in China (See Chapter 10). The largest dam ever built (1.4 miles long), Three Gorges has displaced some 1.2 million people in order to generate

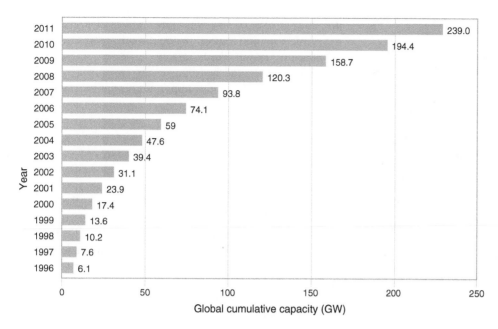

Figure 16–15 **Global development of wind energy.** As the cost of wind energy has dropped to the level of being very competitive with conventional energy sources, wind turbine capacity has risen dramatically. (*Source:* Data from Global Wind Energy Council.)

22,000 MW of electricity and control the flood-prone river. Offsetting the human and economic costs is the fact that it would take more than a dozen large coal-fired power plants to produce the same amount of electricity.

A special World Commission on Dams, convened to examine the impacts and controversies surrounding large dams, reported its findings in 2000. The commission began with the assertion that dams are only a means to an end, the end being "the sustainable improvement of human welfare." The report found dams to be a mixed blessing, concluding that large dams should be built only if no other options exist.[3] Many guidelines were presented for assessing costs and benefits of specific projects—in particular, for finding ways to incorporate participatory decision making, sustainability, and accountability in the planning and implementation of projects. Following up the World Commission work, the United Nations Environment Program (UNEP) established the Dams and Development Forum, which meets annually to participate in debate and decision making over dam development in various countries. Many more dams will be built, largely in the developing countries (especially China, Brazil, Turkey, and India), and these will certainly play a role in the energy future of those countries.

Wind Power

Once a standard farm fixture, windmills fell into disuse as transmission lines brought abundant lower-cost power from central generating plants. Not until the energy crisis and rising energy costs of the 1970s did wind begin to be seriously considered again as a potential source of sustainable energy. Growing rapidly, wind power now supplies around 2.5% of global electricity demand, but there are no technical, economic, or resource limitations that would prevent wind power from supplying at least 12% of the world's electricity by 2020, with a generating capacity of 1.2 thousand GW. In Denmark, which is hard pressed by a lack of fossil fuel energy, wind now supplies more than 22% of the electricity.

China is the world leader in wind energy (65 GW), with the United States close behind (47 GW capacity in 2011). In the past five years, global wind power capacity has increased at a rate of 26% per year, to 239 GW at the start of 2012 (Fig. 16–15). Wind is the second-largest component of renewable electricity in the world (behind hydropower), because it has become economically competitive with conventional energy sources, and countries all over the world are encouraging the installation of wind turbines by setting targets and providing subsidies.

A new feature of the American landscape is the "wind farm," a collection of wind turbines in the same location whose power generation can occur while the land beneath the turbines can be used for traditional agricultural purposes. These are getting huge: The Horse Hollow Wind Farm near Abilene, Texas, consists of 421 turbines with a capacity of 735 MW (Fig. 16–16); the Shepherd's Flat Wind Farm in eastern Oregon is under construction and when finished will occupy 30 square miles, house 338 turbines, have an installed capacity of 845 MW, and be the world's largest land-based wind farm (for a while!).

Design. Many different designs of wind machines have been proposed and tested, but the one that has proved most practical is the age-old concept of wind-driven propeller blades. The propeller shaft is geared directly to a generator. (A wind-driven generator is more properly called a wind turbine than a windmill.) As the reliability and efficiency of wind turbines have improved, the cost of wind-generated electricity has decreased. Wind farms are now producing

---

[3]*Dams and Development: A New Framework for Decision-Making. The Report of the World Commission on Dams.* Earthscan Publications. 2000.

Figure 16–16 Horse Hollow Wind Farm. Located near Abilene, Texas, this wind farm consists of 421 turbines with a capacity of 735 MW.

pollution-free, sustainable power for around five cents per kilowatt-hour, a rate that is competitive with the rates of traditional sources. Moreover, the amount of wind that can be tapped is immense. The American Wind Energy Association calculates that wind farms located throughout the Midwest could meet the electrical needs of the entire country, while the land beneath the turbines could still be used for farming. Hundreds of new turbines are sprouting from midwestern farms, and the farmers are paid royalties ($3,000 to $5,000 per turbine per year) for leasing their land to wind developers. The U.S. Department of Energy (DOE) is promoting a scenario where wind energy will provide 20% of U.S. electricity needs by 2030—an ambitious, but by no means impossible, target.

Drawbacks. Still, wind power does have some drawbacks. First, it is an intermittent source, so problems of backup or storage must be considered. Second is an aesthetic consideration: One or two wind turbines can be charming, but a landscape covered with them can be visually unappealing (to some). Third, wind turbines can be a hazard to birds and bats. Locating wind farms on migratory routes or near critical habitats for endangered species such as condors could be a problem for soaring birds in particular. Mortality from wind turbines may be upward of 40,000 per year, but this number pales in comparison to the hundreds of millions of birds killed annually by cats, automotive traffic, and glass windows.

As discussed earlier, plans for offshore wind farms are putting a new spin on wind energy. Denmark already has many offshore turbines, as do the Netherlands, the United Kingdom, and Sweden. Belgium, France, and Germany are also in the development stage. The primary lure of offshore wind is the dependability and strength of the maritime winds. Siting is perhaps easier, too, as the turbines will be far enough offshore to have much less of a visual impact than onshore sites and land does not have to be purchased. Whether offshore or onshore, the global drive to install wind power is generating electricity that is emission free; in fact,

the 43,000 MW of new wind turbines installed in 2011 displaced 125 million tons of carbon dioxide, or emissions from 65 coal-fired power plants.

Wind power and hydropower are two forms of indirect solar energy; another highly important form is biomass energy.

Biomass Energy

Burning firewood for heat is the oldest form of energy that humans have used throughout history. However, there is nothing like a new name to put life into an old concept. Thus, "burning firewood" has become "utilizing biomass energy." **Biomass energy** means energy derived from present-day photosynthesis. As Figure 16–3 indicates, biomass energy leads hydropower in renewable-energy production in the United States. (Most uses of biomass energy are for heat.)

In addition to burning wood in a stove, major means of producing biomass energy include burning municipal wastepaper and other organic waste, generating methane from the anaerobic digestion of manure and sewage sludges, running power plants on wastes from timber operations, and producing alcohol from fermenting grains and other starchy materials.

Burning Firewood. Wherever forests are ample relative to the human population, firewood—or fuelwood, as it is called—can be a sustainable energy resource; and, indeed, wood has been a main energy resource over much of human history. Fuelwood is the primary source of energy for heating and cooking for some 2.6 billion people, amounting to about 9% of total energy use from all sources.

In the United States, woodstoves have enjoyed a tremendous resurgence in recent years: About 5 million homes rely entirely on wood for heating, and another 20 million use wood for some heating. The most recent development in woodstoves is the *pellet stove*, a device that burns compressed wood pellets made from wood wastes (Fig. 16–17). The pellets are loaded into a hopper (controlled by computer

Figure 16–17 Pellet stove. Pellet stoves use pelletized wood waste to achieve an efficient burn that requires much less care than burns from conventional woodstoves.

chips) that feeds fuel when it is needed. The stove requires very little attention and burns efficiently, relying on one fan to draw air into it and another fan to distribute heated air to the room.

Fuelwood Crisis? Recall that two patterns of use determine how forest resources will be exploited: consumptive use and productive use (Chapter 7). Most fuelwood use in developing countries fits the *consumptive* pattern: People simply forage for their daily needs in local woodlands and forests. However, gathering wood, converting wood into charcoal, and selling the wood products in urban areas translates into important *productive* use activities for many in developing countries. All these activities have the potential to degrade local forests and woodlands. There was serious concern in the later decades of the 20th century about deforestation due to wood gathering, but though there are local shortages, it appears that global use of fuelwood peaked in the late 1990s and is now declining. As development progresses, people have more disposable income and shift up the "energy ladder" from wood to charcoal to fossil fuels. The Millennium Ecosystem Assessment judged that fuelwood demand has not become a significant cause of deforestation, though there are local areas of concern. This could change if the cost of fossil fuels continues to rise.

Burning Wastes. Facilities that generate electrical power from the burning of municipal wastes (waste-to-energy conversion) are discussed in another chapter (Chapter 21). Many sawmills and woodworking companies are now burning wood wastes, and a number of sugar refineries are burning cane wastes to supply all or most of their power. In Virginia, three 63 MW coal-fired power plants are being converted to biomass power, primarily wood waste from timber operations. Power from these sources may not meet more than a small percentage of a country's total electrical needs, but it represents a productive and relatively inexpensive way to dispose of biological wastes as well as to prevent more fossil fuel combustion.

Producing Methane. The anaerobic digestion of sewage sludge yields *biogas*, which is two-thirds methane, plus a nutrient-rich treated sludge that is a good organic fertilizer (examined further in Chapter 20). Animal manure can be digested likewise. When the disposal of manure, the production of energy, and the creation of fertilizer can be combined in an efficient cycle, great economic benefit can be achieved. In China and India, millions of small farmers maintain a simple digester in the form of an underground brick masonry fermentation chamber with a fixed dome on top for storing gas (Fig. 16–18). Agricultural wastes, such as pig manure and cattle dung, are put into the chamber and diluted 1:1 with water, and the anaerobic digestion produces the biogas, which is used for cooking, heating, and lighting. The residue slurry makes an excellent fertilizer. The concept has been expanded throughout the developing world to provide an alternative to fuelwood. Currently, some 25 million households employ these

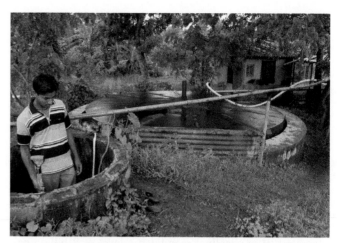

Figure 16–18 Biogas power. Animal wastes are introduced to this unit in rural India and mixed with water. The wastes then decompose under anaerobic conditions, producing biogas.

devices. Both India and China provide subsidies for these family-scale biogas plants.

16.4 Renewable Energy for Transportation

Declining oil reserves and the enormous impact of transportation's demands for oil on our economy and on global climate suggest that the most critical need for a sustainable energy future is a new way to fuel our vehicles. Renewable energy is already answering a small but growing part of this need in the form of biofuels and may have the answer for the long term in the form of hydrogen and fuel cells.

Biofuels

Complex organic matter (primarily plants, but also animal wastes) can be processed to make fuels for vehicles. Currently, two fuels are seeing rapid expansion globally: **ethyl alcohol** (ethanol) and **biodiesel**. High oil prices, strong farmer support, government subsidies, and environmental concerns have led to a major expansion of global ethanol and biodiesel production since 2000. Although these two biofuels currently provide only 2.7% of global transportation fuels, this is just the beginning, as new technologies and government support promise to make biofuels a major competitor for fossil fuels. The current sources of biofuels are agricultural and food commodities.

Ethanol. Ethanol is produced by the fermentation of starches or sugars. The usual starting material is corn, sugarcane, sugar beets, or other grains. Fermentation is the process used in the production of alcoholic beverages. The only new part of the concept is that, instead of drinking the brew, we distill it and put it in our cars. However, production costs make ethanol more expensive than gasoline unless oil sells for more than $55 a barrel. To stimulate the industry in the United States, federal tax credits have been extended to biofuels, which make them even more competitive. **Gasohol,** 10% ethanol and 90% gasoline, is now marketed in most parts of the country.

Farm Products. In 2011, 13.9 billion gallons (334 million barrels) of ethanol for fuel, the equivalent of 221 million barrels of oil, were produced in the United States (ethanol contains about two-thirds the energy of regular gasoline, gallon for gallon). One-third of the nation's corn crop is dedicated to this use; however, an ethanol factory also produces corn oil and livestock feed. A tax credit of 45 cents a gallon helps ethanol compete with gasoline, and a **renewable fuel standard** (or RFS, which requires a minimum volume of renewable fuel in gasoline) mandated a level of 9 billion gallons of renewable fuel in 2008 (all corn-based ethanol), to rise to a limit of 15 billion gallons of corn-based ethanol by 2015. The RFS target rises to 36 billion gallons in 2022, but the increase beyond 2015 must be met by using sources other than corn.

Can we expect ethanol production from corn to make serious inroads on the oil import and greenhouse gas emissions problems? Currently, biofuels represent about 8% of U.S. fuel consumption. This could rise to 20% if the country's entire corn crop were devoted to ethanol production—an impossible assumption, given the importance of corn for animal feed and export. With some 84 million acres devoted to corn harvest in the United States, there is little suitable farmland for significant expansion. There are serious concerns that biofuel production has contributed significantly to recent rising prices of food grain, diverting corn from hungry people to ethanol production (Chapter 12).

Another issue is the energy efficiency of corn-based ethanol. For corn-based ethanol, fossil fuel energy is required to produce the corn (fertilizer, pesticides, farm machinery), to transport it, and to operate the ethanol plant. A recent analysis[4] has calculated that using ethanol instead of gasoline reduces greenhouse gas emissions, mile for mile, by only 12–18%. However, some biofuel critics argue that if new land is cleared of its forests or grasslands, the carbon emissions from the land-use change should be added to the debit from fossil fuel greenhouse gas emissions. When this is done, corn-based ethanol is a net loser in its impact on climate change. Thus, it could be reasoned that the primary strategy in using corn-based ethanol is to reduce our reliance on imported oil.

Second-Generation Biofuel. A more likely long-run technology for producing ethanol is the use of cellulosic feedstocks such as agricultural crop residues, grasses (such as switchgrass), logging residues, fast-growing trees, and fuelwoods from forests. Ethanol produced this way is called second-generation biofuel (current starch-based processes produce first-generation biofuel). One crop with exceptional potential is Miscanthus **(Fig. 16–19),** a giant perennial grass

Figure 16–19 Miscanthus x giganteus. This hardy perennial grass grows to a height of four meters and is a prime candidate for a second-generation cellulosic biofuel.

that can be grown in poor soils and that outproduces corn and other grasses.

With the use of enzymes to break down the cellulose to sugars, demonstration facilities have shown that cellulosic feedstock technology can be a cheaper and more energy-efficient process than corn-based production. The technology is challenging, however, and the output of 6.6 million gallons in 2011 is way below the RFS target of 250 million gallons. However, several industrial-scale cellulosic plants are under construction, and production should increase dramatically once these are on line. Recall that the RFS requires that all of the increase in the target biofuel after 2015 be derived from second-generation biofuel sources. An available tax credit of $1.01 per gallon of cellulosic biofuel is moving this industry forward rapidly.

Brazil has also invested heavily in fuel ethanol; there the feedstock is sugarcane, which is much less costly to farm than corn. Brazil used to lead the world in ethanol production but has been surpassed by the United States. For years, ethanol has been added at a level of 25% of fuel in Brazil, but recently, the country mandated the production of flex-fuel vehicles that can run on any mixture of alcohol and gasoline. With the lower production costs and the capacity to shift all sugarcane acreage to ethanol production, Brazil is on the road to meeting all of its domestic fuel demand with biofuels.

Biodiesel. Imagine a truck exhaust that smells like french fries. That is not only an improvement over diesel exhaust, but also an indication that the truck is burning biodiesel, made largely from soybean oil. Sales have reached 800 million gallons of the fuel, which is very competitive with petroleum diesel fuel because of a hefty $1-per-gallon production tax credit. Still, this is only 1% of diesel fuel transportation use in the United States. Standard biodiesel is a 20% mix of soybean oil in normal diesel fuel, but practically any natural oil or fat can be mixed with an alcohol to make the fuel; one excellent source is recycled vegetable oil from frying. However, like corn-based ethanol, there are competing uses for the vegetable oils.

[4]Earley, Jane, and Alice McKeown. *Red, White and Green: Transforming U.S. Biofuels.* Worldwatch Report 180. Worldwatch Institute, Washington, DC. 2009.

There are some offbeat technologies surfacing to produce biodiesel, such as the factory in Missouri that takes in truckloads of turkey wastes from a Butterball turkey-processing plant and turns them into biofuels. The patented process belongs to Changing World Technologies, and its founder, Brian Appel, says that it can handle almost any organic waste imaginable and turn it into useful oil. Currently, the Missouri plant turns a profit, converting 250 tons of turkey waste per day into 20,000 gallons of oil and also selling a fertilizer product from the rendered wastes. In another technology, genetic engineering is being applied to algae to induce them to produce oils and complex alcohols. Some serious money is being invested in these enterprises, and commercial-scale production is only a few years away.

Hydrogen: Highway to the Future? Over the past decade, there has been increasing interest in powering cars with hydrogen. Conventional cars with internal combustion engines can be adapted to run on hydrogen gas in the same manner as they can be adapted to run on natural gas. (Hydrogen is not really a fuel, but an energy carrier, like electricity; it must be generated using some other energy source.) Neither carbon dioxide nor hydrocarbon pollutants are produced during the burning of hydrogen. Indeed, the only major by-product of H_2 combustion is water vapor:

$$2H_2 + O_2 \longrightarrow 2H_2O + energy$$

(Some nitrogen oxides will be produced because the burning still uses air, which is nearly four-fifths nitrogen.)

A Good Idea, But . . . If hydrogen gas is so great, why aren't we using it? The answer is that there is virtually no hydrogen gas on Earth. Any hydrogen gas in the atmosphere has long since been ignited by lightning and burned to form water. And although many bacteria in the soil produce hydrogen in fermentation reactions, other bacteria are quick to use the hydrogen because it is an excellent source of energy. Thus, there are abundant amounts of the *element* hydrogen, but it is all combined with oxygen in the form of water (H_2O) or other compounds.

Although hydrogen can be extracted from water via **electrolysis** (the reverse of the preceding reaction), electrolysis requires an *input* of energy. Hydrogen can also be derived chemically from hydrocarbon fuels such as methane, petroleum oil, and methyl alcohol, but these processes are also energy losers; that is, more energy is put into the process than is contained in the hydrogen. Moreover, because these compounds contain carbon, it would be better to use them directly than to obtain hydrogen from them and use it. Therefore, the use of hydrogen as a truly clean energy carrier must await an energy source that is itself suitably cheap, abundant, and nonpolluting—like solar energy.

Plants Do It. The "holy grail" of research and eventual commercialization is to accomplish what plant cells do: produce fuel from water, using solar energy. To date, two ways have been proposed for mimicking this process. The first is to employ a catalyst to do what the photosynthetic pathway does. Two elements are required: (1) a collector that converts photons into electrical energy (electrons), and (2) an electrolyzer that uses the electron energy into split water to hydrogen and oxygen. Recently, researchers from the Massachusetts Institute of Technology (MIT) described a process that employs a water-oxidizing electrolyzer catalyst made from cobalt and a heavy metal alloy, all common chemicals.[5] The process uses light energy captured by a silicon solar cell and generates hydrogen and oxygen in either a wired or a wireless cell. It operates in neutral water and ambient temperature and pressure and achieves a solar-to-fuels efficiency of 4.7% (wired) and 2.5% (wireless). This may be the key step needed to get to that holy grail.

Electrolysis. The second approach is simply to pass an electrical current through water and cause the water molecules to dissociate. Hydrogen bubbles come off at the negative electrode (the cathode), while oxygen bubbles come off at the positive electrode (the anode). (You can demonstrate this process for yourself with a battery, some wire, and a dish of water. A small amount of salt placed in the water will facilitate the conduction of electricity and the release of hydrogen.) The hydrogen gas is collected, compressed, and stored in cylinders, which can then be transported or incorporated into a vehicle's chassis. One important drawback to this technology is that it is difficult to store enough hydrogen in a vehicle to allow it to operate over long distances. Also, compressing the hydrogen requires energy, thus reducing the energy efficiency involved. As an alternative, the hydrogen can be combined with metal hydrides, which can absorb the gas and release it when needed; but finding a hydride that is not too heavy has been a challenge. Another pathway that holds promise is to convert the hydrogen into liquid formic acid (HCOOH) by combining it with carbon dioxide. The hydrogen is then released by use of a catalyst.

Solar Energy to Hydrogen. A rather elaborate plan has been suggested for taking solar energy–produced hydrogen for vehicles to its logical conclusion. The plan would start by building arrays of solar-trough or photovoltaic generating facilities in the deserts of the southwestern United States, where land is cheap and sunlight plentiful. The electrical power produced by these methods would then be used to produce hydrogen gas by electrolysis. The most efficient way to move the hydrogen is through underground pipelines; hundreds of miles of such pipelines already exist where hydrogen is transported for use in chemical industries. Although this would be an expensive part of a hydrogen infrastructure, the technology for it is already well known.

Model U. The Ford Motor Company unveiled in the United States a "concept car" it has dubbed the Model U. The Model U sports a 2.3-liter internal combustion engine that runs on hydrogen and is equipped with a hybrid electric drive. The car uses four 10,000 psi tanks to store hydrogen, enough to range 300 miles before a fill-up. And there's the problem: Before such cars can become feasible, there must be a hydrogen-fueling infrastructure. Once that infrastructure is in place, cars like the Model U would likely be replaced by a completely new way of moving a vehicle: by means of fuel cells.

[5]Reece, Steven Y. et al. "Wireless Solar Water Splitting Using Silicon-Based Semiconductors and Earth-Abundant Catalysts." *Science* 334: 645–648. November 4, 2011.

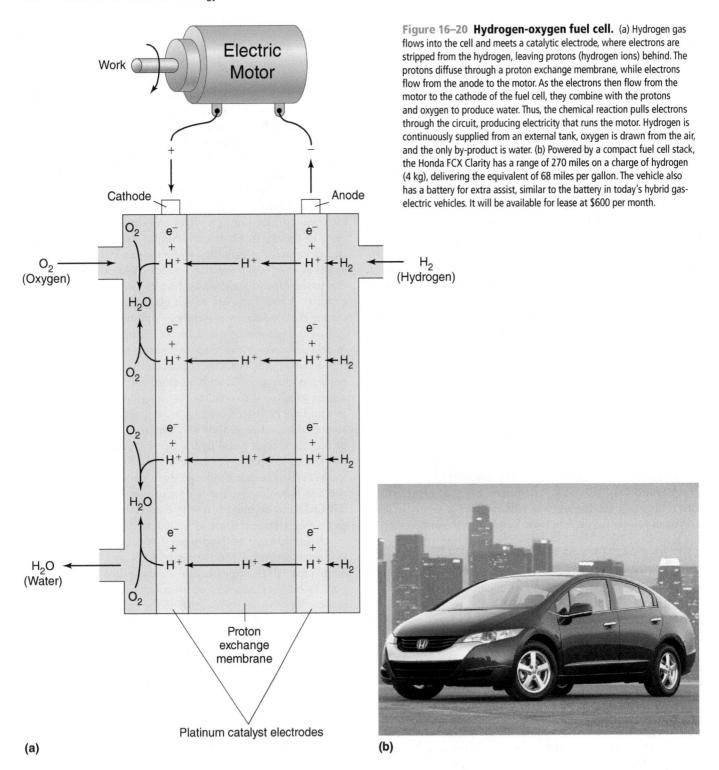

Figure 16–20 Hydrogen-oxygen fuel cell. (a) Hydrogen gas flows into the cell and meets a catalytic electrode, where electrons are stripped from the hydrogen, leaving protons (hydrogen ions) behind. The protons diffuse through a proton exchange membrane, while electrons flow from the anode to the motor. As the electrons then flow from the motor to the cathode of the fuel cell, they combine with the protons and oxygen to produce water. Thus, the chemical reaction pulls electrons through the circuit, producing electricity that runs the motor. Hydrogen is continuously supplied from an external tank, oxygen is drawn from the air, and the only by-product is water. (b) Powered by a compact fuel cell stack, the Honda FCX Clarity has a range of 270 miles on a charge of hydrogen (4 kg), delivering the equivalent of 68 miles per gallon. The vehicle also has a battery for extra assist, similar to the battery in today's hybrid gas-electric vehicles. It will be available for lease at $600 per month.

(a)

(b)

Fuel Cells. An alternative to burning hydrogen in conventional internal combustion engines uses hydrogen in **fuel cells** to produce electricity and power the vehicle with an electric motor. Fuel cells are devices in which hydrogen or some other fuel is chemically combined with oxygen in a manner that produces an electrical potential rather than initiating burning (Fig. 16–20a). Emissions from fuel cells consist solely of water and heat. Because fuel cells create much less waste

heat than conventional engines do, energy is transferred more efficiently from the hydrogen to the vehicle—at a rate of 45–60% versus the 20% for current combustion-engine vehicles. To power a vehicle, hundreds of fuel cells are combined into a fuel-cell stack. The vehicle must also include a hydrogen storage device, a cooling system (fuel cells also generate heat), and a device to force oxygen into the fuel cells. Fuel cells are now powering 150 buses in many cities in the

United States and around the world. The fuel-cell stack develops more than 200 kW of power, from hydrogen in tanks mounted on the roof of the bus.

"Concept" vehicles operating on fuel cells have been developed by all the major car manufacturers. Honda, however, is the first manufacturer to commit to a dedicated fuel-cell vehicle assembly line. The Honda FCX Clarity (Fig. 16–20b) is rolling off the assembly lines, but at a pace of several dozen a year, it will be a long time before it makes an impact on the market. The Clarity is available for lease ($600 a month!) in California regions that are supported by hydrogen refueling stations.

If a hydrogen infrastructure is put in place and vehicles powered by fuel cells are available, we will have entered a **hydrogen economy**—one in which hydrogen becomes a major energy carrier. With solar- and wind-powered electricity also in place, we would no longer be tied to nonrenewable, polluting energy sources and would have made the transition to a sustainable-energy system. Still, the obstacles in the way of the hydrogen economy are formidable, and many believe it will be decades before it even has a chance of happening. Global climate concerns and the costs of importing oil convey an urgency to resolving this issue; reducing our use of oil in the near term is crucial, and many believe that the best pathway is greater use of hybrid vehicles and other technologies already available.

16.5 Additional Renewable-Energy Options

Aside from water, wind, biomass, and hydrogen energy, there are other renewable-energy options that have been developed or are in the concept stage.

Geothermal Energy

In various locations in the world, such as the northwestern corner of Wyoming (Yellowstone National Park), there are springs that yield hot, almost boiling, water. Natural steam vents and other thermal features are also found in such areas. They occur where the hot, molten rock of Earth's interior is close enough to the surface to heat groundwater, particularly in volcanic regions. Using such naturally heated water or steam to heat buildings or drive turbogenerators is the basis of **geothermal energy**. In 2011, geothermal energy had more than 11,200 MW of electrical power capacity (equivalent to the output of 11 large nuclear or coal-fired power stations), in countries as diverse as Nicaragua, the Philippines, Kenya, Iceland, and New Zealand. Today, the largest single facility is in the United States at a location known as The Geysers, 70 miles (110 km) north of San Francisco (Fig. 16–21). With more than 3,000 MW from geothermal energy, the United States is the world leader in the use of this energy source; new projects in the development stage will increase this to more than 4,500 MW. As impressive as this application of geothermal energy is, nearly double the amount

Figure 16–21 Geothermal energy. One of the 11 geothermal units operated by the Pacific Gas & Electric Company at The Geysers in Sonoma and Lake Counties, California. California geothermal energy produces 1,800 MW of power, roughly 4.3% of California's electricity needs.

is being used to directly heat homes and buildings, largely in Japan and China.

A recent study[6] by MIT suggested that the United States employ an emerging technology called enhanced geothermal systems (EGS). EGS involves drilling holes several miles deep into granite that holds temperatures of 400 degrees or more and injecting water under pressure into one hole (where it absorbs heat from the rock) and, as steam, flows up another shaft to a power plant (where it generates electricity). Such plants already exist in Australia, Europe, and Japan. This underground heat is widespread in the United States, unlike the present limited geothermal sources. The MIT team proposed a $1 billion investment to exploit the EGS potential, predicting that by 2050 some 100 gigawatts (GW) of electrical power could be developed in this way.

Heat Pumps. A less spectacular, but far more abundant, energy source than the large geothermal power plants exists anywhere pipes can be drilled into the Earth. Because the ground temperature below six feet or so remains constant, the Earth can be used as part of a heat exchange system that extracts heat in the winter and uses the ground as a heat sink in the summer. Thus, the system can be used for heating and cooling and does away with the need for separate furnace and air-conditioning systems. As **Figure 16–22** shows, a **geothermal heat pump** (GHP) system involves loops of buried pipes filled with an antifreeze solution or a refrigerant, circulated by a pump connected to the air handler (a box containing a blower and a filter). The blower moves house air through the heat pump and distributes it throughout the house via ductwork. In most cases, the up-front costs of the heat pump system are repaid in six to eight years, and then the savings really begin.

---

[6]Tester, Jefferson et al. *The Future of Geothermal Energy: Impact of Enhanced Geothermal Systems (EGS) on the United States in the 21st Century*. Massachusetts Institute of Technology and the Department of Energy. 2006.

Figure 16–22 Geothermal heat pump system. The pipes buried underground facilitate heat exchange between the house and the Earth. This system can either cool or heat a house and can be installed almost anywhere, though at a higher initial cost than a conventional heating, ventilation, and air-conditioning system.

Air handler, with indoor coil and fan connected to air ducts

Heat exchange pipes

Four elementary schools in Lincoln, Nebraska, installed GHP systems for their heating and cooling. Their energy cost savings were 57% compared with the cost of conventional heating and cooling systems installed in two similar schools. Taxpayers will save an estimated $3.8 million over the next 20 years with the GHP systems. According to the EPA, GHP systems are by far the most cost-effective, energy-saving systems available. Although they are significantly more expensive to install than conventional heating and air-conditioning systems, they are trouble-free and save money over the long run. New heat pump installations in the United States are growing rapidly, with more than 1 million in operation by 2010.

Tidal and Wave Power

A phenomenal amount of energy is inherent in the twice-daily rise and fall of the ocean tides, brought about by the gravitational pull of the Moon and the Sun. Many imaginative schemes have been proposed for capturing this limitless, pollution-free source of energy. The most straightforward idea is the **tidal barrage**, in which a dam is built across the mouth of a bay and turbines are mounted in the structure. The incoming tide flowing through the turbines would generate power. As the tide shifted, the blades would be reversed so that the outflowing water would continue to generate power.

In about 30 locations in the world, the shoreline topography generates tides high enough—20 feet (6 m) or more—for this kind of use. Large tidal power plants already exist in two of those places: France and Canada. The only suitable location in North America is the Bay of Fundy, where the Annapolis Tidal Generating Station has operated since 1984, at 20 MW capacity. Thus, this application of tidal power has potential only in certain localities, and even there, it would not be without adverse environmental impacts. The barrage would trap sediments, impede the migration of fish and other organisms, prevent navigation, alter the circulation and mixing of saltwater and freshwater in estuaries, and perhaps have other, unforeseen ecological effects.

Other techniques are being explored that harness the currents that flow with the tides. For example, in 2006, Verdant Power began a project to harness the tidal energy of the East River in New York City. The project has passed its first demonstration phase, connecting six turbines to local electric customers. Verdant plans to install 30 turbines that will connect to the grid and generate 1 MW of power. San Francisco is eyeing a similar scheme to tap the energy of the 400 billion gallons of water that flow under the Golden Gate Bridge with every tide.

Standing on the shore of any ocean, an observer would have to be impressed with the energy arriving with each wave, generated by offshore winds. It might be possible to harness some of this energy, but the technological challenge is daunting. The ideal location is one that receives the wave's force before it hits the shoaling seafloor, is close enough to shore to facilitate hookup with transmission cables, and is deep enough so that the equipment will not crash on the seafloor during storm turbulence. There are a number of proposed mechanisms for capturing wave energy, and it is fair to say that this technology is in the early research-and-development stage. The U.S. DOE is supporting research on ocean energy on a 50% cost-share basis.

Ocean Thermal-Energy Conversion

Over much of the world's oceans, a thermal gradient of about 20°C (36°F) exists between surface water heated by the Sun and the colder deep water. **Ocean thermal-energy conversion (OTEC)** is the name of an experimental technology that uses this temperature difference to produce power. The technology involves using the warm surface water to heat and vaporize a low-boiling-point liquid such as ammonia. The increased pressure of the vaporized ammonia would drive turbogenerators. The ammonia vapor leaving the turbines would then be recondensed by cold water pumped up from as much as 300 feet (100 m) deep and returned to the start of the cycle.

Various studies indicate that OTEC power plants show little economic promise—unless, perhaps, they can be coupled with other, cost-effective operations. For example, in Hawaii, a shore-based OTEC plant uses the cold, nutrient-rich water pumped from the ocean bottom to cool buildings and supply nutrients for vegetables in an aquaculture operation, in addition to cooling the condensers in the power cycle. Even so, interest in duplicating such operations is minimal at present.

16.6 Policies for Renewable Energy

We have examined our planet's energy resources, requirements, and management options (Chapters 14–16). The global issues are clear: Fossil fuels, especially oil and natural gas, will not last long at the current (and increasing) rate at which they are being consumed. Even more important, every use of fossil fuels produces unhealthy pollutants and increases the atmospheric burden of carbon dioxide, accelerating the already-serious climate changes brought on by rising levels of greenhouse gases. Renewable energy means sustainable energy, and a sustainable-energy future does not include significant fossil fuel energy. Global targets, therefore, are (1) *stable atmospheric levels of greenhouse gases, especially carbon dioxide*, and (2) *a sustainable-energy development-and-consumption pattern that is based on renewable energy.* Our main focus in this chapter has been on sustainable energy *development*, but there is another energy strategy that focuses on energy *consumption*—namely, **energy conservation and efficiency.** Energy saved is energy that does not have to be developed or paid for. We laid out two policies that have energy conservation as a goal (Chapter 14). These were *increasing the mileage standards for motor vehicles* and *increasing the energy efficiency of lighting, appliances, and buildings.* Earlier in this chapter, we stressed the Energy Star program, as it encourages municipalities and businesses to achieve energy savings. We turn now to public policy in the United States and the recent and very significant changes that have encouraged renewable energy and energy conservation.

National Energy Policy

Nationally, the United States has a serious *oil-transportation* problem: We import two-thirds of our oil, much of which is consumed in transportation. This problem is an enormous drag on our economy. In fact, more than $600,000 leaves the United States *every minute* to pay for imported oil. We also have an *energy security* problem: Not only are we subject to the whims of the Organization of Petroleum Exporting Countries (OPEC) and other oil producers, but also we are vulnerable to terrorist attacks on various facets of our energy infrastructure.

These national issues, as well as other, global ones, prompted a policy response from the Bush and Obama administrations and Congress. We examined the policies pertaining to fossil fuels and nuclear power as they emerged in the **Energy Policy Act of 2005** and the **Energy Independence and Security Act of 2007** (Chapters 14 and 15). These laws have become the major expression of federal energy policy, though many other laws promoting renewable energy and conservation have been enacted. The **American Recovery and Reinvestment Act of 2009** gave a huge boost ($43 billion) to renewable energy and energy conservation, with the intent of doubling the energy from renewable sources by 2012.

For renewable energy, **supply-side policy provisions** enacted into law:

- Established a renewable fuel standard (RFS) for ethanol and biodiesel that rises from 9 billion gallons in 2008 to 15 billion gallons by 2015.

- Extended the RFS to 36 billion gallons by 2022, but all the increase over 15 billion gallons must be met by feedstocks other than corn (i.e., second-generation sources).

- Continued funding for research and development on renewable energy, including major funding increases for solar energy and biomass programs.

- Extended the production tax credit for electricity generated with wind, hydropower, geothermal, and biomass energy.

- Provided investment tax credits for geothermal heat pumps, solar water heating, biofuel, and PV systems.

- Contained provisions aimed at enabling geothermal energy to compete with fossil fuels in generating electricity.

With their focus on *energy conservation and efficiency*, **demand-side provisions** enacted into law:

- Raised the Corporate Average Fuel Economy standards for the combined fleet of cars and light trucks gradually, to meet a target of 38 miles per gallon for cars and 28 miles per gallon for light trucks by model year 2016.

- Extended the Energy Star energy-efficiency program for buildings, to include schools, retail establishments, private homes, and health care facilities.

- Provided tax credits for many types of improvements to homes and commercial buildings that enhance energy efficiency.

- Required a 30% increase in efficiency for incandescent lightbulbs, which is already met by current compact fluorescent lightbulbs (CFLs). This guarantees that the CFLs will become the light standard of the future.

- Directed EPA to inventory waste-energy potential and establish a grant program to encourage waste-energy recovery (see Chapter 21).

- Developed efficiency standards for most appliances and provided tax credits for manufacturers of energy-saving appliances.

- Continued funding for development of plug-in hybrid electric vehicles (PHEVs).

- Provided an income tax credit applicable to the purchase of new hybrid vehicles, PHEVs, or fuel cell–powered vehicles.

These recent policies did not establish a **federal renewable portfolio standard (RPS)**. This would have required utilities to provide an increasing percentage of power from nonhydroelectric renewable sources (wind, solar, biomass). However, the states are setting the bar for the RPS: 37 states and the District of Columbia have implemented RPS requirements. Most states have adopted target percentages of 10–20%, with deadlines ranging from 2010 to 2025. Globally, at least 64 countries have a national target for renewable energy.

These policies also did not take any direct action on global warming, though they expanded DOE's research program for carbon capture and sequestration. Also, it can be argued that every provision that promotes greater energy efficiency and the use of renewable-energy sources is going to reduce greenhouse gas emissions in the United States.

Final Thoughts

Our look at current energy policy indicates that the United States is making a serious effort to address the need to develop renewable-energy sources and to improve the efficiency of current energy use. One development that has caught everyone's attention in recent years is the rising price of gasoline. Until recently, the United States was the only industrialized country that has seen fit to keep gasoline prices remarkably low. Fuel in all other highly developed countries is so heavily taxed that it costs consumers upward of $6 per gallon—unlike U.S. prices, which were below $1.50 for 12 of the past 20 years. When gasoline rose to $3 a gallon in 2005, consumers began to turn away from gas-guzzling sport-utility vehicles and muscle cars and have been opting for the ris-

ing number of gasoline-electric hybrid cars appearing on the lots of many car manufacturers. This supports the suggestion of a number of economists and environmental groups that we should be paying more—much more—for gasoline (and other fossil fuels). To accomplish this, we would need a policy change: a **carbon tax**—that is, a tax levied on all fuels according to the amount of carbon dioxide that they produce when consumed. Such a tax, proponents believe, would provide both incentives to use renewable sources, which would not be taxed, and disincentives to consume fossil fuels. It is hard to imagine any step that would be more effective (or more controversial!) in reducing greenhouse gas emissions in the United States. A number of European countries have already adopted such a tax.

Are the preceding developments, even the suggested carbon tax, enough to enable us to achieve a sustainable-energy system and to mitigate global climate change? Very likely, no. Yet many of them are moving us in the sustainable direction that is vital to the future of the global environment.

REVISITING THE THEMES

Sound Science

Some elegant technologies have been discussed in this chapter, developed by scientists in research laboratories and then applied to solving some very practical problems. PV devices, for example, are being intensely researched in order to bring down the costs and make solar energy competitive with conventional energy sources. Research at MIT has produced a real breakthrough in the discovery of a catalyst that can split water, imitating photosynthesis. The National Renewable Energy Laboratory in Golden, Colorado, was established by Congress in 1977 and has developed into a cutting-edge research institute that produced the solar-trough and solar-dish systems. It is now exploring hydrogen technologies and improved PV devices, as well as a number of biomass technologies and low-wind-speed turbines and other renewable-energy options. This is science at its best, with public funding put to work to develop new ideas that may revolutionize the energy scene.

Sustainability

At the risk of repetition, global civilization is on an unsustainable energy course. Our intensive use of fossil fuels has created a remarkable chapter in human history, but we are still terribly dependent on maintaining and increasing our use of oil, gas, and coal. The results have already been seen in rising atmospheric greenhouse gases and the climate changes they are producing.

Future use of fossil fuel will bring on more-intense climate changes, and long before we burn all the available oil, gas, and coal, we will have been forced to turn to other energy sources. Renewable-energy sources derived from the Sun can provide a sustainable, inexhaustible supply of energy that is virtually free from harmful environmental impacts. It is imperative that the United States, as well as other countries, embark on a course to bring about a transition to a renewable-energy economy, most likely based on hydrogen and electricity as energy carriers, to be produced from renewable sources.

Stewardship

Stewardship of energy means doing more with less and turning away from the fossil fuels that are generating the greenhouse gases that are responsible for global climate change. Government policies are rapidly moving forward in encouraging renewable energy by providing subsidies for homeowners and businesses to embrace renewable-energy options. Policies are also improving the energy efficiency and conservation picture. After all, energy saved is energy that does not have to be developed. Picture solar panels on every home, church, hospital, and school roof as well as wind turbines on college campuses, grazing lands, and offshore wind farms. Many nongovernmental organizations are involved with programs that distribute PV and biogas systems to people in poor, rural, developing-country communities. The impact is literally being felt around the globe.

REVIEW QUESTIONS

1. Why is it important for renewable energy sources to replace fossil fuels? What are the prospects for getting it done?

2. How much solar energy is available, and what happens when it is used? What are some problems with harnessing solar energy?

3. How do active and passive solar hot-water heaters work?

4. How can a building best be designed to become a passive solar collector for heat?

5. How does a PV system work, and what are some present applications of such cells?

6. What has been happening in recent years in the PV market? How are utilities encouraging PV power?

7. Describe two concentrated solar power systems, how they work, and their potential for providing power.

8. What is the potential for developing more hydroelectric power in North America versus developing countries, and what are the impacts of such development?

9. Where is wind power being harvested, and what is the future potential for wind farms?

10. What are some ways of converting biomass to useful energy, and what is the potential environmental impact of each?

11. Which biofuels are used for transportation, and what is the potential for increasing biofuels in the United States?

12. How can hydrogen gas be produced via the use of solar energy? How might hydrogen be collected and stored to meet the need for fuel for transportation in the future?

13. How do fuel cells work, and what is being done to adapt them to power vehicles?

14. What is geothermal energy, and what are two ways it is being harnessed?

15. Describe current policy for renewable energy and energy efficiency as an outcome of recent government programs.

THINKING ENVIRONMENTALLY

1. What do you believe needs to happen before solar power becomes a thoroughly mainstream form of energy production? Defend your answer.

2. What do you think could be a viable solution for backup power systems for solar heaters in the event of bad weather?

3. How much promise does hydrogen power hold? Is its eventual sustainability just a myth or something to be pursued?

4. Imagine you are charged with building a facility run entirely by renewable resources (with the possible exception of backup power). How would you evaluate which sources have the most potential?

5. Audit all of the energy needs in your daily life. How much energy do you consume? Describe how each need might be satisfied by a renewable-energy option. (Check the Internet for tools for this exercise.)

MAKING A DIFFERENCE

1. Many everyday electrical products can now be powered by photovoltaic (PV) cells. You can find solar-powered chargers for MP3 players, cell phones, digital cameras, and even laptops. While this power may not be as dependable as that from a wall charger, it certainly provides a sustainable alternative while the Sun shines (especially useful on road and camping trips, where conventional power isn't available).

2. If you live close to work, consider not driving there at all and instead taking a bicycle. The benefits are endless; great exercise, low emissions, and no money toward gas are just the beginning.

3. Take advantage of the following services from your electric company: energy conservation, home-energy audits, and subsidized compact fluorescent lighting.

4. Consult the free *Greentips* newsletter of the Union of Concerned Scientists on its Web site (www.ucsusa.org), and follow the advice given in this publication for reducing your energy footprint.

5. Adopt ways to use less fuel and electricity both at home and where you work. (Turn thermostats up in the summer and down in the winter, turn off lights when you leave a room, wear sweaters, use energy-efficient lightbulbs, and so on.)

MasteringEnvironmentalScience®

Go to **www.masteringenvironmentalscience.com** for practice quizzes, Pearson eText, videos, current events, and more.

PART FIVE

Pollution and Prevention

Paper mill at sunset, Georgetown, South Carolina.

A N INDUSTRIAL PLANT sends a steady stream of exhaust gases into the air, and the wind carries the pollutants away. If it didn't, life in the vicinity of the plant would be nasty. But where is "away"? Is it the next county, state, or country? The upper atmosphere? In reality, there is no "away" for the pollution of land, water, and air resulting from the activities of the 7.2 billion people inhabiting Earth. We are fouling our own nest, our only planet.

In his book *Red Sky at Morning*,[1] James Gustave Speth describes four long-term trends in pollution that marked the 20th century:

First, *the volumes of pollutants released increased by huge amounts*—so much so that the developed countries finally began to legislate limits on many pollutants.

Second, *the pollution evolved from gross excesses to microtoxicity,* where major releases of toxic gases and waterborne pathogens were replaced by smaller but much more toxic releases of organic chemicals and trace metals like dioxin and mercury.

Third, *industrial pollutants have shifted from the first world to the third world*—from the developed to the developing countries. China, for example, is reaping the benefits of rapid industrial growth and at the same time suffering from massive and health-damaging pollution.

Fourth, *the effects of pollution have shifted from local to global.* Air pollution, resulting from the use of fossil fuels and industrial chemicals, has brought acid rain on a regional scale and global climate change and ozone depletion on a global scale.

In this part of the book, Chapter 17 begins with a look at the links between environmental hazards (like pollution and disease) and human health. The chapters that follow examine the major forms of pollution, and you will discover that pollution is often a by-product of some useful activity (though sometimes intentionally released). We cover the range of pollutants, from global and regional air pollutants to water pollutants to municipal and industrial wastes. In every chapter, the public policies crafted to deal with each of the problems raised by pollution are discussed. Without exaggeration, the problems of pollution pose some of the most difficult and important issues facing human society.

[1]Speth, James Gustave. *Red Sky at Morning.* Yale University Press, New Haven. 2004.

CHAPTER 18

Global Climate Change

Delegates meet at Durban, South Africa, for the 17th Conference of the Parties to the Framework Convention on Climate Change, December 2011.

"THE MALDIVES IS THE canary in the world's carbon coal mine." This was stated by Mohamed Nasheed, former president of the Maldives, an archipelago of 1190 islands in the Indian Ocean that some 320,000 people call home. Many of the islands are atolls (ring-shaped islands formed of coral), others little more than sandbars, and the capital, Malé, is a square mile of densely packed buildings surrounded by a seawall (Fig. 18–1a). The average elevation in the islands is a mere 3 feet (1 meter) above sea level, and seafront erosion has claimed many beaches and some buildings. Nasheed was working on a sovereign-wealth fund that would enable the Maldivians to purchase land somewhere (India, Sri Lanka?); the fund was to be financed by the tourism industry that is the economic engine of the islands. Over in the South Pacific, residents of numerous island nations and islands are bracing for the rising sea level that is already submerging parts of their lands. Kiribati and Tuvalu are two such island nations whose existence is threatened by environmental changes linked to global warming; as salt water encroaches on the freshwater lenses that support plant life on the islands, it is likely that the entire populations of these two countries—some 110,000—will, like the Maldivians, be forced to emigrate.

SEA LEVEL RISE. The relentless rise of sea level, now at 3.2 mm/yr, is accelerating as the oceans continue to warm and ice sheets and glaciers melt. The estimates of total sea level rise at year 2100 range from a low of 20 cm to a high of 1.8 meters,[1] and because the low estimates do not take into consideration any melting of the polar ice sheets, low-lying regions like the Maldives and Pacific

LEARNING OBJECTIVES

1. **Atmosphere, Weather, and Climate:** Describe the structure of the atmosphere and its gases; distinguish between weather and climate.

2. **Climate Change Science:** Explore the science that describes the greenhouse effect, summarize the evidence for recent climate change, and evaluate the various greenhouse gases and their impacts on present and future climates.

3. **Response to Climate Change:** Examine the international and U.S. measures taken to mitigate climate change and evaluate their effectiveness.

---

[1]Robert J. Nicholls and Anny Cazenave. "Sea-Level Rise and Its Impact on Coastal Zones." *Science*, 328: 1517–1520. June 18, 2010.

(a)

(b)

Figure 18–1 **Regions under threat from rising seas.** (a) The city of Malé, capital of the Maldives, in the Indian Ocean. (b) A view of Shishmaref, on the Alaskan coast.

islands are paying more attention to the high range estimates of sea level rise.

Far to the north, the island village of Shishmaref, Alaska, is falling into the sea. Built on permafrost and normally protected from ocean waves by sea ice, Shishmaref is now battered by waves as the summer sea ice is melted away, and the soil is shifting as the permafrost is melted by the unusual summer warmth. Every year, some 20 feet of the shoreline is washed away (Fig. 18–1b), sometimes taking with it the villagers' homes. The 600 inhabitants of Shishmaref are actively working toward relocating the entire community to higher ground elsewhere in Alaska. Scientists point out that the populations of these isolated islands will be merely the first wave of climate change refugees unless the global community of nations takes rapid steps to curb the fossil fuel emissions that are largely responsible for global climate change.

THE FUTURE. Fast forward to 2050. Could it be that whatever happens this far into the future depends on the actions taken by the leading nations in the world now and in the next decade to address the issue of global climate change? Ethicists claim that we are in the predicament of having to make decisions now, costly and far-reaching decisions, in order that our children and grandchildren will not be living in a world that experiences unprecedented and dangerous environmental conditions.

Can all this be true? What is happening with our climate? Indeed, what controls the climate? We will seek answers to these questions as we first investigate the atmosphere, how it is structured, and how it brings us our weather and climate. Then we will consider the scientific evidence for global climate change, examine the future projections of conditions made by elegant computer modeling, and then look at the varied responses to address global climate change.

18.1 Atmosphere, Weather, and Climate

The atmosphere is a collection of gases that gravity holds in a thin envelope around Earth. The gases within the lowest layer, the **troposphere,** are responsible for moderating the flow of energy to Earth and are involved with the biogeochemical cycling of many elements and compounds—oxygen, nitrogen, carbon, sulfur, and water, to name the most crucial ones. The troposphere ranges in thickness from 10 miles (16 km) in the tropics to 5 miles (8 km) in higher latitudes, due mainly to differences in solar energy. This layer contains practically all of the water vapor and clouds in the atmosphere; it is the site and source of our weather. Except for local temperature inversions, the troposphere gets colder with altitude (Fig. 18–2). Air masses in this layer are well mixed vertically, so pollutants can reach the top within a few days. Substances entering the troposphere—including pollutants—may be changed chemically and washed back to Earth's surface by precipitation (Chapter 19). Capping the

troposphere is the **tropopause,** a boundary region where air shifts from cooling with height and begins to warm.

Above the tropopause is the **stratosphere,** a layer within which temperature *increases* with altitude, up to about 40 miles above the surface of Earth. The temperature increases primarily because the stratosphere contains ozone (O_3), a form of oxygen that absorbs high-energy radiation emitted by the Sun. Because there is little vertical mixing of air masses in the stratosphere and no precipitation from it, substances that enter it can remain there for a long time. Beyond the stratosphere are two more layers, the **mesosphere** and the **thermosphere,** where the ozone concentration declines and only small amounts of oxygen and nitrogen are found. Table 18–1 summarizes the characteristics of the troposphere and stratosphere.

Weather

People sometimes make the mistake of assuming that one snowstorm or one hurricane is evidence for or against climate change. It is simply evidence that weather is happening. The

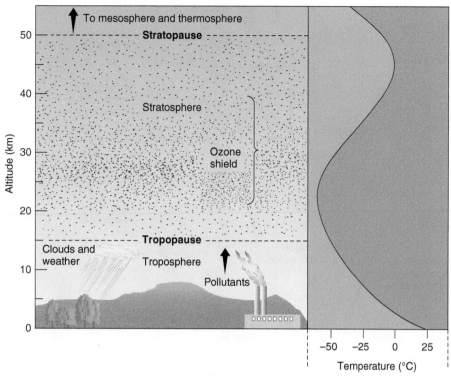

Figure 18–2 **Structure and temperature profile of the atmosphere.** The image on the left shows the layers of the atmosphere and the ozone shield, while the plot on the right shows the vertical temperature profile.

TABLE 18–1 Characteristics of Troposphere and Stratosphere

Troposphere	Stratosphere
Extent: Ground level to 10 miles (16 km)	Extent: 10 miles to 40 miles (16 km to 65 km)
Temperature normally decreases with altitude, down to −70°F (−59°C)	Temperature increases with altitude, up to +32°F (0°C)
Much vertical mixing, turbulent	Little vertical mixing, slow exchange of gases with troposphere, via diffusion
Substances entering may be washed back to Earth	Substances entering remain unless attacked by sunlight or other chemicals
All weather and climate take place here	Isolated from the troposphere by the tropopause

day-to-day variations in temperature, air pressure, wind, humidity, and precipitation—all mediated by the atmosphere—constitute our **weather**. **Climate** is the result of long-term weather patterns in a region, patterns that involve decades or longer. The scientific study of the atmosphere—both of weather and of climate—is **meteorology**. You can think of the atmosphere-ocean-land system as an enormous weather engine, driven by solar power and strongly affected by the rotation of Earth and its tilted axis. Solar radiation enters the atmosphere and then takes a number of possible courses (Fig. 18–3). Some (29%) is reflected by clouds and Earth's surfaces, but most is absorbed by the atmosphere, oceans, and land, which are heated in the process. The land and oceans

then release energy back upward through evaporation, convection, and reradiation of infrared energy.

Flowing Air. Some of the energy that is released from Earth's surface is transferred to the atmosphere. Thus, air masses grow warmer at the surface of Earth and will tend to expand, becoming lighter. The lighter air will then rise, creating *vertical* air currents. On a large scale, this movement creates major *convection currents* (Chapter 10, Fig. 10–6). Air must flow in to replace the rising warm air, and the inflow leads to *horizontal* airflows, or wind. The ultimate source of the horizontal flow is cooler air that is sinking, and the combination produces the Hadley cell (Fig. 10–6). These

Figure 18–3 Solar-energy balance. Much of the incoming radiation from the Sun (29%) is reflected back to space, but the remainder (71%) is absorbed by the oceans, land, and atmosphere, where it creates our weather and fuels photosynthesis. Eventually, this absorbed energy is radiated back to space as infrared energy (heat).

(*Source:* Rebecca Lindsey, Climate and Earth's Energy Budget, NASA Earth Observatory, January 14, 2009.)

major flows of air create regions of high rainfall (equatorial), deserts (25° to 35° north and south of the equator), and horizontal winds (trade winds).

Convection. On a smaller scale, **convection currents** bring us the day-to-day changes in our weather as they move in a general pattern from west to east. Weather reports inform us of regions of high and low pressure, but where do these come from? Rising air (due to solar heating) creates high pressure up in the atmosphere, leaving behind a region of lower pressure close to Earth. Conversely, once the moist, high-pressure air has cooled by reradiating heat to space and losing heat through condensation (thereby generating precipitation), it flows horizontally toward regions of sinking, cool, dry air (where the pressure is lower). There the air is warmed at the surface and creates a region of higher pressure (Fig. 18–4). The differences in pressure lead to airflows, which are the winds we experience. As the figure shows, the winds tend to flow from high-pressure regions toward low-pressure regions.

Jet Streams. The larger-scale air movements of Hadley cells are influenced by Earth's rotation from west to east. This creates the trade winds over the oceans and the general flow of weather from west to east. Higher in the troposphere, Earth's rotation and air-pressure gradients generate veritable rivers of air, called **jet streams**, that flow eastward at

speeds of more than 300 mph and meander considerably. Jet streams are able to steer major air masses in the lower troposphere. One example is the polar jet stream, which steers cold air masses into North America when it dips downward in latitude.

Put Together. . . Air masses of different temperatures and pressures meet at boundaries we call **fronts,** which are regions of rapid weather change. Other movements of air masses due to differences in pressure and temperature include hurricanes and typhoons and local, but very destructive, tornadoes. Finally, there are also major seasonal airflows—**monsoons**—which often represent a reversal of previous wind patterns. Monsoons are created by major differences in cooling and heating between oceans and continents. The summer monsoons of the Indian subcontinent are famous for the beneficial rains they bring and notorious for the devastating floods that can occur when the rains are heavy. Putting these movements all together—taking the general atmospheric circulation patterns and the resulting precipitation, then adding the wind and weather systems generating them, and finally mixing all this with the rotation of Earth and the tilt of the planet on its axis, which creates the seasons—yields the general patterns of weather that characterize different regions of the world. In any given region, these patterns are referred to as the region's **climate.**

Figure 18–4 **A convection cell.** Driven by solar energy, convection cells produce the main components of our weather as evaporation and condensation occur in rising air and precipitation results, followed by the sinking of dry air. Horizontal winds are generated in the process.

18.2 Climate Change Science

Climate is the average temperature and precipitation expected throughout a typical year in a given region (Chapter 5). Different temperature and moisture regimes in different parts of the world have generated different types of ecosystems called biomes, reflecting the adaptations of plants, animals, and microbes to the prevailing weather patterns, or climate, of a region. The temperature and precipitation patterns themselves are actually caused by other forces—namely, the major determinants of weather previously outlined. Humans can adjust to practically any climate (short of the brutal conditions of high mountains and burning deserts), but this is not true of the other inhabitants of the particular regions we occupy. If other living organisms in a region are adapted to a particular climate, then a major change in the climate represents a serious threat to the structure and function of the existing ecosystems. The subject of climate change is such a vital issue today because we depend on these other organisms for a host of vital goods and services without which we could not survive (see Chapter 7). If the climate changes, can these ecosystems change with it in such a way that the crucial support they provide us is not interrupted? Is Earth's climate indeed changing? If so, what is causing it to change?

Synopsis of Global Climate Change

In 2007, after sifting through thousands of studies about global warming, scientists from the **Intergovernmental Panel** on Climate Change (IPCC) published the Fourth Assessment Report (AR4) on climate change. They concluded that *warming of the climate system is unequivocal.* Our climate is changing, the scientists said: The atmosphere is warmer (**Fig. 18–5**), the oceans are warmer, there is more precipitation, there are more extreme weather events (like hurricanes,

GLOBAL LAND–OCEAN TEMPERATURE INDEX

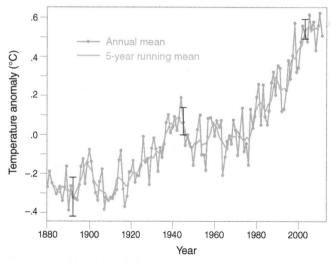

Figure 18–5 **Annual mean global surface temperature anomalies.** The baseline, or zero point, is the period 1951–80. The warming trend since 1975 is conspicuous.

(*Source:* NASA Goddard Institute for Space Studies, 2011.)

ATMOSPHERIC CO₂ AT MAUNA LOA OBSERVATORY

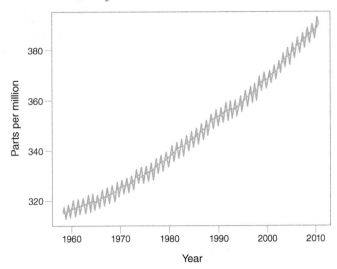

Figure 18–6 Atmospheric carbon dioxide concentrations. The concentration of CO_2 in the atmosphere fluctuates between winter and summer because of seasonal variation in photosynthesis. The average concentration is increasing due to human activities—in particular, burning fossil fuels and deforestation.

(*Source:* NOAA Earth System Research Laboratory, 2011.)

floods, droughts, heat waves), glaciers are melting, and the sea level is rising.

The IPCC report stated that it is *very likely* (i.e., there is 90–100% probability) that the warming is mostly caused by increased concentrations of anthropogenic (human-made) **greenhouse gases** (GHGs), atmospheric gases that trap infrared radiation. The most significant anthropogenic GHG is carbon dioxide (CO_2), which has risen by 40%—from 280 parts per million (ppm) to 394 ppm—since the Industrial Revolution began **(Fig. 18–6)**. The source of this added CO_2 is no surprise: Most of it comes from burning fossil fuels, and a smaller amount comes from burning forests (deforestation). The global use of fossil fuels is rising every year, and if nothing is done to reduce it, computer modeling tells us that the 21st century will see climate changes that are dangerous, possibly catastrophic. Sea levels will keep rising; there will be more frequent heat waves, changed weather patterns, and threats to natural ecosystems. In fact, these changes will go on for hundreds of years. Needless to say, this is not good news, and it has gotten the attention of the world. Efforts are under way to respond by way of **mitigation** (reducing GHG emissions) and **adaptation** (adjusting to coming climate changes). However, our civilization has no experience with a problem like this, and the way forward is still being debated.

IPCC and UNEP

The Fourth Assessment Report is an incredibly detailed and comprehensive study. In 1988, the UN Environment Program (UNEP) and the World Meteorological Society established the IPCC in order to provide accurate and relevant information that would lead to an understanding of human-induced climate change. The IPCC has three working groups: one to assess the scientific issues (Working Group I), another to evaluate the impact of global climate change and the prospects for adapting to it (Working Group II), and a third to investigate ways of mitigating the effects (Working Group III). The latest IPCC assessment working groups consist of more than 2,000 experts in the appropriate fields, from 154 countries. These experts are unpaid and participate at the cost of their own research and other professional activities. Each working group produced a separate report;[2] all reports are available from the IPCC Web site (www.ipcc.ch).

The work of the IPCC has been guided by two basic questions:

Risk assessment—Is the climate system changing, and what is the impact on society and ecosystems?

Risk management—How can we manage the system through adaptation and mitigation?

Building on past assessments (1990, 1995, 2001) and new results of research, the three IPCC working groups released the Fourth Assessment Report in stages during 2007, the final product being *Climate Change 2007: Synthesis Report*, which was released late that year and contained key findings of the working groups.

The UNEP issued a report in 2009 (**Climate Change Science Compendium 2009**[3]) that addressed many new findings since the IPCC's assessment. Other updates have come from the American Meteorological Society[4] and the U.S. Global Change Research Program.[5] Work on the next full IPCC assessment is under way and will be released in 2013. In this chapter, we will explore the information on climate change in some detail, making full use of the IPCC and many other reports. We begin with a look into the past, which harbors "records" of climate change.

Climates in the Past

Searching the past for evidence of climate change has become a major scientific enterprise, one that becomes more difficult the further into the past we try to search. Systematic records of the factors making up weather—temperature, precipitation, storms, and so forth—have been kept for little more than 130 years. Nevertheless, these records clearly inform us that our climate is far from constant. The record of surface temperatures, from weather stations around the world and from literally millions of observations of temperatures at the

---

[2]See, for example, Susan Solomon et al., Eds., *Climate Change 2007: The Physical Science Basis*, Contribution of Working Group I to the Fourth Assessment Report of the Intergovernmental Panel on Climate Change (New York: Cambridge University Press, 2007).

[3]Catherine P. McMullen, Ed. *Climate Change Science Compendium 2009*. United Nations Environment Program. http://www.unep.org/compendium2009. December 13, 2011.

[4]J. Blunden et al., Eds. *State of the Climate in 2010*. Special Supplement to the Bulletin of the American Meteorological Society, Vol. 92, No. 6, June 2011. http://www1.ncdc.noaa.gov/pub/data/cmb/bams-sotc/climate-assessment-2010-lo-rez.pdf. December 13, 2011.

[5]Thomas R. Karl et al., Eds. *Global Climate Change Impacts in the United States*. Cambridge University Press. 2009. www.globalchange.gov/usimpacts. December 13, 2011.

surface of the sea, tells an interesting story (see Fig. 18–5). Since 1880, global average temperature has shown periods of cooling and warming, but since 1976, it has increased 0.6°C (1.1°F). During the 20th century, two warming trends occurred, one from 1910 to 1945 and the latest dramatic increase from 1976 until the present. The first decade of the 21st century has been the warmest decade on record.

Further Back. Observations on climatic changes can be extended much further back in time with the use of **proxies**—measurable records that can provide data on factors such as temperature, ice cover, and precipitation. For example, historical accounts suggest that the Northern Hemisphere enjoyed a warming period from 1100 to 1300 A.D. This was followed by the "Little Ice Age," between 1400 and 1850 A.D. Additional proxies include tree rings, pollen deposits, changes in landscapes, marine sediments, corals, and ice cores.

Some work done quite recently on ice cores has both provided a startling view of a global climate that oscillates according to several cycles and afforded some evidence that remarkable changes in the climate can occur within as little as a few decades. Ice cores in Greenland and the Antarctic have been analyzed for thickness, gas content (specifically, carbon dioxide (CO_2) and methane (CH_4)), two GHGs, and **isotopes**, which are alternative chemical configurations of a given compound, due to different nuclear components. Isotopes of oxygen, as well as isotopes of hydrogen, behave differently at different temperatures when condensed in clouds and incorporated into ice.

The record based on these analyses indicates that Earth's climate has oscillated between ice ages and warm periods (Fig. 18–7a). During major ice ages, huge amounts of water were tied up in glaciers and ice sheets, and the sea level was lower by as much as 400 feet (120 m). Ice cores from Antarctica show eight glacial periods and eight interglacial periods,

over the past 800,000 years. During the glacial periods, temperatures and GHGs were low; during the warm interglacial periods, just the opposite was true. The GHG and temperature data match exactly. Carbon dioxide levels ranged between 150 and 280 ppm.

The most likely explanation for these major oscillations is the existence of known variations in Earth's orbit, where, in different modes of orbital configuration, the distribution of solar radiation over different continents and latitudes varies substantially. These oscillations take place according to several periodic intervals, called **Milankovitch cycles** (after the Serbian scientist who first described them), of 100,000, 41,000, and 23,000 years.

Rapid Changes. Superimposed on the major oscillations is a record of rapid climatic fluctuations during periods of glaciation and warmer times (Fig. 18–7b). One such rapid change, called the **Younger Dryas** event (*Dryas* is a genus of Arctic flower), occurred toward the end of the last ice age. Earth had been warming up for 6,000 years and then plunged again into 1,150 years of cold weather. At the end of this event, 11,700 years ago, Arctic temperatures rose 7°C in 50 years. The impact on living systems must have been enormous. It is unlikely that this warming was due to variations in solar output: There is simply no evidence that the Sun has changed over the past million years, let alone undergone major changes in just a few decades. Instead, scientists have narrowed the field of possible explanations to the link between the atmosphere and the oceans.

Ocean and Atmosphere

More than two-thirds of Earth is covered by oceans, making ours mostly a water planet. Because we all live on land, it is hard for us to imagine the dominant role the oceans play

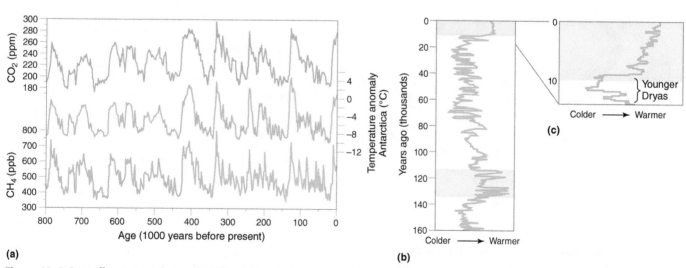

(a)   (b)

Figure 18–7 Past climates, as determined from ice cores. (a) Carbon dioxide, methane, and estimated global temperature from Antarctic ice cores, covering the past 800,000 years, compared with changes of the past century. Note how closely the temperature and GHG concentrations coincide. (b) Temperature patterns of the past 160,000 years, demonstrating climatic oscillations. (c) Higher resolution of the past 12,000 years. The Younger Dryas cold spell occurred at the start of this record. Note how rapidly the cold spell dissipated, at around 10,700 years before the present.

(*Sources:* (a) The Bohr Institute; (b) & (c) Adapted from Robert W. Christopherson, *Geosystems: An Introduction to Physical Geography,* 5th ed. (Upper Saddle River, NJ: Pearson Prentice Hall, 2005).)

in determining our climate. Nevertheless, the oceans are the major source of water for the hydrologic cycle and the main source of heat entering the atmosphere. The *evaporation of ocean water* supplies the atmosphere with water vapor, and when water vapor condenses in the atmosphere, it supplies the atmosphere with heat (latent heat of condensation, Fig. 10–4). The oceans also play a vital role in climate because of their innate *heat capacity*—the ability to absorb energy when water is heated. Indeed, the entire heat capacity of the atmosphere is equal to that of just the top 3 meters of ocean water. It is this property that makes the climate milder in coastal areas. Finally, through the movement of currents, the oceans *convey heat* throughout the globe.

Thermohaline Circulation. For many years, oceanographers have described the existence of a **thermohaline** circulation pattern that dominates oceanic currents, where *thermohaline* refers to the effects that temperature and salinity have on the density of seawater. This pattern, known formally as the **Atlantic Meridional Overturning Circulation (AMOC)** (Fig. 18–8), has been pictured as a giant, complex conveyor belt, moving water masses from the surface to deep oceans and back again. A key area is the high-latitude North Atlantic, where salty water from the Gulf Stream moves northward on the surface and is cooled by Arctic air currents. Cooling increases the density of the water, which then sinks to depths of up to 4,000 meters—the **North Atlantic Deep Water (NADW)**. This deep-water current spreads southward through the Atlantic to the southern tip of Africa, where it is joined by cold Antarctic waters. Together, the two streams spread northward into the Indian and Pacific Oceans as deep currents. Gradually, the currents slow down and warm,

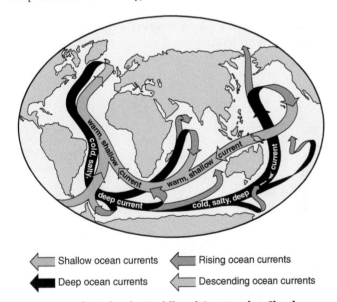

Shallow ocean currents — Rising ocean currents
Deep ocean currents — Descending ocean currents

Figure 18–8 The Atlantic Meridional Overturning Circulation. Salty water flowing to the North Atlantic is cooled and sinks, forming the North Atlantic Deep Water system. This deep flow extends southward and is joined by Antarctic water, whereupon it extends into the Indian and Pacific Oceans. Surface currents then proceed in the opposite direction, returning the water to the North Atlantic.

(*Source:* Adapted from Figure 3.15 from *Our Changing Planet*, 2nd ed., by Fred T. MacKenzie. Copyright © 1998 by Prentice Hall, Inc. Reprinted by permission of Pearson Education, Inc., Upper Saddle River, NJ 07458.)

becoming less dense and welling up to the surface, where they are further warmed and begin to move as surface waters back again toward the North Atlantic. This movement transfers enormous quantities of heat toward Europe, providing a climate that is much warmer than the high latitudes there would suggest.

Recently, the conveyor-belt paradigm has been challenged.[6] Instead of the neat flows pictured in Figure 18–8, research has revealed that eddies and oceanic winds inject and subtract water masses at many points in the overall circulation, and the actual driving force for the turnover of ocean waters is unclear. What is clear is that the turnover does occur—deep waters are formed by sinking at the poles, and warm water does return northward to affect the climate of northern Europe. This new work has called into question some of the conjecture that changes in the climate might trigger abrupt changes in the AMOC.

Abrupt Change. Recent evidence indicates that the AMOC has been interrupted in the past, changing climate abruptly. One mechanism that could have accomplished such a change is the appearance of unusually large quantities of freshwater in the North Atlantic. This would have the effect of lowering the density of the water (and, therefore, preventing much of the massive sinking that normally occurs there). With this stagnation occurring in surface Arctic waters, the northward movement of warmer, saltier water would slow down. North Atlantic marine sediments show evidence of the periodic invasion (six times in the past 75,000 years) of icebergs from the polar ice cap, which supplied huge amounts of freshwater as they melted—called Heinrich events, after the scientist who first described them. The evidence indicates that these invasions coincided with rapid cooling, as recorded in ice cores, and suggests that the AMOC shifted southward, with the NADW forming nearer to Bermuda than to Greenland. When this shift occurred, a major cooling of the climate took place within a few decades. Although it is not clear how, the normal thermohaline pattern returned and brought about another abrupt change, this time warming conditions in the North Atlantic. The Younger Dryas event likely involved just such a shift in the AMOC, brought on by the sudden release of dammed-up water from glacial Lake Agassiz into the St. Lawrence drainage. Referring to these abrupt changes in a recent article, oceanographer Wallace Broecker commented, "Earth's climate system has proven itself to be an angry beast. When nudged, it is capable of a violent response."[7]

What If . . . ? Among the likely consequences of extended global warming are increased precipitation over the North Atlantic and more melting of sea ice and ice caps. If such a pattern is sustained, it could lead to a weakening in the normal operation of the AMOC and a change in climate, especially in the northern latitudes—a possibility that Broecker has called "the Achilles' heel of our climate system." Such a

---

[6]M. Susan Lozier. "Deconstructing the Conveyor Belt." *Science* 328: 1507–1511. June 18, 2010.
[7]Wallace S. Broecker. "Does the Trigger for Abrupt Change Reside in the Ocean or in the Atmosphere?" *Science* 300 (June 6, 2003): 1519–1522.

change could bring major cooling to Europe. However, there are doubts about the functioning of the conveyor-belt paradigm, especially as it is presented as a smooth, simple set of ocean currents. Accordingly, most observers believe that expected increases in GHGs and the overall warming that this brings will prevent anything like a new ice age (as portrayed by the movie *The Day After Tomorrow*).

Ocean-Atmosphere Oscillations. Regional climates are notoriously erratic on time scales from a few days to decades. Studies of a number of ocean-atmosphere processes—processes that produce erratic climates on a global scale—have provided new insights into natural climate variability. There is, for example, the **North Atlantic Oscillation (NAO)**, where atmospheric pressure centers switch back and forth across the Atlantic, switching winds and storms in the process. There is also a warm-cool cycle, the **Interdecadal Pacific Oscillation (IPO)**, that swings back and forth across the Pacific over periods of several decades.

Then there is the **El Niño/La Niña Southern Oscillation (ENSO)**, where major shifts in atmospheric pressure over the central equatorial Pacific Ocean lead to a reversal of the trade winds. Incredibly, these reversals dominate the climate over much of the planet, and they can last for a year or two at a time. The 1997–2000 ENSO was the most intense of recent decades, and it spawned powerful global weather patterns that caused more than $36 billion in damages and more than 22,000 deaths. *El Niños* tend to encourage warming, while *La Niñas* do the opposite; 2010 had a strong *El Niño*, but 2011 was a strong *La Niña* year, with corresponding warmer and cooler global temperatures.

These processes are becoming better understood, and as they are, they are beginning to provide explanations for some previously puzzling developments. For example, it is clear (Fig. 18–5) that a global warming trend was halted in the mid-1940s and that it resumed 30 years later. Researchers have found evidence that this mid-century cooling was the result of shifting ocean circulation linked to the NAO. Forecasters have suggested that this and the other ocean-atmosphere oscillations have been turning greenhouse-based warming off and on. The *El Niño/La Niña* events have been happening more frequently and with greater intensity in recent decades, changes in the climate that may be linked to global warming.

The Earth as a Greenhouse

Factors that influence the climate include interactive *internal components* (oceans, the atmosphere, snow cover, sea ice) and *external factors* (solar radiation, the Earth's rotation, slow changes in our planet's orbit, and the gaseous makeup of the atmosphere). **Radiative forcing** is the influence any particular factor has on the energy balance of the atmosphere-ocean-land system. A *forcing factor* can be *positive*, leading to *warming*, or *negative*, leading to *cooling*, as it affects the energy balance. Forcing is expressed in units of watts per square meter (W/m^2); averaged over all of the planet, solar radiation entering the atmosphere is about $340 \ W/m^2$. It is this radiation that is acted on by the various forcing factors.

Warming Processes. The interior of a car heats up when the car is sitting in sunlight with the windows closed. This heating occurs because sunlight comes in through the windows and is absorbed by the seats and other interior objects, thus converting light energy into heat energy, which is given off in the form of infrared radiation. Unlike sunlight, infrared radiation is blocked by glass and so cannot leave the car. The trapped heat energy causes the interior air temperature to rise. This is the same phenomenon that keeps a greenhouse warmer than the surrounding environment.

Greenhouse Gases. On a global scale, water vapor, CO_2, and other gases in the atmosphere play a role analogous to that of the glass in a greenhouse, hence the term *greenhouse gases (GHGs)*. Light energy comes through the atmosphere and is absorbed by Earth and converted to heat energy at the planet's surface. The infrared heat energy radiates back upward through the atmosphere and into space. The GHGs that are naturally present in the troposphere absorb some of the infrared radiation and reradiate it back toward the surface; other gases (N_2 and O_2) in the troposphere do not (**Fig. 18–9**). This greenhouse effect was first recognized in 1827 by French scientist Jean-Baptiste Fourier and is now firmly established. The GHGs are like a heat blanket, insulating Earth and delaying the loss of infrared energy (heat) to space. Without this insulation, average surface temperatures on Earth would be about $-19°C$ instead of $+14°C$, and life as we know it would be impossible. Therefore, our global climate depends on Earth's concentrations of GHGs. If these concentrations increase or decrease significantly, their influence as positive forcing agents will change, and our climate will change accordingly.

Ozone in the troposphere has a positive forcing effect, whereas its impact in the stratosphere is negative. However, the positive forcing predominates. Tropospheric ozone has a strong anthropogenic component linked to pollution (discussed in Chapter 19). It varies greatly in time and location and is highest in the vicinity of industrial societies.

Cooling Processes. Earth's atmosphere is also subject to negative forcing factors. For example, on average, clouds cover 50% of Earth's surface and reflect some 23% of solar radiation away to space before it ever reaches the ground. Sunlight reflected in this way is called the **planetary albedo**, and it contributes to overall cooling by preventing a certain amount of warming in the first place. The effect of the albedo is especially true for *low-lying*, fluffy clouds and can be readily appreciated if you think of how you are comforted on a hot day when a large cloud passes between you and the Sun. The radiation that was heating you and your surroundings is suddenly intercepted higher up in the atmosphere, and you feel cooler. However, *high-lying*, wispy clouds have a positive forcing effect, absorbing some of the solar radiation and emitting some infrared radiation themselves. Recent work indicates that the current net impact of clouds is a slightly positive forcing.

Snow and sea ice (the **cryosphere**) also reflect sunlight, contributing to the planetary albedo. Arctic warming has reduced this effect in recent decades, as open water and darker, unfrozen ground absorb sunlight. Cryosphere albedo is

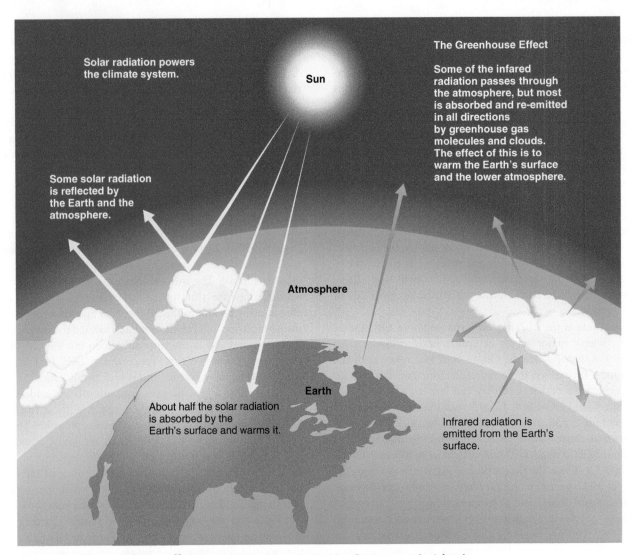

Figure 18–9 **The greenhouse effect.** Solar radiation that reaches Earth's surface is converted to infrared radiation and is radiated upward. Greenhouse gases in the atmosphere intercept this radiation and are warmed. The greenhouse gases in turn reradiate heat energy, and much of this is directed back toward Earth's surface.

(*Source:* S. Solomon et al., Eds. *Climate Change 2007: The Physical Science Basis,* Contribution of Working Group I to the Fourth Assessment Report of the Intergovernmental Panel on Climate Change (Cambridge, England: Cambridge University Press, 2007), FAQ 1.3, Figure 1.)

reduced even more by the widespread black carbon soot originating from anthropogenic sources (diesel engine exhaust and fires). By darkening the snow and ice, the soot promotes the absorption of radiant energy rather than its reflection.

Volcanoes. Volcanic activity can also lead to planetary cooling. When Mount Pinatubo in the Philippines erupted in 1991, some 20 million tons of particles and aerosols entered the atmosphere and contributed to a significant drop in global temperature as radiation was reflected and scattered away. This global cooling effect lasted until the volcanic debris was finally cleansed from the atmosphere by chemical change and deposition, a process that took several years. However, some sulfate aerosols from volcanic sources enter the stratosphere, where they have a longer-term cooling effect; these have increased since 2000, effectively reducing some of the global warming that otherwise might have occurred.[8]

Aerosols. Aerosols are microscopic liquid or solid particles originating from land and water surfaces (Chapter 10). Climatologists have found that industrial aerosols (from ground-level pollution) play a significant role in canceling out some of the warming from GHGs. Sulfates, nitrates, dust, and soot from industrial sources and forest fires enter the atmosphere and react with compounds there to form a high-level aerosol haze. This haze reflects and scatters some sunlight; the aerosols also contribute to the formation of clouds, which likewise increase the planetary albedo. *Sooty* aerosol (from fires) has an overall warming effect, but industrial *sulfate* aerosol creates substantial cooling, mainly through its tendency to increase global cloud cover. The mean residence time of the sulfates and soot forming the aerosol is about a week, so the aerosol does not increase over time, as the GHGs do. However, because anthropogenic sulfate is more than double that coming from natural sources, its effect is substantial and persistent. Climatologists estimate that the cooling effect of these pollutants has counteracted much of the potential global warming in recent decades. Because of progress made in curbing industrial pollutants in the United States and Europe, this impact has been declining over those regions. However, industrial growth in China and India has created a major rise in aerosols over Asia.

Solar Variability. Because the Sun is the source of radiant energy that heats Earth, any variability in the Sun's radiation reaching Earth will likely influence the climate. Direct monitoring of solar irradiance goes back only a few decades, but it has confirmed that there is an 11-year cycle of changes involving solar radiation increases during times of high sunspot activity. Sunspots are known to block cosmic ray intensity, and because cosmic rays help seed clouds, the diminished cloud cover allows more solar radiation to reach Earth's surface. Indeed, variations in solar forcing are thought to be partly responsible for the early-20th-century warming trend. However, solar output began declining around 1985 and continued for at least 20 years, yet global temperatures were rising rapidly at that time and have continued to rise. The IPCC AR4 assigned a slight warming role to fluctuations in solar radiation, but found that GHGs were some 13 times more responsible for the rising global temperatures than were solar changes.

Thus . . . Global atmospheric temperatures are a balance between the positive and negative forcing from natural causes (volcanoes, clouds, natural GHGs, solar irradiance) and anthropogenic causes (sulfate aerosols, soot, ozone, increases in GHGs). The net result varies, depending on one's location. The various forcing agents bring us year-to-year fluctuations in climate and make it difficult to attribute any one event or extreme season to human causation. Nevertheless, there has clearly been enough of a shift in many features of our climate in recent decades to generate international attention.

Evidence of Climate Change

There is much natural variation in weather from year to year, and local temperatures do not necessarily follow globally averaged ones. It is a fact, however, that the first decade of the 21st century is the warmest on record (Fig. 18–5). The years 2005 and 2010 tied for a new record for global temperature—the warmest years since recordkeeping began. Since the mid-1970s, the average global temperature has risen about 0.6°C (1.1°F), almost 0.2°C per decade. The warming is happening everywhere but is greater at high latitudes in the Northern Hemisphere. Because of the continued increases in anthropogenic GHGs in the atmosphere, the observed warming is considered to be the consequence of an "enhanced greenhouse effect."

Satellites. An interesting and controversial aspect of the warming trend involves measurements of tropospheric temperatures (from Earth's surface to 8 km above) made by 13 different satellites over two decades. One early analysis of the data indicated virtually no temperature increase in the troposphere. Much was made of this apparent discrepancy with the surface temperature trends by skeptics eager to disprove global warming. This situation was addressed by the Climate Change

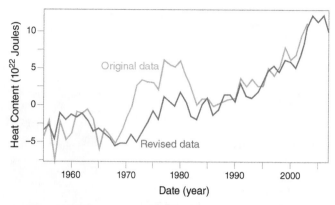

Figure 18–10 Heat capture by the oceans. The plot shows the changes in heat content of the upper 2,290 feet (700 m) of the world's oceans, as plotted by the Global Oceanographic Data Archaeology and Rescue Project (GODAR). Heat content is measured in joules (J). Two plots are seen: an original data plot and a revised data plot after corrections were made. See Sound Science, "Getting It Right."

(*Source:* Rebecca Lindsey, *Correcting Ocean Cooling,* Earth Observatory, November 5, 2008.)

Science Program (CCSP), which was created in 2002 by the Bush administration to address apparent unresolved questions about global climate change. The CCSP study, reported in May 2006, found that "the discrepancy no longer exists because errors in the satellite . . . data have been identified and corrected. New data sets have also been developed that do not show such discrepancies." Indeed, the study found a remarkable agreement between surface temperatures and tropospheric temperatures, all of which indicate a continued rise in temperature consistent with "our understanding of the effects of radiative forcing agents [showing] clear evidence of human influences on the climate system."[9] This report, the first of 21 assessments planned by the program, was approved by the Bush White House.

Ocean Heat Content. The upper 3,000 meters of the ocean have warmed measurably since 1955 (Fig. 18–10), a warming that dwarfs the observed warming of the atmosphere, accounting for 90% of the heat increase of Earth systems in the past several decades. There is a fascinating story about the actual measurements of ocean heat content shown in Figure 18–10 (described in Sound Science, "Getting It Right"). A key analysis of Earth's energy imbalance[10] makes the case for the ocean's continuing absorption of heat; over the past decade, the ocean has absorbed essentially all of the heat not yet seen in the atmosphere. This net absorption of heat energy has one long-term consequence and one that is more immediate.

The long-term consequence is *the impact of this stored heat* as it eventually comes into equilibrium with the atmosphere, raising temperatures over land and in the atmosphere even more. The immediate consequence is *the rise in sea level* that occurs because of thermal expansion. Sea level rose

[9]Climate Change Science Program. *Temperature Trends in the Lower Atmosphere: Steps for Understanding and Reconciling Differences,* A Report by the Climate Change Science Program and the Subcommittee on Global Change Research (Washington, DC: CCSP, 2006).

[10]James Hansen et al. "Earth's Energy Imbalance: Confirmation and Implications," *Science* 308 (June 2005): 1431–1435.

SOUND SCIENCE

Getting It Right

Josh Willis works at NASA's Jet Propulsion Laboratory and specializes in measurements of the ocean's response to global warming. He publishes his results in peer-reviewed journals like the *Journal of Geophysical Research*. In a 2004 paper, he presented work that showed the ocean heat content increasing between 1993 and 2003, in agreement with what climatologists were seeing with the atmospheric temperature measurements. This is no trivial matter; the oceans absorb some 90% of the heat from global warming. However, Willis then did a follow-up study with colleague John Lyman, updating the time series from 2003 to 2005, showing that the oceans suddenly began to cool, and in a large way. This alarmed many climatologists and, at the same time, fed the climate change skeptics, who pounced on the data as proof that global warming wasn't happening.

One climatologist who was especially dubious about Willis's new data was Takmeng Wong, who works at NASA's Langley Research Center. Wong had been measuring the exchange of energy between the Earth and space, and his data showed that the amounts of entering and outgoing energy at the top of the atmosphere were gradually climbing out of balance. More energy was entering than leaving. This was true for the

Josh Willis, NASA Jet Propulsion Laboratory. Willis is shown here receiving the Presidential Early Career Award for Scientists and Engineers in January 2010 from John Holdren (White House Office of Science and Technology Policy Director) and Lori Garver (NASA Associate Administrator)

2003–2005 time period as well, and Wong politely asked Willis to reexamine his data because there was a clear discrepancy between the two studies. When Willis measured an even deeper ocean cooling in 2006, he began to entertain serious doubts about his data.

The source of the temperature data being employed by Willis was a flotilla of Argo floats—underwater robots that would sink to 2,000 meters, drift with the ocean currents, and then pop up to the surface, taking water temperatures as they ascended. They then transmitted the data to a satellite. Willis found

that, when tested, many new Argo floats were giving bad data—in fact, indicating cooler temperatures than other devices being employed. He also consulted an independent set of data on satellite measurements of sea level. When water heats up, it expands, and the sea level data were showing a continual rise. One final factor in the data relates to a different data set on ocean temperatures from devices called XBTs (for expandable bathythermographs, which are dropped into the ocean and relay temperatures as they sink). An independent paper had shown that the XBT data from previous years were too warm. When Willis corrected his ocean warming time series with the too-warm XBT measurements and the too-cool Argo measurements, the indications of ocean cooling went away. The warm pulses of the 1970s and 1980s disappeared, and the time series showed a gradual warming (Fig. 18–10).

The conclusion to this story is that you can never have too many independent measurements if you want to measure something as huge as a warming planet. Taken together, ocean warming, sea level rise, and energy exchange with space are now telling a consistent story, one of a warming that can be attributed only to rising GHG emissions.

Source: Rebecca Lindsey, *Correcting Ocean Cooling*, NASA Earth Observatory, November 5, 2008.

about 6 inches (15 cm) during the 20th century, a rate of 1.5 millimeters per year. It is now rising more rapidly, at a rate of 3.2 millimeters per year (Fig. 18–11). About half of this rise is due to thermal expansion, and the remainder results from the melting of glaciers and ice fields. The IPCC AR4 documents a general loss of land ice as glaciers and ice caps have thinned and melted. Significantly, historical sea level data indicate that the sea level was unchanged until 100 years ago; this modern sea level rise is a new phenomenon and is consistent with the known pattern of anthropogenic climate warming.

Other Observed Changes. The IPCC AR4 and other recent reports document a number of climate impacts, all of which are consistent with and contribute to the picture of GHG-caused climate change (note that most of these changes have potentially serious consequences for human and natural systems):

- Broad increases in warm temperature extremes and decreases in cold temperature extremes have been documented. There are also seasonal changes: Spring comes earlier and fall is later in the Northern Hemisphere,

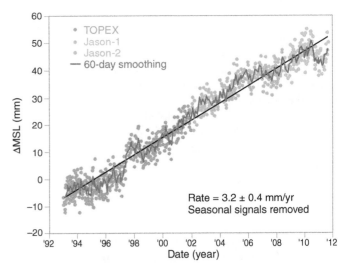

Figure 18–11 The rise in global mean sea level. Satellite radar altimeters have provided estimates of global sea level since 1993. The current rate is 3.2 mm/year. Note the 6 mm decline in 2010–2011, a consequence of the strong La Niña that produced massive rainfall events over land. Note, too, that the sea level started back up in mid-2011 as the La Niña began to subside.

(*Source:* Colorado University Sea Level Research Group, 2011. Used with permission.)

shifting ecosystems and populations out of sync. More tree deaths and forest insect damage have also been traced to the warmer temperatures. Heat waves, like those that scorched Europe in 2010 and the United States in 2011 and 2012, are increasing in intensity and frequency.

- Droughts are also increasing in frequency and intensity; the fraction of land area experiencing drought has more than doubled over the past 30 years, leading to a global decline in net primary productivity and significant reductions in corn and wheat crops. More than 60% of the United States has been under a drought that started in the late 1990s, seriously affecting agricultural crops and water resources. East Africa is experiencing its worst drought in 60 years, overwhelming refugee camps and available food aid. The increased forest fire activity in the western United States is clearly related to droughts, warmer temperatures, and earlier springs; more than 8.5 million acres burned in 2011, the third largest burn in history.

- Rising Arctic temperatures have brought about a major shrinkage of Arctic sea ice, with an accelerating decrease (Fig. 18–12). According to a recent assessment,[11] the Arctic Ocean is likely to have an ice-free summer by 2030.

[11]Arctic Monitoring and Assessment Program. Snow, Water, Ice and Permafrost in the Arctic, Executive Summary. 2011. www.amap.no/swipa. December 19, 2011.

While overall global temperature has increased a moderate 1.1°F, temperatures in Alaska, Siberia, and north-western Canada have risen 5°F in summer and 10°F in winter. Spring comes two weeks earlier in the Arctic than it did at the turn of the 21st century. The polar ice cap has lost nearly 20% of its volume in the past two decades, and permafrost has been melting all over the polar regions—lifting buildings, uprooting telephone poles, and breaking up roads.

- The Greenland Ice Sheet, a huge reservoir of water, is melting and calving icebergs at unprecedented rates, undoubtedly a response to the rise in temperatures in the northern latitudes. A net loss of 530 cubic miles of water has occurred between 2003 and 2011 (Fig. 18–13). Record warm summers have accelerated Greenland ice melt; the largest loss (114 cubic miles) was in 2011. The two-mile-high ice sheet contains enough water to raise ocean levels 23 feet (7 m).

- Temperatures in Antarctica, which holds enough ice to raise sea levels by 185 feet (57 m), have risen by more than 0.5°C over the past 55 years; West Antarctica showed the greatest warming, at 0.85°C. The West Antarctic Ice Sheet (WAIS) is the continent's most vulnerable ice mass because it is grounded below sea level. Ocean water is constantly in contact with the edges of this ice sheet, and the ice sheet has been shrinking as the water eats away at the ice. Melting of this ice sheet would raise global sea level

SEA ICE EXTENT 09/09/2011

—— 1979–2000 (median)

AVERAGE MONTHLY ARCTIC SEA ICE EXTENT
August 1978 to 2010

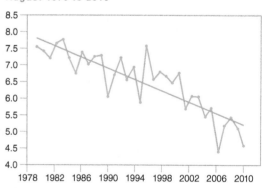

Figure 18–12 Decline of Arctic sea ice. (a) The extent of sea ice in September 2011 was 4.33 million km² (1.67 million mi²), the second lowest measure on record. The orange line is the median ice extent for September from 1979 to 2000. (b) Tracking with satellites shows the 33-year downward decline in the Arctic sea ice at the end of the northern summer. The decline is now 11.2% per decade.

(*Source:* National Snow and Ice Data Center, University of Colorado, October 2011.)

LOSS OF MASS OF THE GREENLAND ICE SHEET

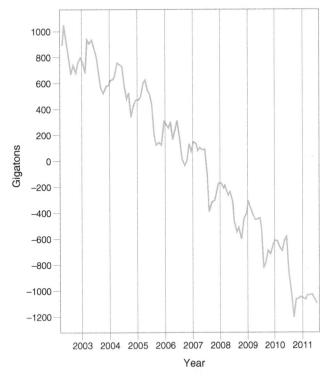

Figure 18–13 Loss of mass of the Greenland Ice Sheet. The ice sheet loss has been measured by the gravity-measuring GRACE satellites. The greatest decline occurred in 2010–2011, a total loss of 430 gigatons (114 cubic miles).

(*Source:* NOAA Arctic Report Card: Update for 2011.)

by 16 to 20 feet (5 to 6 m). The East Antarctic Ice Sheet contains eight times the mass of West Antarctic's.

- Glaciers have resumed a retreat that has been documented for more than a century, but that slowed in the 1970s and 1980s. The World Glacier Monitoring Service has followed the melting and slow retreat of mountain glaciers all over the world. The response time of glaciers to climatic trends is slow—10 to 50 years—but the data collected show an acceleration of glacial "wastage" since 1990 that is likely a response to recent rapid atmospheric warming (Fig. 18–14). Loss of mountain glaciers is especially serious, as these glaciers are often critical water sources for arid lands below.

- Patterns of precipitation are changing, with greater amounts from 30° N and 30° S poleward and with smaller amounts from 10° N to 30° N. Also, there have been widespread increases in heavy precipitation events, leading to more frequent flooding.

- Marine fish species populations are shifting northward as sea temperatures have warmed, impacting the commercial fisheries. Changing sea temperatures have also affected the spatial distribution of phytoplankton production over major ocean areas.

- The oceans have been soaking up some 30% of the CO_2 emissions from human sources, for which we may be thankful because this slows the rise of atmospheric CO_2 considerably. However, in doing so, the oceans are

(a)

(b)

Figure 18–14 Shrinkage of the Muir glacier. The Muir glacier, a tidewater glacier in Alaska's Glacier Bay, has retreated more than 7 miles (12 km) and thinned by more than 2,600 feet (800 m) since 1941. Once covered with ice and snow (a), the land now holds trees and shrubs (b).

(*Source:* NSIDC/WDC for Glaciology, compiled 2002, updated 2006, *Online glacier photograph database,* Boulder, CO: National Snow and Ice Data Center/World Data Center for Glaciology, digital media.)

experiencing a decrease in pH, a process known as **ocean acidification**. Although the decrease is only about 0.1 pH unit to date, there is serious concern about the future state of seawater pH in light of continued anthropogenic CO_2 production. At some level, ocean acidification will make the warm oceans inhospitable to coral reefs; the coral animals depend on an equilibrium for carbon minerals that is affected by acidic conditions. The bottom line: Human use of fossil fuels has begun to change not only the temperature, but also the chemistry of the surface oceans.

Given the accumulating evidence that the climate is changing and that the change is already causing an array of changes in biological, physical, and chemical systems on Earth, it is time to address the causes of these changes in more detail.

Rising Greenhouse Gases

According to the IPCC AR4 Synthesis Report, "Global GHG emissions due to human activities have grown since pre-industrial times, with an increase of 70% between

ESTIMATES OF GLOBAL CARBON EMISSIONS FROM FOSSIL-
FUEL COMBUSTION AND CEMENT MANUFACTURE

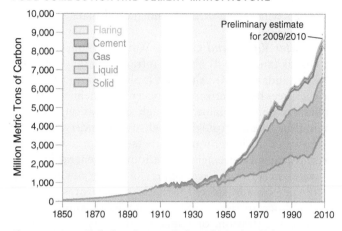

Figure 18–15 Global carbon emissions from fossil fuel combustion. Data from 1850 to 2010, from the Carbon Dioxide Information Analysis Center (CDIAC). The rise in the 2000s decade is conspicuous.

(*Source:* CDIAC, Oak Ridge National Laboratory, 2011.)

TOTAL EMISSIONS: 8.3 BILLION METRIC TONS OF CARBON
PER YEAR

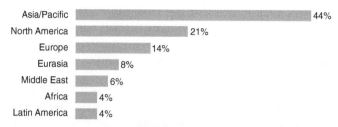

Figure 18–16 Sources of carbon dioxide emissions from fossil fuel burning. Total emissions in 2009 were approximately 8.3 GtC, or 30.3 billion metric tons of CO_2. Half of this (Europe, North America, Japan, South Korea, Taiwan, Saudi Arabia) comes from the industrialized countries.

(*Source:* Data from U.S. Energy Information Administration, December 2011.)

1970 and 2004."[12] They have continued to increase.[13] The most important of these anthropogenic GHGs is carbon dioxide (CO_2).

Carbon Dioxide. More than 100 years ago, Swedish scientist Svante Arrhenius reasoned that differences in CO_2 levels in the atmosphere could greatly affect Earth's energy budget. Arrhenius suggested that, in time, the burning of fossil fuels might change the atmospheric CO_2 concentration, though he believed that it would take centuries before the associated warming would be noticeable. He was not concerned about the impacts of this warming, arguing that such an increase would be beneficial. (He lived in Sweden!)

Carbon Dioxide Monitoring. In 1958, Charles Keeling began measuring CO_2 levels on Mauna Loa, in Hawaii. Measurements there have been recorded continuously, and they reveal a striking increase in atmospheric levels of the gas (Fig. 18–6). The concentrations increased exponentially until the energy crisis in the mid-1970s, rose at a rate of 1.5 ppm/year for several decades, and in the 2000s began rising at a rate of 2.0 ppm/year and higher. The data also reveal an annual oscillation of 5–7 ppm, which reflects seasonal changes of photosynthesis and respiration in terrestrial ecosystems in the Northern Hemisphere. When respiration predominates (late fall through spring), CO_2 levels rise; when photosynthesis predominates (late spring through early fall), CO_2 levels fall. Most salient, however, is the relentless rise in CO_2. As of mid-2012, atmospheric CO_2 levels were at 394 ppm, 40% higher than they were before the Industrial Revolution and higher than they have been for more than 800,000 years (Fig. 18–7a). Thus, our insulating blanket is thickening, and it is reasonable to expect that this will have a warming effect.

Sources. As Arrhenius suggested, the obvious place to look for the source of increasing CO_2 levels is our use of fossil fuels. Every kilogram of fossil carbon burned produces 3.7 kilograms of CO_2 that enters the atmosphere (each carbon atom in the fuel picks up two oxygen atoms in the course of burning and becoming CO_2). Currently, 9.1 billion metric tons (gigatons, or Gt) of fossil fuel carbon (GtC) are burned each year (Fig. 18–15), all added to the atmosphere as CO_2 (about 5% of this total comes from cement production and is usually included in figures reported for fossil fuel emissions). About half of this amount comes from the industrialized countries (Fig. 18–16). Carbon dioxide accounts for about 20% of greenhouse warming, at current levels.

Climate change skeptics sometimes claim that much of the new CO_2 comes from natural sources. This claim can be put to rest by considering the ^{14}C signature of atmospheric CO_2. ^{14}C is a radioactive isotope of carbon that is formed in the atmosphere by bombardment of nitrogen atoms by cosmic rays; it decays over time to regenerate nitrogen atoms. Fossil fuels contain no ^{14}C because of radioactive decay (the half-life of ^{14}C is 5730 years). If significant amounts of CO_2 originating from fossil fuel combustion are added to the atmosphere, the ^{14}C in the atmosphere should be declining, and it clearly is (Fig. 18–17).

CLEAN AIR MEASUREMENTS AT NIWOT RIDGE, COLORADO

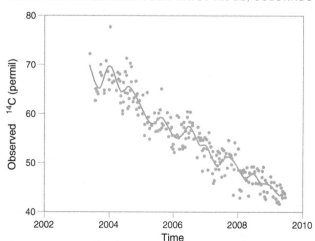

Figure 18–17 ^{14}C trend in the atmosphere. The $\Delta^{14}C$ is the ratio of ^{14}C to normal ^{12}C. The smaller the ratio, the fewer ^{14}C atoms are in the air. The decreasing trend is due to ^{14}C depleted CO_2 emitted from burning fossil fuels.

(*Source:* NOAA Earth System Research Laboratory, Issue 6: Spring 2011.)

[12]Intergovernmental Panel on Climate Change. *Climate Change 2007: Synthesis Report.* Contribution of Working Groups I, II and III to the Fourth Assessment. Report of the Intergovernmental Panel on Climate Change (Core Writing Team, Pachauri, R. K., and Reisinger, A. (Eds.)). IPCC, Geneva, Switzerland, 2007.
[13]S. A. Montzka et al. Non-CO_2 Greenhouse Gases and Climate Change. *Nature* 476: 43–50. August 4, 2011.

It is estimated that land use changes such as deforestation add another 0.9 GtC annually to the carbon already coming from fossil fuel combustion. Over the past 50 years, the release of carbon from fossil fuel use and deforestation has more than tripled. Fortunately, more than half of these carbon emissions are removed annually by so-called *sinks*.

Sinks. Careful calculations show that if all the CO_2 emitted from burning fossil fuels accumulated in the atmosphere, the concentration would rise by 3 or more ppm per year, not the actual 2 ppm charted in Figure 18–6. Thus, there must be carbon sinks that absorb CO_2 and keep it from accumulating at a more rapid rate in the atmosphere. There is broad agreement that the oceans serve as a sink for about 30% of the CO_2 emitted; some of this is due to the uptake of CO_2 by phytoplankton, and some is a consequence of the undersaturation of CO_2 in seawater. There are limitations to the ocean's ability to absorb CO_2, however, because only the top 300 m of the ocean are in direct contact with the atmosphere. (As mentioned earlier, the deep ocean layers do mix with the upper layers, but the mixing time is more than 1,000 years.) And, as the oceans acidify (precisely because they are absorbing CO_2), their capacity to continue this absorption will diminish.

The seasonal swings illustrated in Figure 18–6 show that biota can influence atmospheric CO_2 levels. Measurements indicate that terrestrial ecosystems also serve as carbon sinks. Indeed, these land ecosystems apparently have stored a net 25%, a figure that includes the losses from deforestation. As a result, terrestrial ecosystems, and especially forests, are increasingly valued for their ability to sequester carbon. A simple model of the major dynamic pools and fluxes of carbon, as presently understood, is presented in **Figure 18–18**.

Other Gases. Water vapor, methane, nitrous oxide, ozone, and chlorofluorocarbons (CFCs) also absorb infrared radiation and add to the insulating effect of CO_2 (Table 18–2).

Most of these gases have anthropogenic sources and are increasing in concentration, raising the concern that future warming will extend well beyond the calculated effects of CO_2 alone.

Water Vapor and Clouds. Water as vapor (a gas) or in clouds (an aerosol) absorbs infrared energy and is the most abundant GHG. Although it plays an important role in the greenhouse effect, its concentration in the troposphere is quite variable. Through evaporation and precipitation (the hydrologic cycle), water undergoes rapid turnover in the lower atmosphere (see Chapter 10). However, recent measurements have found a general increase in water vapor in the atmosphere of 400 grams per cubic meter per decade since 1988. As temperatures over the land and oceans rise, evaporation increases, and the water vapor concentration, or humidity, rises. As the humidity rises, it traps more heat in the atmosphere, which causes even more warming. This phenomenon is called **positive feedback** and is one of the more disturbing features of future warming. The recent rise in atmospheric humidity is entirely consistent with the warming that has accompanied the rise in anthropogenic GHGs. Water vapor accounts for about 50% of the greenhouse effect, and clouds an additional 25%.

Methane. Methane (CH_4), the third-most-important GHG, is 25 times more effective a GHG than is CO_2, molecule for molecule. Primarily a product of microbial fermentative reactions, methane's main natural sources are wetlands and green plants. Anthropogenic sources include livestock (methane is generated in the stomachs of ruminants), landfills, coal mines, natural-gas production and transmission, rice cultivation, and manure. Although methane is gradually destroyed in reactions with other gases in the atmosphere, it is being added to the atmosphere faster than it can be broken down. The concentration of atmospheric methane has more than doubled since the Industrial Revolution, as revealed in core samples taken from glacial ice (Table 18–2). After rising at a rate of around 1.8 parts per billion (ppb) per year, methane

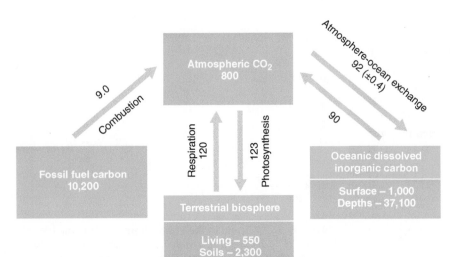

Figure 18–18 Global carbon cycle. Data are given in GtC (billions of metric tons of carbon). Pools are in the boxes, and fluxes (Gt C per year) are indicated by the arrows.

(*Source:* U.S. DOE. 2008. *Carbon Cycling and Biosequestration: Report from the March 2008 Workshop*, DOE/SC-108, U.S. Department of Energy Office of Science, pp. 2–3. http://genomicscience. energy.gov.)

TABLE 18–2 Anthropogenic Greenhouse Gases in the Atmosphere

Gas	Average Preindustrial Concentration (ppb)*	Approximate Current Concentration (ppb)	Radiative Forcing (W/m²)	Average Years in Atmosphere
Carbon dioxide (CO_2)	280,000	392,000	1.76	ca. 120
Methane (CH_4)	714	1,800	0.50	9
Nitrous oxide (N_2O)	270	322	0.17	120
Chlorofluorocarbons and halocarbons	0	1.2	0.30	50–100

Sources: IPCC AR4; recent data from CDIAC.

*Parts per billion; 1,000 ppb = 1 part per million (ppm).

leveled off from 1999–2006 but is now increasing at a rate of 6 ppb/year. Measurements indicate that two-thirds of the present methane emissions are anthropogenic. Like CO_2, methane is more abundant than it has been for at least the past 800,000 years.

Nitrous Oxide. Nitrous oxide (N_2O) levels have increased some 19% during the past 200 years and are still rising at a rate of 0.7 ppb per year. Sources of the gas include agriculture, the oceans, and biomass burning; lesser quantities come from fossil fuel burning and industry. N_2O is produced in agriculture via anaerobic denitrification processes, which occur wherever nitrogen (a major component of fertilizers) is highly available in soils (see Chapter 3). The buildup of nitrous oxide is particularly unwelcome because its long residence time (114 years) makes the gas a problem in not only the troposphere, where it contributes to warming, but also the stratosphere, where it contributes to the destruction of ozone.

Ozone. Although ozone in the troposphere is short-lived and varies at many locations, it is a potent GHG. Some ozone from the stratosphere (where it is formed) descends into the troposphere, but the greatest source is anthropogenic, through the action of sunlight on pollutants (Chapter 19). Estimates indicate that the concentration of ozone in the atmosphere has increased 36% since 1750. Major sources are automotive traffic and burning forests and agricultural wastes.

CFCs and Other Halocarbons. Emissions of halocarbons are entirely anthropogenic. Like nitrous oxide, halocarbons are long lived and contribute to both global warming in the troposphere and ozone destruction in the stratosphere. Used as refrigerants, solvents, and fire retardants, some halocarbons have 10,000 times the capacity to absorb infrared radiation that CO_2 does. The rate of production of halocarbons has declined due to adherence to the Montreal Protocol, and the concentration of halocarbons in the troposphere began declining in 1990 and is now only one-tenth of its former level.

Together the other anthropogenic GHGs are estimated to account for 5% of greenhouse warming, about one-fourth of the impact of CO_2. Although the tropospheric concentrations of some of these gases are rising, it is hoped that they will gradually decline in importance because of steps being taken to reduce their levels in the atmosphere.

The Atmosphere's Control Knob. A recent report from the Goddard Institute for Space Studies[14] examined the role of the different greenhouse gases in maintaining temperatures on Earth. Some skeptics have claimed that because water vapor and clouds contribute the lion's share of the greenhouse effect (75%), CO_2 and the other greenhouse gases are not very important. On the contrary, Lacis and coauthors point out that, in fact, CO_2 and the other *noncondensing* gases (water readily *condenses* and can be removed from the atmosphere) are the essential components of greenhouse warming because their "forcing" role is what sustains the current levels of water vapor and clouds. They point out that without the stability of these noncondensing greenhouse gases, the water vapor and clouds could not maintain our current greenhouse conditions and Earth would be plunged into an icebound state. It is the radiative forcing of CO_2 and the other gases that controls the feedback processes involved with water vapor and clouds, even though these on average contribute 75% of the greenhouse effect. Thus, CO_2, because it is the most abundant noncondensing gas, is the key gas, the "control knob" that governs Earth's temperature.

The IPCC AR4 Synthesis Report states: "Global atmospheric concentrations of CO_2, CH_4 and N_2O have increased markedly as a result of human activities since 1750 and now far exceed pre-industrial values determined from ice cores spanning many thousands of years . . . . There is *very high confidence* (90–100%) that the global average net effect of human activities since 1750 has been one of warming, with a radiative forcing of +1.6 W/m²." **Figure 18–19** shows the understanding of the various radiative forcing. It is evident that positive anthropogenic forcing far outweighs negative.

[14]Andrew A. Lacis et al. "Atmospheric CO_2: Principal Control Knob Governing Earth's Temperature." *Science* 330: 356–359. October 15, 2010.

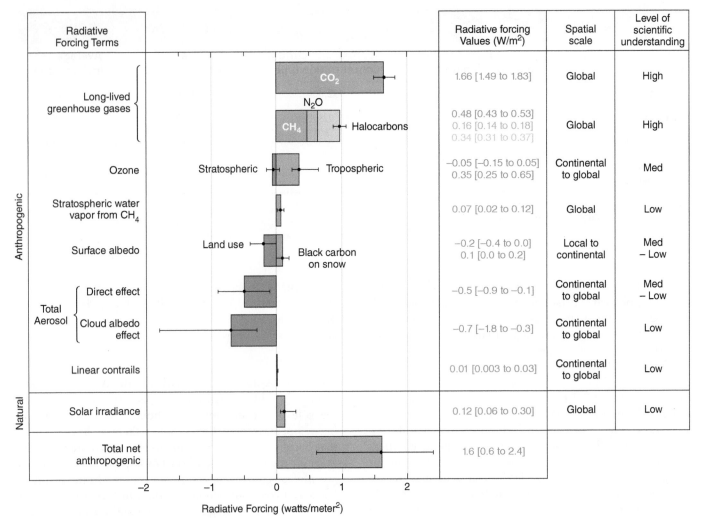

Figure 18–19 Radiative forcing. Positive and negative factors contribute to changes in energy balance within the atmosphere and at the Earth's surface. The figure presents the human factors that have led to the current sustained increase in radiative forcing (RF), in watts per square meter. The 90% confidence limits are indicated, and on the right, the relative radiative forcing and spatial scale of effects are shown, along with the level of scientific understanding.

(*Source:* S. Solomon et al., Eds. *Climate Change 2007: The Physical Science Basis*, Contribution of Working Group I to the Fourth Assessment Report of the Intergovernmental Panel on Climate Change (Cambridge, England: Cambridge University Press, 2007), Figure SPM 2.)

Future Changes in Climate

Higher temperatures, rising sea levels, heat waves, droughts, intense precipitation events, shifts in seasons, melting ice sheets, and Arctic thawing—these are happening right now, and GHG levels are continuing to rise as a result of human agency. The International Energy Agency projects a growing demand for fossil fuels as populations and economies grow. If global fossil fuel use continues on its present trajectory, emissions of GHGs will increase 35% by 2030. By 2050, emissions will increase 100%. Given the huge reserves of coal, ample supplies of natural gas, and remaining oil reserves, there is no reason to doubt this projection. However, it is clear that commitment to this future use of fossil fuels also will commit us to greater changes in climate. How much change, and when, would be a matter of guesswork if it were not for the use of climate models.

Modeling Global Climate. Weather forecasting employs powerful computers that are capable of handling large amounts of atmospheric data and applying mathematical equations to model the processes taking place in the atmosphere, oceans, and land. Forecasts of conditions for 72 hours or more have become quite accurate. Even though computing power has increased greatly in recent years, the somewhat chaotic behavior of weather parameters prevents longer-term forecasting.

Modeling climate is an essential strategy for exploring the potential future impacts of rising GHGs. Climatologists employ similarly powerful computers and have combined global atmospheric circulation patterns with ocean circulation, radiation feedback from clouds, and land surface processes to produce **atmosphere-ocean general circulation models (AOGCMs)** that are capable of simulating long-term climatic conditions. Many

ANTHROPOGENIC AND NATURAL FORCINGS

(a)

NATURAL FORCINGS ONLY

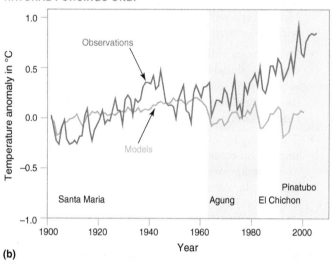

(b)

Figure 18–20 Comparison between modeled and actual data on temperature anomalies, 1900–2000. Observed values are shown by the green line, and runs from 13 models are shown in color. (a) Model results with both anthropogenic and natural forcings. (b) Model results with only natural forcings. The shaded areas mark the timing of major volcanic events.

(*Source:* S. Solomon et al., Eds. *Climate Change 2007: The Physical Science Basis*, Contribution of Working Group I to the Fourth Assessment Report of the Intergovernmental Panel on Climate Change (Cambridge, England: Cambridge University Press, 2007), Figure 23, TS.)

centers around the world are intensely engaged in exploring climate change by running models coupling the atmosphere, oceans, and land.

The best test of such models is the degree to which they can simulate present-day climate. A recent study compared some 50 climate models developed over the past two decades in order to answer this question: How well do coupled models simulate today's climate?[15] The authors concluded that the most recent models, especially those used for the IPCC AR4, have reached an unprecedented level of realism.

Figure 18–20, from the IPCC AR4, shows how closely models track the observed temperature changes from 1900 to 2004, taking into consideration natural and anthropogenic forcing. Earlier assessment reports projected global temperature increases from 0.15 to 0.29°C per decade, based on less sophisticated models. These values compare favorably with the observed values of about 0.2°C per decade occurring since the projections.

Running the Models. The AOGCMs are employed to examine the changes that might take place over the 21st century. A number of assumptions about GHG emissions are combined with a range of climate responses to GHG concentrations (called **climate sensitivity**) to project some 35 scenarios of 21st-century climate changes. In **Figure 18–21**, we show three scenarios to illustrate a range of climate responses. None of the scenarios considers the impacts of *specific policies* to reduce GHGs:

- A2 is a high emissions scenario, reflecting a world of independent countries going their own way, with increasing population and regionally varied economic growth; technological change is slower than in other scenarios.

- A1B, a medium emissions scenario, reflects a world in which population reaches its peak in mid-century and then declines, economic growth is rapid, and new and efficient technologies are introduced; there is a balance across all energy sources, with no specific reliance on any one technology.

- B1 is a lower emissions scenario, reflecting a more globalized world with population developments as in A1B, but with effective global cooperation to reach sustainability; in particular, technologies are clean and resource efficient.

Every scenario employed in the models generates a rise in CO_2 concentrations and a corresponding rise in mean global temperature. Even if there were no increase at all in

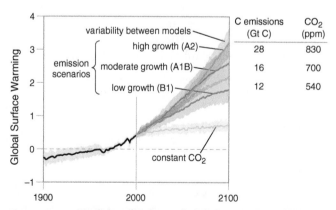

Figure 18–21 Model projections of global mean warming. Projections are for the A2, A1B, and B1 scenarios starting in 2000 and extended to 2100. The orange curve from 2000 shows the forcing "commitment" if greenhouse gas emissions were held constant in 2000. Annual carbon emissions and final CO_2 concentrations corresponding to the three scenarios are also shown.

(*Source:* S. Solomon et al., Eds. *Climate Change 2007: The Physical Science Basis*, Contribution of Working Group I to the Fourth Assessment Report of the Intergovernmental Panel on Climate Change (Cambridge, England: Cambridge University Press, 2007), Figure 32, TS.)

GHGs, current GHG concentrations represent a *commitment* to further temperature increase due to the delay in the release to the atmosphere of energy stored in the oceans. That commitment is on the order of about 0.1°C per decade for the next several decades, as shown in Figure 18–21 (the orange curve). Approximate peak carbon emissions and CO_2 concentrations corresponding with the three scenarios are also shown in Figure 18–21.

Projections. The AR4 examined the implications of the model runs and projected the potential future climate changes that could be expected, given the range of scenarios and also the current picture of climate change already under way. The major consequence of rising GHG levels during the 21st century is *rising temperatures*—the amount of rise depending on energy choices and other factors, such as population growth. Rising global temperatures are linked to two major impacts: *regional climatic changes* and *a rise in sea level*. Both of these effects show up in all of the models, though the details of regional changes from climate models are very uncertain. Some of the most significant findings are presented here:

- **Equilibrium climate sensitivity**—the sustained change in mean global temperature that occurs if atmospheric CO_2 is held at double preindustrial values, or about 550 ppm—is in the range of 2–4.5°C, with a median of 3°C. A more recent estimate of climate sensitivity,[16] based on past glacial temperature ranges, suggests a lower range: 1.7–2.6°C, median 2.3° (though there are many uncertainties in this estimate).

- The actual warming of the 21st century will be a consequence of GHG emissions, whatever they are. The model scenarios project a range of surface warming in 2100 compared with 1980–2000; for the B1, A1B, and A2 scenarios, the estimates average 1.8°C, 2.8°C, and 3.4°C, respectively. The projected rate of warming for the next two decades is 0.2°C per decade.

- The warming is expected to occur in geographical patterns similar to those of recent years: warming greatest at the higher latitudes and in continental interiors and least over the North Atlantic and the southern oceans. However, it will be warmer everywhere.

- Because of the warming climate, snow cover and sea ice will decrease, possibly fully opening up the Arctic Ocean by mid-century. Glaciers and ice caps will continue to shrink, resulting in a rise in sea level. In the Arctic, up to 90% of the upper layer of permafrost is expected to thaw, creating a positive climate feedback as methane and CO_2 are released.

- Because the oceans will be absorbing so much CO_2, they will continue to acidify, threatening coral reefs (which will already be stressed by warming tropical seas) and shellfish everywhere.

- The sea level, currently rising at a rate of 3.2 mm per year, will certainly continue to rise as a consequence of continued thermal expansion and snow and ice melt (Fig. 18–11). The range projected by the IPCC for the end of the 21st century is 7 to 23 inches (19 to 59 cm). Significantly, the projections did not include melting of the Greenland and Antarctic Ice Sheets.

- As the upper layers of the North Atlantic Ocean warm and become more fresh, the thermohaline circulation is expected to slow down, but no models show it collapsing.

- Storm intensities are expected to increase, with higher wind speeds, more extreme wave heights, and more intense precipitation; there will be fewer but more intense hurricanes in the Atlantic Basin.

- Heat waves will become more frequent and longer lasting as the climate warms. Growing seasons will lengthen, and frost days will decrease in middle and high latitudes. Outbreaks of cold air in the Northern Hemisphere will diminish by 50% or more compared with the present.

- Precipitation will decrease in already dry regions and increase in already wet regions; there will be an increase in extremes of daily precipitation. Areas of extreme drought will expand, affecting up to 30% of the world's land surface.

- The changing climatic parameters will have profound impacts on ecosystems and species, the impacts accruing as the temperature warms over time (Fig. 18–22): damage to polar ecosystems (as we have seen), bleached and dying coral reefs, major loss of Amazon rain forests, widespread extinctions of species, and loss of ecosystem resilience.

- Some impacts are positive: growing seasons would be longer in mid- to high latitudes, and temperatures would be more moderate in high-latitude countries like Canada and Russia.

A "business as usual" approach to climate change is best illustrated by the A2 scenario, which projects a temperature change between 3°C and 5°C. Note that the difference in temperature between an ice age and the warm period following it is only 5°C, so in a century, unless some serious measures are taken, Earth's climate will change dramatically. Responding to these changes will likely involve unprecedented and costly adjustments. The impact on natural ecosystems could be highly destabilizing. For the agricultural community, the greatest difficulty in coping with climatic change is *not knowing what to expect*. Already, farmers lose an average of one in five crop plantings because of unfavorable weather. As the climate shifts, the vagaries of weather will become more pronounced, and crop losses are likely to increase.

Sea Level. There is great uncertainty about the magnitude of the rise in sea level. A half-meter rise in sea level will flood many coastal areas and make them much more

---

[16]Andreas Schmittner et al. "Climate Sensitivity Estimated from Temperature Reconstructions of the Last Glacial Maximum." *Science* 334: 1385–1388. December 9, 2011.

Figure 18–22 **Global warming impacts on biological systems.** The impacts build up with greater temperature changes over time. The optimistic scenario is B1 from IPCC AR4; the pessimistic scenario is A2 from IPCC AR4.

(*Source:* Richard Kerr, "How Urgent Is Climate Change?" by Richard A. Kerr, from SCIENCE, November 2007, Volume 318(5854). Copyright © 2007 by AAAS. Reprinted with permission.

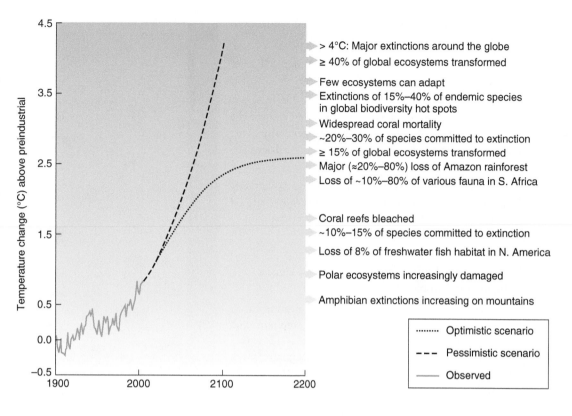

> 4°C: Major extinctions around the globe

≥ 40% of global ecosystems transformed

Few ecosystems can adapt
Extinctions of 15%–40% of endemic species in global biodiversity hot spots
Widespread coral mortality
~20%–30% of species committed to extinction
≥ 15% of global ecosystems transformed
Major (≈20%–80%) loss of Amazon rainforest
Loss of ~10%–80% of various fauna in S. Africa

Coral reefs bleached
~10%–15% of species committed to extinction

Loss of 8% of freshwater fish habitat in N. America

Polar ecosystems increasingly damaged

Amphibian extinctions increasing on mountains

·········· Optimistic scenario

– – – Pessimistic scenario

———— Observed

prone to damage from storms, forcing people to abandon properties and migrate inland. A 1-meter rise would flood 17% of Bangladesh, creating tens of millions of refugees and destroying half of the country's rice lands. As we saw, for many of the small oceanic nations, a rise in sea level means obliteration, not just alteration. Models suggest that if the mean global temperature rises as much as 3°C above present levels, it will set up conditions that could cause widespread loss of the Greenland Ice Sheet. Recent studies have made it clear that the IPCC projections of sea level rise are *strikingly on the low side*. These studies indicate that 21st-century warming would lead to a sea level rise of close to 2 meters, considering the plausible rates of melting of glaciers that run into the sea (in Greenland and Antarctica). And once atmospheric GHG levels are stabilized (assuming they are), temperatures and sea levels will continue to rise for hundreds of years because of the slow response time of the oceans. The expected continued rise would cause disasters in most coastal areas, which are home to half the world's population and its business and commerce.

Climate Change Impacts in the United States

In 2002, the Bush administration launched the Climate Change Science Program (CCSP—now called the Global Change Research Program, or GCRP) to integrate the efforts of many federal agencies involved in the scientific effort to

understand global climate change. One of the tasks of the CCSP has been to communicate the findings of the scientific community to policy makers and the broader public by publishing reports on climate change issues. These reports, covering a broad range of topics, are available on the Internet (www.globalchange.gov) and are very well done. The 2009 report, *Global Climate Change Impacts in the United States*,[17] draws from 19 existing CCSP reports and other peer-reviewed scientific assessments, such as those from the IPCC. It is designated as the **United Synthesis Product (USP)** and provides a detailed look at the impacts of climate change on various *sectors* (e.g., transportation, agriculture, human health) and *regions* (e.g., Northwest, Southwest, Northeast, Alaska) of the United States. Some highlights of the report are worth examining.

National Climate Change. Most of the global impacts of climate change—temperature increases, droughts, intensity of hurricanes, seasonal changes, increased intensity of heavy rain events, floods, rising sea level, large wildfires, and melting glaciers, among others—have already been observed in the United States. The projected future changes just reviewed will certainly also affect the United States. However, national and regional climates vary more than global climate, and the different regions of the United States have experienced different impacts and will do so in the

---

[17]Thomas R. Karl, Jerry M. Melillo, and Thomas C. Peterson (Eds.). *Global Climate Change Impacts in the United States*, Cambridge University Press, 2009.

future. Following are key observations from the report (and more recent updates):

- The average U.S. temperature rose more than 2°F over the previous 50 years and will rise more; heat waves could become commonplace in the next 30 years.

- Precipitation increased an average of about 5% over the previous 50 years. Shifting patterns have generally made wet areas wetter, while dry areas have become drier. This is projected to continue.

- The heaviest downpours have increased approximately 20% on average in the past century, and this is projected to continue, with the strongest increases in the wettest places.

- Southwestern North America is experiencing the worst drought since 1900; future projections suggest that droughts could worsen across the region.

- Many types of extreme weather events, in addition to heavy downpours, have become more frequent and intense during the past 40 to 50 years; 2011 was a record year for devastating weather in the United States, with 12 billion-dollar disasters and more than 1,000 deaths.[18]

- The destructive energy of Atlantic hurricanes has increased in recent decades and is projected to increase further in this century.

- Sea level rose 2 to 5 inches during the previous 50 years along many U.S. coasts; coastal cities with some 40 million people are at risk because of the likely rise in sea level linked to 21st-century GHG emissions.

- For cold-season storms outside the tropics, storm tracks are shifting northward, and the strongest storms are projected to become stronger.

- Arctic sea ice is declining rapidly, and this is projected to continue.

Some interesting graphics are used to illustrate regional climate changes. For example, for the Midwest, the summer climate in Illinois and Michigan is shown shifting southward and westward (Fig. 18–23) as temperatures increase and precipitation decreases. Significantly, the impacts of climate change in Alaska are greater than those in any other region of the United States. Average temperatures are projected to rise 4°F to 7°F by mid-century and could rise 8°F to 13°F by the end of the century if global emissions continue on their present course. The USP report's concluding thoughts emphasize the importance of involving scientists, policy makers, and the public in "designing, initiating, and evaluating mitigation and adaptation strategies. . . . The best decisions about these strategies will come when there is widespread understanding of the complex issue of climate change—the science and its many implications for our nation."

We turn now to our society's response to climate change.

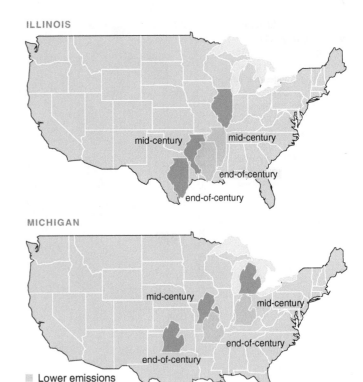

Figure 18–23 Climate on the move in the Midwest. Model projections of summer average temperature and precipitation changes in Illinois and Michigan for mid-century and end of century. The lower emissions scenario is IPPC B1, and the higher emissions scenario is IPPC A2. Note that both states are projected to get considerably warmer and have less summer precipitation. (*Source:* CSSP, *Global Climate Change Impacts in the United States: Unified Synthesis Product,* 2009.)

18.3 Response to Climate Change

The world's industries and transportation networks are so locked into the use of fossil fuels that high emissions of CO_2 and other GHGs seem certain to continue for the foreseeable future, bringing on significant climate change. One possible response to this situation is **adaptation**. That is, we must anticipate some harm to natural and human systems and should plan adaptive responses to lessen the vulnerability of people, their property, and the biosphere to coming changes.

Yet it seems more sensible to reduce the rate at which emissions are added to the atmosphere and, eventually, bring about a sustainable balance—though no one thinks that doing so will be easy. This is the **mitigation** response: Take action to reduce emissions. Before we deal with these responses, we need to address an important question: Why is there still so much doubt about climate change?

Skeptics, Deniers, and Ethics

The scientific consensus on global climate change is clear: Global warming is well under way, and the consequences

---

[18]Climate Central. "Top 10 States Ravaged by Extreme Weather in 2011." *Grist,* December 30, 2011. www.grist.org. December 31, 2011.

of further climate change are potentially catastrophic. International concern about this issue has led to a number of conferences designed to address climate change. In the United States, however, public opinion polls reveal a high level of skepticism about global warming. This attitude has puzzled scientists, who have seen the evidence for global warming growing stronger all the time. Some recent work has reviewed this discrepancy,[19] pointing out that most people do not spend time examining the scientific evidence but instead form their opinions based on the views of organizations and media sources they trust. The high degree of public skepticism, then, can be traced to several factors:

- A deliberate campaign to undermine trust in climate science by organizations and corporations that stand to lose influence and profits if carbon emissions are curtailed.[20] This campaign has systematically spread disinformation in order to confuse the public.[21]

- A political divide that sees conservatives and Republicans showing much more skepticism about climate change than liberals and Democrats; this is especially evident in Congress, where the divide is virtually unanimous.

- An unfortunate release of hacked e-mails from a climate research group in the UK in late 2009 that has been called "Climategate" (more about this later) and led to an erosion of trust in climate scientists.

- The coincidence of an economic crisis in the United States that has focused the public's attention on economic issues and provided fuel for the campaigns determined to attack the public's trust in climate science and policy making.

Which Is It? True skeptics are those who seek after truth, looking for evidence that will guide them to correct conclusions. Given the substantial public skepticism about global warming, it is fair to ask: Is this really skepticism, or is it simply misguided trust?

In a very insightful book, Haydn Washington and John Cook address the issue of those who are denying climate change.[22] The authors charge that this is not a matter of skepticism; on the contrary, it is more accurate to use the label "deniers" to describe those who are challenging climate change science. In effect, they are either refusing to accept the evidence or possibly denying a truth they do not like. Of the numerous arguments presented by the deniers, one in particular has gained credence because of "Climategate." The argument is that the world's climate scientists are engaged in a conspiracy to deceive in order to continue to get lucrative

grants to keep their laboratories and research empires in business.

"Climategate," as it is called, involved the illegal hacking into computers at the University of East Anglia, a center of climate research. Private e-mails between climate researchers were made public, some of which were purported to reveal conspiratorial correspondence to falsify or hide data. In fact, the correspondence was taken out of context and misinterpreted, deliberately, to suggest dishonesty on the part of the scientists. Several high-level investigations into the episode have cleared the scientists of any fraud or scientific malpractice. "Climategate," however, fed into the true conspiracy to deny that climate change was occurring, giving deniers a perfect occasion to question the scientists' integrity and thus influence public opinion against climate change science.

Who are these "deniers"? Very often, they are conservative "think tanks" that are ideologically opposed to regulation. They see the kinds of international agreements and national public policies needed to address climate change as threats to free market capitalism. They are often supported by industries that stand to lose profits if these policy changes are put in place—the fossil fuel industries (especially ExxonMobil), the utilities, and their public supporting body, the U.S. Chamber of Commerce. Washington and Cook document the work of these organizations and the range of arguments they employ, and one of the authors (Cook) supports a Web site that counters virtually every "denialist" argument (www.skepticalscience.com) with careful reasoning and data. If the stakes were not so high, one could pass off this denial phenomenon as a sociological aberration. However, given the high stakes, the denial of climate change lands us firmly in the domain of ethics.

A Perfect Moral Storm. International treaties and national policies are needed to move us in the direction of mitigation and adaptation. But why should we do it? And how should we proceed?

In a recent book,[23] philosopher Stephen Gardiner refers to our flawed attempts to address climate change as an ethical failure—in fact, a "perfect moral storm" (using the metaphor of Sebastian Junger's book *The Perfect Storm*, a true account of the loss of the fishing boat *Andrea Gail* in a rare convergence of three bad storms in the North Atlantic). Gardiner's three factors that converge are of deep moral significance: 1) climate change is a *global* "storm," one where the wealthy nations are able to shape what is done about it, possibly to the detriment of the poorer nations; 2) it is also an *intergenerational* storm, where the present generation has the power to affect future generations, who have no voice in the matter; 3) the third is a *theoretical* storm, in that the climate change threat is unprecedented and lacks adequate moral theories to give guidance for appropriate actions. The convergence of these three interacting "storms," says Gardiner, has led to our present lack of real progress in addressing the looming threat of global climate change.

[19]Sandra T. Marquart-Pyatt et al. "Understanding Public Opinion on Climate Change: A Call for Research." *Environment* 53: 38–42. July/August 2011.

[20]Naomi Oreskes and Erik M. Conway. *Merchants of Doubt*. Bloomsbury Press, New York. 2010.

[21]Steven A. Kolmes. "Climate Change: A Disinformation Campaign." *Environment* 53: 33–37. July/August, 2011.

[22]Haydn Washington and John Cook. *Climate Change Denial: Heads in the Sand*. Earthscan. Washington, DC, 2011.

[23]Stephen M. Gardiner. *A Perfect Moral Storm: The Ethical Tragedy of Climate Change*. Oxford University Press, New York. 2011.

To simplify what could become a complex philosophical discussion, here are three ethical principles that speak to the issue:

1. The first is the **precautionary principle**, as articulated in the 1992 Rio Declaration. The principle states, "In order to protect the environment, the precautionary approach shall be widely applied by States according to their capabilities. Where there are threats of serious or irreversible damage, lack of full scientific certainty shall not be used as a reason for postponing cost-effective measures to prevent environmental degradation." Employing this principle is like taking out insurance: We are taking measures to avoid a highly costly, but uncertain, situation (albeit one that is appearing quite likely). The risk of serious harmful consequences is real, the scientific consensus is strong, but the political response, as we will see, is still inadequate.

2. The second is the **polluter pays principle**. Polluters should pay for the damage their pollution causes. This principle has long been part of environmental legislation. CO_2 is where it is because the developed countries (and now many developing countries) have burned so much fossil fuel since the beginning of the industrial era. It has become clear that CO_2 is a pollutant.

3. The third is the **equity principle**. Currently, the richest 1 billion people produce 55% of CO_2 emissions, while the poorest 1 billion produce only 3%. International equity and intergenerational equity are ethical principles that should compel the rich and privileged to care about those generations that follow—especially those in the poor countries who are even now experiencing the consequences of global climate change. Climate change is going to cause harm, as we have seen. If we are able to take action that will prevent both present and future harm, it would be morally wrong not to do so.

And so, what shall we do?

Mitigation

It will be costly to take the actions needed to mitigate the causes of climate change and to adapt to changes that are unavoidable, but the costs of inaction will be far higher. If climate change is unchecked, every country will be affected, but it will be most disastrous for the world's poorest countries and people. Climatic disruptions will create hundreds of millions of refugees. Conflict and terrorism will surely follow in the wake of such deprivation, as people are radicalized by their plight. The impacts on the natural world will be equally severe, as we have seen (Fig. 18–22).

Some attempts have been made to put a price tag on inaction; these are admittedly rough estimates, but ones based on sound analyses. For the United States, one study by the Natural Resources Defense Council estimates a total economic cost of global warming at 3.6% of gross domestic product (GDP) by 2100, or almost $3.8 trillion (in today's dollars). For just four impacts—hurricane damage, energy costs, real estate losses, and water costs—the price tag comes to almost $1.9 trillion. The Stern Review,[24] an economic analysis commissioned by the British government, estimated that inaction on global climate change would result in economic loss equivalent to 5% to 20% of global GDP per year for the indefinite future. Given the economic, environmental, and social costs of the consequences of unrestrained release of GHGs, it would seem that mitigation is absolutely essential. We need to reduce emissions of GHGs in order to prevent disaster. The next question is: What should be our target?

Achieving Stabilization. The stated objective of the Framework Convention on Climate Change (FCCC) is to *stabilize the GHG content of the atmosphere at levels and on a time scale that would prevent dangerous anthropogenic interference with the climate system.* This means that GHG emissions must be brought under control to the point where they are no longer accumulating in the atmosphere, and it must be done before global temperatures rise to dangerous levels. Earth history tells us that with 3°C global warming, equilibrium sea level could be at least 80 feet (25 m) higher than today. This is clearly dangerous to human civilization and Earth systems in general and to be avoided. However, with current warming at about 0.8°C above pre-industrial levels and more warming already in the pipeline, we could get to 2°C in a couple of decades. Many feel that 2°C could well be a **tipping point**, a point beyond which irreversible—and clearly dangerous—runaway climate change occurs no matter what we do.

So we have a target: hold global temperatures to 2°C above pre-industrial levels, which corresponds to a stable concentration of CO_2 (with the other GHGs included) in the atmosphere of around 450 ppm. To achieve stabilization at 450 ppm will require major changes in our energy systems. Current carbon emissions of 33 $GtCO_2$/year will have to fall to 7 $GtCO_2$/year by 2100 and then drop even further. This is the *inconvenient truth* Al Gore referred to in his 2006 film by the same name on global warming. The IPCC AR4 Synthesis Report presented an analysis of six stabilization scenarios and their correspondence with global temperatures and sea level rise (Table 18–3). Global emissions of GHGs corresponding to the different scenarios are shown in **Figure 18–24a**, along with the time course of allowable emissions. The relationship between temperature increase above preindustrial levels and GHG stabilization-level concentration for the six scenarios is shown in Figure 18–24b. The IPCC states: "In order to stabilize the concentration of GHGs in the atmosphere, emissions would need to peak and decline thereafter. The lower the stabilization level, the more quickly this peak and decline would need to occur."[25] Clearly, the only category in Table 18–3 and Figure 18–24 that is consistent with the FCCC objective of avoiding "dangerous anthropogenic

[24]Nicholas Stern. *The Economics of Climate Change: The Stern Review* (Cambridge, England: Cambridge University Press, 2007).

[25]Intergovernmental Panel on Climate Change. *Climate Change 2007: Synthesis Report*, Contribution of Working Groups I, II and III to the Fourth Assessment. Report of the Intergovernmental Panel on Climate Change (Geneva, Switzerland: IPCC, 2007).

TABLE 18–3 Stabilization Scenarios and Corresponding Global Temperatures and Sea Level Rise

Category	CO$_2$-equivalent concentration at stabilization (including all GHGs) (ppm)	Peaking year for CO$_2$ emissions	Change in global CO$_2$ emissions in 2050 (% of 2000 emissions)	Global avg. temperature increase at equilibrium (°C)	Global avg. sea level rise above preindustrial at equilibrium from thermal expansion (m)
I	445–490	2000–2015	−85 to −50	2.0–2.4	0.4–1.4
II	490–535	2000–2020	−60 to −30	2.4–2.8	0.5–1.7
III	535–590	2010–2030	−30 to +5	2.8–3.2	0.6–1.9
IV	590–710	2020–2060	+10 to +60	3.2–4.0	0.6–2.4
V	710–855	2050–2080	+25 to +85	4.0–4.9	0.8–2.9
VI	855–1130	2060–2090	+90 to +140	4.9–6.1	1.0–3.7

Source: IPCC, *Climate Change 2007: Synthesis Report* (Geneva, Switzerland: IPCC, 2008).

interference" is category I. Again, from the IPCC: "Mitigation efforts over the next two to three decades will have a large impact on opportunities to achieve lower stabilization levels."

We turn now to the question of what the international community has done in response to global climate change.

International Conferences. One of the five documents signed by heads of state at the UN Conference on Environment and Development's Earth Summit in Rio de Janeiro in 1992 was the **Framework Convention on Climate Change (FCCC).** This convention agreed to the goal of *stabilizing GHG levels in the atmosphere*, starting by reducing GHG

emissions to 1990 levels by the year 2000 in all industrialized nations. Countries were to achieve the goal by voluntary means. Five years later, it was obvious that the voluntary approach was failing. All the developed countries except those of the European Union *increased* their GHG emissions by 7% to 9% in the ensuing five years. The developing countries increased theirs by 25%.

Kyoto, 1997. Prompted by a coalition of island nations (whose very existence is threatened by global climate change), the third Conference of Parties to the FCCC met in Kyoto, Japan, in December 1997 to craft a binding agreement on reducing GHG emissions. In Kyoto, 38 industrial and former eastern bloc nations agreed to reduce emissions

(a)

(b)

Figure 18–24 CO$_2$ emissions and equilibrium temperature increases for a range of stabilization levels. (a) Global CO$_2$ emissions for 1940 to 2000 and projected emissions ranges for six categories of stabilization scenarios from 2000 to 2100. The thickness of each band represents the uncertainty inherent in the model projections. The dashed lines (post-SRES range) show the upper and lower emissions range of more recently developed scenarios. (b) Corresponding relationship between a CO$_2$ stabilization target and the likely equilibrium global temperature increase above preindustrial. The black line through the middle shows the best estimate of the response of temperature to GHG concentrations (climate sensitivity); the orange and blue lines show the upper and lower bounds of climate sensitivities.

(*Source:* IPCC, *Climate Change 2007: Synthesis Report,* Contribution of Working Groups I, II and III to the Fourth Assessment. Report of the Intergovernmental Panel on Climate Change (Geneva, Switzerland: IPCC, 2007), Figure 5-1.)

of six GHGs to 5.2% *below* 1990 levels, *to be achieved by 2012* (the **Kyoto Protocol**). The signatories to this agreement are called the *Annex I parties*; all others (the developing countries) are *non–Annex I parties*. At the conference, the developing countries refused to agree to *any* reductions, arguing that the developed countries had created the problem and that it was only fair that the developing countries continue on their path to development as the developed countries had, energized by fossil fuels. This stance was in accord with the FCCC principle of "common but differentiated responsibilities." Under this principle, each nation must address climate change, but its priorities and efforts could differ according to national circumstances. Thus, the developing countries argued that their first priority was to alleviate poverty, whereas the developed countries had no such excuse.

The signers of the Kyoto Protocol had a great deal of flexibility in deciding how they would achieve their GHG reductions. The most obvious choices involve renewable energy, possibly nuclear energy, and a variety of energy conservation strategies. They could plant forests to act as carbon sinks or engage in emissions trading with other Annex I parties, either buying or selling assigned emissions amounts to meet targets. They could even implement projects that reduce emissions in other countries and earn credits toward their target emissions.

The targeted reductions of the Kyoto Protocol will *not* stabilize atmospheric concentrations of GHGs. The IPCC calculates that it would take immediate reductions in emissions of at least 60% worldwide to stabilize GHG concentrations at today's levels. Since this has no chance of happening, the concentration of GHGs in the atmosphere will continue to rise. The major weakness of the Kyoto Protocol is that the world's largest GHG emitters—India, China, and the United States—are not participating. The United States withdrew from the treaty in 2001, and recently, Canada, Japan, and Russia withdrew also, with the result that Kyoto now only covers 13% of global emissions. Nevertheless, Kyoto was an important first step toward binding agreements to stabilize the atmosphere.

Bali, 2007. In December 2007, a UN-sponsored climate conference held in Bali addressed the need for greater cuts in GHG emissions when the Kyoto Protocol expires in 2012. At the Bali meeting, parties to the FCCC agreed to what was essentially a "road map" to future negotiations. It was agreed that "deep cuts in global emissions will be required," to achieve the objective of avoiding dangerous climate change, and a negotiation process was established, to prepare for the next meeting.

Copenhagen, 2009. The next major climate conference was held in December 2009 in Copenhagen. There, delegates from around the world met to once again attempt to find agreement on climate change policy. On the plus side, the **Copenhagen Accord** was agreed to by 187 out of 192 countries. This accord amounted to pledges to implement actions that would limit global temperature increases to 2°C above pre-industrial levels, and a commitment by developed and developing countries to set countrywide emissions targets to be achieved by 2020. Still, nothing in the way of a binding agreement was reached there, nor was there even a timetable for reaching such agreements.

Cancún, 2010. At Cancún, negotiations by delegates appeared to get back on track after the disappointing Copenhagen meeting. Delegates approved the mitigation pledges made by all major GHG emitting countries in accordance with the Copenhagen Accord and established a Green Climate Fund of $30 billion to help the more vulnerable developing countries fund their mitigation pledges and cope with impacts of climate change. Also, mechanisms were set up to reward developing countries for maintaining their forests (REDD, for Reducing Emissions from Deforestation and Forest Degradation). Delegates postponed any decision on extending the Kyoto Protocol. There were still no binding agreements on emissions.

Durban, 2011. Once again, meeting in December as the 17th Conference of the Parties to the FCCC, delegates debated and negotiated what to do. In the end, they reached an agreement (the **Durban Platform**) to begin negotiations that would lead to a legally binding agreement by 2015, to take effect by 2020. The agreement aims at ensuring that emissions reductions will meet the goal of keeping global temperature rise below 2°C. Delegates also agreed to establish a second commitment period of the Kyoto Protocol, to begin when the first period ends (2012).

The Gap. At the Durban meeting, the United Nations Environment Program released a report[26] it was commissioned to develop. The report was based on the question of how the pledges made by each country, based on the Copenhagen Accord, help meet the 2°C target. The report showed that the pledges fall short of the target; thus, there is a *climate emissions gap* to be addressed, a gap of between 6 and 11 $GtCO_2$, depending on how well the pledges are kept (**Fig. 18–25**). The report states that to stay within the 2°C limit, emissions would have to peak before 2020, and that won't happen unless new emissions targets are established. It is possible to

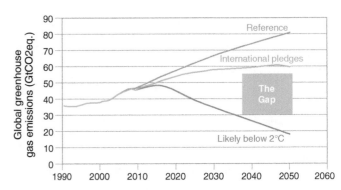

Figure 18–25 The climate emissions gap. The plot shows estimates of global GHG emissions in gigatons of CO2 equivalents (other gases equated to CO2). The reference plot (blue line) shows emissions growth in the absence of the targets and pledges, the orange line shows the pledges made by countries following the Copenhagen Accord, and the brown line shows the emissions pathway needed to keep the growth in global temperature below 2°C.

(*Source:* Climate Action Tracker, Dec. 11, 2011. Copyright © 2009 by Ecofys and Climate Analytics.)

[26]United Nations Environment Program. *Bridging the Emissions Gap: A UNEP Synthesis Report.* November 2011. www.unep.org/publications/ebooks/bridgingemissionsgap. December 28, 2011.

TABLE 18–4 Options for Mitigation of Greenhouse Gas Emissions

Cap-and-trade. Place a cap on GHG emissions; for CO_2, this can be accomplished by limiting the use of fossil fuels in industry and transportation. Rights to emit GHGs are allocated to different companies and are tradable in a market-based system. This has worked well internationally (in the EU), where different countries are allocated permits and can trade with other countries. It is anticipated that the cap will be reduced gradually until a stabilized atmosphere is achieved. This option generates potentially large revenues, which can be put to use in ways that can alleviate some of the problems created by the program.

Renewable energy. Invest in and deploy an increasing percentage of energy in the form of renewable-energy technologies: wind power, solar collectors, solar thermal energy, photovoltaics, biofuels, hydrogen-powered vehicles, and geothermal energy, among others.

Carbon capture and sequestration. Sequester CO_2 emitted from burning fossil fuels at power plants by capturing it at the site of emission and pumping it into deep, porous underground formations. This is especially vital for coal-burning power plants, as coal is the most abundant fossil fuel energy source for many major GHG emitters. This is expected to push electricity prices up about $0.04 per kilowatt-hr.

Nuclear power. Encourage the development of nuclear power, first resolving issues concerning cost-effectiveness, reliability, spent fuel, and high-level waste.

Reforestation. Stop the loss of tropical forests and encourage the planting of trees and other vegetation over vast areas now suffering from deforestation. Trees and other vegetation provide a sink for carbon that removes CO_2 from the atmosphere.

Efficiency. Make energy conservation rules much more stringent. (Tighten building codes to require more insulation, use energy-efficient lighting, and so forth.)

Mileage standards. Reduce the amount of fuels used in transportation by raising mileage standards, encouraging car pooling, and stimulating mass transit in urban areas.

Subsidies. Remove fossil fuel subsidies like depletion allowances, tax relief to consumers, support for oil and gas exploration, and the substantial costs of maintaining access to Middle Eastern oil.

Population growth. Reducing population growth would make a substantial contribution to GHG emissions reduction, especially in the economically robust developing countries.

Carbon tax. Levy a tax on all fuels according to the amount of carbon dioxide that they produce when consumed. Such a tax, proponents believe, would provide both incentives to use renewable sources, which would not be taxed, and disincentives to consume fossil fuels. This puts the polluter-pays principle into practice.

close the gap, says the report, but countries need to realize that what they are pledging just won't cut it.

Clearly, international accords are important, but *it is legislative action at the national level that brings about emissions reductions.* A research team from the UK recently analyzed national-level legislation in 16 countries that are major GHG emitters.[27] The study was encouraging: It reported on 155 existing climate change-related laws that were in effect in the countries and found that many approaches were used to accomplish the goal of reducing GHG emissions and prepare the country for the impacts of climate change. This brings us to the question: What in fact has the United States been doing about global climate change and the FCCC?

U.S. Policy. Climate change policy in the United States can be described in four venues: (1) scientific research, (2) national legislation, (3) regulatory action, and (4) state and local action. Of course, one major policy move was made by President George W. Bush in 2001 when he announced that the United States would withdraw from the Kyoto Protocol agreement.

Scientific Research. The *Global Change Research Act of 1990* established a policy of support for research on climate change; the act mandates an interagency approach, where all of the agencies and departments that might be involved in climate change research are to coordinate their activities and programs as part of the official Global Change Research Program (GCRP). Lead agencies in this effort have been NOAA, NASA, the U.S. Geological Survey, and the EPA. One example of the GCRP's effort has been the 20 reports of the Climate Change Science Program already mentioned. Budgetary support for the GCRP has been about $2 billion per year. Hundreds of U.S. scientists have been in the lead in conducting research on climate change and publishing their work, especially as they have participated in the IPCC assessments.

National Legislation. The U.S. Congress has failed to enact a comprehensive set of policies to address global climate change. It came close when a Democrat-controlled House passed the *American Clean Energy and Security Act* in 2009, which would establish an emissions reduction and trading plan called cap-and-trade (see Table 18–4), but the bill died in the Senate where Republican opposition was enough to prevent its passage. However, the *American Recovery and Reinvestment Act* has invested more than $43 billion in the

[27]Terry Townshend et al. "Legislating Climate Change on a National Level." *Environment* 53: 5–17. September/October 2011.

TABLE 18–5 Adaptation Strategies

All Countries

- **Agriculture:** Farmers shift to climate-resistant crops or crops more appropriate to the new climate regime. Irrigation is expanded to areas once fed only by rain.
- **Structural concerns:** Societies invest to reduce the costs and disruption from extreme weather events like storms, floods, droughts (e.g., seawalls, new reservoirs, revegetating coastal wetlands).
- **Emergency preparedness:** Societies invest in early-warning systems, high-quality climate information, intervention when needed (e.g., heat wave warnings, heavy precipitation events, shelters for those displaced or affected by events).
- **Reducing risks:** Societies establish a financial safety net to help their poorest members, providing insurance that accurately reflects new risks to discourage poor choices.

Developing Countries

- **Promoting development:** Investments are made in health, education, economic opportunity, and food security (to lower people's vulnerability to climate impacts and help them build adaptive capacity).
- **Controlling diseases:** Malaria, AIDS, tuberculosis, and emerging diseases are brought under control so that a changing climate does not increase their threat.
- **Enhancing economic progress:** Societies promote literacy, electronic communication, road infrastructure, and diversification of economic activity.

Source: Nicholas Stern, *The Economics of Climate Change: The Stern Review* (Cambridge, England: Cambridge University Press, 2007).

support of renewable energy and energy efficiency programs, which will certainly have an impact in lowering GHG emissions. Other legislative actions include laws that established subsidies and rebates for renewable energy sources.

Regulatory Action. The Obama administration, under the Copenhagen Accord, has committed the United States to a reduction of GHG emissions by 17% below 2005 levels, to be achieved by 2020. Major tools to accomplish this include all of the policies to promote renewable energy and energy conservation, especially the regulations that raise the corporate average fuel economy standards (Chapter 16). Most important, however, is the role of the EPA. In 2009, taking its cue from a 2007 Supreme Court ruling, the EPA determined that greenhouse gases pose a danger to public health and welfare, thus giving the agency a green light to regulate CO_2 and other GHGs. This move has infuriated many industry groups and their Republican allies, but their efforts to block the EPA from this role have so far failed. The agency has begun its regulatory efforts with the *New Source Performance Standards* for greenhouse gases from fossil-fueled power plants, announced in 2011. This permitting rule requires all new power plants to hold emissions to 1,000 pounds of CO_2 per megawatt hour, something that natural gas plants can accomplish but coal plants cannot. Limits on existing coal plants are yet to come.

State and Local Action. It is encouraging that states are taking unilateral action to address global climate change. Many states are adopting renewable portfolio standards and are mandating reporting of GHG emissions (see Chapter 16). Several regions have established GHG emissions cap-and-trade programs similar to the Clean Air Act program that was successful in bringing down sulfur dioxide emissions. Many states have set quantitative goals for reducing GHG emissions. More than 1,000 mayors have pledged to move their cities to make GHG reductions under the Climate Protection Agreement.

Mitigation Tools. Many options are available for reducing GHG emissions, many of which are already in place in the United States and globally. Table 18–5 presents a summary of most of the prominent mitigation tools. Appropriately, the majority of the options address the energy sector, where most of the anthropogenic GHGs are originating. What is needed, of course, is to "decarbonize" the energy economy, so that energy needs are met without fossil fuels. Every provision that promotes greater energy efficiency and the use of renewable energy sources is going to reduce GHG emissions in the United States (Chapter 16). Recent legislation has made progress in energy efficiency and renewable energy (as discussed in Chapters 14 and 16).

There will be economic costs and benefits to mitigation efforts. The benefits come in the form of new industries and the jobs they create, savings from efficiency measures, and the ecosystem benefits from forests that are preserved and regrown. The net costs, as calculated by the Stern Review for stabilization at 550 ppm CO_2, amount to around 2% of global GDP by 2050. These are the costs of cutting GHG emissions by reducing demand for emissions-intensive goods and services, increasing efficiencies of energy use, avoiding deforestation, and switching to lower-carbon technologies for power, heat, and transport. Recall that the Stern Review calculated the costs of inaction to be from 5% to 20% of GDP.

As a bottom line, however, climate change is already happening and will likely accelerate in the future. *Mitigation* efforts will reduce the magnitude of future climate change, but *adaptation* will also be needed.

Adaptation

Adaptation means making adjustments in anticipation of changes brought on by the rising sea levels and temperatures of the next decades. It also means reducing vulnerability to the inevitable impacts of climate change. What makes this process difficult is that the adaptations will be aiming at a moving target—and one that is uncertain at best. Adaptation is not cost free. Climate changes are bringing us into ever new situations, and some of them are developing rapidly. Climate-related natural disasters are already happening at a higher rate than ever and will only get worse.

The Stern Review detailed adaptations for developed and developing countries, many of which are presented in Table 18–5. The IPCC also weighed in with the AR4 report. In light of the risks, the IPCC stated, "The effects of climate change are expected to be greatest in developing countries in terms of loss of life and relative effects on investment and the economy." A number of international funds have been established to address these needs, the latest being the *Green Climate Fund*, launched at the Cancún international meeting. The emphasis of these funds is on the developing countries, because it is assumed that the developed countries will be far more able to afford the costs of adaptation (and can also afford to finance the programs).

Poverty and Climate Change. It is painfully evident that climate change will be much harder on the poor, as documented in a recent article by Boorse;[28] they are already struggling to meet their needs for shelter, food, employment, and health care. The article lists several telling points:

1. The poor, especially in the less developed countries, are especially vulnerable to disasters. They lack buffers to help them deal with crop failures, storms, and floods—the kinds of impacts that will increase in the changing climate.

2. The poorer countries are less able to divert resources to adaptation to the changing climate; they are already challenged to provide health care, education, and food. Failure of many to meet the Millennium Development Goals is evidence of their resource limitations (Table 9–2).

3. Rising sea levels and other climate change impacts will inevitably displace millions in the poorer countries; the flood of environmental refugees will challenge the ability (and will) of the international community to provide aid.

4. The lack of resources, especially water and arable land, will lead to greater internal (and possibly international) conflicts. The U.S. Department of Defense has identified climate change as a significant national security issue, pointing out that climate change may act as an accelerant of conflict.

A development worker[29] states, "The last thing most people living in poverty need is climate change . . . It's a very real intensifier of poverty today . . . (it) increases vulnerability to environmental shocks that are outside their control. . . ." Even now, more than 96% of disaster-related deaths take place in developing countries. It seems fair to ask, What kind of society are we if we ignore these needs and just let the climate keep on warming as we reject the changes we need to make to limit GHG emissions?

Geoengineering The threat of climate change is generating a host of futuristic schemes to help the fight against global warming.[30] Some of the schemes are clearly unworkable, while others have been floated as serious proposals. For example, there is a proposal to fertilize vast areas of the oceans with iron, thereby stimulating phytoplankton growth, which would remove CO_2 and sink to the depths. Another proposed scheme erects scrubbers, devices that would chemically absorb CO_2 in the air and then store it in deep reservoirs. Still other methods would block some of the solar radiation from reaching Earth's surface by, for example, injecting sulfate aerosols into the stratosphere or launching satellites into space that would release reflecting particles in the path of the Sun's radiation. Most climate experts dismiss these schemes on the basis of their huge costs or the likelihood of unintended consequences such as interference with weather patterns or ecosystem destruction; besides, they might not work at all.

It is fair to say that none of these schemes compares with what is already happening. Whatever the outcome, it is certain that we are conducting an enormous global experiment in geoengineering, and our children and their descendants will be living with the consequences. Global climate change is perhaps the greatest challenge facing human civilization in the 21st century.

[28]Dorothy Boorse. *Loving the Least of These: Addressing a Changing Environment*. National Association of Evangelicals. 2011. http://www.nae.net/images/content/Loving_the_Least_of_These.pdf. December 31, 2011.

[29]Ibid., p. 35
[30]Catherine P. McMullen, ibid., pp. 51–53.

REVISITING THE THEMES

Sound Science

Much of this chapter reflects some outstanding science, as our knowledge of climate change depends on the solid work of scientists from around the world. It is largely the scientists who are calling attention to the perils of climate change. They were the first to discover the risks involved, and they are now the chief advocates of effective action. The IPCC, with the thousands of scientists involved, has performed a masterful assessment of the scientific basis of climate change. In the United States, the CCSP/GCRP has also produced a portfolio of excellent analyses of climate change and its many dimensions. More and more of the questions and uncertainties about climate change are being resolved as scientists continue to work.

Sustainability

Earth is in the midst of an unsustainable rise in atmospheric GHG levels, the result of our intense use of fossil fuels. In short, we completely depend on a host of technologies that are threatening our future. Projections of business-as-usual fossil fuel use point to global consequences that are disastrous, but not inevitable. The United States and other developed countries will not escape these consequences, but the gravest of them affect the developing countries. A sustainable pathway is still open to us, and it involves a combination of steps we can take to mitigate the emissions and bring the atmospheric concentration of GHGs to a stable, even declining, level.

Stewardship

Stewardly care for Earth is not really something we can ignore. We must face this "perfect moral storm," and several principles have been cited as arguments for effective action to prevent dangerous climate change: the precautionary principle, the polluter-pays principle, and the equity principle. If we care about our neighbors and our descendants, we will take action both to mitigate the production of GHGs and to enable especially the poorer countries to adapt to coming unavoidable climate changes, even if taking such action is costly.

Public skepticism in the United States about climate change is a serious problem, but the public gets its cues from the media and political leaders, where denial of climate change is embedded like a destructive cancer. One can only hope that in time the public will reject the spurious arguments of the climate change deniers and seize the moral high ground in this battle for the future of our children and grandchildren.

REVIEW QUESTIONS

1. What are the important characteristics of the troposphere? Of the stratosphere?

2. What are the main components of our weather, and how is weather related to climate?

3. Provide a brief synopsis of global climate change. What are the main issues and trends?

4. What has been discovered about global climate trends in the past? How do contemporary trends relate to past records?

5. What is the Atlantic Meridional Overturning Circulation? How does it work? What are the impacts of the El Niño/ La Niña Southern Oscillation (ENSO)?

6. What is radiative forcing? Describe some warming and cooling forcing agents.

7. What evidence do global land and ocean temperatures provide for a warming Earth?

8. What additional changes contribute to the picture of human-caused warming?

9. Which of the GHGs are the most significant contributors to global warming? How do they work?

10. Describe the data for atmospheric CO_2. What are significant sources and sinks for atmospheric CO_2? Why can CO_2 be called "the atmosphere's control knob?"

11. How are computer models employed in climate change research? Describe several scenarios for 21st-century climate change.

12. What are the major IPCC projections for climate changes in the 21st century?

13. How does recent work revise the IPCC projections of future sea level rise?

14. What are some possible reasons for current skepticism about climate change in the U.S. public?

15. Give three ethical principles that can be brought to bear on "the perfect moral storm."

16. Trace the political history of the international efforts to address global climate change. What is the "climate emissions gap"?

17. Describe recent U.S. climate change policy. What is the main reason for U.S. inaction to pass climate change legislation?

18. What mitigation steps could be taken to stabilize the GHG content of the atmosphere?

19. What are some adaptation steps that should be taken to anticipate inevitable changes in climate?

THINKING ENVIRONMENTALLY

1. What steps could you take to lower your climate impact? Check the Union of Concerned Scientists Web site for suggestions.

2. Research the deniers of global climate change. What evidence do they offer in support of their views? How does it compare with the evidence from the IPCC? On balance, what do the data indicate? Check www.skepticalscience.com.

3. What recent developments most increase the urgency of action in the international arena?

4. Trace the history of the international conferences and their outcomes. What are the main areas of contention that are blocking any binding agreements?

MAKING A DIFFERENCE

Anything you can do to cut energy use will cut your CO_2 output. In general, cutting CO_2 will also cut your bills. Listed below are just a few examples.

1. Buy items with the smallest amounts of packaging, The more packaging products have, the more space they take up in the distribution trucks, and the more CO_2 emissions they create.

2. Washing your clothes in cold water instead of hot will keep 200 pounds of carbon dioxide from entering the atmosphere a year.

3. The worst form of transportation for the climate is driving alone in a car. Use public transportation when possible, bike, walk, carpool, buy a hybrid—there are many options! When deciding on a car, make fuel economy a high priority. Driving 25 fewer miles a week will earn you 1,500 fewer pounds of CO_2 per year.

4. Replace your incandescent bulbs with compact fluorescent bulbs and the new LED lights.

MasteringEnvironmentalScience®

Go to **www.masteringenvironmentalscience.com** for practice quizzes, Pearson eText, videos, current events, and more.

CHAPTER 19

Atmospheric Pollution

Smog in Mexico City. Because of its geographic location and heavy automobile traffic, Mexico City has had some of the worst air pollution anywhere.

LEARNING OBJECTIVES

1. **Air-Pollution Essentials:** Review normal atmospheric cleansing and the formation of industrial and photochemical smog.

2. **Major Air Pollutants and Their Sources:** Identify the variety and sources of the major air pollutants, and classify them as primary or secondary pollutants.

3. **Impacts of Air Pollutants:** Investigate how air pollutants impact human health and cause damage to agricultural crops and natural ecosystems.

4. **Bringing Air Pollution Under Control:** Summarize the ways that the Clean Air Act and its amendments, and regulations derived from them, have given the Environmental Protection Agency the responsibility of controlling air pollution.

5. **Destruction of the Ozone Layer:** Assess how chlorofluorocarbons and other gases have been implicated in the destruction of stratospheric ozone, and review the steps taken to bring back the ozone layer.

O N TUESDAY MORNING, October 26, 1948, the people of Donora, Pennsylvania (population 13,000), awoke to a dense fog. Donora lies in an industrialized valley along the Monongahela River, south of Pittsburgh. On the outskirts of town, a sooty sign read, "DONORA: NEXT TO YOURS, THE BEST TOWN IN THE U.S.A." The town had a large steel mill that used high-sulfur coal and a zinc-reduction plant that roasted ores laden with sulfur. At the time, most homes in the area were heated with coal. At first, the fog did not seem unusual: Most of Donora's fogs lifted by noon, as the Sun warmed the upper atmosphere and then the land. This one, however, didn't lift for five days.

SICKNESS AND DEATH.

Through Wednesday and Thursday, the air began to smell of sulfur dioxide—an acrid, penetrating odor. By Friday morning, the town's physicians began to get calls from people in trouble. At first, the calls were from elderly citizens and those with asthmatic conditions. They were having difficulty breathing. The calls continued into Friday afternoon. People young and old were complaining of stomach pain, headaches, nausea, and choking (Fig. 19–1). Work at the mills went on, however. The first deaths occurred on Saturday morning. By 10 AM, one mortician

had nine bodies; two other morticians had one each. On Sunday morning, the mills were shut down. Even so, the owners were certain that their plants had nothing to do with the trouble. Mercifully, the rain came on Sunday and cleared the air—but not before more than 6,000 townspeople were stricken and 20 elderly people had died. During the next month, 50 more people died.

MEMORIAL. Eventually, it was determined that the cause of the deaths was a combination of polluting gases and particles, a thermal inversion in the lower atmosphere, and a stagnant weather system that, together, brought home the deadly potential of air pollution. Today, a historical marker in the town and a small storefront museum commemorate the Donora Smog of 1948, but the lasting legacy of the smog and of those who suffered sickness and death are the state and national laws to control air pollution, culminating in the Clean Air Act of 1970 and its amendments. Donora was a landmark event.

In the previous chapter, we looked at the structure and function of the atmosphere and its links to weather and climate, and we examined the effects of greenhouse gas pollutants on climate change. In this chapter, we will consider the impacts of a host of other pollutants on human health and the environment.

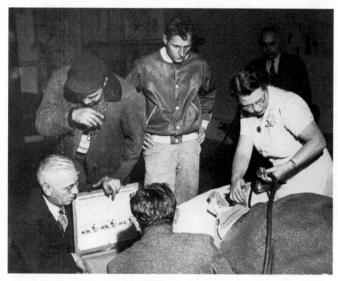

Figure 19–1 Donora Smog Victim. A nurse administers oxygen to a patient in an emergency hospital in Donora, site of a lethal smog in 1948.

19.1 | Air Pollution Essentials

For a long time, we have known that the atmosphere contains numerous *gases*. The major constituents of the atmosphere are nitrogen (N_2), at a level of 78.08%; oxygen (O_2), at 20.95%; water vapor, ranging from 0% to 4%; argon (Ar), at 0.93%; and carbon dioxide (CO_2), at 0.04%. Smaller amounts of at least 40 "trace gases" are normally present as well, including ozone, helium, hydrogen, methane, nitrogen oxides, sulfur dioxide, and neon. In addition, the atmosphere contains *aerosols*: microscopic liquid and solid particles such as dust, carbon particles, pollen, sea salts, and microorganisms, originating primarily from land and water surfaces and carried up into the atmosphere. Outdoor air is a valuable and essential resource, providing gases that sustain life and maintain warmth (Chapter 18). It also shields the Earth from harmful radiation. With the advent of the Industrial Revolution, the mixture of gases and particles in our atmosphere began to change, and we learned the hard way about air pollution.

Pollutants and Atmospheric Cleansing

Air pollutants are substances in the atmosphere—certain gases and aerosols—that have harmful effects. Three factors determine the level of air pollution:

- the amount of pollutants entering the air,

- the amount of space into which the pollutants are dispersed, and

- the mechanisms that remove pollutants from the air.

The lower atmosphere, called the *troposphere* (Fig. 19–2), is the site and source of our weather and contains almost all of the water vapor and clouds of the atmosphere (Chapter 18). Pollutants that enter the troposphere are usually removed within hours or a few days unless they are carried up into the upper troposphere by towering cumulus clouds. If that happens, they can be carried far and persist for many days before they, too, are removed by cleansing agents.

Some pollutants are resistant to most of the cleansing mechanisms and can be carried up into the next higher layer of the atmosphere, the *stratosphere*. The most notorious of these are the ozone-depleting chemicals (chlorine and bromine compounds), which we will consider in Section 19.5.

Atmospheric Cleansing. Environmental scientists distinguish between natural and anthropogenic (human-caused) air pollutants. For millions of years, volcanoes, fires, and dust storms have sent smoke, gases, and particles into the atmosphere. Trees and other plants also emit volatile organic compounds into the air around them as they photosynthesize. However, there are mechanisms in the biosphere that remove, assimilate, and recycle these natural pollutants. First, a naturally occurring compound, the **hydroxyl radical**

Figure 19–2 **Layers of the atmosphere closest to Earth's surface.** The troposphere extends from the surface to roughly 6 miles above the surface, and the stratosphere is above that. The colored band shows the average temperature of the atmosphere at different altitudes. In the troposphere, temperatures generally decrease with height, while in the stratosphere temperatures increase with height.

(*Source:* CCSP 1.1. *Temperature Trends in the Lower Atmosphere: Steps for Understanding and Reconciling Differences.* Thomas R. Karl, Susan J. Hassol, Christopher D. Miller, and William L. Murray, Eds., 2006. A Report by the Climate Change Science Program and the Subcommittee on Global Change Research, Washington, DC.)

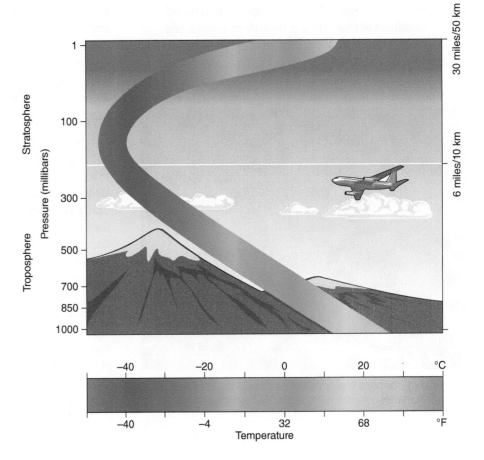

(**OH**), oxidizes many gaseous pollutants to products that are harmless or that can be brought down to the ground or water by precipitation (**Fig. 19–3**). Sea salts—picked up from sea spray as air masses move over the oceans—are a second cleansing agent. These salts, now aerosols, act as excellent nuclei for the formation of raindrops. The rain then brings down many particulate pollutants (other aerosols) from the atmosphere to the ocean, cleansing pollutant-laden air. Third, sunlight breaks organic molecules apart. These three processes hold natural pollutants below toxic levels (except in the immediate area of a source, such as around an erupting volcano).

Figure 19–3 **The hydroxyl radical.** This is a simplified model of atmospheric cleansing by the hydroxyl radical. The first step is the photochemical destruction of ozone, which is the major process leading to ozone breakdown in the troposphere. The second step produces hydroxyl radicals, which react rapidly with many pollutants, converting them to substances that are less harmful (CO_2) or that can be returned to Earth via precipitation (HNO_3, H_2SO_4).

(a) Industrial smog

(b) Photochemical smog

Figure 19–4 Industrial and photochemical smog. (a) Industrial smog occurs when coal is burned and the atmosphere is humid. (b) Photochemical smog occurs when sunlight acts on vehicle pollutants.

Many of the pollutants oxidized by the hydroxyl radical are of concern because human activities have raised their concentrations far above normal levels. Recent studies have shown that the hydroxyl radical plays a key role in the removal of anthropogenic pollutants from the atmosphere. Highly reactive hydrocarbons are oxidized within an hour of their appearance in the atmosphere, and nitrogen oxides (NO_x) are converted to nitric acid (HNO_3) within a day. It takes months, however, for carbon monoxide (CO) to be oxidized by hydroxyl and years in the case of methane (CH_4). As Figure 19–3 shows, the photochemical breakdown of tropospheric ozone is the major source of the hydroxyl radical (not shown is a newly discovered additional source of the hydroxyl radical, from the photoexcitation of nitrogen dioxide). As we will see, higher levels of ozone result from higher concentrations of other polluting gases.

Recent research[1] indicates that the atmospheric levels of hydroxyl are quite stable, suggesting that formation and breakdown are balanced. Some hydroxyl is used up during reactions with CO and CH_4, but hydroxyl is recycled as it reacts with most other pollutants. This is good news for now, but researchers are concerned that future pollutants and climate change could affect the hydroxyl balance.

Smogs and Brown Clouds

Down through the centuries, the practice of venting the products of combustion and other fumes into the atmosphere remained the natural way to avoid their noxious effects within buildings. With the Industrial Revolution of the 1800s came crowded cities and the use of coal for heating and energy. It was then that air pollution began in earnest.

Industrial Smog. In *Hard Times*, Charles Dickens described a typical English scene: "Coketown lay shrouded in a haze of its own, which appeared impervious to the sun's rays. You only knew the town was there because there could be no such sulky blotch upon the prospect without a town." This shrouding haze became known as **industrial smog** (a combination of *sm*oke and f*og*), an irritating, grayish mixture of soot, sulfurous compounds, and water vapor **(Fig. 19–4a)**. This kind of smog continues to be found wherever industries are concentrated and where coal is the primary energy source; such smog events mostly occur in the winter. The Donora incident is a classic example. Currently, industrial smog can be found in the cities of China, India, Korea, and a number of eastern European countries.

Photochemical Smog. After World War II, the booming economy in the United States led to the creation of vast suburbs and a mushrooming use of cars for commuting to and from work. As other fossil fuels were used in place of coal for heating, industry, and transportation, industrial smog was largely replaced by another kind of smog. Increasingly, Los Angeles and other cities served by huge freeway systems began to be enshrouded daily in a brownish, irritating haze that was different from the more familiar industrial smog **(Fig. 19–5)**. Weather conditions were usually warm and sunny rather than cool and foggy, and, typically, the new haze would arise during the morning commute and begin to dissipate only by the time of the evening commute. This **photochemical smog**, as it came to be called, is produced when several pollutants from automobile exhausts—nitrogen oxides and volatile organic carbon compounds—are acted on by sunlight (Fig. 19–4b).

Inversions. Certain weather conditions intensify levels of both industrial and photochemical smogs. Under normal conditions, the daytime air temperature is highest near the ground, because sunlight strikes Earth and the absorbed heat radiates to the air near the surface. The warm air continues

[1]S. A. Montzka et al. "Small Interannual Variability of Global Atmospheric Hydroxyl." *Science* 331: 67–69. January 7, 2011.

(a)

(b)

Figure 19–5 Los Angeles air. (a) Los Angeles on a good day. (b) LA under a blanket of photochemical smog.

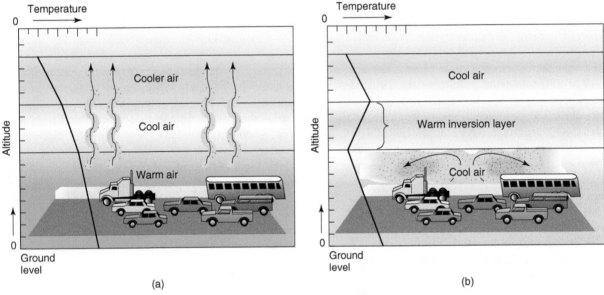

Figure 19–6 Temperature inversion. A temperature inversion may cause episodes of high concentrations of air pollutants. (a) Normally, air temperatures are highest at ground level and decrease at higher elevations. (b) In a temperature inversion, a layer of warmer air overlies cooler air at ground level.

to rise, carrying pollutants upward and dispersing them at higher altitudes (**Fig. 19–6a**). At times, however, a warm air layer occurs above a cooler layer. This condition of cooler air below and warmer air above is called a **temperature inversion** (Fig. 19–6b). Inversions often occur at night, when the surface air is cooled by radiative heat loss. Such inversions are usually short lived, as the next morning's sunlight begins the heating process anew and any pollutants that accumulated overnight are carried up and away. During cloudy weather, however, the Sun may not be strong enough to break up the inversion for hours or even days. A mass of high-pressure air may move in and sit above the cool surface air, trapping it. Topography can also intensify smog as cool ocean air flows into valleys and is trapped there by nearby mountain ranges. Los Angeles has both topographical features.

When such long-term temperature inversions occur, pollutants can build up to dangerous levels, prompting local health

officials to urge people with breathing problems to stay indoors. For many people, smog causes headaches, nausea, and eye and throat irritation. It may aggravate preexisting respiratory conditions, such as asthma and emphysema. In some industrial cities (such as Donora), air pollution reached lethal levels under severe temperature inversions. These cases became known as *air-pollution disasters*. London experienced repeated episodes of inversion-related disasters in the mid-1900s. One episode in 1952 resulted in 4,000 pollution-related deaths.

Atmospheric Brown Clouds. A relative newcomer on the air-pollution scene is the so-called **atmospheric brown cloud (ABC)**, a 1- to 3-kilometer-thick blanket of pollution that frequently hovers over south and central Asia. The ABC is in fact a persistent aerosol, similar to the summer aerosol found over industrial regions in the North Temperate Zone, but dissimilar in that it persists year-round and has a different makeup (see

Chapter 18). Unique to the ABC is the high proportion of black carbon and soot derived from biomass burning (residential cooking, agricultural clearing) and fossil fuel combustion (coal and diesel exhaust). Ozone and acid rain accompany the ABC.

The impacts of the ABC are serious: major dimming, especially over large cities; reductions in rainfall due to the aerosol particles; solar heating of the atmosphere and decreased reflection by snow and ice (both of which are contributing to a shrinking of the Hindu Kush–Himalaya–Tibetan glaciers, vital water sources for the major river systems of eastern Asia); a weakening of the Indian summer monsoon; reduced crop yields due to the dimming and to ozone levels; and heightened acute and chronic health effects typical of exposure to industrial and urban air pollution.

Industrial smog from coal burning, photochemical smog from vehicular exhaust, and atmospheric brown cloud are all caused by the release of pollutants, and we now turn our attention to those pollutants.

19.2 Major Air Pollutants and Their Sources

In large measure, anthropogenic air pollutants are direct and indirect products of the *combustion* of coal, gasoline, other liquid fuels, and refuse (wastepaper, plaster, and so on). These fuels and wastes are organic compounds. With complete combustion, the products of burning organic compounds are carbon dioxide and water vapor. Unfortunately, combustion is seldom complete, and many complex chemical substances are involved. The combustion of fuels and refuse creates a host of gaseous and particulate products that in turn create unwanted problems before they are cleansed from the air. Other processes producing air pollutants are *evaporation* (of volatile substances) and *strong winds* that pick up dust and other particles.

Primary Pollutants

Table 19–1 presents the names, symbols, major sources, characteristics, and general effects of the major air pollutants. The first seven (**particulates, volatile organic compounds, carbon monoxide, nitrogen oxides, sulfur dioxide, lead,** and **air toxics**) are called **primary air pollutants** because they are the direct products of combustion and evaporation. Some primary pollutants may undergo further reactions in the atmosphere and produce additional undesirable compounds, called **secondary air pollutants** (**ozone, peroxyacetyl nitrates, sulfuric acid,** and **nitric acid**). Sources of air pollution are summarized in **Figure 19–7**. Power plants are the major source of sulfur dioxide, particulates originate from all sorts of combustion, and transportation

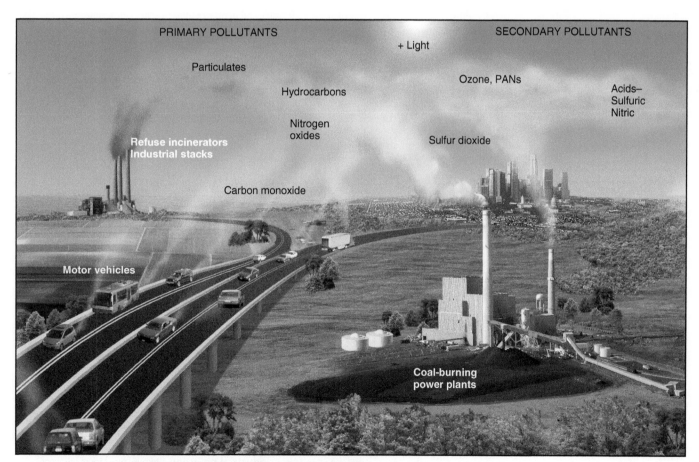

Figure 19–7 The prime sources of the major anthropogenic air pollutants. Industrial processes and transportation generate a toxic brew of primary and secondary air pollutants.

TABLE 19–1 Major Anthropogenic Air Pollutants and Their Effects

Name	Symbol	Source	Description and Effects
Primary Pollutants			
Suspended particulate matter	PM	Soot, smoke, metals, and carbon from combustion; dust, salts, metal, and dirt from wind erosion; atmospheric reactions of gases	Complex mixture of solid particles and aerosols; reduces lung function and affects respiration and cardiovascular disease
Volatile organic compounds	VOC	Incomplete combustion of fossil fuels; evaporation of solvents and gasoline; emission from plants	Mixture of compounds, some carcinogenic; major agent of ozone formation
Carbon monoxide	CO	Incomplete combustion of fuels	Invisible, odorless, tasteless gas; poisonous because of ability to bind to hemoglobin and block oxygen delivery to tissues; aggravates cardiovascular disease
Nitrogen oxides	NO_x	From nitrogen gas due to high combustion temperatures when burning fuels; also from wood burning	Reddish-brown gas and lung irritant; aggravates respiratory disease; major source of acid rain; contributes to ozone formation
Sulfur dioxide	SO_2	Combustion of sulfur-containing fuels, especially coal	Poisonous gas that impairs breathing; major source of acid rain; contributes to particle formation
Lead	Pb	Battery manufacture; lead smelters; combustion of leaded fuels and solid wastes	Toxic at low concentrations; accumulates in body and can lead to brain damage in children
Air toxics	Various	Fuel combustion in vehicles; industrial processes; building materials; solvents	Toxic chemicals, many of which are known human carcinogens (e.g., benzene, asbestos, vinyl chloride); Clean Air Act identifies 187 air toxics
Radon	Rn	Rocks and soil; natural breakdown of radium and uranium	Invisible and odorless radioactive gas can accumulate inside homes; second leading cause of lung cancer in United States
Secondary Pollutants			
Ozone	O_3	Photochemical reactions between VOCs and NO_x	Toxic to animals and plants and highly reactive in lungs; oxidizes surfaces and rubber tires
Peroxyacetyl nitrates	PAN	Photochemical reactions between VOCs and NO_x	Damages plants and forests; irritates mucous membranes of eyes and lungs
Sulfuric acid	H_2SO_4	Oxidation of SO_2 by OH radicals	Produces acid deposition, damages lakes, soils, artifacts
Nitric acid	HNO_3	Oxidation of NO_x by OH radicals	Produces acid deposition, damages lakes, soils, artifacts

accounts for the lion's share of carbon monoxide and nitrogen oxides. This diversity suggests that strategies for controlling air pollutants will be different for the different sources.

When fuels and wastes are burned, particles consisting mainly of carbon are emitted into the air; these are the particulates we see as soot and smoke (Fig. 19–8). In addition, various unburned fragments of fuel molecules are given off; these are the VOC emissions. Incompletely oxidized carbon is carbon monoxide (CO), in contrast to completely oxidized carbon, which is carbon dioxide (CO_2). Combustion takes place in the air, a mixture of 78% nitrogen and 21% oxygen. At high combustion temperatures, some of the atmospheric nitrogen gas is oxidized to form the gas nitric oxide (NO). In the air, nitric oxide immediately reacts with additional oxygen to form nitrogen dioxide (NO_2) and nitrogen tetroxide (N_2O_4).

Figure 19–8 Industrial pollution. Because the stack of this wood-products mill in New Richmond, Quebec Province, Canada, lacks electrostatic precipitators, the plume contains substantial amounts of suspended particulate matter that can be seen from a great distance.

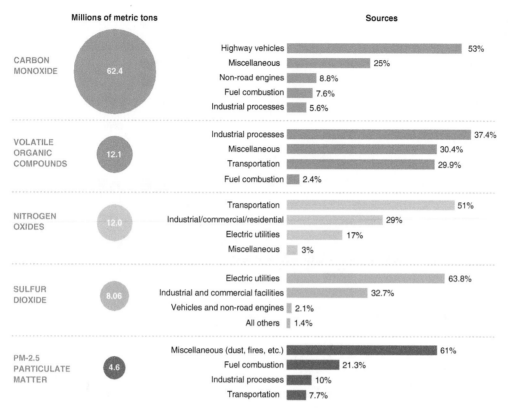

Figure 19–9 **U.S. emissions of five primary air pollutants, by source, for 2011.** *Fuel combustion* refers to fuels burned for electrical power generation and for space heating. Note especially the different contributions by transportation and fuel combustion/electric utilities, the two major sources of air pollutants.

(*Source:* EPA National Emissions Inventory, 2012. http://www.epa.gov/ttn/chief/trends/index.html.)

These compounds are collectively referred to as the nitrogen oxides, or NO_x. Nitrogen dioxide absorbs light and is largely responsible for the brownish color of photochemical smog.

In addition to organic matter, fuels and refuse contain impurities and additives, and these substances are also emitted into the air during burning. Coal, for example, contains from 0.2% to 5.5% sulfur. In combustion, this sulfur is oxidized, giving rise to several gaseous oxides, the most common being sulfur dioxide (SO_2). Coal also contains heavy-metal impurities such as mercury, and refuse contains an endless array of "impurities."

Tracking Pollutants. The Environmental Protection Agency (EPA) operates the Clearinghouse for Inventories and Emissions Factors, which tracks trends in national emissions of the primary pollutants from all sources. The EPA also follows air quality by measuring ambient concentrations (where *ambient* means "present in the air") of the pollutants at thousands of monitoring stations across the country. According to EPA data, 2011 emissions in the United States of the first five primary pollutants amounted to 99 million tons. By comparison, in 1970, when the first Clean Air Act became law, these same five pollutants totaled 301 million tons. The relative amounts emitted in the United States in 2011, as well as their major sources, are illustrated in **Figure 19–9**. The general picture shows remarkable improvement for emissions over the past 40 years (**Fig. 19–10**), reflecting the effectiveness of Clean Air Act regulations. This progressively improving trend over time has occurred in spite of large increases in the gross

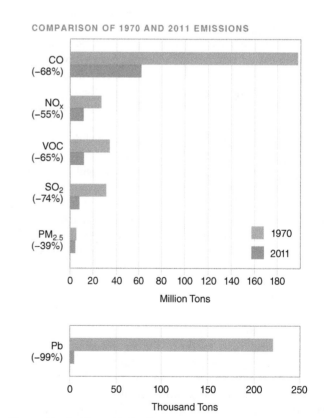

COMPARISON OF 1970 AND 2011 EMISSIONS

Figure 19–10 **Clean Air Act impacts.** Comparison of percent reductions in the emission of six criteria air pollutants between 1970 and 2011. $PM_{2.5}$ comparison values are from 1990, when data were first gathered, and 2011.

(*Source:* EPA National Emissions Inventory, 2012. http://www.epa.gov/ttn/chief/trends/index.html.)

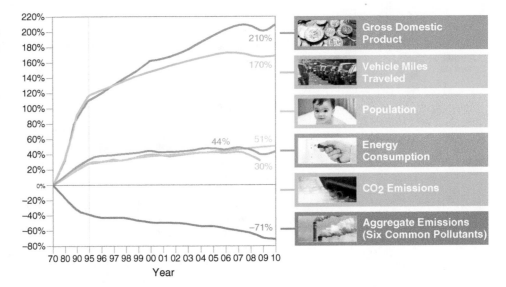

Figure 19–11 Comparison of growth versus emissions. Gross domestic product, vehicle miles traveled, energy consumption, CO_2 emissions, and population are compared with aggregate reductions in emissions of the six principal pollutants from 1970 to 2010.

(*Source:* EPA Air Trends, 2012. http://epa.gov/airtrends/aqtrends.html.)

domestic product, vehicular miles traveled, and population and energy consumption (Fig. 19–11).

Getting the Lead Out. The sixth type of primary pollutant—lead and other heavy metals—is discussed separately because the quantities emitted are far less than the levels for the first five. Before the EPA-directed phaseout in the 1980s and 1990s, lead was added to gasoline as an inexpensive way to prevent engine knock. Emitted with the exhaust from gasoline-burning vehicles, lead remained airborne and traveled great distances before settling as far away as the glaciers of Greenland. Since the phaseout, concentrations of lead in the air of cities in the United States have declined remarkably. However, lead levels are elevated around airports where piston-engine aircraft operate, the reason being that aviation gasoline still uses leaded gasoline (jet fuel has no added lead). Between 1980 and 2010, lead levels in air fell 89%. At the same time, levels of lead in children's blood have dropped 92% (some children still get lead from dust and paint chips). Lead concentrations in Greenland ice have also decreased significantly. All these declines indicate that lead restrictions in the United States and most other Northern Hemisphere nations have had a global impact. The data indicate that we have reached a steady state in lead emissions and that any new reductions must target leaded aviation gasoline, which accounts for half of the current lead air emissions. Lead smelters and battery manufacturers also add to the burden of lead.

Toxics and Radon. As with lead, the concentrations of toxic chemicals and radon in the air are small compared with those of the other primary pollutants. Some of the air's toxic compounds—benzene, for example—originate with transportation fuels. Most, however, are traceable to industries and small businesses. Radon, by contrast, is produced by the spontaneous decay of fissionable material in rocks and soils. Radon escapes naturally to the surface and seeps into buildings through cracks in foundations and basement floors, sometimes collecting in the structures.

Secondary Pollutants

Ozone and numerous reactive organic compounds are formed as a result of chemical reactions between nitrogen oxides and volatile organic carbons. Because sunlight provides the energy necessary to propel the reactions, these products are also known as **photochemical oxidants**. Note that these reactions and the ozone they produce are entirely in the troposphere; ozone in the stratosphere is "good" ozone, protecting life from damaging ultraviolet (UV) radiation. In preindustrial times, ozone concentrations ranged from 10 to 15 parts per billion (ppb), well below harmful levels. Summer concentrations of ozone in unpolluted air in North America now range from 20 to 50 ppb. Polluted air may contain ozone concentrations of 150 ppb or more, a level considered quite unhealthy if encountered for extended periods. EPA data indicate that ambient ozone levels, monitored across the United States at some 1,100 sites, declined by 20% between 1980 and 1992, leveled off during the 1990s, and then declined 11% in the first decade of the 2000s. Ozone air quality standards are the leaders in nonattainment across the country; 108 million people live in counties that still do not meet ozone standards.

Ozone Formation. A simplified view of the major reactions in the formation of ozone and other photochemical oxidants is shown in Figure 19–12. Nitrogen dioxide absorbs light energy and splits to form nitric oxide and atomic oxygen, which rapidly combines with oxygen gas to form ozone. If other factors are not involved, ozone and nitric oxide then react to form nitrogen dioxide and oxygen gas. A steady-state concentration of ozone results, and there is no appreciable accumulation of the gas (Fig. 19–12a). When VOCs are present, however, the nitric oxide reacts with them instead of with the ozone, causing several serious problems. First, the reaction between nitric oxide and the VOCs leads to highly reactive and damaging compounds known as peroxyacetyl nitrates, or

Major pollutants from vehicles

Figure 19–12 Formation of ozone and other photochemical oxidants. (a) Nitrogen oxides, by themselves, would not cause ozone and other oxidants to reach damaging levels, because reactions involving nitrogen oxides are cyclic. (b) When VOCs are also present, however, reactions occur that lead to the accumulation of numerous damaging compounds—most significantly, ozone, the most injurious.

PANs (Fig. 19–12b). Second, numerous aldehyde and ketone compounds are produced as the VOCs are oxidized by atomic oxygen, and these compounds are also noxious. Finally, with the nitric oxide tied up in this way, the ozone tends to accumulate. Because of the complex air chemistry involved, ozone concentrations may peak 30 to 100 miles (50 to 160 km) downwind of urban centers where the primary pollutants were generated. As a result, ozone concentrations above the air quality standards are sometimes found in rural and wilderness areas.

Sulfuric acid and nitric acid are considered secondary pollutants because they are products of sulfur dioxide and nitrogen oxides, respectively, reacting with atmospheric moisture and oxidants such as hydroxyl. Sulfuric and nitric acids are the acids in acid rain (technically referred to as acid deposition). We now turn our attention to this important and widespread problem.

Acid Precipitation and Deposition

Acid precipitation refers to any precipitation—rain, fog, mist, or snow—that is more acidic than usual. Because dry acidic particles are also found in the atmosphere, the combination of precipitation and dry-particle fallout is called **acid deposition.** In the late 1960s, Swedish scientist Svante Odén first documented the acidification of lakes in Scandinavia and traced it to air pollutants

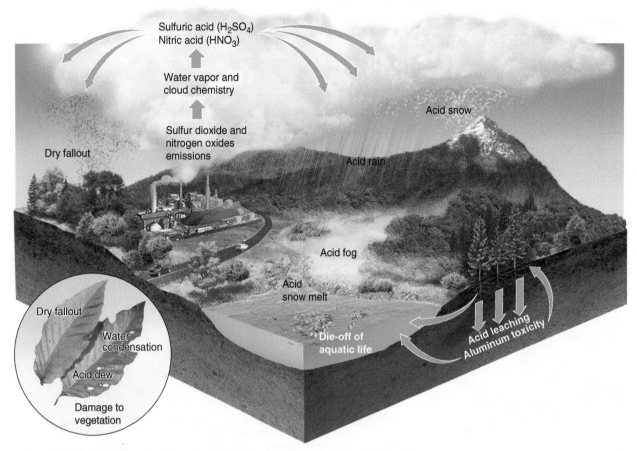

Figure 19–13 Acid deposition. Emissions of sulfur dioxide and nitrogen oxides react with hydroxyl radicals and water vapor in the atmosphere to form their respective acids, which return to the surface either as dry acid deposition or, mixed with water, as acid precipitation. Various effects of acid deposition are noted.

originating in other parts of Europe and Great Britain. Since then, careful monitoring has shown that broad areas of North America, as well as most of Europe and other industrialized regions of the world, have been experiencing precipitation that is between 10 and 1,000 times more acidic than usual. This has affected ecosystems in diverse ways, as illustrated in Figure 19–13.

To understand the full extent of the problem, we must first understand some principles about acids and how we measure their concentration.

Acids, Bases, and pH. Acidic properties (for example, a sour taste and corrosiveness) are due to the presence of hydrogen ions (H^+, hydrogen atoms without their electron), which are highly reactive. Therefore, an **acid** is any chemical that releases hydrogen ions when dissolved in water. The chemical formulas of a few common acids are shown in Table 19–2. Note that all of them ionize—that is, their components separate—to create hydrogen ions plus a negative ion. The higher the concentration of hydrogen ions in a solution, the more acidic the solution.

A **base** is any chemical that releases hydroxide ions (OH^-, oxygen-hydrogen groups with an extra electron) when dissolved in water. (See Table 19–2.) The bitter taste and caustic properties of alkaline, or basic, solutions are due to the presence of hydroxide ions.

The concentration of hydrogen ions is expressed as **pH**. The pH scale goes from 0 (highly acidic) through 7 (neutral) to 14 (highly basic) (Fig. 19–14). As the pH scale numbers go from 0 to 7, the concentration of hydrogen ions (H^+) decreases, and the solution becomes less acidic and more neutral. As the numbers go from 7 to 14, the concentration of hydrogen ions gets lower, but the concentration of hydroxide ions (OH^-) increases, and the solution becomes more basic. The numbers on the scale (0–14) represent the negative logarithm (power of 10) of the hydrogen ion concentration, expressed in grams per liter (g/L). For example, a solution with a pH of 1 has an H^+ concentration of 10^{-1} g/L, a pH of 2 has a concentration of 10^{-2} g/L, and so on.

Because numbers on the pH scale represent powers of 10, there is a *tenfold difference* between each unit and the next. For example, pH 5 is 10 times as acidic (has 10 times as many H^+ ions) as pH 6, pH 4 is 10 times as acidic as pH 5, and so on.

Extent and Potency of Acid Precipitation. In the absence of any pollution, rainfall is normally somewhat acidic, with a pH of 5.6, because carbon dioxide in the air readily dissolves in, and combines with, water to produce carbonic acid. **Acid precipitation,** then, is any precipitation with a pH less than 5.5.

Since the middle of the 20th century, acid precipitation has been the norm over most of the Western world. The pH of rain and snowfall over a large portion of eastern North America used

TABLE 19–2 Common Acids and Bases

	Formula	Yields	H[1] Ion(s)	Plus	Negative Ion
Acid					
Hydrochloric acid	HCl	→	H$^+$	+	Cl$^-$ Chloride
Sulfuric acid	H$_2$SO$_4$	→	2H$^+$	+	SO$_4^{2-}$ Sulfate
Nitric acid	HNO$_3$	→	H$^+$	+	NO$_3^-$ Nitrate
Phosphoric acid	H$_3$PO$_4$	→	3H$^+$	+	PO$_4^{3-}$ Phosphate
Acetic acid	CH$_3$COOH	→	H$^+$	+	CH$_3$COO$^-$ Acetate
Carbonic acid	H$_2$CO$_3$	→	H$^+$	+	HCO$_3^-$ Bicarbonate
	Formula	**Yields**	**OH[2] Ion(s)**	**Plus**	**Positive Ion**
Base					
Sodium hydroxide	NaOH	→	OH$^-$	+	Na$^+$ Sodium
Potassium hydroxide	KOH	→	OH$^-$	+	K$^+$ Potassium
Calcium hydroxide	Ca(OH)$_2$	→	2OH$^-$	+	Ca^{2+} Calcium
Ammonium hydroxide	NH$_4$OH	→	OH$^-$	+	NH$_4^+$ Ammonium

to be quite acidic, reflecting the west-to-east movement of polluted air from the Midwest and industrial Canada. Many areas in this region once regularly received precipitation having a pH of 4.0 and, occasionally, as low as 3.0 (Fig. 19–15a). Acid precipitation was heavy in Europe in the latter half of the 20th century, from the British Isles to central Russia. Like North America, acid precipitation has declined greatly in these regions. It is on the rise in China and India as these countries increasingly exploit their coal resources. It has not disappeared in eastern North America, but pH values lower than 4.6 are now uncommon (Fig. 19–15b).

Sources of Acid Deposition. Chemical analysis of acid precipitation reveals the presence of two acids, sulfuric acid (H$_2$SO$_4$) and nitric acid (HNO$_3$). As we have seen, burning fuels produce sulfur dioxide and nitrogen oxides, so one source of the acid deposition problem is evident. These oxides enter the troposphere in large quantities from both anthropogenic and natural sources. Once in the troposphere, they are oxidized by hydroxyl radicals (Fig. 19–3) to sulfuric

and nitric acids, which dissolve readily in water or adsorb to particles and are brought down to Earth in acid deposition. This usually occurs within a week of the oxides entering the atmosphere. Another important source of acidification is traced to the use of nitrogen fertilizers, made by the Haber-Bosch process whereby atmospheric N$_2$ (a nonreactive form of nitrogen) is converted into reactive ammonia (NH$_3$) and incorporated into urea ((NH$_2$)$_2$CO). In turn, urea gives off NH$_3$ in the presence of water, which is volatile and enters the atmosphere. Whether in the atmosphere, soil, or natural waters, ammonia is eventually oxidized to nitrate (NO$_3^-$) by bacterial action, a process that generates acidity.

Natural sources contribute substantial quantities of pollutants to the air, including 50 million to 70 million tons per year of sulfur dioxide (from volcanoes, sea spray, and microbial processes) and 30 million to 40 million tons per year of nitrogen oxides (from lightning, the burning of biomass, and microbial processes). *Anthropogenic sources* per year are estimated at 115 million tons of sulfur dioxide, 60 million

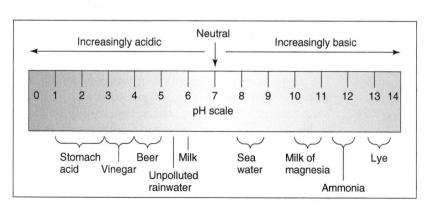

Figure 19–14 The pH scale. Each unit on the scale represents a tenfold difference in hydrogen ion concentration.

Hydrogen ion concentration as pH from measurements
made at the Central Analytical Laboratory, 1994

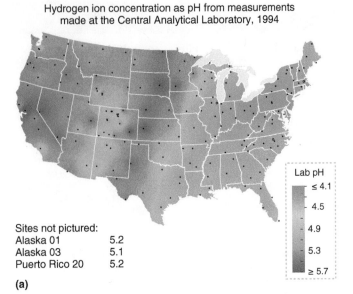

Sites not pictured:
Alaska 01   5.2
Alaska 03   5.1
Puerto Rico 20   5.2

Lab pH

≤ 4.1
4.5
4.9
5.3
≥ 5.7

(a)

Hydrogen ion concentration as pH from measurements
made at the Central Analytical Laboratory, 2010

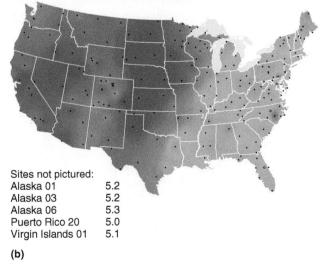

Sites not pictured:
Alaska 01   5.2
Alaska 03   5.2
Alaska 06   5.3
Puerto Rico 20   5.0
Virgin Islands 01   5.1

(b)

Figure 19–15 Acid deposition in eastern North America. (a) 1994 rainfall pH distribution across the United States; dots show locations of measuring stations. (b) 2010 rainfall pH distribution.

(*Source:* National Atmospheric Deposition Program (NRSP-3). 2012. NADP Program Office, Illinois State Water Survey. 2204 Griffith Dr., Champaign, IL 61820).

to 70 million tons of nitrogen oxides, and 50 million tons of ammonia.[2] The vital difference between natural and anthropogenic sources is that anthropogenic sources are strongly concentrated in industrialized and agricultural regions, whereas the emissions from natural sources are spread out and are a part of the global environment. Levels of the anthropogenic oxides have increased sixfold[3] since 1900, while levels of the natural emissions have remained fairly constant.

As Figure 19–9 indicates, 8.06 million tons of sulfur dioxide were released into the air in 2011 in the United States; 92% was from fuel combustion (mostly from coal-burning power plants). Some 12.0 million tons of nitrogen oxides were released, 51% of which can be traced to transportation emissions and 41% to fuel combustion at fixed sites. In addition, 4.1 million tons of ammonia were released to the atmosphere in 2011 from fertilizer use and livestock. Nitrogen oxides and ammonia are doubly damaging because the nitrogen contributes to eutrophication in aquatic ecosystems (Chapter 20). In the eastern United States, the source of much of the acid deposition was identified as the tall stacks of 50 huge, older coal-burning power plants located primarily in the Midwest (Fig. 19–16a). The tall stacks were built to alleviate local sulfur dioxide pollution at ground level. The good news is that many of these same plants are now reducing their emissions as a result of the Clean Air Act. Figure 19–16b shows the current geographic distribution of coal power plants with and without scrubbers (emissions control devices). Acid-generating emissions have decreased by 65% over the past 20 years, but there is obviously more that can be done. Of great significance, the

pattern of sources has shifted from predominantly sulfur dioxide to nitrogen oxides and ammonia.

19.3 Impacts of Air Pollutants

Air pollution is an alphabet soup of gases and particles, mixed with the normal constituents of air. The amount of each pollutant present varies greatly, depending on its proximity to the source and various conditions of wind and weather. As a result, we are exposed to a mixture that varies in makeup and concentration from day to day—even from hour to hour—and from place to place. Consequently, the effects we feel or observe are rarely, if ever, the effects of a single pollutant. Instead, they are the combined impact of the whole mixture of pollutants acting over our life span up to that point.

For example, plants may be so stressed by pollution that they become more vulnerable to other environmental factors, such as drought or attack by insects. Humans may develop lung disease due to the combined effects of ozone and NO_x. Given the complexity of this situation, it is often difficult to determine the role of any particular pollutant in causing an observed result. Nevertheless, some significant progress has been made in linking cause and effect.

Human Health

The air-pollution disasters in Donora and London demonstrated that exposure to air pollution can be deadly. Every one of the primary and secondary air pollutants (Table 19–1) is a threat to human health, particularly the health of the respiratory system (Fig. 19–17). *Acute* exposure to some pollutants can be life threatening, but many effects are *chronic*, acting over a period of years to cause a gradual deterioration of physiological functions and

[2]Karen C. Rice and Janet S. Herman. "Acidification of Earth: An Assessment Across Mechanisms and Scales." *Applied Geochemistry* 27: 1–14. 2012.

[3]S. J. Smith et al. "Anthropogenic Sulfur Dioxide Emissions: 1850–2005." *Atmospheric Chemistry and Physics* 11: 1101–1116. 2011.

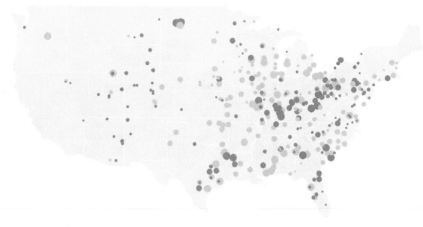

SO₂ Emissions Short Tons	Flue Gas Desulfurization Status

SO₂ Emissions Short Tons
○ 25,000 to 60,000
○ 15,000 to 24,999
○ 7,000 to 14,999
○ 3,000 to 6,999
○ 1,000 to 2,999
○ 1 to 999

Flue Gas Desulfurization Status
FGD
Planned FGD
No FGD

(a)　　　　　　　　　**(b)**

Figure 19–16 Midwestern coal-burning power plant. (a) Standard smokestacks of this coal-burning power plant were replaced by new 1,000-foot (330-m) stacks to aid in the dispersion of pollutants into the atmosphere. The taller stacks alleviated local air-pollution problems, but created a more widespread distribution of acid-generating pollutants. (b) Distribution of coal-burning power plants and their SO₂ emissions (2010); green indicates plants with flue gas scrubbers, blue shows plants with planned scrubbers, and gold shows plants without scrubbers to remove emissions.

(*Source:* U.S. Energy Information Administration, *Today in Energy,* Dec. 21, 2011.)

eventual premature mortality. Moreover, some pollutants are *carcinogenic*, adding significantly to the risk of lung cancer as they are breathed into the lungs.

Chronic Effects. Many people living in areas of urban air pollution suffer from chronic effects. Long-term exposure to *sulfur dioxide* can lead to bronchitis (inflammation of the bronchi). Chronic inhalation of *ozone* can cause inflammation and, ultimately, fibrosis of the lungs, a scarring that permanently impairs lung function. *Carbon monoxide* reduces the capacity of the blood to carry oxygen, and extended exposure to carbon monoxide can contribute to heart disease. Chronic exposure to *nitrogen oxides* impairs lung function and is known to affect the immune system, leaving the lungs open to attack by bacteria and viruses. Exposure to airborne *particulate matter* can bring on a broad range of health problems, including respiratory and cardiovascular pathology. Other factors—such as poor diet, lack of exercise, preexisting diseases, and individual genetic makeup—may add to the effects of pollution to bring on adverse health outcomes.

COPD. Any one or combination of these exposures can develop into **chronic obstructive pulmonary disease (COPD)**, a slowly progressive lung disease that makes it increasingly hard to breathe. COPD is estimated to affect 15 million people in the United States and is the fourth leading cause of death (128,000 deaths/year). Worldwide, COPD afflicts up to 10% of adults ages 40 and older.

The leading cause of this disease is smoking, but in many developing countries, the burning of wood and dung in indoor stoves for heating and cooking delivers much the same burden of pollutants as smoking to the women who tend the stoves and the children who are with them. COPD involves three separate disease processes: emphysema (destruction of the lung alveoli—see Fig. 19–17), bronchitis (inflammation and obstruction of the airways), and asthma.

Asthma. Those most sensitive to air pollution are small children, asthmatics, people with chronic pulmonary or heart disease, and the elderly. Asthma is an immune-system disorder characterized by impaired breathing caused by constricted air passageways. Asthma episodes are triggered by contact with allergens (dust mites, molds, pet dander) and compounds in polluted air (ozone, particulate matter, SO₂). According to the National Center for Health Statistics, almost 456,000 hospitalizations for asthma occur yearly, together with 1.75 million visits to hospital emergency departments. The highest prevalence is among children from birth to 4 years of age. In the past decade, the incidence of asthma in the United States doubled, affecting 25 million people (including 7 million children).

Strong Evidence. Two key studies recently analyzed by the Health Effects Institute provide strong evidence of the harmful effects of fine particles and sulfur pollution. These studies followed thousands of adult subjects living in 154

(a)

(b)

Figure 19–17 The respiratory system. (a) In the lungs, air passages branch and rebranch and finally end in millions of tiny sacs called alveoli. These sacs are surrounded by capillaries. As blood passes through the capillaries, oxygen from inhaled air diffuses into the blood from the alveoli. Carbon dioxide diffuses in the reverse direction and leaves the body in the exhaled air. (b) On the left is normal lung tissue, and on the right is lung tissue from a person who suffered from emphysema, a chronic lung disease in which some of the structure of the lungs has broken down. Cigarette smoking and heavy air pollution are associated with the development of emphysema and other chronic lung diseases.

U.S. cities for as long as 16 years. In the studies, higher concentrations of fine particles were correlated with increased mortality, especially from cardiopulmonary disease and lung cancer. The more polluted the city, the higher the mortality. The studies were used by the EPA to step up its regulatory attention to fine particles.

Fine particles were also cited as a key to heightened costs of air pollution in Southern California, along with ozone. Both pollutants exceed federal standards and were judged to cause more deaths in the region than did traffic accidents. Meeting those standards would save $28 billion annually in avoided health care costs, missed work, school absences, and premature deaths, according to a research study from California State University, Fullerton, in 2008. Health impacts of the excess pollutants include asthma, chronic bronchitis, and cardiovascular problems.

Mercury. One of the heavy-metal pollutants, mercury, deserves special attention. It is a toxic element, one that binds to key proteins in the body and can lead to many neurological disorders. In fetuses and small children, mercury impairs brain development. Power plants are the major source of mercury reaching the environment, and once present in aquatic systems, mercury is converted to a highly toxic form, methylmercury, which accumulates in fish as a consequence of bioaccumulation (Chapter 13). In recent tests, the EPA reported methylmercury concentrations that exceeded recommendations in the game fish of 49% of lakes and reservoirs. Every state has advisories warning consumers about the dangers of mercury in locally caught fish. As we will see, the EPA has recently stepped up the regulatory restrictions on mercury releases from power plants.

Acute Effects. In severe cases, air pollution reaches levels that cause death, though such deaths usually occur among people already suffering from critical respiratory or heart disease or both. The gases present in air pollution are known to be lethal in high concentrations, but such concentrations occur nowadays only in cases of accidental poisoning. Nevertheless, intense air pollution puts an additional stress on the body, and if a person is already in a weakened condition (as are, for example, the elderly or asthmatics), this additional stress may be fatal. Most of the deaths in air-pollution disasters reflect the acute effects of air pollution. However, recent research shows that even moderate air pollution can cause changes in cardiac rhythms of people with heart disease, triggering fatal heart attacks.

Carcinogenic Effects. The heavy-metal and organic constituents of air pollution include many chemicals known to be carcinogenic in high doses. According to the industrial reporting required by the EPA, 4.7 million tons of hazardous air pollutants (the air toxics—see Table 19–1) are released annually into the air in the United States. The presence of trace amounts of these chemicals in the air may be responsible for a significant portion of the cancer observed in humans. One major source of such carcinogens is diesel exhaust (Fig. 19–18). The EPA has classified diesel exhaust as a likely human carcinogen and has established the National Clean Diesel Campaign to reduce emissions from the current diesel truck fleet and establish standards for new diesel-powered engines.

In some cases, exposure to a pollutant can be linked directly to cancer and other health problems by way of epidemiological evidence. One pollutant that clearly and indisputably is correlated with cancer and other disorders is **benzene**. This organic chemical is present in motor fuels and is also used as a solvent for fatty substances and in the manufacture of detergents, explosives, and pharmaceuticals. Environmentally, benzene is found in the emissions from fossil fuel combustion that result from operating motor vehicles and burning coal and oil. Benzene

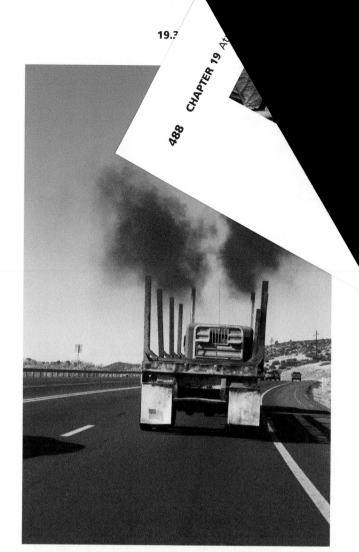

Figure 19–18 Diesel truck exhaust. Diesel truck exhaust is a major source of hazardous air pollutants as well as particulates, and the exhaust from diesel engines has been classified as a probable human carcinogen.

is also present in tobacco smoke, which accounts for half of the public's exposure to the chemical. The EPA has classified benzene as a known human carcinogen, linked to leukemia in persons encountering the chemical through occupational exposure. Chronic exposure to benzene can also lead to numerous blood disorders and damage to the immune system.

The Environment

Experiments show that plants are even more sensitive to air pollutants than are humans. Before emissions were controlled, it was common to see wide areas of totally barren land or severely damaged vegetation downwind from smelters and coal-burning power plants. The pollutant responsible was usually sulfur dioxide.

Crop Damage. Nowadays, damage to crops, orchards, and forests downwind of urban centers is caused mainly by exposure to ozone. The ozone gains access to plants through their stomata, the respiratory pores in all plant leaves. Symptoms of ozone damage include black flecking

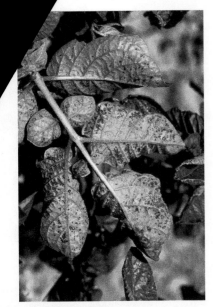

Figure 19–19 Ambient ozone injury. This potato leaf shows the black flecking symptomatic of ozone damage.

(*Source:* U.S. Department of Agriculture Agricultural Research Service. Effects of Ozone Air Pollution on Plants. 2009. www.ars.usda.gov/Main/docs.htm?docid=12462.)

and yellowing of leaves (**Fig. 19–19**). Crops vary in their susceptibility to ozone, but damage to many important crops (such as soybeans, corn, and wheat) is observed at common ambient levels of ozone (**Fig. 19–20**). Unfortunately, ozone levels are highest in summer, when crops are growing, and rural areas often experience high ozone levels as ozone forms downwind of pollution sources. The $27 billion U.S. soybean crop suffers a loss of almost $2 billion annually due to ozone. Much of the world's grain production occurs in regions that receive enough ozone pollution to reduce crop yields. India loses $5 billion yearly to ozone crop damage, China loses $2.5 billion, and farmers in Europe lose more than $7.5 billion yearly to ozone.

Forest Damage. The negative impact of air pollution on wild plants and forest trees may be even greater than on agricultural crops.

Ozone Damage. Studies have shown that ozone damage to forest trees begins at about 40 ppb and gets more intense with higher levels. In California and southern Appalachian forests, ozone levels often reached 60 ppb and above, and seasonal losses in tree stem growth in the latter were measured at 30–50% for most species. Studies in European forests found that ozone stress affects photosynthetic carbon uptake, increases respiration of foliage, amplifies water loss, and generally disrupts carbon and nutrient metabolism. In sum, research has suggested that as temperatures climb and moisture is less predictable under conditions of expected global climate change, ozone levels will have an increasingly serious impact on forest growth.

Damage from Acid Deposition. From the Green Mountains of Vermont to the San Bernardino Mountains of California, the die-off of forest trees in the 1980s caused great concern. Red spruce forests were especially vulnerable. In New England, 1.3 million acres of high-elevation forests were devastated. Commonly, the damaged trees lost needles as acidic water drew calcium from them, rendering them more susceptible to winter freezing. Sugar maples, important forest trees in the Northeast, have shown extensive mortality, ranging from 20–80% of all trees in some forests.

Much of the damage to forests from acid precipitation is due to chemical interactions within the forest soils. Sustained acid precipitation at first adds nitrogen and sulfur to the soils, which stimulate tree growth. In time, though, these chemicals leach out large quantities of the buffering chemicals (usually calcium and magnesium salts). When these buffering salts no longer neutralize the acid rain, aluminum ions, which are toxic, are dissolved from minerals in the soil. The combination of aluminum and the increasing scarcity of calcium, which is essential to plant growth, leads to reduced tree growth. Research at the Hubbard Brook Experimental Forest in the White Mountains

Figure 19–20 Ozone impact on crop yields. Some crop species react more strongly to ozone than others.

(*Source:* U.S. Department of Agriculture Agricultural Research Service: Effects of Ozone Air Pollution on Plants. 2009. www.ars.usda.gov/Main/docs.htm?docid=12462.)

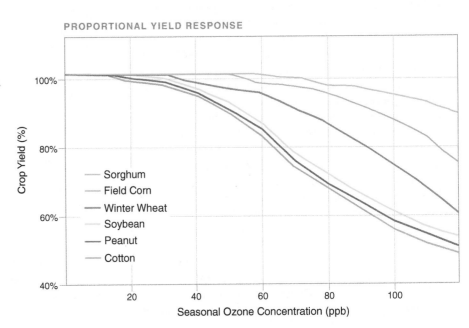

of New Hampshire has shown a marked reduction in calcium and magnesium in the forest soils from the 1960s on, which is reflected in the amount of calcium in tree rings over the same period. The net result of these changes has been a decline in forest growth. Experimental liming of soils in forests showing maple tree dieback was able to restore the trees to health, and aluminum ion concentrations were seen to decrease greatly. Although acid deposition has declined since the 1980s, few studies have actually tracked the recovery of terrestrial ecosystems.

Impacts on Aquatic Ecosystems. Some 50 years ago, anglers started noticing sharp declines in fish populations in many lakes in Sweden, Ontario, and the Adirondack Mountains of upper New York State. Since that time, as ecological damage continued to spread, studies have revealed many ways in which air pollution—especially acid deposition—alters and may destroy aquatic ecosystems.

The pH of an environment is extremely critical because it affects the function of virtually all enzymes, hormones, and other proteins in the bodies of all organisms living in that environment. Ordinarily, organisms are able to regulate their internal pH within the narrow limits necessary to function properly. A consistently low environmental pH, however, often overwhelms the regulatory mechanisms in many life forms, thus weakening or killing them. Most freshwater lakes, ponds, and streams have a natural pH in the range from 6 to 8, and organisms have adapted accordingly. The eggs, sperm, and developing young of these organisms are especially sensitive to changes in pH. Most are severely stressed, and many die, if the environmental pH shifts as little as one unit from the optimum.

As aquatic ecosystems become acidified, a shift occurs from acid-sensitive to acid-tolerant species. The acid-sensitive species die off, either because the acidified water kills them or because it keeps them from reproducing. Figure 19–13 shows that acid precipitation may leach aluminum and various heavy metals from the soil as the water percolates through it. Normally, the presence of these elements in the soil does not pose a problem because they are bound in insoluble mineral compounds and, therefore, are not absorbed by organisms. As the compounds are dissolved by low-pH water, however, the metals are freed. They may then be absorbed by and are highly toxic to both plants and animals. For example, mercury tends to accumulate in fish as lake waters become more acidic.

Acid deposition hit some regions especially hard in the latter part of the 20th century. In Ontario, Canada, approximately 1,200 lakes lost their fish life. In the Adirondacks, a favorite recreational region for New Yorkers, 346 lakes were without fish in 1990. In New England and the eastern Catskills, more than 1,000 lakes have suffered from recent acidification. The physical appearance of highly acidified lakes is deceiving. From the surface, they are clear and blue, the outward signs of a healthy condition. However, the only life found below the surface is acid-loving mosses growing on the bottom.

Neutralizing Capacity. As Figure 19–15a indicates, wide regions of eastern North America receive substantial amounts of acid precipitation, yet not all areas have acidified lakes.

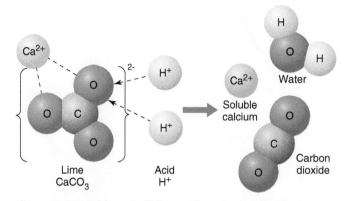

Figure 19–21 Acid neutralizing. Acids may be neutralized by certain nonbasic compounds. A chemical such as limestone (calcium carbonate) reacts with hydrogen ions as shown. Hence, the pH of a lake or river remains close to neutral despite the additional acid, when it contains adequate acid neutralizing capacity.

Apparently, many areas remain healthy, whereas others have become acidified to the point of becoming lifeless. How is this possible? The key lies in the system's **acid neutralizing capacity (ANC)**. Despite the addition of acid, a system may be protected from changes in pH by a neutralizer—a buffer that, when present in a solution, has a large capacity to absorb hydrogen ions and thus maintain the pH at a relatively constant value.

Limestone ($CaCO_3$) is a natural acid neutralizer (Fig. 19–21) that protects lakes from the effects of acid precipitation in many areas of the North American continent, particularly in the Midwest. Lakes and streams receiving their water from rain and melted snow that have percolated through soils derived from limestone will contain dissolved limestone. The regions that are sensitive to acid precipitation are those containing much granitic rock, which does not yield good ANC. The good news is that the sensitive regions (New England, the Adirondacks, the Northern Appalachian Plateau) are recovering their ANC, and the percentage of acidic lakes has declined in the past 18 years.[4] The decline is consistent with the decrease in acid deposition in these regions, which has been brought about by the reductions of SO_2 and NO_x emissions mandated by the Clean Air Act.

Visibility. A clear blue sky and good visibility are matters of health, but they also carry significant aesthetic value and can have a deep psychological impact on people. Can a value be put on these benefits? Many of us spend thousands of dollars and hundreds of hours commuting long distances to work so that we can live in a less polluted environment than the one in which we work. Ironically, the resulting traffic and congestion cause much of the very pollution we are trying to escape. Then we travel to national parks and wilderness areas and too often find that the visibility in *these* natural areas is impaired by what has been called "regional haze," coming from particulates and gases originating hundreds of miles away. In an encouraging move, the EPA established a

---

[4]Executive Office of the President. National Acid Precipitation Assessment Program Report to Congress 2011: An Integrated Assessment. USGS, 2011. http://ny.water.usgs.gov.

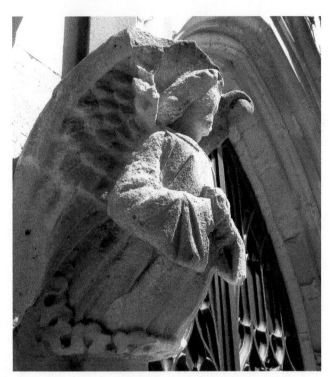

Figure 19–22 Effect of pollution on monuments. The corrosive effects of acids from air pollutants are dissolving away the features of many monuments and statues, as seen in the angel perched on this building buttress.

Regional Haze Rule in 1999, aimed at improving the visibility at 156 national parks and wilderness areas. The regulations call on all 50 states to establish goals for improving visibility and to develop long-term strategies for reducing the emissions (especially particles) that cause the problem.

Effects on Materials and Aesthetics. Walls, windows, and other exposed surfaces turn gray and dingy as particulates settle on them. Paints and fabrics deteriorate more rapidly, and the sidewalls of tires and other rubber products become hard and checkered with cracks because of oxidation by ozone. Metal corrosion is increased dramatically by sulfur dioxide and acids derived from sulfur and nitrogen oxides, as are weathering and the deterioration of stonework.

Limestone and marble (which is a form of limestone) are favored materials for the outsides of buildings and for monuments (collectively called artifacts). The reaction between acid deposition and limestone is causing these structures to erode at a tremendously accelerated pace. Monuments and buildings that have stood for hundreds or even thousands of years with little change are now dissolving and crumbling away (Fig. 19–22). The corrosion of buildings, monuments, and outdoor equipment by acid precipitation costs billions of dollars for replacement and repair each year in the United States. In an extreme case of corrosion, a 37-foot bronze Buddha in Kamakura, Japan, is slowly dissolving away as precipitation from Korea and China bathes the statue in highly acidic rain.

Although the decay of artifacts is a tragic loss in itself, it should also stand as a grim reminder of how we are dissolving away the buffering capacity of ecosystems. As the saying goes, "What goes up must come down." The sulfur and nitrogen

oxides pumped into the troposphere in the United States gradually increased from some 11.4 million tons in 1900 to their peak of 53 million tons in 1973. Although this number has been reduced by almost two-thirds, the pollutants still come back down as acid deposition, generally to the east of their origin because of the way weather systems flow. And the soils retain much of the sulfate deposition they have received. The deposits cross national boundaries, too. As a result, Canada receives half of its acid deposition from the United States, and Scandinavia gets it mostly from Great Britain and other western European nations. Japan receives the wind-borne pollution from widespread coal burning in Korea and China. For good reason, the problem of acid deposition has been addressed at national and international levels. Accordingly, we turn next to the efforts made to curb air pollution.

19.4 Bringing Air Pollution Under Control

By the 1960s, it was obvious that pollutants produced by humans were overloading natural cleansing processes in the atmosphere. The unrestricted discharge of pollutants into the atmosphere could no longer be tolerated.

Clean Air Act

Federal legislation regarding air pollution was first introduced in 1955 as the **Air Pollution Control Act.** Several minor amendments followed until, under grassroots pressure from citizens, the U.S. Congress enacted a major bill, the **Clean Air Act Amendments of 1970 (CAA).** Together with amendments passed in 1977 and 1990, this law, administered by the EPA, represents the foundation of U.S. air-pollution control efforts. The act called for identifying the most widespread pollutants, setting **ambient standards** (levels that need to be achieved to protect environmental and human health), and establishing control methods and timetables to meet standards.

NAAQS. The CAA mandated the setting of standards for four of the primary pollutants—particulates, sulfur dioxide, carbon monoxide, and nitrogen oxides—and for the secondary pollutant ozone. At the time, these five pollutants were recognized as the most widespread and objectionable ones. Today, with the addition of lead, they are known as the **criteria pollutants** and are covered by the **National Ambient Air Quality Standards (NAAQS)** (Table 19–3). The primary standard for each pollutant is based on the presumed highest level that can be tolerated by humans without noticeable ill effects, minus a 10–50% margin of safety. For some of the pollutants, long-term and short-term levels are set. The short-term levels are designed to protect against acute effects, while the long-term standards are designed to protect against chronic effects and damage to crops, animals, vegetation, and buildings. The EPA is required to review the pollutants every five years and make adjustments if the science justifies changes. The NAAQS have far-reaching impacts on many regulations, and proposed changes always generate controversies.

TABLE 19–3 National Ambient Air Quality Standards for Criteria Pollutants (NAAQS)

Pollutant	Averaging Time*	Primary Standard
PM_{10} particulates	24 hours	150 $\mu g/m^3$
$PM_{2.5}$ particulates**	1 year	15 $\mu g/m^{3}$***
	24 hours	35 $\mu g/m^3$
Sulfur dioxide	1 hour	0.075 ppm
	3 hours	0.5 ppm
Carbon monoxide	8 hours	9 ppm
	1 hour	35 ppm
Nitrogen dioxide	Annual mean	0.053 ppm
	1 hour	0.100 ppm
Ozone	8 hours	0.075 ppm
Lead	3 months	0.15 $\mu g/m^3$

Source: U.S. EPA, Office of Air Quality Planning and Standards, *National Ambient Air Quality Standards.* October 2011. www.epa.gov/air/criteria.html.

*The averaging time is the period over which concentrations are measured and averaged.

**$PM_{2.5}$ is the particulate fraction having a diameter smaller than or equal to 2.5 micrometers.

***New proposed standard is 12 to 13 $\mu g/m^3$.

NESHAPs. In addition, the CAA required the EPA to establish **National Emission Standards for Hazardous Air Pollutants (NESHAPs)** for a number of toxic substances (the air toxics). The Clean Air Act Amendments of 1990 greatly extended this section of the EPA's regulatory work by specifically naming 187 toxic air pollutants for the agency to track and regulate. The EPA tracks both the criteria pollutants and the hazardous air pollutants in a database, the National Emissions Inventory. This database serves as an essential source of information for the EPA in carrying out its regulatory responsibilities.

Control Strategy. The basic strategy of the 1970 Clean Air Act was to regulate the emissions of air pollutants so that the *ambient* criteria pollutants would remain below the primary standard levels. This approach is called **command-and-control** because regulations were enacted requiring industry to achieve a set limit on each pollutant through the use of specific control equipment. The assumption was that human and environmental health could be significantly improved by a reduction in the output of pollutants. If a particular region was in violation for a given pollutant, a local government agency would track down the source(s) and order reductions in emissions until the region came into compliance.

Unfortunately, this strategy proved difficult to implement. Most of the regulatory responsibility fell on the states and cities, which were often unable or unwilling to enforce control.

In spite of these difficulties, however, total air pollutants were reduced by some 25% during a time when both population and economic activity increased substantially, and even in the noncompliant regions, the severity of air-pollution episodes lessened. Accordingly, some significant changes were made in the law and in the regulations that followed.

1990 Amendments. The Clean Air Act Amendments of 1990 (CAAA) targeted specific pollutants more directly and enforced compliance more aggressively, through such means as the imposition of sanctions. As with the earlier law, the states do much of the work in carrying out the mandates of the 1990 act. Each state must develop a State Implementation Plan (SIP) that is designed to reduce emissions of every NAAQS pollutant whose control standard (Table 19–3) has not been attained. One major change was the addition of a permit application process (already in place for the release of pollutants into waterways). Polluters must apply for a permit that identifies the kinds of pollutants they release, the quantities of those pollutants, and the steps they are taking to reduce pollution. Permit fees provide funds the states can use to support their air-pollution control activities.

Under the CAAA, regions of the United States that have failed to attain the required levels must submit *attainment plans* based on **reasonably available control technology (RACT)** measures. Offending regions must convince the EPA that the standards will be reached within a certain time frame. The state SIPs and attainment performances are enforced by EPA sanctions that impose costly withholding of federal funds in case of failures.

Dealing with the Pollutants

The Clean Air Act and its amendments give the EPA broad authority to write regulations for reducing air pollutants, using a process known as rulemaking. The process involves a proposed rule stage and a final rule stage. EPA will give notice first of a proposed rule, which allows a period of one to three months for public review and comments. Next, the agency is required to consider the comments received, and when the final rule is published, responses to the comments are usually discussed, and any changes made on the basis of the comments are noted. Then the final rule is published in the Federal Register (available on the Internet), the official daily publication for a host of federal notices, regulations, executive orders, and other presidential documents. Once published, a final rule has the force of law until it is amended or repealed. We will consider the air pollution regulations by the different categories of pollutants.

Reducing Particulates. Prior to the 1970s, the major sources of particulates were industrial stacks and the open burning of refuse. The CAA mandated the phaseout of open burning of refuse and required that particulates from industrial stacks be reduced to "no visible emissions." To reduce stack emissions, industries were required to install filters, electrostatic precipitators, and other devices (though many facilities in place before the 1970 CAA were exempted). These measures markedly reduced the levels of particulates since the 1970s, but particulates continued to be released from steel mills, power plants, cement plants, smelters, construction sites, and diesel engines. Wood-burning stoves and wood and grass fires also contribute to the particulate load, making regulation even more difficult. Before 1987, the NAAQS particulate standard was "total suspended particulates," and this was replaced in 1987 by the PM_{10} standard (all particles 10 micrometers or less in diameter), based on the understanding at the time of particles that could reach the interior regions of the respiratory tract.

The EPA added a new ambient air quality standard for particulates—$PM_{2.5}$—in 1997, on the basis of information indicating that smaller particulate matter (less than 2.5 micrometers in diameter) has the greatest effect on health. The coarser material (PM_{10}) is still regulated but is not considered to play as significant a role in health problems as do the finer particles. There is overwhelming evidence that the finer particles (2.5 microns or less) go right into the lungs when breathed. Responding to this evidence, the EPA announced a revision to the NAAQS in 2006, reducing the 24-hour primary standard for $PM_{2.5}$ from 65 µg/m³ to 35 µg/m³. The EPA left the annual standard at 15 µg/m³, in spite of recommendations from the EPA's Clean Air Scientific Advisory Committee that it be lowered. More recently (June, 2012), the EPA proposed strengthening the annual standard by lowering it to a range of 12 to 13 µg/m³. This proposal came as a response to legal action by the American Lung Association. Industry groups maintain that the current standard is protective enough, but the EPA defended the change by showing benefits far outweighing the costs of implementation.

Controlling Air Toxics. By EPA estimates, the amount of air toxics emitted annually into the air in the United States is around 4.7 million tons. These come from stationary sources (factories, refineries, power plants), mobile sources (cars, trucks, buses), and indoor sources (solvents, building materials). Cancer and other adverse health effects, environmental contamination, and catastrophic chemical accidents are the

major concerns associated with this category of pollutants. Under the CAAA, Congress identified 187 toxic pollutants. It then directed the EPA to identify major sources of these pollutants and to develop **maximum achievable control technology (MACT)** standards, the NESHAPs. Besides affecting control technologies, the standards include options for substituting nontoxic chemicals, giving industry some flexibility in meeting MACT goals. State and local air-pollution authorities are responsible for seeing that industrial plants achieve the goals. In response to the CAAA, the EPA has mobilized more than 300 monitoring sites to track emissions of the affected substances **(Fig. 19–23)**. To reduce the contribution from vehicles, the agency requires cleaner burning fuels (reformulated gasoline) in urban areas. Industrial sources are being addressed by setting emission standards for some 82 stationary-source categories (e.g., paper mills, oil refineries).

After years of piecemeal and delayed regulations, the EPA published final rules in December 2011 that for the first time will force the older coal- and oil-fired power plants to control their pollutants. The major focus of these new standards is mercury, a contaminant in coal and oil that is released to the air when these fuels are burned. The standards—the **Mercury and Air Toxics Standards**—require all coal- and oil-fired power plants to limit their emissions of mercury, acid gases, and other metallic toxic pollutants, preventing 90% of the mercury and 88% of acid gases from being emitted. Because of the controls needed to accomplish these reductions, emissions of SO_2 and fine particles will also be greatly reduced. The human health value of these new controls is estimated at $37 billion to $90 billion and will prevent 11,000 premature deaths per year; the estimated costs to industry to effect these controls is $9.6 billion per year. The industry has up to four years to comply with these new standards. Industry lobbies claimed that this and other new rule changes amount to a "train wreck" for the electric power industry, predicting a wave of coal-plant closures and major increases in electricity costs. A recent Congressional Research Service report[5] found these claims to be wildly overstated. The study concluded that there will be closures of old coal-fired power plants, but these are inefficient and dirty and are largely being replaced by newer natural gas–fired plants.

Limiting Pollutants from Motor Vehicles. Cars, trucks, and buses release nearly half of the pollutants that foul our air. Vehicle exhaust sends out VOCs, carbon monoxide, and nitrogen oxides that lead to ground-level ozone and PANs. Additional VOCs come from the evaporation of gasoline and oil vapors from fuel tanks and engine systems. The 1970 CAA mandated a 90% reduction in these emissions by 1975. This timing proved to be unrealistic, but enough improvements have been made over the years that today's new cars have actually achieved a 90% emissions reduction. This improvement is fortunate because driving in the United States has been increasing much more rapidly than the population has. Between

Figure 19–23 Air toxics monitoring station. A radiation monitoring device has been added to this air toxics monitoring station located on the grounds of a school in Anaheim, California.

[5]James E. McCarthy and Claudia Copeland. "EPA's Regulation of Coal-Fired Power: Is a 'Train Wreck' Coming?" *Congressional Research Service* R41914. August 8, 2011. www.crs.gov.

Figure 19–24 **Cutaway of a catalytic converter.** Engine gas is routed through the converter, where catalysts promote chemical reactions that change the harmful hydrocarbons, carbon monoxide, and nitrogen oxides into less harmful gases, such as carbon dioxide, water, and nitrogen.

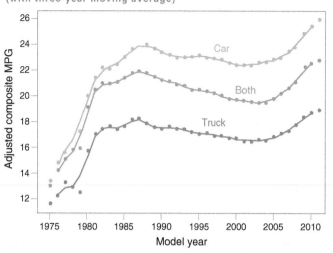

Figure 19–25 **Fuel economy and light-duty vehicles.** Changes in the fuel economy in model years from 1975 to 2011. "Truck" refers to pickups, family vans, and SUVs.

(*Source*: EPA, Office of Transportation and Air Quality. Light-Duty Automotive Technology, Carbon Dioxide Emissions, and Fuel Economy Trends: 1975 Through 2011. EPA-420-R-12-001a, March 2012. April 30, 2012.)

1970 and 2011, the number of vehicle miles increased from 1 trillion to 3 trillion miles per year, and between 1980 and 2010, the number of registered vehicles increased more than 56%. It is hard to imagine what the air would be like without the improvements mandated by the CAA.

Emissions. The reductions in automobile emissions have been achieved with a general reduction in the size of passenger vehicles, along with a considerable array of pollution-control devices, among which is one that affords the computerized control of fuel mixture and ignition timing, allowing more complete combustion of fuel and decreasing VOC emissions. To this day, however, the most significant control device on cars is the **catalytic converter** (Fig. 19–24). As exhaust passes through this device, two different catalysts are at work: a reduction catalyst that converts NO_x emissions to harmless nitrogen gas and an oxidation catalyst that oxidizes unburned hydrocarbons and carbon monoxide to carbon dioxide.

Emissions standards set in 1968 were subsequently tightened because of continuing failure to meet air quality standards in many regions of the United States. The latest of these were the Tier 2 standards, phased in over the 2004 to 2009 model years. Emissions standards require attainment of specific levels or below of volatile organic carbons, carbon monoxide, nitrogen oxides, formaldehyde, and particulate matter. All vehicles used for personal transportation, up to larger SUVs and passenger vans, are subject to the Tier 2 standards. These are the emissions that are tested by state-certified inspection stations, now required in most states.

Efficiency. Although the Clean Air Act does not address fuel efficiency, it is obvious that less fuel burned means fewer pollutants emitted. Two negative factors have recently affected fuel efficiency and consumption rates. First, the elimination of federal speed limits in 1996 reduced fuel efficiencies because of the higher speeds. Second, the sale of

sport-utility vehicles (SUVs), vans, and pickup trucks surged from 25% of the combined light-duty vehicle sales in 1990 to 50% in 2004. Automobile sales finally passed those of heavier vehicles in 2008, a response to both high fuel prices and the economic recession. The EPA's "adjusted" fuel economy estimates for model year 2011 are as follows (these are real-world estimates, based on five different driving conditions): automobiles 25.9 mpg and "trucks" (includes minivans, SUVs, and pickups) 18.9 mpg, giving a fleet average of 22.8 mpg. The efficiencies have risen above earlier peak values (achieved in 1987) since model year 2009 and are getting better every year (Fig. 19–25).

CAFE Standards. Under the authority of the Energy Policy and Conservation Act of 1975 and its amendments, the National Highway Traffic Safety Administration was given the authority to set *corporate average fuel economy (CAFE)* standards for motor vehicles. The intention of the law was to conserve oil and promote energy security. The standard set in 1984 for passenger cars required a fleet average of 27.5 mpg. The standard for light trucks (pickups, SUVs, minivans) was set at 20.7 mpg and eventually raised to 22.2 mpg. Note that the EPA's "adjusted" vehicle performances are lower than CAFE standards by 25% due to the different measurement methods used; the "unadjusted" EPA measurements of fuel economy are the basis for manufacturers' compliance with the CAFE standards.

The **Energy Independence and Security Act of 2007** mandated a new CAFE fuel economy standard of 35 mpg for the combined fleet of cars and light trucks, to be achieved by 2020. Congress passed this legislation as a major step toward a new energy future of reduced reliance on foreign oil and increased renewable energy, with a view toward reducing CO_2 greenhouse gas emissions (Chapter 18). In 2009, the Obama EPA set more stringent fuel-economy standards, calling for an annual fuel economy increase of 5%, beginning with the 2011 model year. By 2016, the CAFE fleet standard would reach 35.5 mpg. For the first time, regulations also were set for greenhouse gas emissions, to be lowered to 250 grams of CO_2 per mile by 2016. Then, working with automakers, unions, and environmental groups, the Obama administration announced a new round of CAFE standards: the combined fleet would have to achieve a 54.5 mpg and 163 g/mile CO_2 emissions target by 2025. Achieving these goals will certainly require some innovative technological advances in vehicle design, but at the same time, achieving the goals will cut oil imports in half, eliminate billions of tons of CO_2 emissions, and save drivers thousands of dollars per year in fuel costs.

Getting Around. Even though many Americans continue to prefer SUVs and larger automobiles, there are definite signs of change, particularly in light of the sustained high prices of gasoline in recent years. One option is the **hybrid electric vehicle,** which combines a conventional gasoline engine and a battery-powered electric motor to achieve substantial improvements in fuel economy. Such vehicles have been marketed by Honda and Toyota for almost a decade and are the most fuel-efficient cars in the United States. The Toyota Prius averages 46 mpg, while the Honda Insight gets 43 mpg, according to EPA figures.

All of the major automakers are jumping on the hybrid bandwagon, and higher prices of gasoline have boosted hybrid sales in the United States. Sales of hybrids soared in 2007, with 352,000 units sold, but with the downturn in the economy, hybrid sales dropped to 268,000 vehicles in 2011, about 2.1% of the passenger vehicle sales. Most newer hybrids are "green" versions of standard vehicles, including SUVs. For example, the Toyota Camry hybrid employs the same 2.5-liter gasoline engine as the standard four-cylinder Camry, but combines it with a large battery nestled behind the rear seat. Two electric motors work as generators that charge the battery as the car slows down. The car starts out under electric power, and with acceleration, the gasoline engine kicks in. When the car is sitting at a stoplight or coasting down a hill, the gasoline engine shuts off and starts automatically when speeding up. The EPA rates the 2012 Camry hybrid at 43 mpg, tops for all mid-sized hybrid sedans.

Prices for hybrids are several thousand dollars above those for comparable standard vehicles, but with gasoline ranging as high as $4 or more a gallon, the savings catch up with the extra cost in a few years. As more and more of the new hybrids are sold, prices are expected to drop substantially. For a time, a federal tax credit was available for hybrid buyers that offset much of the cost differential. Many states still offer tax incentives for hybrid buyers.

Another encouraging trend is the development of plug-in hybrid cars and electric cars. The plug-in hybrid has a larger battery pack than the conventional hybrid and can be driven up to 40 miles on a charge; after that, a down-sized gasoline engine either recharges the battery or serves as the source of propulsion. Electric vehicles are just that—all electric, with rechargeable batteries that give the vehicle a range up to 100 miles, depending on the speed of driving. Both in-home and commercial charging stations are becoming available to enable speedy recharging of the batteries. Both types of vehicles have now hit the mass market but, except for the Nissan Leaf, are somewhat pricey. It is certain that all of these innovative vehicles will become commonplace as the United States moves toward the 2025 fuel efficiency target.

Managing Ozone. Because ozone is a secondary pollutant, the only way to control ozone levels is to address the compounds that lead to ozone formation. For a long time, it was assumed that the best way to reduce these levels was simply to reduce emissions of VOCs. The steps pertaining to motor vehicles in the CAAA addressed the sources of about half of the VOC emissions. Point sources (industries) accounted for another 45% of such emissions, and area sources (numerous small emitters, such as dry cleaners, print shops, and users of household products) represented the remaining 5%. RACT measures have already been mandated for many point sources, and much progress has been made through EPA, state, and local regulatory efforts to reduce emissions from those sources. Since passage of the CAAA, VOC emissions have declined by 50%.

However, recent understanding of the complex chemical reactions involving NO_x, VOCs, and oxygen has thrown some uncertainty into this strategy of simply emphasizing a reduction in VOCs. The problem is that *both* NO_x and VOC concentrations are crucial to the generation of ozone (Fig. 19–12). Either one or the other can become the rate-limiting factor in the reaction that forms ozone. Thus, as the ratio of VOCs to NO_x changes, the concentration of NO_x can become the controlling chemical factor, pointing to the need to reduce NO_x emissions as well. This happens more commonly in air-pollution episodes that occur over a period of days than in the daily photochemical smog of the urban city.

New Ozone Standards? The revised ozone standard announced in 1997 (0.08 ppm instead of 0.12 ppm) met with strong opposition from industry groups, which obtained a court injunction in 1999 prohibiting the EPA from enforcing the new standard. However, the U.S. Supreme Court upheld the EPA in the dispute. This and other delays put off implementation of the revised standard to 2004. Cost-benefit estimates indicated that the anticipated health benefits far outweighed the costs of compliance. Then the EPA's Science Advisory Committee recommended in 2007 that a new ozone standard in the range of 0.06–0.07 ppm be set, based on human health concerns. EPA Administrator Stephen Johnson decided on a level of 0.075 ppm and published the new standard in early 2008—to the dismay of public-health advocates. The new ozone standard is expected to prevent a substantial number of premature deaths, but only a third of those that the lower standard would have prevented. EPA Administrator Lisa Jackson proposed lowering the standard but was asked by President Obama to withdraw the recommendation because the NAAQS would be reconsidered in 2013 anyway.

Down with NO_x. In a response to petitions from states in the Northeast that were having trouble achieving ozone and particulates ambient standards because of out-of-state emissions, the EPA has implemented regulations to reduce NO_x emissions from *mobile sources* and from *power plants and large industrial boilers and turbines*. For the mobile sources, which account for 59% of the smog-generating emissions in the eastern United States, the EPA established the Tier 2 standards, which were phased in gradually between 2004 and 2009. Under these regulations, emissions for all SUVs, pickup trucks, and passenger vans are held to the same standards as those for passenger cars. For NO_x, this means a gradual reduction to 0.07 grams per mile for the fleet of cars sold by each manufacturer, an 83% reduction over 2003 passenger car standards.

CAIR. States in the eastern half of the country continue to bear the burden of pollutants that are carried long distances by wind and weather, making it more difficult for them to attain the NAAQS levels for ozone and particulate matter. To address this, the Bush EPA announced a new rule in 2005 to accomplish further reductions of SO_2 and NO_x emissions. The **Clean Air Interstate Rule (CAIR)** set new lower caps on SO_2 and NO_x in 28 states in the Midwest and East, many of which are upwind of states experiencing nonattainment of ozone and particulate matter. CAIR would reduce SO_2 emissions 50% beginning in 2010 and 65% beginning in 2015. NO_x emissions would be reduced by similar percentages.

The new rules had a mixed reception. The industries and utilities were disappointed because the rules lacked the curb on lawsuits that a congressional act would provide, but they were pleased with the extended time frame for compliance. However, CAIR received a legal setback when a federal appeals court overturned the CAIR regulations, stating that the program had "more than several fatal flaws," including not being strict enough. However, the EPA, numerous states, and the Environmental Defense Fund successfully petitioned the

court to reconsider its decision. In December 2008, the court reversed its ruling and kept CAIR in force until the EPA fixed the rule in accord with CAA requirements.

CSAPR. In 2011, the Obama EPA announced the **Cross-State Air Pollution Rule (CSAPR)** to replace CAIR. This rule addresses the same pollutants as CAIR and several additional states in the Midwest **(Fig. 19–26)**. The rule requires reductions in NO_x and SO_2 to begin in 2012 and tighten further in 2014, with the final reductions in power plant SO_2 emissions of 73% from 2005 levels and NO_x reductions of 54%. The rule involves some significant improvements in the manner in which upwind states are required to protect downwind states. In late 2012, the CSAPR rule was overturned by a US Court of Appeals, claiming that EPA overstepped its authority. CAIR is back in force.

To accomplish the emissions reductions, both CAIR and CSAPR involve a system that was first implemented with the Acid Rain Program (ARP), called **cap-and-trade.** A target cap, or budget, is set by EPA for SO_2 or NO_x, in units of millions of tons of emissions. At the start, power plants are granted emission allowances based on formulas in the regulations. The plants are free to choose how they will achieve their allowances, whether by installing emissions control systems or purchasing allowances from utilities that are under their budgeted allowance. The exchange of allowances occurs as a market, with prices fluctuating in response to supply and demand. For example, the price for SO_2 at the end of 2010 was $19 per ton, while NO_x went for $325 per ton.

The impacts of these regulations for human health are significant. The EPA estimates that the regulations would, by 2014, have prevented 13,000 to 34,000 premature deaths, 15,000 nonfatal heart attacks, and 400,000 cases of aggravated asthma, among other benefits. The monetary benefits were estimated at $120 billion to $280 billion per year, while the costs of implementation would have been approximately $2.4 billion per year.[6]

Coping with Acid Deposition

Scientists working on acid-rain issues in the 1980s calculated that a 50% reduction in acid-causing emissions in the United States would effectively prevent further acidification of the environment. This reduction was not expected to correct the already bad situations, but together with natural buffering processes, it was estimated to be capable of preventing further environmental deterioration. Because we knew that about 50% of acid-producing emissions came from coal-burning power plants, control strategies focused on these sources.

Political Developments. Although evidence of the link between power-plant emissions and acid deposition was well established by the early 1980s, no legislative action was taken until 1990. The problem was one of different regional interests. Throughout the 1980s, a coalition of politicians from the Midwestern states, representatives of high-sulfur

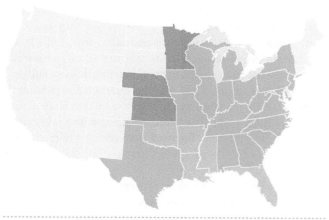

Figure 19–26 Map of states covered by the Cross-State Air Pollution Rule (CSAPR). The CSAPR is the 2011 EPA rule that replaces the Clean Air Interstate Rule (CAIR), designed to prevent downwind states from NO_x and SO_2 pollutants.

(*Source:* EPA CSAPR Fact Sheet. www.epa.gov/airtransport/statesmap.html. May 2, 2011.)

States controlled for both fine particles (annual SO_2 and NO_x) and ozone (ozone season NO_x) (20 States)
States controlled for fine particles only (annual SO_2 and NO_x) (3 States)
States controlled for ozone only (ozone season NO_x) (5 States)
States not covered by the Cross-State Air Pollution Rule

[6]EPA. Cross-State Air Pollution Rule (CSAPR). www.epa.gov/airtransport/. April 20, 2012.

coal producers, and representatives from the electric power industry effectively blocked all attempts at passing legislation that would take action on acid deposition.

On the other side of the issue were New York and the New England states, as well as most of the environmental and scientific communities, which argued that it was both possible and necessary to address acid deposition and that the best way to do so was to control emissions from power plants. Also, since 70% of Canada's acid-deposition problem came from the United States, diplomatic pressure toward a resolution was applied.

Action. With the passage of Title IV of the CAAA, the outcome of the controversy became history. However, two decades of action were lost because of political delays. In the wake of the passage of the 1990 act, Canada and the United States signed a treaty stipulating that Canada would cut its power plant SO_2 emissions by half and cap them at 3.5 million tons by the year 2000. Canada has done well; its emissions are now about 1.8 million tons and are expected to stay down. So has the United States.

Title IV of the Clean Air Act Amendments of 1990. Title IV of the CAAA addressed the acid-deposition problem by mandating reductions in both sulfur dioxide and nitrogen oxide levels. The major provisions of the Title IV ARP are as follows:

1. By 2010, total power plant SO_2 emissions were to be reduced 10 million tons below 1980 levels. This is the 50% reduction called for by scientists, and it involved the setting of a permanent cap of 8.9 million tons on such emissions.

2. In a major departure from the command-and-control approach, Title IV promoted a free-market approach to regulation of SO_2. This was the original cap-and-trade program that the CAIR and CSAPR have been grafted on.

3. New utilities do not receive allowances. Instead, they have to buy into the system by purchasing existing allowances. Thus, there are a finite number of allowances.

4. Nitrogen oxide emissions from power plants were to be reduced by 2 million tons by 2001. This was to be accomplished by regulating the boilers used by the utilities and by mandating the continuous monitoring of emissions.

Accomplishments of Title IV. The utilities industry responded to the new law with three actions:

1. Many utilities have switched to low-sulfur coal, available in Appalachia and the western United States.

2. Many older power plants have added scrubbers—"liquid filters" that put exhaust fumes through a spray of water containing lime. SO_2 reacts with the lime and is precipitated as calcium sulfate ($CaSO_4$). Because the technology for high-efficiency scrubbing is well established, more and more power plants are installing scrubbers, which have been required for all coal-burning power plants built after 1977.

3. Many utilities are trading their emission allowances. The purchase of allowances often represents a less costly way to achieve compliance than by purchasing low-sulfur coal or adding a scrubber. A typical transaction might involve a trade in the rights to emit, say, 10,000 tons of sulfur dioxide at a cost of $19 a ton. The combination of approaches has created so many efficiencies that it has cut compliance costs to 10% of what was expected.

To carry out Title IV of the CAAA, the EPA initiated a two-phase approach. Phase I aimed at a reduction of 3.5 million tons of SO_2 by 2000. Remarkably, the goal was met and even exceeded—at a cost far below the gloomy industry predictions (Fig. 19–27). Phase II began in 2000 and targeted the remaining sources of SO_2 in order to reach the 8.9-million-ton cap by 2010. This goal was met for the first time in 2007, when power plant SO_2 emissions totaled 8.9 million tons of SO_2. The emissions continue to drop, reaching 5.17 million tons in 2010, as CAIR reductions have been implemented and as more and more power plants have switched from coal to natural gas. This is a decrease of 67% from 1990 levels (Fig. 19–27).

The 2001 goal for a 2-million-ton reduction in NO_x emissions by fixed sources was met in 2000 and every year since; in fact, emissions reductions of NO_x are more than double the Title IV reduction objective. The Acid Rain Reduction Program was responsible for a large portion of these reductions, but the CAIR has also played a significant role in recent years, as we have seen. Current (2010) fixed source emissions of NO_x are 2.1 million tons, a decrease of 67% from 1990 levels. However, these sources account for less than half of all NO_x emissions, and the trend in total NO_x emissions has been a slower decline than that for SO_2.

Field News. The news from the field reflects the trends. Under the Acid Rain Program, air quality has improved, with significant benefits to human health, reductions in acid deposition, some recovery of freshwater lakes and streams, and improved forest conditions. Concentrations of sulfate in rain and deposition on the land have shown a significant decline (41–69%) over a large part of the eastern United States in the past 18 years. The acidified streams and lakes of the Adirondacks and New England have seen some recovery, in the form of pH increases and increases in acid neutralizing capacity.

One reason for the slow recovery is the continued impact of nitrogen deposition. Apparently, nitrogen plays a much larger role in acid deposition than was once believed. In passing the CAAA, Congress did not set curbs on nitrogen emissions, but simply opted to reduce the emissions from fixed sources. The other reason that slow progress has been made in recovery is the long-term buildup of sulfur deposits in soils. Residual sulfur takes a long time to flush from natural ecosystems. Accordingly, most scientists believe that the recovery of the affected ecosystems will require further reductions in both sulfur and nitrogen emissions. Acid rain still falls on eastern forests, as Figure 19–15b indicates.

SO₂ EMISSIONS FROM CAIR SO₂ ANNUAL PROGRAM AND ARP SOURCES, 1980–2010

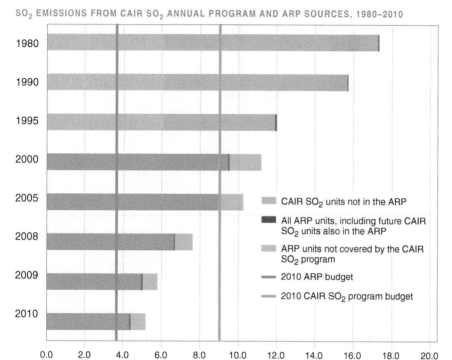

Figure 19–27 Power plant SO₂ emissions covered under the Acid Rain and CAIR programs. Emissions from all power plants were under ARP allowances for the first time in 2006 and even more so in 2007.

(*Source:* Executive Office of the President. National Acid Precipitation Assessment Program Report to Congress 2011: An Integrated Assessment. USGS, 2011. http://ny.water.usgs.gov.)

The 2011 *National Acid Precipitation Assessment Program Report to Congress*[7] concluded that further reductions in SO₂ and NOₓ will be needed in order to achieve substantial recovery of acidic lakes and streams and improvement of forest soils. These reductions are in the pipeline, as we have seen.

Costs and Benefits

We have air pollution because we want the goods and services that inevitably generate it. We want to be warm or cool, depending on the weather; we use electricity to power our homes, institutions, and manufacturing facilities; we crave freedom of movement, so we have our motor vehicles, trains, boats, and planes; and we want the array of goods produced by industries, from food to DVDs to computers to toys—the list is endless. We embrace all of these because we derive some benefit from them. The benefits may be essential or trivial, but we are accustomed to having them, as long as we can pay for them. Satisfying all of these needs and wants is what drives the American economy—and it produces millions of tons of pollutants in the process.

In recent decades, we have been learning that air pollution does not have to get worse—that in fact it can be remedied enough to keep most of us from getting sick and the environment from being degraded. But the remedies come with a price. Without question, measures taken to reduce air pollution carry an economic cost. Some critics have charged that air-pollution controls are not cost effective; that is, the benefits are not nearly as great as the costs. They see lost

opportunities for economic growth and tend to disregard the *costs avoided* (from improved health).

The Acid Rain Program has recently been examined from a benefit-cost perspective.[8] Benefits from improvements in human health have received the greatest attention from economic and scientific analyses, but some progress has been made in evaluating the aesthetic and environmental benefits as well. Health benefits extend well beyond the acid deposition issues, because the reductions in NOₓ and SO₂ reduce the levels of PM₂.₅ particulates and ozone. The estimated value of the program's health benefits in the year 2010 ranges from $174 billion to $427 billion, and the program prevented some 160,000 premature deaths. Two environmental benefit assessments have been made: Benefits from improved visibility were $40 billion in 2010, while environmental benefits to New York State alone were estimated at $1.1 billion per year. The estimated 2010 costs of administering and implementing the ARP were $3 billion, far below early estimates. The benefit-cost ratio speaks for itself. Acid rain is just one of many problems brought on by our involvement in major technologies, and although decades of inaction passed before it was addressed by public policy, the CAAA has made real improvements in the troposphere, ecosystems suffering from acidification, and human health.

We turn now to yet another problem of unintended consequences, where the use of some apparently harmless chemicals led to destruction of the stratospheric ozone that protects Earth from harmful ultraviolet radiation.

---

[7]Executive Office of the President, op cit.

[8]U.S. Environmental Protection Agency, Office of Air and Radiation. The Benefits and Costs of the Clean Air Act from 1990 to 2020. Summary Report, March 2011. www.epa.gov/air/sect812/aug10/summaryreport.pdf.

TABLE 19–4 Key Findings of the 2010 Scientific Assessment of Ozone Depletion

1. The Montreal Protocol is working as intended: There is clear evidence of a decrease in the atmospheric burden of ozone-depleting substances (ODS) and some early signs of stratospheric ozone recovery.

2. Springtime polar ozone depletion continues to be severe in cold stratospheric winters. Large Antarctic holes continue, and large Arctic ozone depletion occurs during colder Arctic winters. Antarctic ozone levels are projected to return to normal levels around 2060–2075.

3. Ozone abundances over regions outside of the poles no longer continue to decline, in spite of contributions of polar ozone depletion to extrapolar regions. It is likely that global ozone will return to normal levels around the middle of the 21st century.

4. Our basic understanding that anthropogenic ODS have been the principle cause of the ozone depletion over the past decades has been strengthened.

5. The abundances of anthropogenic ODS in the troposphere and the stratosphere show a downward trend from their peak values in the 1990s.

6. There are significant connections between ozone depletion efforts and climate change: Some of the replacements for ODS are potent greenhouse gases, and some greenhouse gases promote cooling in the stratosphere, which affects ozone depletion reactions.

Source: World Meteorological Organization, *Scientific Assessment of Ozone Depletion: 2010,* Global Ozone Research and Monitoring Project Report No. 52 (Geneva, Switzerland: World Meteorological Organization), 20.

19.5 Destruction of the Ozone Layer

The stratospheric ozone layer protects Earth from harmful ultraviolet radiation. The depletion of this layer is another major atmospheric challenge that is the result of human technology. Environmental scientists have traced the problem to a widely used group of chemicals: the **chlorofluorocarbons, or CFCs.** As with global warming, there were skeptics who were unconvinced that the problem was serious. However, scientists have achieved a strong consensus on the ozone depletion problem, reflected

in the work of the Scientific Assessment Panel of the Montreal Protocol. Table 19–4 summarizes some of the major findings of the panel's 2010 assessment.[9]

Radiation and Importance of the Shield

Solar radiation emits electromagnetic waves with a wide range of energies and wavelengths (**Fig. 19–28**). Visible light is that part of the electromagnetic spectrum that can be detected by the eye's photoreceptors. Ultraviolet (UV) wavelengths are slightly shorter than the wavelengths of violet light, which are the shortest

Figure 19–28 **The electromagnetic spectrum.** Ultraviolet radiation, visible light, infrared radiation, and many other forms of radiation are at different wavelengths on the electromagnetic spectrum.

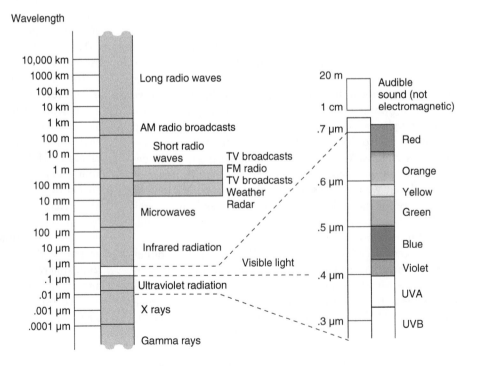

[9]World Meteorological Organization. Global Ozone Research and Monitoring Project—Report No. 52. Scientific Assessment of Ozone Depletion: 2010. http://ozone.unep.org/Assessment_Panels/SAP/Scientific_Assessment_2010/index.shtml.

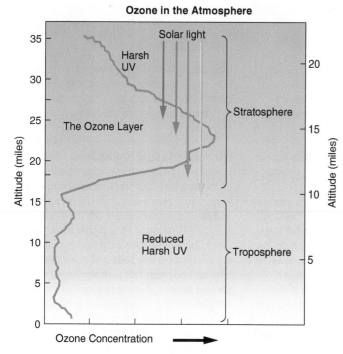

Figure 19–29 Ozone in the atmosphere. The vertical distribution of ozone in the troposphere (green) and stratosphere (red), showing the location of the stratospheric ozone layer that absorbs 99% of UV radiation.

(*Source:* Synthesis and Assessment Product 2.4. Report by the U.S. Climate Change Science Program and the Subcommittee on Global Change Research. November 2008.)

wavelengths visible to the human eye. UVB radiation consists of wavelengths that range from 280 to 315 nanometers (0.28 μm to 0.32 μm), whereas UVA radiation is from 315 to 400 nanometers (0.32 μm to 0.40 μm). Because energy is inversely related to wavelength, UVB is more energetic and, therefore, more dangerous, but UVA can also cause damage.

Upon penetrating the atmosphere and being absorbed by biological tissues, UV radiation damages protein and DNA molecules at the surfaces of all living things. (This damage is what occurs when you get a sunburn.) If the full amount of UV radiation falling on the stratosphere reached Earth's surface, it is doubtful that any life could survive. We are spared the more damaging effects from UV rays because most UV radiation (more than 99%) is absorbed by ozone in the stratosphere. For that reason, stratospheric ozone is commonly referred to as the **ozone shield** (Fig. 19–29).

However, even the small amount (less than 1%) of UVB radiation that does reach us is responsible for sunburns and more than 700,000 cases of skin cancer and precancerous ailments per year in North America as well as for damage to plant crops and other life-forms. (See Sound Science, "Coping with UV Radiation.")

Formation and Breakdown of the Shield

Ozone is formed in the stratosphere when UV radiation acts on oxygen (O_2) molecules. The high-energy UV radiation first causes some molecular oxygen (O_2) to split apart into free

oxygen (O) atoms, and these atoms then combine with molecular oxygen to form ozone via the following reactions:

$$O_2 + UVB \rightarrow O + O \qquad (1)$$

$$O + O_2 \rightarrow O_3 \qquad (2)$$

Not all of the molecular oxygen is converted to ozone, however, because free oxygen atoms may also combine with ozone molecules to form two oxygen molecules in the following reaction:

$$O + O_3 \rightarrow O_2 + O_2 \qquad (3)$$

Finally, when ozone absorbs UVB, it is converted back to free oxygen and molecular oxygen:

$$O_3 + UVB \rightarrow O + O_2 \qquad (4)$$

Thus, the amount of ozone in the stratosphere is dynamic. There is an equilibrium due to the continual cycle of reactions of formation (Eqs. 1 and 2) and reactions of destruction (Eqs. 3 and 4). Because of seasonal changes in solar radiation, ozone concentration in the Northern Hemisphere is highest in summer and lowest in winter. Also, in general, ozone concentrations are highest at the equator and diminish as latitude increases—again, a function of higher overall amounts of solar radiation. However, the presence of other chemicals in the stratosphere can upset the normal ozone equilibrium and promote undesirable reactions there.

Halogens in the Atmosphere. Chlorofluorocarbons (CFCs) are a type of halogenated hydrocarbon (see Chapter 22). CFCs are nonreactive, nonflammable, nontoxic organic molecules in which both chlorine and fluorine atoms have replaced some hydrogen atoms. At room temperature, CFCs are gases under normal (atmospheric) pressure, but they liquefy under modest pressure, giving off heat in the process and becoming cold. When they revaporize, they reabsorb the heat and become hot. These attributes led to the widespread use of CFCs (more than 1 million tons per year in the 1980s) for the following applications:

- In refrigerators, air conditioners, and heat pumps as the heat-transfer fluid;
- In the production of plastic foams;
- By the electronics industry for cleaning computer parts, which must be meticulously purified; and
- As the pressurizing agent in aerosol cans.

Rowland and Molina. All of the preceding uses led to the release of CFCs into the atmosphere, where they mixed with the normal atmospheric gases and eventually reached the stratosphere. In 1974, chemists Sherwood Rowland and Mario Molina published a classic paper[10] (for which they were awarded the Nobel Prize in Chemistry in 1995) concluding that CFCs could damage the stratospheric ozone layer through the release of chlorine atoms and, as a result, UV radiation would increase and cause more skin cancer (their story is described in Chapter 2

[10]M. J. Molina and F. S. Rowland, "Stratospheric Sink for Chlorofluoro-Methanes: Chlorine-Atom Catalyzed Distribution of Ozone," *Nature* 249 (1974): 810–812.

SOUND SCIENCE

People living in Chile, Australia, and New Zealand are no strangers to the effects of the thinner ozone shield. UV alerts are given in those parts of the Southern Hemisphere during spring months as lobes of ozone-depleted stratospheric air move outward from the Antarctic. At times, the ozone above those countries can be less than half its normal concentration, which means that greater intensities of UV radiation reach Earth's surface. It is predicted that one out of every three Australians will develop serious and perhaps fatal skin cancer in his or her lifetime.

Even without a thinner ozone layer, UV radiation is a serious problem. Concerned over the rising incidence of skin cancer and cataract surgery in the United States, the EPA, together with the National Oceanic and Atmospheric Administration and the Centers for Disease Control and Prevention, has initiated a new *UV Index* (see the table at the end of the essay). The index takes the form of daily forecasts of UV exposure, issued by the Weather Service for 58 cities. Satellite measurements of stratospheric ozone are combined with other weather patterns. The goal of the index is to remind people of the dangers of UV radiation and to prompt them to take appropriate action to avoid cancer, premature aging of the skin, eye damage, cataracts, and blindness. For at least the next two decades, the dangers will be quite noticeable, ranging from a greater incidence of sunburn to a likely epidemic of malignant melanoma.

Less obvious, but no less important, are the chronic effects of exposure to the Sun. The normal aging of skin—coarse wrinkling, yellowing,

and the development of irregular patches of heavily pigmented and unpigmented skin—is now known to be largely the result of damage from the Sun. This can happen even in the absence of episodes of sunburn. Further, a large proportion of the million cataract operations performed annually in the United States can be traced to UV exposure, another of the chronic effects of this kind of radiation.

The most serious impact of chronic exposure to the Sun is skin cancer; more than 1 million new cases occur each year in the United States, according to the National Cancer Institute. Three types of skin cancer are traced to UV exposure: basal cell carcinoma (BCC), squamous cell carcinoma (SCC), and melanoma. Most of the skin cancers (75%) are BCCs, slow growing and therefore treatable. SCC accounts for about 20% of skin cancers and can also be cured if treated early. However, it metastasizes (spreads away from the source) more readily than BCC and thus is potentially fatal. Melanoma (6%) is the

most deadly form of skin cancer, as it metastasizes easily. Melanoma is often traced to occasional sunburns during childhood or adolescence or to sunburns in people who normally stay out of the sun.

What is an appropriate response to this disturbing information? First, know when UV intensity is greatest (three hours on either side of midday), and take precautions accordingly. Protect your eyes with sunglasses and a hat, and apply sunscreen with a sun protection factor (SPF) rating of 15 or higher during such times. Think twice before considering sunbathing or using tanning beds, and never proceed without sunscreen that is strong enough to prevent sunburn. Always protect children with sunscreen. Their years of potential exposure are many, and their skin is easily burned. And if you detect a patch of skin or a mole that is changing in size or color or that is red and fails to heal, consult a dermatologist for treatment.

UV Index (EPA)

Exposure Category	Index Value	Minutes to Burn for "Never Tans" (Most Susceptible)	Minutes to Burn for "Rarely Burns" (Least Susceptible)
Minimal	0–2	35	>120
Low	3–4	20	>120
Moderate	5–6	12	90
High	8–9	8	55
Very high	10–12	6	40

to illustrate the public-policy life cycle). Rowland and Molina reasoned that, although CFCs would be stable in the troposphere (where they have been found to last 70 to 110 years), in the stratosphere they would be subjected to intense UV radiation, which would break them apart, releasing free chlorine atoms via the following reaction:

$$CFCl_3 + UV \rightarrow Cl + CFCl_2 \qquad (5)$$

Ultimately, all of the chlorine of a CFC molecule would be released as a result of further photochemical breakdown. The free chlorine atoms would then attack stratospheric ozone to form chlorine monoxide (ClO) and molecular oxygen:

$$Cl + O_3 \rightarrow ClO + O_2 \qquad (6)$$

Furthermore, two molecules of chlorine monoxide may react to release more chlorine and an oxygen molecule:

$$ClO + ClO \rightarrow 2Cl + O_2 \qquad (7)$$

Reactions 6 and 7 are called the **chlorine catalytic cycle** because chlorine is continuously regenerated as it reacts with ozone. Thus, chlorine acts as a **catalyst,** a chemical that promotes a chemical reaction without itself being used up in the reaction. Because every chlorine atom in the stratosphere can last from 40 to 100 years, it has the potential to break down 100,000 molecules of ozone. Thus, CFCs are judged to be damaging because they act as transport agents that continuously move chlorine atoms into the stratosphere. The damage persists because the chlorine atoms are removed from the stratosphere only very slowly. Figure 19–30 shows the basic processes of ozone formation and destruction, including recent refinements to our knowledge of those processes that will be explained shortly.

EPA Action. After studying the evidence, the EPA became convinced that CFCs were a threat and, in 1978, banned their

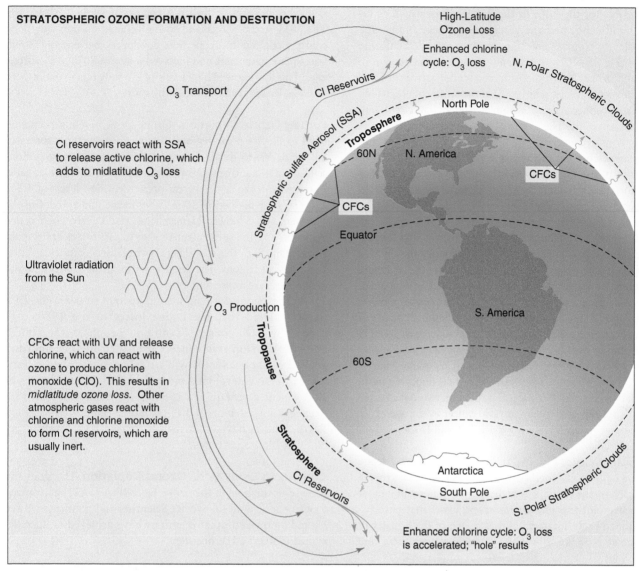

STRATOSPHERIC OZONE FORMATION AND DESTRUCTION

High-Latitude Ozone Loss

Enhanced chlorine cycle: O₃ loss

N. Polar Stratospheric Clouds

O₃ Transport

Cl Reservoirs

North Pole

Stratospheric Sulfate Aerosol (SSA)

Troposphere

60N

N. America

CFCs

Cl reservoirs react with SSA to release active chlorine, which adds to midlatitude O₃ loss

CFCs

Equator

Ultraviolet radiation from the Sun

O₃ Production

Tropopause

CFCs

S. America

60S

CFCs react with UV and release chlorine, which can react with ozone to produce chlorine monoxide (ClO). This results in *midlatitude ozone loss*. Other atmospheric gases react with chlorine and chlorine monoxide to form Cl reservoirs, which are usually inert.

Stratosphere

Cl Reservoirs

Antarctica

South Pole

S. Polar Stratospheric Clouds

Enhanced chlorine cycle: O₃ loss is accelerated; "hole" results

Figure 19–30 Stratospheric ozone formation and destruction. UV radiation stimulates ozone production at the lower latitudes, and ozone-rich air migrates to high latitudes. At the same time, CFCs and other compounds carry halogens into the stratosphere, where they are broken down by UV radiation, to release chlorine and bromine. Ozone is subject to high-latitude loss during winter, as the chlorine cycle is enhanced by the polar stratospheric clouds. Midlatitude losses occur as chlorine reservoirs are stimulated to release chlorine by reacting with stratospheric sulfate aerosol.

use in aerosol cans in the United States. Manufacturers quickly switched to nondamaging substitutes, such as butane, and things were quiet for several years. CFCs continued to be used in applications other than aerosols, however, and skeptics demanded more convincing evidence of their harmfulness.

Atmospheric scientists reasoned that any substance carrying reactive halogens to the stratosphere had the potential to deplete ozone. These substances include halons, methyl chloroform, carbon tetrafluoride, and methyl bromide. Chemically similar to chlorine, bromine also attacks ozone and forms a monoxide (BrO) in a catalytic cycle. Because of its extensive use as a soil fumigant and pesticide, bromine plays a major role in ozone depletion. (Bromine is 16 times as potent as chlorine in ozone destruction.)

The Ozone "Hole." In the fall of 1985, British atmospheric scientists working in Antarctica reported a gaping

"hole" (actually, a serious thinning) in the stratospheric ozone layer over the South Pole. There, in an area the size of the United States, ozone levels were 50% lower than normal. The hole would have been discovered earlier by NASA satellites monitoring ozone levels except that computers were programmed to reject data showing a drop as large as 30% as being due to instrument anomalies. Scientists had assumed that the loss of ozone, if it occurred, would be slow, gradual, and uniform over the whole planet. The ozone hole came as a surprise, and if it had occurred anywhere but over the South Pole, the UV damage would have been extensive. As it is, the limited time and area of ozone depletion there have not apparently brought on any catastrophic ecological events so far.

News of the ozone hole stimulated an enormous scientific research effort. A unique set of conditions was found to be responsible for the hole. In the summer, gases such as nitrogen dioxide and methane react with chlorine monoxide and chlorine to trap the chlorine, forming so-called chlorine reservoirs (Fig. 19–30) and preventing much ozone depletion.

Polar Vortex. When the Antarctic winter arrives in June, it creates a vortex (like a whirlpool) in the stratosphere, which confines stratospheric gases within a ring of air circulating around the Antarctic. The extremely cold temperatures of the Antarctic winter cause the small amounts of moisture and other chemicals present in the stratosphere to form the south polar stratospheric clouds. During winter, the cloud particles provide surfaces on which chemical reactions release molecular chlorine (Cl_2) from the chlorine reservoirs.

When sunlight returns to the Antarctic in the spring, the Sun's warmth breaks up the clouds. UV light then attacks the molecular chlorine, releasing free chlorine and initiating the chlorine cycle, which rapidly destroys ozone. By November, the beginning of the Antarctic summer, the vortex breaks down, and ozone-rich air returns to the area. However, by that time, ozone-poor air has spread around the Southern Hemisphere. Shifting patches of ozone-depleted air have caused UV radiation to increase to 20% above normal in Australia. Television stations there now report daily UV readings and warnings for Australians to stay out of the sun. On the basis of current data, estimates indicate that in Queensland, where the ozone shield is thinnest, two out of three Australians are expected to develop skin cancer by the age of 70. The ozone hole intensified during the 1990s and has leveled off between 22 million and 27 million square kilometers, an area as large as North America (Fig. 19–31). Because severe ozone depletion occurs under polar conditions, observers have been keeping a close watch on the Arctic. The higher temperatures and weaker vortex formation there prevent the severe losses that have become routine in the Antarctic. However, one of the impacts of global climate change is lower stratospheric temperatures, and this is beginning to influence Arctic ozone levels (Chapter 18). The 2011 Arctic winter and spring brought an unusually long cold period, and an ozone hole developed that covered 2 million square kilometers and involved a loss of 80% of the ozone layer. This loss allowed high levels of UV radiation over northern Canada, Russia, and Europe in the spring.

Further Ozone Depletion. Ozone losses have not been confined to Earth's polar regions, though they are most spectacular there. A worldwide network of ozone-measuring stations sends data to the World Ozone Data Center in Toronto, Canada. Reports from the center reveal ozone depletion levels of 3.5% and 6% over the period 2006–2009 in the midlatitudes of the Northern and Southern Hemispheres, respectively. Polar ozone depletion and the subsequent mixing of air masses are responsible for much of this loss. There is virtually no ozone depletion over tropical regions. The good news from the network is that ozone levels are improving.

Is the ozone loss significant to our future? The EPA has calculated that the ozone losses of the 1980s will eventually have caused 12 million people in the United States to develop skin cancers over their lifetime and that 93,000 of these cancers will be fatal. Americans are estimated to have developed more than 900,000 new cases of skin cancer a year in the 1990s. The ozone losses of that decade allowed more UVB radiation than ever to reach Earth. Studies have confirmed increased UVB levels, especially at higher latitudes.

Coming to Grips with Ozone Depletion The dramatic growth of the hole in the ozone layer (Fig. 19–31) galvanized a response around the world. Scientists and politicians in the United States and other countries have achieved treaties designed to avert a UV disaster.

Figure 19–31 Ozone loss and extent of ozone hole. (a) The decline in ozone from 1980 to 2011 is shown in Dobson units for September 21 to October 16 each year (the average amount of ozone in the stratosphere is 300 Dobson units). (b) The size of the ozone hole is plotted for the same time frame, showing the origin of the hole and its leveling off in the last few years. No data were acquired in 1995, shown as a blue column in both plots.

(*Source:* NASA Ozone Hole Watch. http://ozonewatch.gsfc.nasa.gov/. May 15, 2012.)

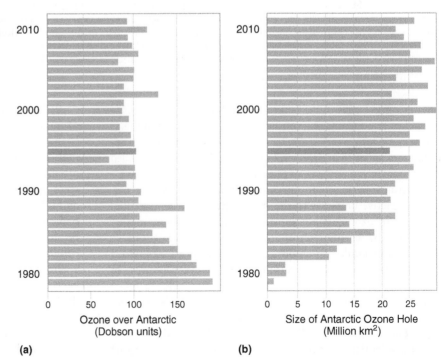

(a) Ozone over Antarctic (Dobson units)

(b) Size of Antarctic Ozone Hole (Million km²)

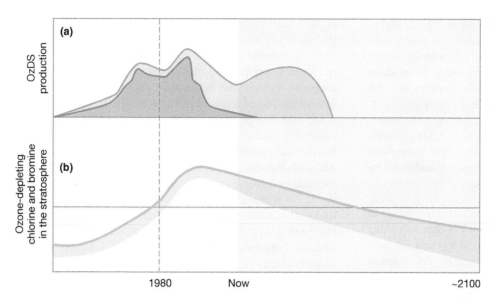

Figure 19–32 Production and presence of ozone-depleting substances in the atmosphere: Past, present, and future. (a) Production of ozone-depleting substances (ODS); CFCs are shown in green, and HCFCs, being used to replace CFCs, are shown in blue. (b) Relative abundances of ozone-depleting chlorine and bromine in the stratosphere. The impact of the Montreal Protocol and its amendments is clear.

(*Source:* UN Environment Program, Scientific Assessment of Ozone Depletion: 2006.)

Montreal Protocol. In 1987, under the auspices of its environmental program, the United Nations convened a meeting in Montreal, Canada, to address ozone depletion. Member nations reached an agreement, known as the **Montreal Protocol,** to scale back CFC production 50% by 2000. All 196 United Nations member countries have ratified the agreement.

The Montreal Protocol was written even before CFCs were so clearly implicated in driving the destruction of ozone and before the threat to Arctic and temperate-zone ozone was recognized. Because ozone losses during the late 1980s were greater than expected, an amendment to the protocol was adopted in June 1990. The amendment required participating nations to phase out the major chemicals destroying the ozone layer by 2000 in developed countries and by 2010 in developing countries. In the face of evidence that ozone depletion was accelerating even more, another amendment to the protocol was adopted in November 1992, moving the *target date for the complete phaseout of CFCs to January 1, 1996.* Timetables for phasing out all of the suspected ozone-depleting halogens were shortened at the 1992 meeting.

Quantities of CFCs were still being manufactured after 1992 to satisfy legitimate demand in the developing countries. However, according to the Montreal Protocol, all manufacturing of CFCs was to have been halted by December 31, 2005. The results of the protocol can be seen clearly in **Figure 19–32,** which shows the time course of production of ozone-depleting substances (ODS) and the abundance of those chemicals in the stratosphere. Ozone depletion continues to occur because the ODS are long-lived in the stratosphere.

Action in the United States. The United States was the leader in the production and use of CFCs and other ODS, with DuPont Chemical Company being the major producer. Following years of resistance, DuPont pledged in 1988 to phase out CFC production by 2000. In late 1991, a company spokesperson announced that, in response to new data on ozone loss, DuPont would accelerate its phaseout. Many of the large corporate users of CFCs (AT&T, IBM, and Northern Telecom, for example) phased out their CFC use by 1994.

The Clean Air Act Amendments of 1990 also address this problem—in Title VI, Protecting Stratospheric Ozone. Title VI is a comprehensive program that restricts the production, use, emissions, and disposal of an entire family of chemicals identified as ozone depleting. For example, the program calls for a phase out schedule for the hydrochlorofluorocarbons (HCFCs), a family of chemicals being used as less damaging substitutes for CFCs until nonchlorine substitutes are available. Halons—used in chemical fire extinguishers—were banned in 1994. The CAAA also regulates the servicing of refrigeration and air-conditioning units.

The Montreal Protocol had its 25th anniversary in 2012. As a result of this and subsequent agreements, CFCs are no longer being produced or used. Substitutes for CFCs are readily available and, in some cases, are even less expensive than CFCs. The most commonly used substitutes are HCFCs, which still contain some chlorine and are scheduled for a gradual phaseout (by 2030). Although they contain chlorine, HCFCs are largely destroyed in the troposphere and are much less capable of destroying stratospheric ozone than CFCs. The most *promising* substitutes are hydrofluorocarbons (HFCs), which contain no chlorine and are judged to have no ozone-depleting potential. They do, however, have significant global warming potential. Because CFCs are potent greenhouse gases, phasing out CFCs and other ozone-depleting substances is helping the efforts to slow down global climate change (Chapter 18). Ironically, HFCs are likely to have a marked influence on global climate change if their use increases in the future.

Other ozone-depleting substances are still a concern. Methyl bromide continues to be produced and released into the atmosphere; the compound is employed as a soil fumigant to control agricultural pests. Under the Montreal Protocol, it was scheduled to be completely phased out by 2005 in the developed countries and 10 years later in the developing countries. In the meantime, bromine is likely to play a greater role in ozone depletion relative to chlorine. Responding to requests from the agricultural industry, the United States has repeatedly received "critical use" exemptions to the ban for use of this ozone-depleting chemical. However, the EPA is phasing out these uses, and the current (2012) level is just 4.6% of 1991 use (1,180 tons vs. 25,500 tons).

Another ODS is nitrous oxide (N_2O). Figure 19–12a shows how nitric oxides are able to destroy ground-level ozone. This can also happen in the stratosphere, where N_2O is broken down into NO_x and the nitrogen oxides deplete ozone there, along with the chlorine and bromine compounds. Even though the current ozone depletion in the stratosphere is largely due to accumulated chlorine and bromine compounds from past releases, nitrous oxide is the predominant anthropogenic ODS currently being released and is expected to remain the largest throughout the 21st century. Oddly, this substance is not yet addressed by the Montreal Protocol and its amendments.[11]

Final Thoughts. The ozone story is a remarkable episode in human history. From the first warnings in 1974 that something might be amiss in the stratosphere because of a practically inert and highly useful industrial chemical, through the development of the Montreal Protocol and the final steps of CFC phaseout, the world has shown that it can respond collectively and effectively to a clearly perceived threat. The ozone layer is expected to recover completely by midcentury in the midlatitudes and a couple of decades later in the polar regions. The scientific community has played a crucial role in this episode, first alerting the world and then plunging into intense research programs to ascertain the validity of the threat. Scientists continue to influence the political process, which has forged a response to the threat. Although skeptics were stressing the uncertainties in our understanding of ozone loss and its consequences, the strong consensus in the scientific community convinced the world's political leaders that action was clearly needed. This is a most encouraging development as we look forward to the actions that must be taken during the 21st century to prevent catastrophic global climate change.

REVISITING THE THEMES

Sound Science

Atmospheric science has come a long way in the past half-century. Some of its triumphs include understanding causes and effects that are operative in photochemical smog, discovering the cleansing role of the hydroxyl radical, tracing the sources of lead and mercury in humans, working out causes and effects in the acid-rain story, and alerting the world to ozone shield destruction. Sound science is increasingly important in measuring ambient pollutant levels and in devising technologies to prevent more pollution. Many scientists have put their reputations and careers on the line as they have fought for policy changes to correct the human and environmental damage they have uncovered.

Sustainability

Air pollution was on an unsustainable track, with industrial smog producing health disasters, photochemical smog making city living intolerable for many, crops and natural ecosystems deteriorating seriously, and the ozone shield being destroyed. Less obvious, but just as important, chronic exposure to air pollutants was responsible for poor health and increased mortality for millions. Are we now back on a more sustainable track? The important indicators would be long-term declines in the following: lead in the environment, annual amounts of emissions of pollutants, acid and sulfate deposition in the Northeast, ambient levels of pollutants, asthma hospitalizations, and locations that are noncompliant. Most of these parameters are moving in the right direction, but much remains to be done. The ozone story represents a sustainable pathway. Levels of ozone-destroying chemicals are now declining, and it is very likely that the ozone layer will be "healthy" by midcentury.

Stewardship

Stewardship means doing the right thing when faced with difficult problems and choices. It is fair to say that our society has responded well in caring for children threatened by high lead levels in their blood and, in general, in taking the costly actions we have documented in this chapter. Further, in addressing acid deposition, we have even shown care for the natural world. The need for stewardship is still very strong, however, and thankfully, there are many in nongovernmental and other organizations, and indeed many in the EPA, that are determined to stay the course and make sure that effective action is taken. Often, though, they have to do battle with industry lobbies and special interests that are concerned with the economic bottom line and that seem unable to embrace the common good represented by effective action to curb pollution.

REVIEW QUESTIONS

1. What naturally occurring cleanser helps to remove pollutants from the atmosphere? Where does it come from? What other mechanisms also act to cleanse the atmosphere of pollutants?

2. Describe the origins of industrial smog, photochemical smog, and atmospheric brown clouds. What are the differences in the cause and appearance of each?

3. What are the seven major primary air pollutants and their sources?

4. What are the major secondary pollutants, and how are they formed?

5. What is the difference between an acid and a base? What is the pH scale?

---

[11]A. R. Ravishankara et al. "Nitrous Oxide (N_2O): The Dominant Ozone-Depleting Substance Emitted in the 21st Century." *Science* 326: 123–125. October 2, 2009.

6. What two major acids are involved in acid deposition? Where does each come from?

7. What impacts does air pollution have on human health? Give the three categories of impact, and distinguish among them.

8. Describe the negative effects of pollutants on crops, forests, and other materials. Which pollutants are mainly responsible for these effects?

9. How can a shift in environmental pH affect aquatic ecosystems? What protects these ecosystems in some regions?

10. What are the criteria pollutants and the National Ambient Air Quality Standards, and how are the standards used?

11. Discuss ways in which the Clean Air Act Amendments of 1990 address the failures of previous legislation.

12. Describe the new Mercury and Air Toxics Standards and the impacts they will have on industry and on human health.

13. What are the major steps being taken to reduce emissions from passenger vehicles? What are the CAFE standards, and how are they changing?

14. How do CAIR and CSAPR address downwind ozone pollution?

15. What has been happening in the United States to reduce acid deposition, and how successful has it been?

16. How is the protective ozone shield formed? What causes its natural breakdown?

17. How do CFCs affect the concentration of ozone in the stratosphere and contribute to the formation of the ozone hole?

18. Describe the international efforts that are currently in place to protect our ozone shield. What evidence is there that such efforts have been effective?

THINKING ENVIRONMENTALLY

1. Motor vehicles release close to half the pollutants that dirty our air. What alternatives might be introduced to encourage a decrease in our use of automobiles and other vehicles with internal combustion engines?

2. How would our pattern of life be different in the absence of the Clean Air Act and its amendments? Write a short essay describing the possibilities.

3. The wind blows across Country A and into Country B. Country A has fossil fuel–burning power plants, but a relatively low level of air pollution. Country B has power plants run by moving water (hydroelectric plants), but a higher level of pollution. What's happening? What could the two countries do to correct the situation? Explain how this pertains to international air-pollution laws.

4. A large amount of air pollution is attributed to manufacturing. Some would argue that it is not technologically possible, or economically efficient, to eliminate this pollution. How would you respond to this argument?

5. What arguments might the auto and utility industries present to delay regulatory action on particulates and ozone? How would health officials respond to their arguments?

MAKING A DIFFERENCE

1. At all costs, avoid burning trash in your yard. It's illegal in many places and can lead to birth defects, cancers, and lung diseases.

2. Check your home heating system. Simple wood smoke contains fine particles that are associated with serious negative health effects. The tiny size of these pollutants allows them to be easily inhaled, traveling deep into your lungs where they can cause respiratory and cardiovascular problems, including premature death. Woodstoves, fireplaces, and other wood-burning devices put out hundreds of times more air pollution than other sources of heat such as natural gas, propane, oil, and electricity.

3. Discuss air-pollution issues with your employer. Many employers are realizing the benefits of considering air quality issues. Green travel plans, alternative-powered vehicles, and the provision of cycling facilities are just three ways employers can help to reduce their impacts on air quality, realize a financial saving, and maintain a healthy workforce.

4. If you live in an urban area, take advantage of public transportation. It helps ease urban congestion as well as atmospheric conditions in the area.

5. When you buy a new car, consider purchasing a hybrid-electric or an all-electric vehicle.

MasteringEnvironmentalScience®

Go to **www.masteringenvironmentalscience.com** for practice quizzes, Pearson eText, videos, current events, and more.

PART SIX

Stewardship for a Sustainable Future

Denver, Colorado. As this view from Ferril Lake in City Park shows, Denver's setting, with the snow-capped Rockies to the west, makes it a very attractive place to live. The "Mile High City" is considered one of the most livable cities in America.

CHAPTER 23
Sustainable Communities and Lifestyles

HOW WILL WE SHAPE a sustainable future? In previous chapters, we discussed many issues that need to be addressed and resolved if we are indeed to achieve a sustainable relationship with the environment. In Chapter 23, the last one of the book, we explore one of the most difficult problems faced by every nation today: promoting livable and sustainable communities. With half of humanity now living in cities, urbanization is an irresistible trend, particularly in the developing world, where 95% of urban population growth is occurring. There, one of the most profound challenges is the slums and shantytowns that receive so many migrants from the countryside. How can the people living under such deplorable conditions be brought into the mainstream of a country's economy and achieve a sustainable well-being?

THERE ARE MANY CHALLENGES in the developed countries as well. How can these countries reverse the urban blight that plagues many older cities, dooming so many to second-class citizenship? How should both developed and developing countries deal with the urban sprawl that spreads out from cities into the countryside, consuming prime agricultural land and wildlife habitat?

IN THIS PART SIX, we explore answers to these questions. We consider examples of cities moving in a sustainable direction. We also look at some of the work being done by organizations that are grappling with the question of sustainability. Finally, we look at the vital, but difficult, task of adopting lifestyles that embrace the stewardship values capable of shaping a sustainable future. The outcome is uncertain, but we know enough now to be able to point in a sustainable and stewardly direction.

CHAPTER 23

Sustainable Communities and Lifestyles

Atlanta, Georgia

LEARNING OBJECTIVES

1. **Urban Sprawl:** Explain the connections between urban sprawl, car dependency, and highway construction; examine the ways in which "smart growth" can prevent further urban sprawl.

2. **Urban Blight:** Summarize the factors leading to urban blight in older cities of the developed world; describe the reasons why cities of the developing world are also experiencing urban blight and vast slums.

3. **Moving Toward Sustainable Communities:** Examine the steps that can make cities more livable and attractive and even make them more ecologically sustainable than the suburbs.

4. **Lifestyles and the Common Good:** Evaluate some good things that can happen to move our society toward greater sustainability, and include an assessment of lifestyle options open to people who want to be responsible stewards.

HE WORD *BELTLINE* conjures up images of a megalane highway that runs around the outskirts of a major metropolitan area, facilitating commuting and stimulating a ring of industries, all of which guarantees that not long after such a highway is built, it will become congested. Atlanta, Georgia, has such a belt, Interstate Route 285, a notorious 10-lane highway built at first to allow through traffic to avoid the city, but now heavily used by commuters between the expanding suburbs and the corporations that have located along the highway. This is the Atlanta Beltway. The **Atlanta BeltLine** (http://beltline.org) is something else altogether, an ambitious makeover of an abandoned rail and industrial corridor that loops around the heart of Atlanta, well inside the Beltway (see photo above). One writer has called it "the country's most ambitious smart growth project."[1]

We'll talk about what smart growth means later, but this project is a remarkable visionary effort that will provide parks, trails, transit system, brownfields remediation, revitalization of distressed city neighborhoods, and much more. The BeltLine loop will be linked by

Martin Luther King Jr.'s birth house in the Old Fourth Ward, on the east side of the BeltLine.

[1]Kaid Benfield. "The Atlanta BeltLine: The Country's Most Ambitious Smart Growth Project." *Natural Resources Defense Council Switchboard.* July 26, 2011. http://switchboard.nrdc.org/blogs/kbenfield/the_countrys_most_ambitious_sm.html. February 29, 2012.

Figure 23–1 Historic Fourth Ward Park. This park, one of the new features of the Atlanta BeltLine, has replaced a drab urban landscape with a mix of green space, lakes, jogging paths, and playgrounds.

a 22-mile trail system that will include pedestrian-friendly rail-based transit segments, with spur segments that will extend into neighborhoods and existing parks and trails around the BeltLine. The east side of the BeltLine connects with the Old Fourth Ward, a neighborhood that includes the birth site of Dr. Martin Luther King, Jr., and Ebenezer Baptist Church, where King and his father served as pastors. Those buildings are now part of the Martin Luther King, Jr., National Historic Site. As part of the BeltLine project, the 17-acre Historic Fourth Ward Park has recently been completed. It has dramatically transformed a blighted neighborhood into a lovely public space connected to a small lake (Fig. 23–1).

HISTORY. The "Belt Line" was originally a loop of tracks that provided rail transportation to local industry and commerce in post–Civil War Atlanta. When trucks and highways came on the scene, most of the rail tracks were abandoned. The new BeltLine concept was the brainchild of Georgia Tech graduate student Ryan Gravel, who, in 1999, proposed a new transit system that would link the inner city neighborhoods. Gravel's concept quickly attracted grassroots attention, and soon the BeltLine plan included parks, trails, affordable housing, and neighborhood renewal. Public support grew as more and more civic organizations enthusiastically endorsed the BeltLine plan. Input from more than 10,000 citizens helped craft the first five-year work plan, and with funding from private and public sectors, work began in 2006. The total price tag is estimated at

$2.8 billion, but considering the potential benefits for the city of Atlanta, that seems like a bargain.

FUTURE. In concept, the Atlanta BeltLine will create:

- 2,000 acres of parks, all linked by the multi-use trail and transit loop
- 33 miles of continuous trails
- a 22-mile light rail transit system that will connect to Atlanta's regional transit network
- the cleanup and redevelopment of 1,100 acres of contaminated brownfield sites
- 5,600 units of workforce housing
- 30,000 permanent jobs and thousands of temporary construction jobs
- a $20 billion increase in the city's tax base over the next 25 years
- the connection to and renewal of some 40 city neighborhoods

Many obstacles remain before Atlanta BeltLine reaches completion. Some key right-of-way parcels of land must be acquired for the transit system, and much of the funding is uncertain. It is now in the hands of Atlanta BeltLine, Inc., a body created by the city to oversee implementation of the project; Atlanta BeltLine Partnership is a sister organization responsible for fundraising and outreach. Several parks and pieces of the trails have been built, and master plans have been completed for 10 segments of land the BeltLine comprises. There is no doubt that the Atlanta BeltLine will be years in the making, but when it is finished, it will represent a monumental improvement in urban Atlanta, making the city more livable and viable. Atlanta, with its BeltLine, joins a bevy of cities intent on transforming unused and blighted neighborhoods into showplaces of urban renewal: New York's High Line (illustrated on the cover of this text), Chicago's Millennium Reserve, Boston's Public Market, Los Angeles' River of Dreams, and Seattle's waterfront, among others.

Our objective in this chapter is first to show how urban sprawl and urban blight are related and how they can be remedied. Then we will consider the global and national efforts being undertaken to forge sustainable cities and communities. Finally, we will look at some ethical concerns and personal lifestyle issues as we consider the urgent needs of people and the environment in this new millennium.

23.1 Urban Sprawl

What is urban sprawl? Sprawl's signature manifestation is a far-flung urban-suburban network of low-density residential areas, shopping malls, industrial parks, and other facilities loosely laced together by multilane highways. The word *sprawl* is used because the perimeters of the city have simply been extended outward into the countryside,

one development after the next, with little plan as to where the expansion is going and no notion as to where it will stop. Almost everywhere we go near urban areas, we are confronted by farms and natural areas giving way to new subdivisions being built, new highways being constructed, and old roadways being upgraded and expanded (Fig. 23–2). In fact, cars and sprawl are codependent; they need each other!

Figure 23–2 New-highway construction. The hallmark of development over the past several decades has been the construction of new highways, which, however, have only fed the environmentally damaging car-dependent lifestyle.

Figure 23–3 The integrated city. Before the widespread use of automobiles, cities had an integrated structure. A wide variety of small stores and offices on ground floors, with residences on upper floors, placed everyday needs within walking distance. This scene is from a historic section of Philadelphia.

The Origins of Urban Sprawl

Until the end of World War II, a relatively small percentage of people owned cars. Cities had developed in ways that allowed people to meet their needs by means of the transportation that was available—mainly, walking. Every few blocks had small groceries, pharmacies, and other stores as well as professional offices integrated with residences. Often, buildings had stores at the street level and residences above (Fig. 23–3). Schools were scattered throughout the city, as were parks for outdoor recreation or relaxation. Walking distances were generally short, and bicycling made going somewhere even more convenient. For more specialized needs, people boarded public transportation—electric trolleys, cable cars, and buses—that took them from neighborhoods to the "downtown" area, where big department stores, specialty shops, and offices were located. Public transportation did not change the compact structure of cities, because people

still needed to walk to the transit line. At the outer ends of the transit lines, cities gave way abruptly to natural areas and farms, which provided most of the food for the city. The small towns and villages surrounding cities—the original suburbs—were compact for the same reasons and mainly served farmers in the immediate area. At the end of World War II, this pattern began to change dramatically.

Despite the many advantages of urban life, many people found cities less-than-pleasant places to live. Especially in industrial cities, poor housing, inadequate sewage systems, inadequate refuse collection, pollution from home furnaces and industry, and generally congested, noisy conditions were common. Hence, many people had the desire—the "American dream"—to live in their own house, on their own piece of land, away from the city.

Suburbs. Because of the massive production of war materiel, consumer goods were in short supply during World War II. As a result, when the war ended, there was a pent-up demand for consumer goods. When mass production of cars resumed at the end of the war, people flocked to buy them. With private cars, people were no longer restricted to living within walking distance of their workplaces or transit lines. They could move out of their cramped city flats and into homes of their own outside the city. Their cars would allow them to drive back and forth easily to their jobs, shopping, recreation, and so on.

Housing Boom. Returning veterans and the accompanying baby boom created a housing demand that rapidly exhausted the existing inventory. Developers responded quickly to the demand for private homes. They bought farmlands and natural areas outside the cities and put up houses. The government aided this trend by providing low-interest mortgages through the Veterans Administration and the Federal Housing Administration, and interest payments on mortgages and local property taxes were made tax deductible (rent was not). These financial factors meant that, for the first time in history, making monthly payments on one's own home in the suburbs was cheaper than paying rent for equivalent or less living space in the city.

Thus, the mushrooming development around cities did not proceed according to any plan; rather, it happened wherever developers could acquire land (Fig. 23–4). No governing body existed to devise—much less enforce—an overall plan. Cities were usually surrounded by a maze of more or less autonomous local jurisdictions (towns, villages, townships, and counties). Local governments were quickly thrown into the catch-up role of trying to provide schools, sewers, water systems, other public facilities, and, most of all, roads to accommodate the uncontrolled growth. Local zoning laws kept residential and commercial uses separate. It became more difficult to walk to a grocery store or an office.

Rust Belt. Pittsburgh, Cleveland, Youngstown, Gary—these and many other cities of the Midwest can be counted as full-fledged representatives of what has been called the **Rust Belt.** Once known as the "Foundry of the Nation," these cities and their outskirts had specialized in heavy manufacturing of industrial and consumer products up to the mid-20th

Figure 23–4 Urban sprawl. Prime land is being sacrificed for development around most U.S. cities and towns. The locations of developments are determined more by the availability of land than by any overall urban planning. Here we see sprawl surrounding the fastest-growing major city in the United States: Las Vegas, Nevada.

century. Then a combination of factors contributed to a decline in the Rust Belt: the migration of manufacturing to southern states where labor was less costly, the globalization of trade that gave foreign manufacturers with their far lower labor costs access to U.S. markets, the expansion of free trade agreements, and the outsourcing of jobs and factories because of these two developments. The result was a wholesale loss of the economic foundations of cities of the Rust Belt during the latter half of the 20th century, and this loss added to the mass migration of people from the cities to the suburbs. The term "Rust Belt" is a consequence of the all-too-common images of rusting and crumbling buildings and factories (**Fig. 23–5**).

Highways. The influx of commuters into previously rural areas soon resulted in traffic congestion, creating a need for new and larger roads. To raise money to build and expand highways, Congress passed the Highway Revenue Act of 1956, which created the **Highway Trust Fund**. This

legislation placed a tax on gasoline and earmarked the revenues to be used exclusively for building new roads.

Ironically, the Highway Trust Fund perpetuates development. A new highway not only alleviates existing congestion, but also encourages development at farther locations, because *time*, not *distance*, is the limiting factor for commuters. (When people describe how far they live from work, it is almost always put in terms of minutes, not distance.) The average person is willing to spend 20 to 40 minutes each way on a daily commute. With cars and expressways, people can live many miles from work and still get there in an acceptable amount of time.

Vicious Cycle. New highways that were intended to reduce congestion actually fostered the development of open land and commuting by more drivers from more distant locations (**Fig. 23–6**). Soon traffic conditions became as congested as ever. Average commuting distance has doubled since 1960, but average commuting time has remained about the same. The increase in commuting distance, however, requires more fuel, which generates more money for the Highway Trust Fund. Thus, the whole process is repeated in a continuous

(a)

(b)

Figure 23–6 The new-highway traffic-congestion cycle.
(a) Growing traffic congestion creates the need for new and upgraded highways.
(b) However, upgraded highways encourage development in more distant locations, thus creating more traffic congestion and, hence, the need for more highways.

Figure 23–5 Rust Belt image. This abandoned factory is symbolic of many such relics of the heavy manufacturing that once took place in large midwestern cities.

TABLE 23–1 Decline in Population of American Cities, 1950–2009

City	Population (thousands)						Percent Change, 1950–2009
	1950	1970	1990	2000	2005	2009	
Baltimore, MD	950	905	736	651	640	637	–33
Boston, MA	801	641	574	589	597	645	–19
Buffalo, NY	580	463	328	293	278	270	–53
Cleveland, OH	915	751	505	478	450	431	–53
Detroit, MI	1,850	1,514	1,028	951	921	911	–51
Minneapolis, MN	522	434	368	383	375	385	–26
Philadelphia, PA	2,072	1,949	1,586	1,517	1,460	1,547	–26
St. Louis, MO	857	662	396	348	353	357	–58
Washington, DC	802	757	607	572	582	600	–25
U.S. population (millions)	151	218	249	281	296	307	+103

Source: Data from Population Division, U.S. Bureau of the Census, 2012.

cycle. As a result, government policy, as an unintended consequence, helped support and promote sprawl.

Residential developments are inevitably followed (or sometimes led) by shopping malls, industrial parks, big-box stores, and office complexes. These commercial centers are usually situated in such a way that the only possible access to them is by car. This situation, in turn, has only changed the direction of commuting: Whereas, in the early days of suburban sprawl, the major traffic flow was into and out of cities, it is now between suburban centers. Multilane highways connecting suburban centers are perpetually congested with traffic going in both directions.

Exurbs, Too. In broad perspective, then, urban sprawl is a process of **exurban migration**—that is, a relocation of residences, shopping areas, and workplaces from their traditional spots in the city to outlying areas. The populations of many eastern and midwestern U.S. cities, excluding the suburbs, have been declining over the past 60 years as a result of exurban migration and the loss of large-scale manufacturing around Rust Belt cities (Table 23–1). At the same time, the suburban population has increased from 35 million in 1950 to 150 million in 2010, half of the U.S. population. Exurban migration is continuing in a leapfrog fashion as people from older suburbs move to **exurbs** (communities farther from cities than suburbs are).

The "love affair" with cars is not just a U.S. phenomenon: Around the world, in both developed and developing countries, people aspire to own cars and adopt the car-dependent lifestyle. Consequently, urban sprawl is occurring around many developing-world cities as people become affluent enough to own cars. Love of the car-dependent lifestyle, however, is insufficient to make it sustainable. In fact, this lifestyle is at the crux of a number of the unsustainable trends described in earlier chapters.

Measuring Sprawl

A team of researchers from Rutgers University, Cornell University, and Smart Growth America (a nongovernmental

organization) worked for several years on a comprehensive effort to define, measure, and evaluate sprawl and its impacts. The research team labeled sprawl as "the process in which the spread of development across the landscape far outpaces population growth."[2] The team members described four dimensions characterizing sprawl and used them to analyze metropolitan regions in order to create a *sprawl index:*

- Population widely dispersed in low-density development; thus, measure *residential density.*

- Sharply separated homes, stores, and workplaces; thus, measure *neighborhood mix* of these three.

- A network of roads marked by poor connections and huge superblocks that concentrate traffic onto a few routes; thus, measure *accessibility of the street networks.*

- A general lack of well-defined downtowns and activity centers; thus, measure *strength of activity centers and downtowns.*

Each of the preceding four dimensions was standardized numerically so as to give 100 points as the average of the factor; higher means less sprawl, and lower means more. Scores for each factor were combined into a total *sprawl score* that also averaged 100. The team analyzed 83 metropolitan areas, representing almost half of the U.S. population. The results ranged from 14 to 178 (Fig. 23–7), with the Riverside–San Bernardino, California, metropolitan area the most sprawled and New York City the least. The 10 most sprawling metropolitan regions are ranked in Table 23–2. The Smart Growth America authors pointed out that, even though an area ranks higher on the sprawl score, this does not mean that sprawl is not a problem. Each of the four dimensions and the overall score were used to examine a range of travel- and transportation-related outcomes as the authors examined the impacts of sprawl on daily life.

---

[2]Reid Ewing, Rolf Pendall, and Don Chen, *Measuring Sprawl and Its Impact* (Washington, DC: Smart Growth America, 2002). Available at www.smartgrowthamerica.org/research/measuring-sprawl-and-its-impact.

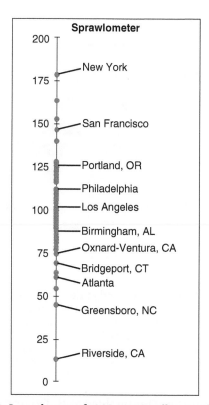

Figure 23–7 Sprawl scores for 83 metropolitan regions. The "sprawlometer" shows rankings of numerous metropolitan areas (each round dot represents a separate area). Low scores mean high sprawl, and vice versa.

(*Source: Measuring Sprawl and Its Impact, 2002*, Smart Growth America.)

TABLE 23–2 Ten Most Sprawling Metropolitan Regions

	Overall Sprawl Index Score	Rank
Riverside–San Bernardino, CA	14.2	1
Greensboro–Winston-Salem–High Point, NC	46.8	2
Raleigh–Durham, NC	54.2	3
Atlanta, GA	57.7	4
Greenville–Spartanburg, SC	58.6	5
West Palm Beach–Boca Raton–Delray Beach, FL	67.7	6
Bridgeport–Stamford–Danbury, CT	68.4	7
Knoxville, TN	68.7	8
Oxnard–Ventura, CA	75.1	9
Forth Worth–Arlington, TX	77.2	10

Source: Reid Ewing, Rolf Pendall, and Don Chen. *Measuring Sprawl and Its Impact* (Washington, DC: Smart Growth America, 2002).

Sprawl and the Recession

The expansion of the suburbs and exurbs in recent years has been remarkable. Builders and developers embarked on the creation of subdivisions of large, expensive homes (McMansions, as they are called), and new buyers were lured by the prospect of ownership of properties that would simply increase in value, as housing had done in the late 1900s and early 2000s. (Between 1997 and 2006, typical American home prices rose by 124%.) They were further encouraged by banks and mortgage companies that extended loans (called subprime mortgages) to many high-risk buyers. A high percentage of these loans were adjustable-rate mortgages (ARMs), in which the interest rates were low for the first few years but in time went up. Many loans required little or no down payment. At the same time, financial firms bought up the subprime mortgages and used these to offer securities to investors. Speculation by buyers and investors was the primary engine that fed this financial bubble.

Bubble Burst. Eventually, the building boom led to a surplus of unsold homes, and housing prices began to decline in 2006. The ARMs were soon reset to higher interest rates, and homeowners were not able to refinance at lower rates. Thousands, and eventually millions, of owners of the new properties defaulted on their loans. Property values declined, and fully one-fourth of all homes in the United States were worth less than their mortgaged amount (called underwater mortgages). Foreclosures soon followed in epidemic numbers. This resulted in the precipitous decline in value of securities backed by the bad loans, and the crisis extended to other sectors of the economy. Job layoffs and business failures followed, and unemployment numbers rose. The country, and indeed the global community, was plunged into a deep recession, with huge investment losses and financial crises that are still reverberating around the global economy.

Recovery. It is significant that areas with the most booming housing markets before the recession are now areas with the most underwater mortgages—regions in California, Florida, and the Southwest.[3] For example, the Las Vegas–Paradise metropolitan area in Nevada has 64% of mortgaged homes underwater; 35% of the homes were built since 2000, and 17% of homes there are now vacant. The unemployment rate there is 14%, and housing prices have dropped 60% from prerecession values. Although recovery from the recession is under way, the housing market is going to take a long time to recover because of the high inventory of foreclosed homes. Most of these homes are in the suburbs—and in sprawling subdivisions.

Environmental Impacts of Urban Sprawl

In addition to its contribution to the decline in home values and the recession, urban sprawl affects the quality of life and the environment in numerous ways. The *environmental impacts* of urban sprawl are many and serious, as the following discussion indicates.

Energy Resources. Shifting to a car-dependent lifestyle has created an ever-increasing demand for petroleum, with many

---

[3]Michael B. Sauter and Charles B. Stockdale. "American Cities with the Most Underwater Mortgages." *24/7 Wall Street*, December 28, 2011.

consequences (Chapter 14). From 1950 to 2010, U.S. oil consumption tripled, while population doubled—a 63% increase in per capita consumption. Transportation accounts for 28% of the U.S. greenhouse gas emissions that are causing climate change.

Air Pollution. Despite improvements in pollution control, many cities still fail to meet desired air quality standards. Vehicles are responsible for an estimated 80% of the air pollution in metropolitan regions. The higher use of gasoline produces greater amounts of carbon dioxide, the most serious anthropogenic greenhouse gas.

Water Resources. All the highways, parking lots, driveways, and other paved areas associated with urban sprawl lead to a substantial increase in runoff, resulting in increased flooding and erosion of stream banks. Also, water quality is degraded by the runoff of fertilizer, pesticides, crankcase oil (the oil that drips from engines), pet droppings, and so on. These nonpoint-source pollutants are the leading cause of water quality problems, according to the EPA.

Loss of Agricultural Land. Perhaps most serious in the long run is the loss of prime agricultural land. In the United States, the National Resources Inventory shows that cropland is declining at a rate of 1.1 million acres per year. Most of the food for cities used to be locally grown on small, diversified family farms surrounding the city. With so many of these farms turned into housing developments, it is estimated that food now travels an average of 1,000 miles (1,500 km) from where it is produced—mostly on huge commercial farms—to where it is eaten. The loss is not just the locally grown produce, but also the social interactions and ties with the farm community.

Loss of Landscapes and Wildlife. New developments are consuming land at an increasing pace. According to the National Resources Inventory, 1.7 million acres a year were developed from 1997 to 2007, compared with 1.4 million acres a year from 1982 to 1992 (Fig. 23–8). The result is the sacrifice of aesthetic, recreational, and wildlife values in metropolitan areas—the very places where they are most important.

The fragmentation of wildlife habitat due to urban sprawl has led to marked declines in many species, ranging from birds to amphibians. A 2005 report[4] found that the 35 fastest-growing metropolitan areas are home to nearly one-third of the nation's rarest and most endangered species of plants and animals.

Impacts of Sprawl on Quality of Life

Urban sprawl can also have major negative impacts on *quality of life* for people in the surrounding areas.

[4]Reid Ewing and John Kostyack, with Don Chen, Bruce Stein, and Michelle Ernst. *Endangered by Sprawl: How Runaway Development Threatens America's Wildlife* (Washington, DC: National Wildlife Federation, Smart Growth America, and NatureServe, January 2005).

Figure 23–8 Conversion of land to developed uses. The buildup of developed land in the United States is shown. From 1982 to 2007, 40 million acres were converted to developed uses from natural lands and farmlands. (*Source:* U.S. Department of Agriculture. 2007 National Resources Inventory, Natural Resources Conservation Service, Washington, DC, and Center for Survey Statistics and Methodology, Iowa State University, Ames, Iowa. July 2009.)

Higher Vehicle Ownership and Driving Mileages

Cars are driven greater distances per person in high-sprawl areas. In Atlanta (sprawl score of 58), for example, daily use per person was 34 miles each day, while in Portland, Oregon (sprawl score of 126), it was only 24 miles each day. In the top 10 sprawl areas, there were 180 vehicles per 100 households, while in the lowest 10, there were 162. Chauffeuring kids to and from school or after-school activities requires more driving in sprawl areas. As these values for miles driven and cars owned aggregate over many metropolitan areas, they add up to millions more miles driven and cars on the road as well as higher gas costs for families. The higher rates of vehicle use also lead to more highway fatalities. In Riverside, California, at the top of the sprawl index, 18 of every 100,000 people die each year in highway accidents. In the eight lowest areas on the index, fewer than eight of 100,000 residents die annually on the highways.

Less Physical Activity and Greater Health Risks. The percentage of commuter trips by mass transit in the 10 highest-sprawl areas was 2% compared with 7% in the 10 lowest-sprawl areas. Similar trends are found for people walking to their workplace. People living in high-sprawl areas drive more, while those in more compact communities walk and take mass transit more. Walking and other moderate physical activities have many health benefits. The study of sprawl and its health effects found a highly significant correlation between the degree of sprawl, on the one hand, and weight, obesity, and high blood pressure, on the other.

Congestion and Higher Costs. There is no difference in commute times between high- and low-sprawl areas. This indicates that moving out to the suburbs or exurbs to get away from traffic congestion does not work. As more people move to the suburbs, the car traffic increases, and the congestion reaches out farther. Thus, metropolitan regions cannot sprawl their way out of congestion. The developments in outlying regions of metropolitan areas also all have to be serviced with schools, sewers, water, electricity, roads, and other infrastructure elements, often forcing county and town budgets (and, therefore, taxes) to escalate. More compact forms of development are less expensive to service.

The Benefits of Urban Sprawl

With all of these undesirable effects of sprawl, one might question why people put up with it. The answer is that people *perceive* that it is better to live in such areas, so they move there. There are benefits to sprawl, and it is important to examine them and compare them with the costs. This comparison was made in a study sponsored by the Federal Transit Administration.[5]

Quality-of-life issues tend to be decisive for most people, and these issues seem to be heavily weighted *in favor of sprawl*. In general, sprawl involves lower-density residential living, larger lot sizes (often 2 acres or more), larger single-family homes, better quality public schools, lower crime rates, better social services, and greater opportunity for participation in local governments. As people move farther out from an urban center, housing costs often decline, and communities tend to be more homogeneous. Given these actual or perceived benefits, it is no wonder that sprawl is the dominant form of growth occurring in major metropolitan areas.

Net Benefits? As we have seen, there is little or no advantage in commute times or traffic congestion and actually greater distances to drive for those in the outlying suburbs and exurbs. With gasoline prices approaching $4 a gallon, the commuting distance exacts a major cost to families (close to $15,000 a year for many suburban regions). Also, the traffic fatality rate is worse because speed alone allows people to drive greater distances and achieve an equivalent commuting time. Several of the perceived benefits of sprawl have serious negative side effects for society as a whole. People move to the exurbs to live in neighborhoods with lower crime rates, to have access to better schools, or to live in more homogeneous communities. In one way or another, these choices are often exclusionary in their effects. The result of thousands of people making these choices is to accentuate the concentration of poorer people in high-density, inner-city, or aging suburban communities.

Common Good? The environmental costs of sprawl are very real, but these are seldom perceived as decisive by the people moving to the sprawling suburbs. These costs are more a matter of the common good, and people tend to make choices based on *personal good* rather than the *common good*. On the whole, most observers who have studied

sprawl and its impacts believe that the costs of sprawl outweigh the benefits. They feel it is worth the effort to bring sprawl under control. The key to controlling sprawl is to provide those quality-of-life benefits that attract people, but to do it without incurring the serious environmental and social costs that are clearly associated with sprawl. This is what "smart growth" intends to do.

Reining in Urban Sprawl: Smart Growth

The way to curtail urban sprawl might appear to be simply to pass laws that bring exurban development under control. Indeed, a number of European countries and Japan have such laws. However, laws cannot be passed without the support of the public. In the United States, the strong sentiment favoring the right of a property owner to develop property as he or she sees fit has made such restrictions, with few exceptions, politically impossible to pass.

Yet there are signs that a sea change is occurring in the attitudes of Americans toward uncontrolled growth. For example, the recently emerged concept of **smart growth** is inviting communities and metropolitan areas to address sprawl and purposely choose to develop in more environmentally sustainable ways. The concept recognizes that some growth will occur and focuses on economic, environmental, and community values that together will lead to more sustainable communities. Table 23–3 presents the basic principles of smart growth. Zoning laws are being changed in many localities, and a new generation of architects and developers is beginning to focus on creating integrated communities, as opposed to disassociated facilities. By directing growth to particular places, smart growth provides protection for sensitive lands. Early indications in the marketplace—the final determining factor—are that the new communities are a great success.

TABLE 23–3 Principles of Smart Growth
Create a range of housing opportunities and choices for people of all income levels.
Create walkable neighborhoods.
Encourage the collaboration of citizens, corporations, businesses, and municipal bodies within communities.
Foster distinctive, attractive communities with a strong sense of place, setting standards for development that respond to community values.
Make development decisions predictable, fair, and cost effective.
Mix land uses to provide a more attractive and healthy place to live.
Preserve open space, farmland, natural beauty, and critical environmental areas.
Provide a variety of transportation choices.
Strengthen and direct development toward existing communities (called *infilling*).
Take advantage of compact building design instead of conventional land-hogging development.

[5]Robert W. Burchell, George Lowenstein, William R. Dolphin, and Catherine C. Galley. *The Costs of Sprawl—2000*. Washington, DC: National Academies Press, 2002.

Initiatives. Smart-growth initiatives are appearing on the ballot in many states and municipalities. These initiatives involve several key strategies:

1. **Setting boundaries on urban sprawl.** Oregon led the way in passing a land-use law in the 1970s that requires every city to set a boundary beyond which urban growth is prohibited. The boundary is a line permitting expected future growth—but controlled growth. Portland has had great success with this strategy, and today it is a highly desirable place to live and work.

2. **Saving open space.** The best way to preserve open space is to own it or the development rights to it, and states are enacting programs to acquire crucial remaining open spaces. For example, in 2004 (before the recession), voters approved 162 state and local ballot measures to provide $4.1 billion for the protection of natural areas.

3. **Developing existing urban space.** In 1997, Maryland's General Assembly passed the Smart Growth and Neighborhood Conservation initiative, which includes measures to channel new growth to community sites where key infrastructure is already in place. Abandoned and brownfield sites in metropolitan areas are already well served with roads, electricity, water, and sewerage and can be developed into communities with new homes, workplaces, and shopping areas.

4. **Creating new towns.** A key to developing sustainable communities is changing zoning laws to allow stores, light industries, professional offices, and higher-density housing to be integrated. Affordable and attractive housing can be created around industrial parks and shopping malls for the people who work and shop in those places. Safe bicycle and pedestrian access can be provided between residential areas and workplaces. Reston, Virginia; Columbia, Maryland; and Valencia, California, were established as self-contained towns along these lines in the 1960s, and they are still highly desirable as business and residential locations. Fairfax County, Virginia (next to Washington, DC), by contrast, is now almost 100% covered by sprawl-type development. It is estimated that if Fairfax had pursued smart-growth policies, the county would still be 70% open space and would be far less congested and less polluted.

Raiding the Fund. In addition to the foregoing key strategies, there have been successful moves to break the cycle created by the Highway Trust Fund, by allowing revenues to be used for purposes other than the construction of more highways. People live too far from where they work, and there are often better ways to get to work than driving automobiles. The first significant inroad was made in 1991 with the passage of the Intermodal Surface Transportation Efficiency Act (ISTEA). Under this act, a substantial amount of the money levied by the Highway Trust Fund was eligible to be used for other modes of transportation, including cycling, walking, and mass transit. The objectives of ISTEA were extended with the passage of the Transportation Equity Act for the Twenty-First Century (TEA–21) in 1998. Then the Safe, Accountable, Flexible, Efficient Transportation Equity Act—A Legacy for Users (SAFETEA–LU) was passed in 2005. This act authorized $244 billion for 2005–2009 for the highway and transit programs, a significant increase over TEA–21 funding; mass transit has received 18% of these funds.

However, the Highway Trust Fund is not bringing in enough to sustain this level; SAFETEA-LU has expired, and the programs have been continued through short-term extensions, at lower funding levels. A new transportation act is long overdue. However, the economic stimulus package (the **American Recovery and Reinvestment Act of 2009**) contained $64 billion for roads, bridges, rail, and transit, and mass transit has been receiving much of this money, given President Obama's expressed desire to promote projects that will counteract urban sprawl and reduce our dependence on oil.

Highway Trust Fund monies are only part of the reason for the resurgence of mass transit; the high gasoline costs of 2008 drove many commuters to buses, trains, and subways, and mass transit ridership has remained high. Mass transit issues fared well in the 2008 election, with voters approving initiatives that would infuse $75 billion into transportation systems.

Fixing Suburbia. The recession and its accompanying impacts on suburbs have created a unique opportunity to redevelop suburbs in more desirable patterns. Two recent books provide some key guidelines for repairing suburban sprawl.[6] A recent survey[7] found that most Americans prefer a walkable neighborhood to a large house, especially the Baby Boomers (largely empty nesters now) and many Gen Y people (20s and 30s) who are looking for places where they can socialize. The books *Retrofitting Suburbia* by Ellen Dunham-Jones and June Williamson and *Sprawl Repair Manual* by Galina Tachieva are for planners and developers, providing specific examples of what can be done to abandoned malls and poorly designed suburban streets and roadways to convert them to more desirable neighborhoods with places to walk and village centers and greenery. For example, a 100-acre mall in Lakewood, Colorado, has been replaced with 22 blocks of green buildings and public streets, creating a real downtown for the suburban town. The authors of both books state that sprawl has many faces, and some of them are more amenable to makeover than others.

Another key strategy for reducing sprawl is to revitalize the cities. This means coping with urban blight.

23.2 Urban Blight

In the developed world, the other end of the exurban migration is the city from which people are moving. *Exurban migration* is the major factor underlying urban decay,

---

[6]Ellen Dunham-Jones and June Williamson. *Retrofitting Suburbia: Urban Design Solutions for Redesigning Suburbs.* Hoboken, NJ. John Wiley & Sons, Inc. 2011. Galina Tachieva. *Sprawl Repair Manual.* Washington, DC. Island Press. 2010.

[7]Belden Russonello and Stewart LLC. "The 2011 Community Preference Survey: What Americans Are Looking for When Deciding Where to Live." March 2011. www.Brspoll.com. Washington, DC.

or blight, that has occurred over the past 60 years. A completely different set of factors is responsible for urban blight in the developing world. In that case, people are moving *to* the cities at a rate that far exceeds the capacity of the cities to assimilate them. The result is urban slums that surround virtually every city in the poorer developing countries. UN–HABITAT estimates that more than 800 million people live in urban slums in the developing world, often under conditions so squalid that they defy description.

We look first at urban blight in the developed countries, with the United States as our focus.

Economic and Ethnic Segregation

Historically, U.S. cities have included people with a wide diversity of economic and ethnic backgrounds. However, moving to the suburbs required some degree of affluence—at least the ability to manage a down payment and mortgage on a home and the ability to buy and drive a car. Therefore, exurban migration often excluded the poor, the elderly, and persons with disabilities. The poor were mostly minorities because a history of racial discrimination had kept them from good education and well-paying jobs and because many had recently immigrated to the United States and were still at the bottom of the social order. Discriminatory lending practices by banks and dishonest sales practices by real estate agents (called *redlining*) kept minorities out of the suburbs even when money was not a factor. Civil rights laws passed in the 1960s made such practices illegal, but there is evidence that they still persist in various forms. Even without racial segregation, economic segregation continues to exist and has even intensified.

In short, exurban migration and urban sprawl have led to segregation of the population into groups sharing common economic, social, and cultural backgrounds. Moving into the new suburban and exurban developments (often labeled *white flight*) were the economically advantaged, whereas many areas of the cities and older suburbs were effectively abandoned to the economically depressed, who in large part were ethnic minorities, persons with disabilities, and the elderly (Fig. 23–9).

The Vicious Cycle of Urban Blight

Affluent people moving to the suburbs set into motion a vicious cycle of exurban migration and urban blight that continues today. To understand how this downward cycle occurs, we must note several points about local governments. First, local (usually city or county) governments are responsible for providing public schools, maintaining local roads, furnishing police and fire protection, collecting and disposing of refuse, maintaining public water and sewers, and providing welfare services, libraries, and local parks. Second, a local government's major source of revenue to pay for these services is local property taxes, a yearly tax proportional to the market value of the property and home or other buildings on it. If property values increase or decrease, property taxes are adjusted accordingly. Third, in most cases, the central city is

(a)

(b)

Figure 23–9 Segregation by exurban migration. Exurban migration, the driving force behind urban sprawl, has also led to segregation of the population along economic and racial lines. In (a) an area of suburbia and (b) an area of inner-city Baltimore, you see the contrast.

a government jurisdiction that is separate from those of the surrounding suburbs.

Economic Dysfunction. Because of the preceding three characteristics of local government, exurban migration has the following consequences: By the economics of supply and demand, property values in the suburbs escalate with the influx of affluent newcomers. Thus, suburban jurisdictions enjoy increasing tax revenues with which they can improve and expand local services. At the same time, property values in the city decline because of decreasing demand. The lower property taxes create a powerful disincentive toward maintaining property. Many properties end up being abandoned by the owner for nonpayment of taxes. The city "inherits" such abandoned properties, but they are a liability rather than a source of revenue (Fig. 23–10). The declining tax revenue resulting from falling property values is referred to as an **eroding**, or **declining, tax base**, and it has been a serious handicap for most U.S. cities since the exurban migration started in the late 1940s. Adding to the problem is the fact that many immigrants tend to settle in the inner cities, drawn there by ethnic bonds and the hope

Figure 23–10 Abandoned buildings. Many cities' ills are caused by too *little* population, not too much. When the exurban migration causes a city's population to drop below a certain level, businesses are no longer supported. The result is abandonment and urban blight. Shown here is a section of Baltimore only a few blocks from the redeveloped Inner Harbor seen in Figure 23–11.

Figure 23–11 Inner Harbor, Baltimore. High population densities help make a city, not destroy it. Redeveloping key areas of cities with heterogeneous mixtures of office buildings, shopping, restaurants, residences, and recreational facilities—all of which attract people—has helped to bring new life back into the cities.

of employment. The result is that many inner-city dwellers require public assistance of one sort or another. Thus, besides the declining tax revenues, cities bear a disproportionate burden of welfare obligations.

The eroding tax base forces city governments to cut local services, increase the tax rate, or, generally, both. Hence, the property tax on a home in a city is often two to three times greater than that on a comparably priced home in the suburbs. At the same time, schools, refuse collection, street repair, libraries, parks, and other services and facilities deteriorate from neglect. Increasing taxes and deteriorating services cause yet more people to leave the city and become part of urban sprawl, even if the car-dependent lifestyle is not their primary choice. However, it is still only the relatively more affluent individuals who can make this move; thus, the whole process of exurban migration, a declining tax base, deteriorating real estate, and worsening schools and other services and facilities is perpetuated in a vicious cycle. This downward spiral of conditions is referred to as **urban blight** or **urban decay**. It is made worse by the manufacturing losses in Rust Belt cities.

Economic Exclusion of the Inner City. The exurban migration includes more than just individuals and families: The flight of affluent people from the city removes the purchasing power necessary to support stores, professional establishments, and other enterprises. Faced with declining business, merchants and practitioners of all kinds are forced either to go out of business or to move to new locations in the suburbs. Either way, vacant storefronts are the result, and people remaining in the city lose convenient access to goods, services, and, most importantly, jobs because each business also represents employment opportunities.

Unemployment rates run at 50% or more in depressed areas of inner cities, and the jobs that do exist are mostly at the minimum wage. By contrast, the new jobs being created are in the shopping malls and industrial parks in the outlying areas, which are largely inaccessible to inner-city residents

for lack of public transportation. Therefore, not only are people who remain in the inner city poor from the outset, but also the cycle of exurban migration and urban decay has now led to their economic exclusion from the mainstream. As a result, drug dealing, crime, violence, and other forms of deviant social behavior are widespread in such areas.

To be sure, in the past two decades, many cities have redeveloped core areas. Shops, restaurants, hotels, convention and entertainment centers, office buildings, residences, and places for walking and relaxing are all combining to bring a new spirit of life and hope, as well as the practical assets of taxes and employment, back into cities (**Fig. 23–11**). This is an encouraging new trend, so far as it goes. However, walk a few blocks in any direction from the sparkling, revitalized core of most U.S. cities, and you will find urban blight continuing unabated.

Urban Blight in Developing Countries

Two million residents of Nairobi, Kenya's capital, live in slums consisting of flimsy shacks made of scrap wood, metal, plastic sheeting, rocks, and mud (**Fig. 23–12**). The slum neighborhoods of Nairobi surround the outskirts of the city. Burning trash and charcoal cooking fires cloud the air, and the lack of sewers adds to the smell. People get water from private companies because the city does not provide water or any other public amenities. There is no land ownership because the settlements are built on public land or on private land where landowners exact high rents. Crime and disease are endemic, and AIDS and tuberculosis spread readily in such slums.

Similar slum neighborhoods can be found around most of the developing-world cities; **UN–HABITAT** estimates that one out of every three people in the developing-world cities lives in slums. Yet in spite of the conditions, the cities are expected to continue growing well into the middle of the century. The continued rapid growth is a function of both natural population growth (which is high in many

Figure 23–12 Shantytown in Nairobi, Kenya. More than half of Nairobi's residents live in such slums, where conditions defy description.

developing countries) and migration into the city from rural areas (Chapters 8 and 9). The economies of rural areas, often based only on subsistence farming, simply do not provide the jobs needed by a growing population. So people move to the cities, where they at least have the hope of employment. The city housing supply is overwhelmed by the influx of migrants, who could not afford the rents even if housing was available. The slums actually represent a great deal of entrepreneurial energy, because the residents build the dwellings and erect their own infrastructure, usually including food stands, coffee shops, barber shops, and, in some cases, schools for their children. Indeed, the slum residents are of necessity amazing entrepreneurs, engaging in a widespread informal economy. The signature of this economy is the umbrella that covers a booth by the side of the road where goods are exchanged or sold—hence the term "umbrella people."[8]

The Needs

The vast slums, or shantytowns, surrounding the cities are a tremendous challenge to the institutional structure of developing countries. Because slum areas are unauthorized, cities rarely provide them with electricity, water, sanitation facilities, and other social amenities. Yet the slums often represent a workforce essential to the city, taking the low-paying jobs that keep the city and its inhabitants functioning. A great need in such neighborhoods is *home security*. People live in fear of bulldozers coming at any time and leveling the shantytown. In Brazil, governments are providing legal status to existing slums (*favelas*), granting lawful titles to the land. Peru has undertaken a huge titling program, giving recognition to some 1 million urban land parcels in a four-year period. Providing this level of security to the inhabitants is often the key to mobilizing further assets, such as acquiring access to credit and negotiating with the city government for utilities or additional services. People will improve their living conditions if they are given the assurance that they can stay where they are.

The people in the shantytowns also need more *jobs*, and again, local governments could provide employment at low cost to accomplish many improvements in their own neighborhoods and elsewhere—collecting trash, building sewers, composting organic wastes, and growing food. Providing *cheap transportation* is another need. People need to get to where the jobs are and could often do so if they had bicycles or could afford to ride public transportation. Perhaps the greatest need of people living in the informal neighborhoods of city slums is *government representation*. Their voices are seldom heard because they are among the poorest and most powerless in a society. They are often plagued by government corruption, wherein nothing gets done unless accompanied by bribes (which these people can ill afford).

In some regions, however, community organizations are emerging to deal with the basic issues of the city slums. People are organizing and demanding their rights as citizens. Shack/Slum Dwellers International (SDI) now represents these communities to institutions like the World Bank and city governments and even held its first international conference in 2006. Change can happen, and people are learning how to make it happen. As cities devote energy and resources to providing the essential services and infrastructure to the informal slums that surround them, they will only be strengthened. The cities, and even the slums, will then become more livable.

23.3 Moving Toward Sustainable Cities and Communities

The environmental consequences of urban sprawl and the social consequences of urban blight are two sides of the same coin. A sustainable future will depend on both reining in urban sprawl and revitalizing cities. The urban blight of cities in the developing world requires deliberate policies to address the social needs of the people flocking to the shantytowns. UN–HABITAT reports that half of the world's people now live in cities, with 3 million people added weekly to developing-world cities. Looking to the future, the only possible way to sustain the global population is by having viable, resource-efficient cities, leaving the countryside for agriculture and natural ecosystems. The key word is *viable*, which means *livable*. No one wants to, or should be required to, live in the conditions that have come to typify urban blight and urban slums.

What Makes Cities Livable?

Livability is a general concept based on people's response to the question "Do you like living here, or would you rather live somewhere else?" Crime, pollution, and recreational, cultural, and professional opportunities, as well as many other social and environmental factors, are summed up in the subjective answer to that question. Although many people assume that the social ills of the city are an outcome of high population densities, crime rates and other problems in U.S. cities have climbed while populations have dwindled as a result of the exurban migration.

[8]Robert Neuwirth. "Global Bazaar: Shantytowns, Favelas and Jhopadpattis Turn Out to Be Places of Surprising Innovation." *Scientific American* 305: 56–63. September 2011.

Figure 23–13 Livable cities. The key to having a livable city is to provide a heterogeneity of residences, businesses, and stores and to keep layouts on a human dimension so that people can meet or conduct business incidentally over coffee in a sidewalk café or stroll on a promenade through an open area. In short, the space is designed for, and devoted to, people. Shown here is Quincy Market, Boston.

Figure 23–14 Car-centered cities. In contrast to what is required for livability, city development of the past several decades has focused on moving and parking cars and creating homogeneity. Note the sterility of parking lots surrounding buildings in the foreground of this photograph of Los Angeles.

Looking at livable cities around the world, we find that the common denominators are

1. Maintaining a high population density;

2. Preserving a heterogeneity of residences, businesses, stores, and shops; and

3. Keeping layouts on a human dimension so that people can meet, visit, or conduct business informally over coffee at a sidewalk café or stroll on a promenade through an open area.

In short, the space is designed for, and devoted to, people (Fig. 23–13). In contrast, city development of the past 60 years has focused on accommodating automobiles and traffic. Two-thirds of the land in cities that have grown up in the era of the automobile is devoted to moving, parking, or servicing cars, and such space is essentially alien to the human psyche (Fig. 23–14). William Whyte, a well-known city planner, remarked, "It is difficult to design space that will not attract people. What is remarkable is how often this has been accomplished."[9]

A Matter of Design. The world's most livable cities are not those with "perfect" auto access between all points. Instead, they are cities that have taken measures to reduce outward sprawl, diminish automobile traffic, and improve access by foot and bicycle in conjunction with mass transit. For example, Geneva, Switzerland, prohibits automobile parking at workplaces in the city's center, forcing commuters to use the excellent public transportation system. Copenhagen bans all on-street parking in the downtown core. Paris has removed 200,000 parking places in the downtown area. Curitiba, Brazil, with a population of 1.6 million, is cited as the most livable city in all of Latin America. The achievement of Curitiba is due almost entirely to the efforts of Jaime

Lerner, who, while serving as mayor for many decades, guided development with an emphasis on mass transit rather than cars. The space saved by not building highways and parking lots has been put into parks and shady walkways, causing the amount of green area per inhabitant to increase from 4.5 square feet in 1970 to 450 square feet today.

Charinkos. In Tokyo, millions of people ride *charinkos*, or bicycles (Fig. 23–15), either all the way to work or to subway stations from which they catch fast, efficient trains to their destination. Tokyo residents own more than 9 million bicycles. By sharply restricting development outside certain city limits, Japan has maintained population densities within cities and along metropolitan corridors that ensure the viability of commuter trains. Japan's cities have maintained a heterogeneous urban structure that mixes small shops, professional offices, and residences in such a way that a large portion of the population meets its needs without cars. In maintaining an economically active city, it is probably no coincidence that street crime, vagrancy, and begging are

Figure 23–15 Bicycles in Tokyo. Most people in Tokyo do not own automobiles and instead ride bicycles or walk to stations from which they take fast, efficient, inexpensive subways to reach their destinations.

---

[9]William H. Whyte. "The Design of Spaces," in *The City Reader*, 3rd ed., Ed. Richard T. LeGates (New York: Routledge, 2003), 432.

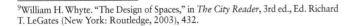

virtually unknown in the vast expanse of Tokyo, despite the seeming congestion.

Bicycles are a growing feature of many cities. In exchange for making special lanes, safe bikeways, and secure parking for bicycles, cities gain a great deal: decreased pollution and congestion and better health for their people because of increased physical activity. Because of its pro-biking policies, the city of Amsterdam in the Netherlands holds the record for large cities in the developed countries; fully 38% of trips within the city are made on bicycles. To be sure, cyclists are at risk of accidents with motor vehicles, but the data show that cities with the highest cycling rates have the best safety records.[10]

Portland. Portland, Oregon, is a pioneering U.S. city that has taken giant steps to curtail automobile use. The first step was to encircle the city with an urban growth boundary, a line outside of which new development was prohibited. Thus, compact growth, rather than sprawl, was ensured. Second, an efficient light-rail and bus system was built, which now carries 45% of all commuters to downtown jobs. (In most U.S. cities, only 10% to 25% of commuters ride public transit systems.) By reducing traffic, Portland was able to convert a former expressway and a huge parking lot into the now-renowned Tom McCall Waterfront Park. Portland is now ranked among the world's most livable cities and has been recognized by SustainLane (see below) as the most sustainable city in the United States.[11]

The Big Dig. Other U.S. cities are discovering hidden resources in their inner core areas. Expressways, which were built with federal highway funds to speed vehicles through the cities, frequently dissected neighborhoods, separating people from waterfronts and consuming existing open space. Now, with federal help, many cities are removing or burying the intruding expressways. Boston, for example, has recently put the finishing touches on the "Big Dig," a $15 billion project that has moved its central freeway below ground, added parks and open space, and reconnected the city to its waterfront (Fig. 23–16). The waterfronts themselves are often the neglected relics of bygone transportation by water and rail. In recent years, cities such as Cleveland, Chicago, San Francisco, and Baltimore have redeveloped their waterfronts, turning rotting piers and abandoned freight yards into workplaces, high-rise residences, and public and entertainment space.

Livable Equals Sustainable. Even though cities are concentrations of energy use, resource use, and pollution, there are certain environmental benefits to urbanization. Decreased auto traffic and a greater reliance on foot and public transportation reduce energy consumption and pollution. If the cities effectively provide the basic infrastructure needs—clean water, solid-waste and sewage disposal, electricity—the economies of scale greatly reduce per capita resource consumption in comparison with suburbs and rural areas. For example, urban populations use half as much electricity

Figure 23–16 Boston, Massachusetts. The Rose Fitzgerald Kennedy Greenway, on land once covered by an elevated expressway, is a series of four parks made up of gardens, plazas, and tree-lined promenades. The "Big Dig" project has revitalized the core city of Boston by replacing the central freeway with an underground tunnel system that allows traffic to flow to and through the city without disrupting city life above.

(*Source:* Rose Fitzgerald Kennedy Greenway Conservancy.)

per capita as those in the suburbs. A number of factors—economic opportunities for women, access to health services, and less need for children's household labor—work to reduce fertility rates in urban populations versus rural populations.

Beyond these basics, housing can be retrofitted with passive solar space heating and heating for hot water. Landscaping can provide cooling (described in Chapter 16). A number of cities are developing vacant or cleared areas into garden plots (Fig. 23–17), and rooftop hydroponic gardens are becoming popular. Such gardens do not make cities agriculturally self-sufficient, but they add to urban livability, provide an avenue for recycling compost and nutrients removed from sewage, give a source of fresh vegetables, and

---

[10]Gary Gardner. "Power to the Pedals." *World Watch* 23: 6–11. July/August 2010.
[11]www.sustainlane.com/us-city-rankings.

Figure 23–17 Urban gardens. Urban garden plots on formerly vacant lots in Philadelphia. Urban gardening is becoming recognized as having sociological, economic, environmental, and aesthetic benefits.

have the potential to generate income for many unskilled workers. All of these factors have the important added advantage of reducing the per capita use of fuel and energy, important in the battle against climate change.

SustainLane. In the United States, the 50 most populous cities have been ranked for sustainability by the organization SustainLane. The organization's Web site is a great source of advice, personal accounts, local business and product reviews, and news about sustainability lifestyles. Its most prominent product, however, is a ranking of cities based on 16 criteria, including transit ridership, street congestion, air and water quality, green building, local food and agriculture, energy and climate change, and green economy. At the top of the ranking was Portland, Oregon, followed by San Francisco, Seattle, Chicago, New York, Boston, Minneapolis, Philadelphia, Oakland, and Baltimore. At the bottom were Las Vegas (#47), Tulsa, Oklahoma City, and Mesa. The goal of the process has been "not to shame, but to inspire, to facilitate the sharing of best practices, and to see all cities continually raise the bar on their efforts," in the words of SustainLane CEO James Elsen.[12]

To the Point. The preceding discussion of urban issues may seem to have strayed far from nature and environmental science. However, there is a close connection between the two: The decay of our cities is hastening the degradation of our larger environment. As the growing human population spreads outward from the old cities in developed countries, we are co-opting natural lands and prime farmlands and ratcheting up the rate of air pollution and greenhouse gases. Similarly, as increasing numbers in the developing world stream *into* the cities, they are degrading the human and social resources that are vital to all environmental issues. Thus, without the creation of sustainable human communities, there is little chance for the sustainability of the rest of the biosphere.

By making urban areas more appealing and economically stable, we not only improve the lives of those who choose to remain or must remain in cities, but also spare surrounding areas. Our parks, wildernesses, and farms will not be replaced by exurbs and shopping malls, but rather will be saved for future generations. In the past decade, some remarkable developments have begun to accelerate the movement toward building sustainable communities. We turn to these developments now.

Sustainable Communities

Recall that the 1992 UN Conference on Environment and Development (UNCED) created the Commission on Sustainable Development (Chapter 1). This new body was given the responsibility of monitoring and reporting on the implementation of the agreements that were made at UNCED—in particular, those related to sustainability. Following Agenda 21, one of the accords signed at UNCED, countries agreed to work on sustainable-development strategies and action plans that would put them on a track toward sustainability. Some 106 countries have now developed national sustainable-development strategies that lay out public-policy priorities. Most of these countries are actively engaged in transforming the policies into action plans, and we will investigate one of the outcomes of these activities: the *sustainable communities movement*.

Revitalizing urban economies and rehabilitating cities requires coordinated efforts on the part of all sectors of society. In fact, such efforts are beginning to occur. What is termed a *sustainable communities movement* is taking root in cities around the United States and elsewhere. In the United States, the Department of Housing and Urban Development sponsors the **Sustainable Communities and Development** program, providing grants to foster the development of more-livable urban neighborhoods. The Internet resources Sustainable Communities Online and Smart Communities Network provide a cornucopia of information, help, case studies, and linkages, demonstrating that the movement is gaining ground throughout the nation. Chattanooga, Tennessee, is now regarded as a prototype of what can occur with such a movement.

Chattanooga. Forty years ago, Chattanooga, which straddles the Tennessee River, was a decaying industrial city with high levels of pollution. Employment was falling and residents were fleeing to the suburbs, leaving abandoned properties and increasing crime. In 1969, the EPA presented the city with a special award for "the dirtiest city in America." Then Chattanooga Venture, a nonprofit organization founded by community leaders, launched *Vision 2000*, the first step of which was to bring people from all walks of life together to build a consensus about what the city *could* be like. Literally thousands of ideas were gradually distilled into 223 specific projects. Then, with the cooperation of all sectors—including government, businesses, lending institutions, and average persons—and an investment of more than $800 million, work on the projects began, providing employment in construction for more than 7,300 people and permanent employment for 1,380. Among the projects were the following:

- With the support of the Clean Air and Clean Water Acts, local government clamped down hard on industries to control pollution.

- The Chattanooga Neighborhood Enterprise fostered the building or renovation of more than 4,600 units of low- and moderate-income housing.

- A new industry to build pollution-control equipment was spawned, as was another industry to build electric buses, which now serve the city without noise or pollution.

- A recycling center employing adults with mental disabilities to separate materials was built.

- An urban greenway demonstration farm, which schoolchildren may visit, was created.

- A zero-emissions industrial park utilizing pollution-avoidance principles was built.

- The river was cleaned up, and a 22-mile Riverwalk reclaimed the waterfront, with parks, playgrounds, and walkways built along the riverbanks.

- Theaters and museums were renovated, and freshwater and saltwater aquariums were built.

- All facilities and a renovated business district were made pedestrian friendly and accessible.

Revision. With these and numerous other projects, many of them still ongoing, Chattanooga has changed its reputation from one of the worst to one of the best places to live (Fig. 23–18). Chattanooga Venture developed a step-by-step guide to assist community groups in similar efforts to build sustainable communities, and the city's experience is being modeled in other cities throughout the United States as well as internationally. Recently, Chattanooga sponsored *Revision 2000*, with more than 2,600 participants taking up where

Figure 23–18 Chattanooga, Tennessee. With numerous projects to reduce pollution and traffic and to provide attractions and amenities for people, Chattanooga, Tennessee, has changed its reputation from one of the worst to one of the best places to live in the United States.

Vision 2000 left off. Revision 2000 identified an additional 27 goals and more than 120 recommendations for further improving Chattanooga. The city's experience demonstrates that visioning and change must occur and continue in order to successfully create and maintain sustainable community development. Although Chattanooga Venture is no longer in operation, its past work has built an expectation throughout the city that public projects will involve the public and that the process will produce results. The latest manifestation of this expectation was *Recreate 2008*, in which hundreds of people engaged in a visioning process that created a plan for revitalizing the city's park system.

23.4 Lifestyles and the Common Good

Sound Science, Stewardship, and *Sustainability*—these are the three strategic themes that have kept our eyes on the basics of how we must live on our planet. Sound science is the basis for our understanding of how the world works and how human systems interact with it, stewardship is the actions and programs that manage natural resources and human well-being for the common good, and sustainability is the practical goal that our interactions with the natural world should be working toward (Chapter 1). Are we making progress in incorporating these concepts into our society?

Our Dilemma

Our intention in this book has been to avoid dwelling on the bad news and instead to raise the hope—indeed, the certainty—that all environmental problems can be addressed successfully. Throughout the text, we have pointed to policies and possibilities that can help move human affairs in a sustainable direction. There is much at stake. When 2015 arrives, will we be able to say that we have met all the Millennium Development Goals, alleviating much of the developing world's grinding poverty and its consequences? Will we reduce our use of fossil fuels to halt global warming and the rising sea level? Can we feed the billions who will join us by midcentury and simultaneously reduce the malnutrition and hunger that still plague more than 900 million people?

Human Decisions. As the late Nobel Laureate Henry Kendall said, "Environmental problems at root are human, not scientific or technical."[13] Even though our scientific understanding is incomplete and our grasp of sustainable development is still tentative, we know enough to be able to act decisively in most circumstances. Therefore, it is human decisions, at both the personal and the societal levels, that can bring about change, and it is these decisions that define our stewardship relationship with Earth.

---

[13]Union of Concerned Scientists. *Keeping the Earth: Scientific and Religious Perspectives on the Environment*, videotape transcript (Pittsburgh, PA: New Wrinkle, 1996), p. 4.

However, making stewardly decisions is not a simple task. Decision making is affected by our personal values and needs, and competing values and needs exist at every turn. One group wins, and another loses. If we stop all destruction of the rain forests, the peasant who needs land to farm will not eat. If we force a halt to the harvesting of shrimp because of concerns about the bycatch, thousands of shrimpers will be out of work. Making decisions means considering competing needs and values and reaching the best conclusion in the face of the numbing complexity of demands and circumstances. It is the nature of our many dilemmas that business as usual resolves only a very small fraction of them. Even though public policies at the national and international levels are absolutely essential elements of our success in turning things around, these in the end are the outcome of decisions by very human people; and even if thoughtful decisions are made by those in power, they will fail unless they are supported by the people who are affected by them.

Here are a few examples of significant changes at the level of governments, municipalities, and industries:

- The EPA has established the Green Power Partnership, a program that encourages organizations to buy green power. The number one purchaser is Intel Corp., buying more than 2.5 billion kilowatt-hours of green power annually.

- Transition Towns (connected by the Transition Network) are more than 400 communities that are working together to respond to the challenges of peak oil and climate change.

- The American Recovery and Reinvestment Act of 2009 (the stimulus package) has invested more than $43 billion in green energy initiatives.

- The World Business Council for Sustainable Development is a network of more than 200 global companies promoting greater resource productivity and sustainable product manufacture.

- Mayors from more than 1,000 cities in the United States have signed the U.S. Mayors' Climate Protection Agreement, which pledges the cities to reduce greenhouse gas emissions to 1990 levels or below (in the absence of a federal commitment).

- Australia led the way in 2007 to eliminate incandescent lightbulbs, an action that has been followed by the European Union nations and other countries; U.S. action to remove them was put on hold by congressional conservatives, but the industry is moving ahead to switch to compact fluorescents and LEDs.

- California established the Million Solar Roofs initiative and hit the 250,000 mark (more than 1 gigawatt) at the beginning of 2012. The state's target now is 12 gigawatts of local green energy by 2020.

The Common Good. We defined the common good in the context of public policy: *to improve human welfare and to protect the natural world* (Chapter 1). What compels people to act to promote the common good? We can identify a number of values that can be the basis of stewardship and help us in our decisions involving both public policies and personal lifestyles:

- *Compassion for those less well off,* or those suffering from extreme poverty or other forms of deprivation—making compassion a major element of our foreign policy, which would energize our country's efforts in promoting sustainable development in the countries that are most in need. Compassion can motivate young people to spend two years of their life in the Peace Corps or a hunger relief agency, for example.

- *Concern for justice*—working to make just policies the norm in international economic relations. A concern for justice can move people to protest the placement of hazardous facilities in underprivileged communities.

- *Honesty,* or a concern for the truth—keeping the laws of the land and openly examining issues from different perspectives.

- *Sufficiency*—simplifying lifestyles rather than ever increasing our consumption; using no more than is necessary of Earth's resources.

- *Humility*—instead of demanding our rights, being willing to share and even defer to others.

- *Neighborliness*—being concerned for other members of our communities (even the global community), such that we do not engage in activities that are harmful to them, but instead make positive contributions to their welfare.

To achieve sustainability, we will have to couple values like these with the knowledge that can come from our understanding of how the natural world works and what is happening to it as a result of human activities. For this to work, people must be willing to grapple with scientific evidence and basic concepts and to develop a respect for the consensus that scientists have reached in areas of environmental concern. It has been our objective to convey that consensus to you in this text. Recall also that sustainable solutions have to be economically feasible, socially desirable, and ecologically viable (see Figure 1–9). This applies directly to the political decisions that are shaping our future in so many of our environmental concerns.

The good news is that many people are engaging environmental problems—working with governments and industries, bringing relief to people in need, and making exactly the kinds of decisions that are needed for effective stewardship. (See Stewardship, "The Tangier Island Covenant.") Community groups are organizing around sustainable principles, providing models of larger-scale changes that will be essential if we are to achieve a sustainable world. Traditional environmental organizations, as well as people from other sectors of society, are working together on the many issues that we have highlighted in this text, bringing about policy changes as well as changes in personal lifestyles.

STEWARDSHIP   The Tangier Island Covenant

The Chesapeake Bay, the largest estuary in the United States, is famous for its blue crabs and the unique "watermen" who fish for the crabs and other marine animals. Watermen are independent fishermen who have lived on the bay for generations and who defend their way of life fiercely. In recent years, the watermen of Tangier, a small island in the Virginia part of the eastern shore of the bay, have been in frequent battles with the Chesapeake Bay Foundation and the state regulators over crab and oyster laws that restrict when and where they can harvest. The watermen skirted restrictions by keeping undersized crabs and dredging clams and oysters out of season. They were also accustomed to throwing their trash overboard, causing the shores of the island to be littered with debris.

In 1997, the island community of Tangier became part of an unusual, but significant, process called *values-based stewardship*, a form of conflict resolution that requires parties to work within the value system of the community to bring about sustained changes in behavior toward the environment. Susan Drake, a doctoral candidate in environmental science at the University of Wisconsin, came to the island to carry out her thesis research on how conflicts are dealt with in homogeneous communities such as Tangier. Originally attracted to the project because of the highly religious community present on the island—the two churches are the center of life and authority there—Drake knew that most of the watermen considered themselves the beneficiaries of a rich bounty in an environment created by God. After working with watermen on their boats and spending time in their churches and with their families, Drake became concerned about the apparent lack of a connection between what the God-fearing watermen believed and what they actually did in their profession.

Convinced that she might be able to intervene in a positive way, Drake requested permission from her thesis committee to engage in "participatory action research," wherein the researcher may enter the conflict and attempt to bring about a resolution. Working within the value system of the community—in this case, a value system based on faith—Drake addressed a joint meeting of the two churches on the island one Sunday morning. Referring to an image of Jesus standing behind a young fisherman at the wheel of a boat in rough seas that almost all Tangier watermen displayed in the cabins of their vessels, Drake addressed the issues of dumping trash overboard and skirting the laws. She showed the picture to the congregation and then put paper blinders over the eyes of Jesus as she listed the ways in which the watermen were disobeying the law. The day of her sermon coincided with a very high tide that gathered the debris from around the shores of the island and washed it up into the streets and people's yards.

The meeting ended with a call by Drake to the watermen to adopt a covenant she had drafted earlier with the help of some of the island's women. Fifty-six watermen went to the altar and promised to abide by the following covenant:

> The Watermen's Stewardship Covenant is a covenant among all watermen, regardless of their profession of religious faith. As watermen, we agree to (1) be good stewards of God's creation by setting a high standard of obedience to civil laws (fishery, boat, and pollution laws) and (2) commit to brotherly accountability. If any person who has committed to this covenant is overtaken in any trespass against this covenant, we agree to spiritually restore such a one in a spirit of gentleness. We also agree to fly a red ribbon on the antennas of our boats to signify that we are part of the covenant.

The next day, scores of watermen began flying red ribbons, taking trash bags out on their boats, and fishing according to the laws. Trucks began to pick up the trash on the island early in the morning. The two churches proceeded to work with the entire island community to draft a plan for the future sustainability of the island and its way of life. They formed the Tangier Watermen's Stewardship for the Chesapeake in order to implement the plan, which is far reaching and involves the women of the island lobbying the state legislature and opening up lines of communication with scientists and government regulators involved in overseeing the bay's health. In recent years, Tangier Islanders have implemented cleanup, waste reduction, and recycling campaigns; environmental education programs; and a Coastal America Project for shoreline and wetland restoration. Island stewardship leaders also contacted a faith-based farming community in Pennsylvania, located on a tributary of the Chesapeake Bay watershed. After meeting with the watermen, the farmers decided to do all they could to prevent runoff from their farmlands that could make its way into the bay. The full story of the original covenant and later contact with the farm community is documented in a recent film.[14]

Values-based stewardship is a call to life-changing stewardship, put within the value system of a community. In this case, putting the call within the context of the faith of the watermen resulted in the establishment of structures within the community that show great promise in helping to bring the entire island toward a sustainable future.

The Tangier Island Covenant.
Susan Drake Emmerich.

---

[14]Center for Law and Culture. *When Heaven Meets Earth.* 2012. www.whenheavenmeetsearth.org.

Lifestyle Changes

What are some of the lifestyle changes that are needed, and are they in fact occurring? We should be encouraged and inspired by the literally millions of people in all walks of life who are acutely aware of the problems and who are making outstanding efforts to bring about solutions.

Every pathway toward solutions that we have mentioned represents the work of thousands of dedicated professionals and volunteers, ranging from scientists and engineers to businesspeople, lawyers, and public servants. Indeed, we are all involved, whether we recognize it or not. Simply by our existence on the planet, everything we do—the cars we drive, the products we use, the wastes we throw away, virtually every choice we make and action we take—has a certain environmental impact and a certain consequence for the future. Therefore, it is not a matter of choosing to have an effect, but a matter of what and how great that effect will be. It is a matter of each of us asking ourselves: Will I be part of the problem or part of the solution? The outcome will depend on how each of us responds to the challenges ahead.

There are a number of levels on which we can participate to work toward a sustainable future:

- Individual lifestyle choices
- Political involvement
- Membership and participation in nongovernmental environmental organizations
- Volunteer work
- Career choices

Lifestyle choices may involve such things as switching to a more fuel-efficient car or walking or using a bicycle for short errands; recycling paper, cans, and bottles; retrofitting your home with solar energy; starting a backyard garden and composting and recycling food and garden wastes into your soil; putting in time at a soup kitchen to help the homeless; choosing low-impact recreation, such as canoeing rather than jet-skiing; and living closer to your workplace.

Political involvement ranges from supporting and voting for particular candidates to expressing your support for particular legislation through letters or phone calls. In effect, you are exercising your citizenship on behalf of the common good.

Membership in nongovernmental environmental organizations can enhance both lifestyle changes and political involvement. As a member of an environmental organization, you will receive, and can help disseminate, information, making you and others more aware of specific environmental problems and things you can do to help. Also, your membership and contribution serve to support the lobbying efforts of the organization. A lobbyist representing a million-member organization that can follow up with thousands of phone calls and letters (and, ultimately, votes) can have a powerful impact.

In cases where enforcement of the existing law has been the weak link, some organizations, such as the Public Interest Research Groups, the Natural Resources Defense Council, and the Environmental Defense Fund, have been highly influential in bringing polluters or the government to court to see that the law is upheld. Again, this can be done only with the support of members.

Another form of involvement is *joining a volunteer organization*. Many effective actions that care for people and the environment are carried out by groups that depend on volunteer labor. Political organizations and virtually all NGOs depend highly on volunteers. Many helping organizations, such as those dedicated to alleviating hunger and to building homes for needy families (Fig. 23–19), are adept at mobilizing volunteers to accomplish some vital tasks that often fill in the gaps left behind by inadequate public policies.

Finally, you may choose to devote your *career* to implementing solutions to environmental problems. Environmental careers go far beyond the traditional occupations of wildlife

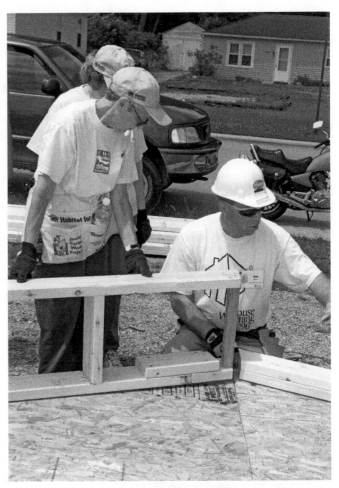

Figure 23–19 Habitat for Humanity volunteers. By using charitable contributions and volunteer labor, Habitat for Humanity creates quality homes—more than 500,000 built throughout the world by 2012—that needy families can afford to buy with no-interest mortgages, enabling the money to be recycled to build more homes. Prospective home buyers participate in the construction and may gain valuable skills in the process.

ranger and park manager. Many lawyers, journalists, teachers, research scientists, engineers, medical personnel, agricultural extension workers, and others are focusing their talents and training on environmental issues or hazards. Business and job opportunities exist in pollution control, recycling, waste management, ecological restoration, city planning, environmental monitoring and analysis, nonchemical pest control, the production and marketing of organically grown produce, the manufacture of solar and wind energy components, and so on. Some developers concentrate on rehabilitation and the reversal of urban blight, as opposed to contributing more to urban sprawl. Some engineers are working on the development of pollution-free vehicles to help solve the photochemical smog dilemma of our cities. Indeed, it is difficult to think of a vocation that cannot be directed toward promoting solutions to environmental problems.

Human society is well into a new millennium, and it promises to be an era of rapid changes unprecedented in human history. Will we just survive, or will we thrive and become a sustainable global society? We are engaged in an environmental revolution—a major shift in our worldview and practice from seeing the natural world as resources to be exploited to seeing it as life's supporting structure that needs our stewardship. You are living in the early stages of this revolution, and we invite you to be one of the many who will make it happen. We close with this quote:

No one could make a greater mistake than he who did nothing because he could do only a little.

Edmund Burke, Irish orator, philosopher, and politician (1729–1797)

REVISITING THE THEMES

Sound Science

City planners and highway engineers have a new set of challenges as our society makes the changes that will move us toward greater sustainability. Creating sustainable cities and towns requires the dedicated work of social scientists, natural scientists, engineers, and many average people as they meet to provide a vision of what they would like their future to look like and then carry out that vision. Many scientific careers are great avenues for work on green solutions.

Sustainability

The story of urban sprawl is a story of poor or nonexistent public policy. Land use is traditionally under local control (if it is under any control at all), and absent any public policy dealing with land use, sprawl happens. In fact, public policy fed sprawl, as the Highway Trust Fund taxed gasoline sales in order to build roads and highways. Crafting effective policy to deal with sprawl means recognizing why people choose to live on the suburban fringes in low-density houses and changing the way we organize our communities. It requires changing public policy to do this, but smart-growth initiatives are taking root in state after state. Reining in sprawl and redesigning suburbia are essential moves toward greater sustainability of our urban surroundings.

Urban blight, too, was the outcome of poor or nonexistent public policy. Cities stood by helplessly and watched the flight of wealthier people and businesses out to the suburbs and even out of the country. In a similar way, developing-world cities are simply watching the poor flock in. It often takes people with compassion and a vision to bring about

change in these situations. Frequently, change can be brought about at the grassroots level, but it helps immensely to have leaders who care about the poor in their midst. Whether in developed or developing countries, addressing urban blight will make cities more livable and, therefore, more sustainable.

Sustainable solutions are becoming more mainstream, in the United States and around the world. Cities and towns are making an effort to respond to global climate change and limited resources as they engage in community efforts to promote sustainability and encourage sustainable lifestyle changes in their people.

Stewardship

The stewardship ethic includes a concern for justice. "White flight" into the suburbs has left minorities trapped in the inner cities, held down by racial and economic discrimination. Equally important is the migration of rural people into the cities of the developing world, where they are forced to live in slums and are unjustly denied ordinary social and environmental services. Both of these developments have energized many individuals and numerous NGOs to make common cause with those who are suffering the injustice and to help them mobilize their human and social resources to bring about change. A similar motivation to bring about change led Ryan Gravel to propose the Atlanta BeltLine, and Chattanooga Venture to begin the visioning process that eventually turned that city around. This is exactly what stewards should be doing. It is a fact that every one of us is given many opportunities to work together to create a truly sustainable society, and stewardship is the ethic that is there to guide our actions.

REVIEW QUESTIONS

1. What is the Atlanta BeltLine, and how does it propose to change urban Atlanta?

2. How did the structure of cities begin to change after World War II? What factors were responsible for the change?

3. Why are the terms *car dependent* and *urban sprawl* used to describe our current suburban lifestyle and urban layout?

4. What federal laws and policies tend to support urban sprawl?

5. Compare the costs and benefits of urban sprawl, looking at the environmental impacts and the impacts on quality of life.

6. What is *smart growth*? What are four smart-growth strategies that address urban sprawl?

7. What services do local governments provide, and what is their prime source of revenue for these services?

8. What is meant by *erosion of a city's tax base*? Why does it follow from exurban migration? What are the results?

9. How do exurban migration, urban sprawl, and urban decay become a vicious cycle?

10. What is meant by *economic exclusion*? How is it related to the problems of crime and poverty in cities?

11. What are the reasons for urban blight in the cities of many developing countries? What do the people in the shantytowns need most?

12. What are some characteristics of livable cities?

13. What is the Sustainable Communities Program? How does Chattanooga illustrate the program?

14. What are some stewardship virtues, and what role could they play in fostering sustainability?

15. State five levels at which people can participate in working toward a sustainable future.

THINKING ENVIRONMENTALLY

1. Interview an older person (say, 75 years of age or older) about what his or her city or community was like before 1950 in terms of meeting people's needs for shopping, participating in recreation, getting to school or work, and so on. Was it necessary to have a car?

2. Do a study of your region. What aspects of urban sprawl and urban blight are evident? What environmental and social problems are evident? Are they still going on? Are efforts being made to correct them?

3. Identify nongovernmental organizations in your region that are working toward reining in urban sprawl or toward preserving or bettering the city. What specific projects are under way in each of these areas? What roles are local governments playing in the process? How can you become involved?

MAKING A DIFFERENCE

1. Analyze your environmental impacts as a consumer. What modes of transportation do you use, where do you shop, what foods do you consume or throw away, what appliances do you own, how do you heat or cool your home, and how much water do you use? Consider especially your impact on the four leading consumption-related environmental problems: air pollution, global climate change, changes in natural habitats, and water pollution.

2. Investigate land-use planning and policies in your region. Is urban sprawl or urban blight a problem? Become involved in zoning issues, and support zoning and policies that will promote, rather than hinder, ecologically sound land use (*smart growth*).

3. Contact local conservation organizations or land trusts, and offer your help in protecting and preserving open land in your region.

4. Find out if there is a Habitat for Humanity project or group in your area, and if there is, volunteer some time to support its work.

MasteringEnvironmentalScience®

Go to **www.masteringenvironmentalscience.com** for practice quizzes, Pearson eText, videos, current events, and more.

APPENDIX A

Environmental Organizations

This appendix presents a list of selected nonprofit, nongovernmental organizations that are active in environmental matters. Listed are national organizations as well as some smaller, specialized ones. These organizations offer a variety of fact sheets, brochures, newsletters, publications, educational materials, and annual reports, most of which are available on the Internet. Some organizations have internship positions available for those wishing to do work for an environmental group. Web addresses are provided in the list. Most of the Web sites also provide connections via Facebook, Twitter, RSS feeds, Flickr, and YouTube. Also, a useful directory of many more environmental organizations can be accessed at **http://environmentdirectorywildlifeconservation.com**

AMERICAN FARMLAND TRUST. Focuses on the preservation of American farmland. 1200 18th St. NW, Suite 800, Washington, DC 20036. **www.farmland.org**

AMERICAN LUNG ASSOCIATION. Research, education, legislation, lobbying, advocacy: indoor and outdoor air pollution effects, smoking. 1301 Pennsylvania Ave. NW, Suite 800, Washington, DC 20004. **www.lung.org**

AMERICAN RIVERS, INC. Mission is "to preserve and restore America's rivers' systems and to foster a river stewardship ethic." Education, litigation, lobbying: wild and scenic rivers, hydropower relicensing. Information on specific rivers available. 1101 14th St. NW, Suite 1400, Washington, DC 20005. **www.amrivers.org**

BREAD FOR THE WORLD. National advocacy group that lobbies for legislation dealing with hunger. 425 3rd St. SW, Suite 1200, Washington, DC 20024. **www.bread.org**

CENTER FOR CLIMATE AND ENERGY SOLUTIONS. The successor to the Pew Center on Global Climate Change, this organization is an independent, nonpartisan, nonprofit organization working to advance strong policy and action to address the twin challenges of energy and climate change. 2101 Wilson Blvd., Suite 550, Arlington, VA 22201. **www.c2es.org**

CENTER FOR SCIENCE IN THE PUBLIC INTEREST. Research and education: alcohol policies, food safety, health, nutrition, organic agriculture. 1220 L St. NW, Suite 300, Washington, DC 20005. **www.cspinet.org**

CHESAPEAKE BAY FOUNDATION. Research, education, and litigation: environmental defense and management of the Chesapeake Bay and surrounding area. Philip Merrill Environmental Center, 6 Herndon Ave., Annapolis, MD 21403. **www.cbf.org**

CLEAN WATER ACTION PROJECT. Lobbying, education, research: water quality. 1010 Vermont Ave. NW, Suite 400 Washington, DC 20005. **www.cleanwateraction.org**

COMMON CAUSE. Lobbying: government reform, energy reorganization, clean air. 1133 19th Street NW, Washington, DC 20036. **www.commoncause.org**

CONGRESS WATCH. Lobbying: consumer health and safety, pesticides (a function of Public Citizen). 215 Pennsylvania Ave. SE, Washington, DC 20003. **www.citizen.org/congress**

CONSERVATION INTERNATIONAL. Education and research to preserve and promote awareness about the world's most endangered biodiversity. 2011 Crystal Dr., Suite 500, Arlington, VA 22202. **www.conservation.org**

CORAL REEF ALLIANCE. Works with the diving community and others to promote coral reef conservation around the world. 351 California St., Suite 650, San Francisco, CA 94104. **www.coral.org**

CLIMATE AND ENERGY. Research, education, and advocacy: affordable, clean and sustainable energy (a function of Public Citizen). 215 Pennsylvania Ave. SE, Washington, DC 20003. **www.citizen.org/cmep**

DEFENDERS OF WILDLIFE. Research, education, and lobbying: all native animals and plants, especially endangered species. 1130 17th St. NW, Washington, DC 20036. **www.defenders.org**

DUCKS UNLIMITED, INC. Hunters working to fulfill the annual life-cycle needs of North American waterfowl by protecting, enhancing, restoring, and managing important wetlands and associated uplands. One Waterfowl Way, Memphis, TN 38120. **www.ducks.org**

EARTHWATCH INSTITUTE. Environmental research is encouraged by organizing teams to make expeditions to various locations all over the world. Team members contribute to the expenses and spend from several weeks to several months on the site. 114 Western Ave., Boston, MA 02134. **www.earthwatch.org**

ENVIRONMENTAL DEFENSE FUND. Research, litigation, and lobbying: cosmetics safety, drinking water, energy, transportation, pesticides, wildlife, air pollution, cancer prevention, radiation. 257 Park Ave. South, New York, NY 10010. **www.edf.org**

ENVIRONMENTAL LAW INSTITUTE. Training, educational workshops, and seminars for environmental professionals, lawyers, and judges on institutional and legal issues affecting the environment. 200 L St. NW, Suite 620, Washington, DC 20036. **www.eli.org**

FOREST STEWARDSHIP COUNCIL. Promotes sustainable forest management and a system of certification of sustainable forest products. 212 Third Ave. North, Suite 504, Minneapolis, MN 55401. **www.fscus.org**

FREEDOM FROM HUNGER. Develops programs for the elimination of hunger worldwide. 1644 DaVinci Court, Davis, CA 95618. **www.freedomfromhunger.org**

FRIENDS OF THE EARTH. Research, lobbying: all aspects of energy development, preservation, restoration, and rational use of the Earth. 1100 15th St. NW, 11th Floor, Washington, DC 20005. **www.foe.org**

GREENBELT MOVEMENT. Environmetal organization that empowers communities, especially women, to improve livelihoods by conserving the environment, especially by planting trees in Africa. Adams Arcade, Kilimani Lane off Elgeyo Marakwet Rd. PO BOX 67545-00200, Nairobi, Kenya. **www.greenbeltmovement.org**

GREENPEACE, USA, INC. An international environmental organization dedicated to protecting the planet through nonviolent, direct action providing public education, scientific research, and legislative lobbying. 702 H St. NW, Washington, DC 20001. **www.greenpeace.org**

GROWING POWER, an urban farm organization begun in Milwaukee, WI, that grows food and provides youth employment and education in sustainable urban farming. 5500 W.

Silver Spring Drive, Milwaukee, Wisconsin 53218. **www .growingpower.org/about_us.htm**

HABITAT FOR HUMANITY INTERNATIONAL. Fosters homebuilding and ownership for the poor. Education on housing issues. 121 Habitat St., Americus, GA 31709-3498. **www.habitat.org**

HEIFER PROJECT INTERNATIONAL. Works throughout the developing world to bring domestic animals to poor families. 1 World Ave., Little Rock, AR 72203. **www.heifer.org**

INSTITUTE FOR LOCAL SELF-RELIANCE. Research and education: appropriate technology for community development. 2001 S St. NW, Suite 570, Washington, DC 20009. **www.ilsr.org**

INTERNATIONAL FOOD POLICY RESEARCH INSTITUTE. Mission is to identify and analyze policies for sustainably ending hunger and poverty. 2033 K St. NW, Washington, DC 20006. **www .ifpri.org**

IZAAK WALTON LEAGUE OF AMERICA, INC. Research, education, endowment grants: conservation, air and water quality, streams. 707 Conservation Lane, Gaithersburg, MD 20878. **www.iwla.org**

KUPENDA FOR THE CHILDREN. Bringing help to the handicapped children of the Malindi region of the Kenyan coast, Kupenda organizes sponsorships to educate and house the children. PO Box 473, Hampton, NH 03843. **www.kupenda.org**

LAND TRUST ALLIANCE. Works with more than 1,700 local and regional land trusts to enhance their work. 1660 L St. NW, Suite 1100, Washington, DC 20036. **www.landtrustalliance.org**

LEAGUE OF CONSERVATION VOTERS. Political arm of the environmental community. Works to elect candidates to the U.S. House and Senate who will vote to protect the nation's environment and holds them accountable by publishing the National Environmental Scorecard each year, available from its Web site. 1920 L St. NW, Suite 800, Washington, DC 20036. **www.lcv.org**

LEAGUE OF WOMEN VOTERS OF THE UNITED STATES. Education and lobbying, general environmental issues. Publications on groundwater, agriculture, and farm policy, with additional topics available. 1730 M St. NW, Suite 1000, Washington, DC 20036. **www.lwv.org**

MANZANAR PROJECT. Provides low-tech solutions to hunger and poverty. Funding for women to plant mangroves along the Eritrean coast, which improves fisheries, food for domestic animals, and family income. PO Box 98, Gloucester, MA 01931. **www.themanzanarproject.com**

MILLENNIUM GOALS. The United Nations site providing information on and monitoring progress toward achieving the Millennium Development Goals. **www.un.org/millenniumgoals**

MILLENNIUM ECOSYSTEM ASSESSMENT (MA). An international work program designed to meet the needs of decision makers and the public for scientific information concerning the consequences of ecosystem change for human well-being and options for responding to those changes. The MA completed its numerous reports in 2005, many of which are referenced in this edition of the text. **www.millenniumassessment.org**

NATIONAL AUDUBON SOCIETY. Research, lobbying, education, litigation, and citizen action: broad-based environmental issues. 225 Varick St., New York, NY 10014. **www.audubon.org**

NATIONAL COUNCIL FOR SCIENCE AND THE ENVIRONMENT. Mission is to improve the scientific basis for making decisions about environmental issues. One important service provides access to the Congressional Research Service (briefings on environmental issues and the legislation addressing them). 1101 17th Street NW, Suite 250, Washington, DC 20036. **ncseonline.org**

NATIONAL PARK FOUNDATION. Partners with the National Park Service to encourage education, land acquisition, management of endowments, grant making. 1201 Eye St. NW, Suite 550B, Washington, DC 20005. **www.nationalparks.org**

NATIONAL PARKS CONSERVATION ASSOCIATION. A private organization with a mission to protect and enhance America's National Park System for present and future generations. 777 6th St. NW, Suite 700 Washington, DC 20001-3723. **www .npca.org**

NATIONAL RELIGIOUS PARTNERSHIP FOR THE ENVIRONMENT. An association of independent faith groups promoting stewardship of Creation in the context of different faiths. 110 Maryland Ave. NE, Suite 108, Washington, DC 20002. **www.nrpe.org**

NATIONAL WILDLIFE FEDERATION. Research, education, lobbying: general environmental quality, wilderness, and wildlife. 11100 Wildlife Center Drive, Reston, VA 20190. **www.nwf.org**

NATURAL RESOURCES DEFENSE COUNCIL. Research and litigation: water and air quality, land use, energy, pesticides, toxic waste. 40 W. 20th St., New York, NY 10011. **www.nrdc.org**

NATURE CONSERVANCY. A land conservation agency working around the world to protect ecologically important lands and waters for nature and people. 4525 N. Fairfax Dr., Suite 100, Arlington, VA 22203. **www.nature.org**

OXFAM AMERICA. Funding agency for projects to benefit the "poorest of the poor" in South America, Africa, India, Central America, the Caribbean, and the Philippines. Provides whatever resources are needed. 226 Causeway St., 5th Floor, Boston, MA 02114. **www.oxfamamerica.org**

PLANNED PARENTHOOD FEDERATION OF AMERICA. Education, reproductive health care services, and research: fertility control, family planning. 1110 Vermont Ave. NW, Suite 300, Washington, DC, 20005. **www.plannedparenthood.org**

POPULATION CONNECTION. Public education, lobbying, and research toward stable populations. 2120 L St. NW, Suite 500, Washington, DC 20037 **www.populationconnection.org**

THE POPULATION INSTITUTE. Education, research, and speaking engagements: population control. 107 2nd St. NE, Washington, DC 20002. **www.populationinstitute.org**

POPULATION REFERENCE BUREAU, INC. Organization engaged in collection and dissemination of objective population information. Excellent publications. 1875 Connecticut Ave. NW, Suite 520, Washington, DC 20009. **www.prb.org**

PUBLIC EMPLOYEES FOR ENVIRONMENTAL RESPONSIBILITY. A service organization that helps public employees work as "anonymous activists," enabling them to inform the public and their agencies about environmental abuses. 2000 P St. NW, Suite 240, Washington, DC 20036. **www.peer.org**

RACHEL CARSON COUNCIL, INC. Publication and distribution of information on pesticides and toxic substances, educational conferences, and seminars. PO Box 10779, Silver Spring, MD 20914. **www.rachelcarsoncouncil.org**

RAIN FOREST ACTION NETWORK. Information and educational resources: world's rain forests. 221 Pine St., 5th Floor, San Francisco, CA 94104. **www.ran.org**

RAINFOREST ALLIANCE. Education, medicinal plants project, timber project to certify "smart wood," and news bureau. 665 Broadway, Suite 500, New York, NY 10012. **www.rainforest -alliance.org**

RESOURCES FOR THE FUTURE. Research and education think tank: connects economics and conservation of natural resources, environmental quality. Publishes *Resources*. 1616 P St. NW, Washington, DC 20036. **www.rff.org**

SHACK/SLUM DWELLERS INTERNATIONAL. Promoting awareness of and support for the urban poor in developing countries; 14 federations and 34 country affiliates, head office in 1st Floor Campground Centre, Cnr Raapenberg and Surrey Rd. Mowbray, Cape Town 7700, S.A. **www.sdinet.org**

SIERRA CLUB. Education and lobbying: broad-based environmental issues. 85 Second St., 2nd Floor, San Francisco, CA 94105. **www.sierraclub.org**

TRUST FOR PUBLIC LAND. Works with citizen groups and government agencies to acquire and preserve open space. 101 Montgomery St., Suite 900, San Francisco, CA 94104. **www.tpl.org**

UNION OF CONCERNED SCIENTISTS. Connects citizens and scientists; works through programs and lobbying to inform the public and policy makers on science-related issues. 2 Brattle Square, Cambridge, MA 02238. **www.ucsusa.org**

U.S. PUBLIC INTEREST RESEARCH GROUP (PIRG). A federation of state PIRGs focusing on research, education, and lobbying: alternative energy, consumer protection, utilities regulation, public interest. 44 Winter St., 4th Floor, Boston, MA 02108. **www.pirg.org**

WATER ENVIRONMENT FEDERATION. Research, education, and lobbying to preserve the global water environment; provides technical education and training for water quality professionals. 601 Wythe St., Alexandria, VA 22314. **www.wef.org**

WILDERNESS SOCIETY. Research, education, and lobbying: wilderness, public lands; mission is to protect wilderness and inspire Americans to care for our wild places. 1615 M St. NW, Washington, DC 20036. **wilderness.org**

WORLD RESOURCES INSTITUTE. Global think tank that conducts research and publishes reports for educators, policy makers, and organizations on environmental issues. 10 G St. NE, Suite 800, Washington, DC 20002. **www.wri.org**

WORLD VISION. Christian humanitarian organization dedicated to working with children, families, and their communities worldwide to help them reach their full potential by tackling the causes of poverty and injustice. 34834 Weyerhaeuser Way S, Federal Way, WA 98001. **www.worldvision.org**

WORLDWATCH INSTITUTE. Research and education: energy, food, population, health, women's issues, technology, the environment. Publications: *State of the World, Vital Signs,* Worldwatch papers and reports. 1776 Massachusetts Ave. NW, Washington, DC 20036. **www.worldwatch.org**

WORLD WILDLIFE FUND. Preservation of wildlife habitats and protection of endangered species. 1250 24th St. NW, PO Box 97180, Washington, DC 20037. **www.worldwildlife.org**

APPENDIX B

Units of Measure

DISTANCE	1 centimeter (cm)	× 10 =	1 decimeter (dm)	× 10 =	1 meter (m)	× 1,000 =	1 kilometer (km)
	1 cm = 0.39 in 1 in = 2.54 cm		1 dm = 3.94 in 1 foot = 3.05 dm		1 m = 1.09 yards 1 yard = 0.91 m		1 km = 0.62 miles 1 mile = 1.61 km

AREA	square centimeter (cm²)	× 10,000 =	square meter (m²)	× 10,000 =	1 hectare (ha)	× 100 =	1 square kilometer (km²)
	1 cm² = 1.55 sq in 1 sq in = 6.45 cm²		1 m² = 10.8 sq ft = 1.20 sq yard 1 sq yd = .836 m²		1 ha = 2.47 acres 1 acre = 0.405 ha		1 km² = 0.39 sq mi 1 sq mile = 2.6 km²

VOLUME	cubic centimeter (cm³) 1 milliliter (mL)	× 1,000 =	cubic decimeter (dm³) 1 liter (L)	× 1,000 =	1 cubic meter (m³)		
	1 mL = 0.203 teaspoons 1 teaspoon = 4.9 mL		1 L = 1.06 qts 1 qt = 0.95 L		1 m³ = 1.31 cubic yards 1 cubic yd = 0.76 m³		

MASS (WEIGHT)	1 mL of water at 4°C has a mass of 1 gram (g)	× 1,000 =	1 L of water at 4°C has a mass of 1 kilogram (kg)	× 1,000 =	1 m³ of water at 4°C has a mass of 1 metric ton (t)		10⁶ metric tons = 1 teragram 10⁹ metric tons = 1 petagram
	1 gram = 0.035 ounces 1 oz = 28.4 g		1 kg = 2.2 pounds 1 lb = 0.45 kg		1 t = 1000 kg 1 English (short) ton = 2 000 lbs = 0.91 t		

Energy Units and Equivalents

1 Calorie, food calorie, or kilocalorie – The amount of heat required to raise the temperature of one kilogram of water one degree Celsius (1.8°F)

1 BTU (British Thermal Unit) – The amount of heat required to raise the temperature of one pound of water one degree Fahrenheit.

1 joule – a force of one newton applied over a distance of one meter (a newton is the force needed to produce an acceleration of 1 m per sec to a mass of one kg)

1 Calorie = 3.968 BTUs = 4,186 joules

1 BTU = 0.252 Calories = 1,055 joules

1 Therm = 100,000 BTUs

1 Quad = 1 quadrillion BTUs

1 watt = standard of electrical power

1 watt = 1 joule per second

1 watt-hour (wh) = 1 watt for 1 hr. = 3.413 BTUs

1 kilowatt (kw) = 1000 watts

1 kilowatt-hour (kwh) = 1 kilowatt for 1 hr = 3,413 BTUs

1 megawatt (Mw) = 1,000,000 watts

1 megawatt-hour (Mwh) = 1 Mw for 1 hr. = 34.13 therms

1 gigawatt (Gw) = 1,000,000,000 watts or 1,000 megawatts

1 gigawatt-hour (Gwh) = 1 Gw for 1 hr = 34,130 therms

1 horsepower = .7457 kilowatts

1 horsepower-hour = 2545 BTUs

1 cubic foot of natural gas (methane) at atmospheric pressure = 1031 BTUs

1 gallon gasoline = 125,000 BTUs

1 gallon No. 2 fuel oil = 140,000 BTUs

1 short ton coal = 25,000,000 BTUs

1 barrel = 42 gallons

APPENDIX C

Some Basic Chemical Concepts

Atoms, Elements, and Compounds

All matter, whether gas, liquid, or solid; living or nonliving; or organic or inorganic, is composed of fundamental units called **atoms**. Atoms are extremely tiny. If all the world's people, 7 billion of us, were reduced to the size of atoms, there would be room for all of us to dance on the head of a pin. In fact, we would only occupy a tiny fraction (about 1/10,000) of the pin's head. Given the incredibly tiny size of atoms, even the smallest particle that can be seen with the naked eye consists of billions of atoms.

The atoms making up a substance may be all of one kind, or they may be of two or more kinds. If the atoms are all of one kind, the substance is called an **element**. If the atoms are of two or more kinds bonded together, the substance is called a **compound**.

Through countless experiments, chemists have ascertained that there are only 94 distinct kinds of atoms that occur in nature. (An additional 21 have been synthesized.) These natural, and most of the synthetic, elements are listed in Table C–1, together with their chemical symbols. By scanning the table, you can see that a number of familiar substances—such as aluminum, chlorine, carbon, oxygen, and iron—are elements; that is, they are a single, distinct kind of atom. However, most of the substances with which we interact in everyday life—such as water, stone, wood, protein, and sugar—are not on the list. Their absence from the list is indicative that they are not elements; rather, they are compounds, which means that they are actually composed of two or more different kinds of atoms bonded together.

TABLE C–1 The Elements

Element	Symbol	Atomic Number	Atomic Weight	Element	Symbol	Atomic Number	Atomic Weight
Actinium	Ac	89	(227)	Chlorine	Cl	17	35.5
Aluminum	Al	13	27.0	Chromium	Cr	24	52.0
*Americium	Am	95	(243)	Cobalt	Co	27	58.9
Antimony	Sb	51	121.8	Copper	Cu	29	63.5
Argon	Ar	18	39.9	*Curium	Cm	96	(245)
Arsenic	As	33	74.9	*Dubnium	Db	105	(262)
Astatine	At	85	(210)	Dysprosium	Dy	66	162.5
Barium	Ba	56	137.3	*Einsteinium	Es	99	(254)
*Berkelium	Bk	97	(245)	Erbium	Er	68	167.3
Beryllium	Be	4	9.01	Europium	Eu	63	152.0
Bismuth	Bi	83	209.0	*Fermium	Fm	100	(254)
*Bohrium	Bh	107	(262)	Fluorine	F	9	19.0
Boron	B	5	10.8	Francium	Fr	87	(223)
Bromine	Br	35	79.9	Gadolinium	Gd	64	157.3
Cadmium	Cd	48	112.4	Gallium	Ga	31	69.7
Calcium	Ca	20	40.1	Germanium	Ge	32	72.6
*Californium	Cf	98	(251)	Gold	Au	79	197.0
Carbon	C	6	12.0	Hafnium	Hf	72	178.5
Cerium	Ce	58	140.1	*Hassium	Hs	108	(265)
Cesium	Cs	55	132.9	Helium	He	2	4.00

TABLE C–1 The Elements (*continued*)

Element	Symbol	Atomic Number	Atomic Weight	Element	Symbol	Atomic Number	Atomic Weight
Holmium	Ho	67	164.9	Promethium	Pm	61	(145)
Hydrogen	H	1	1.01	Protoactinium	Pa	91	231.0
Indium	In	19	114.8	Radium	Ra	88	226.0
Iodine	I	53	126.9	Radon	Rn	86	(222)
Iridium	Ir	77	192.2	Rhenium	Re	75	186.2
Iron	Fe	26	55.8	Rhodium	Rh	45	102.9
Krypton	Kr	36	83.8	Ruthenium	Ru	44	101.1
Lanthanum	La	57	138.9	*Rutherfordium	Rf	104	(261)
*Lawrencium	Lr	103	(257)	Samarium	Sm	62	150.4
Lead	Pb	82	207.2	Scandium	Sc	21	45.0
Lithium	Li	3	6.94	*Seaborgium	Sg	106	(263)
Lutetium	Lu	71	175.0	Selenium	Se	34	79.0
Magnesium	Mg	12	24.3	Silicon	Si	14	28.1
Manganese	Mn	25	54.9	Silver	Ag	47	107.9
*Meitnerium	Mt	109	(265)	Sodium	Na	11	23.0
*Mendelevium	Md	101	(256)	Strontium	Sr	38	87.6
Mercury	Hg	80	200.6	Sulfur	S	16	32.1
Molybdenum	Mo	42	95.9	Tantalum	Ta	73	180.9
Neodymium	Nd	60	44.2	Technetium	Tc	43	98.9
Neon	Ne	10	20.2	Tellurium	Te	52	127.6
*Neptunium	Np	93	237.0	Terbium	Tb	65	158.9
Nickel	Ni	28	58.7	Thallium	Tl	81	204.4
Niobium	Nb	41	92.9	Thorium	Th	90	232.0
Nitrogen	N	7	14.0	Thulium	Tm	69	168.9
*Nobelium	No	102	(254)	Tin	Sn	50	118.7
Osmium	Os	76	190.2	Titanium	Ti	22	47.9
Oxygen	O	8	16.0	Tungsten	W	74	183.8
Palladium	Pd	46	106.4	Uranium	U	92	238.0
Phosphorus	P	15	31.0	Vanadium	V	23	50.9
Platinum	Pt	78	195.1	Xenon	Xe	54	131.3
Plutonium	Pu	94	(242)	Ytterbium	Yb	70	173.0
Polonium	Po	84	(210)	Yttrium	Y	39	88.9
Potassium	K	19	39.1	Zinc	Zn	30	65.4
Praseodymium	Pr	59	140.9	Zirconium	Zr	40	91.2

*Elements that do not occur in nature.
Parentheses indicate the most stable isotope of the element.

Atoms, Bonds, and Chemical Reactions

In chemical reactions, atoms are neither created nor destroyed, nor is one kind of atom changed into another. What occurs in chemical reactions, whether mild or explosive, is simply a rearrangement of the ways in which the atoms involved are bonded together. An oxygen atom, for example, may be combined and recombined with different atoms to form any number of different compounds, but a given oxygen atom always has been, and always will be, an oxygen atom. The same can be said for all the other kinds of atoms. To understand how atoms may bond and undergo rearrangement to form different compounds, it is necessary to examine several concepts concerning the structure of atoms.

Structure of Atoms

Every atom consists of a central core called the **nucleus** (not to be confused with a cell nucleus). The nucleus of an atom contains one or more **protons** and, except for hydrogen, one or more **neutrons**. Surrounding the nucleus are particles called **electrons**. Each proton has a positive (+) electric charge, and each electron has an equal and opposite negative (–) electric charge. Thus, in any atom, the charge of the protons may be balanced by an equal number of electrons, making the whole atom neutral. Neutrons have no charge.

Atoms of all elements have this same basic structure, consisting of protons, electrons, and neutrons. The distinction between atoms of different elements is in the number of protons. The atoms of each element have a characteristic number of protons that is known as the **atomic number** of the element. (See Table C–1.) The number of electrons characteristic of the atoms of each element also differs, in a manner corresponding to the number of protons. The combined total of protons and neutrons in the nucleus of an element is the **mass number**, or **atomic weight**. The general structure of the atoms of several elements is shown in **Figure C–1**.

The number of protons and electrons in an atom of an element (i.e., the atomic number of the element) determines the chemical properties of the element. The number of neutrons may vary. For example, most carbon atoms have six neutrons in addition to the six protons, as indicated in Figure C–1. But some carbon atoms have eight neutrons. Atoms of the same element that have different numbers of neutrons are known as **isotopes** of the element. The total number of protons plus neutrons is used to define different isotopes. For example, the usual isotope of carbon is referred to as carbon-12, while the isotope with eight neutrons is referred to as carbon-14. The chemical reactivities of different isotopes of the same element are identical. (However, certain other properties may differ.) Many isotopes of various elements prove to be radioactive, such as carbon-14. The atomic weights in Table C–1 are expressed as the average of the isotopes of an element as they occur in nature. The weights listed in parentheses are those of the most stable known isotope.

Bonding of Atoms

The chemical properties of an element are defined by the ways in which the element's atoms will react and form bonds with other atoms. By examining how atoms form bonds, we shall see how the number of electrons and protons determines these properties. There are two basic kinds of bonding: (**1**) **covalent bonding** and (**2**) **ionic bonding**.

In both kinds of bonding, it is important to recognize that electrons are not randomly distributed around the atom's nucleus. Rather, there are, in effect, specific spaces in a series of layers, or **orbitals**, around the nucleus. If an orbital is occupied by one or more electrons but is not filled, the atom is unstable; it will then tend to react and form bonds with other atoms to achieve greater stability. A stable state is achieved by having all the spaces in the orbital filled with electrons. It is important, however, to keep the charge neutral (i.e., the total number of electrons should be equal to that of the protons).

Covalent Bonding

These two requirements—filling all the spaces and keeping the charge neutral—may be satisfied by adjacent atoms sharing one or more pairs of electrons, as shown in **Figure C–2**. The sharing of a pair of electrons holds the atoms together in what it is called a **covalent bond**.

Covalent bonding, by satisfying the charge-orbital requirements, leads to discrete units of two or more atoms bonded together. Units of two or more covalently bonded atoms are called **molecules**. A few simple, but important, examples are shown in Figure C–2.

A chemical formula is simply a shorthand description of the number of each kind of atom in a given molecule. The element is given by the chemical symbol, and a subscript following the symbol gives the number of atoms of that element present in the molecule; if there is no subscript, there is only one atom of that chemical. A molecule with two or more different kinds of atoms may be called a compound, but a molecule composed of a single kind of atom—oxygen (O_2), for example—is still defined as an element.

Only a small number of elements—carbon, hydrogen, oxygen, nitrogen, phosphorus, and sulfur—have configurations of electrons that lend themselves readily to the formation of

Figure C–1 Structure of atoms. All atoms consist of fundamental particles: protons (p), which have a positive electric charge; neutrons (n), which have no charge; and electrons, which have a negative charge.

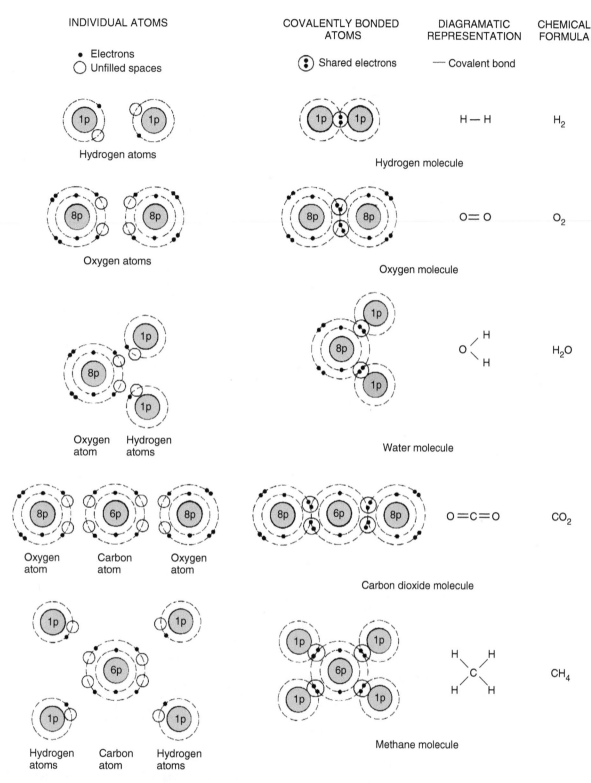

INDIVIDUAL ATOMS

COVALENTLY BONDED ATOMS

DIAGRAMATIC REPRESENTATION

CHEMICAL FORMULA

- Electrons
○ Unfilled spaces

(:) Shared electrons   — Covalent bond

Hydrogen atoms

Hydrogen molecule

H — H H_2

Oxygen atoms

Oxygen molecule

O = O O_2

Oxygen atom   Hydrogen atoms

Water molecule

H_2O

Oxygen atom   Carbon atom   Oxygen atom

Carbon dioxide molecule

O = C = O CO_2

Hydrogen atoms   Carbon atom   Hydrogen atoms

Methane molecule

CH_4

Figure C–2 Atoms to molecules. Molecules are composed of atoms covalently bonded to each other in stable configurations in which electrons are shared.

covalent bonds. Carbon in particular, with its ability to form four covalent bonds, can produce long, straight, or branched chains or rings (Fig. C–3). Thus, an infinite array of molecules can be formed by using covalently bonded carbon atoms as a "backbone" and filling in the sides with atoms of hydrogen or other elements. Accordingly, it is covalent bonding among atoms of carbon and these few other elements that produces all natural organic molecules, those molecules that make up all the tissues of living things, and also synthetic organic compounds such as plastics.

Figure C–3 **Covalent bonding and organic molecules.** The ability of carbon and a few other elements to readily form covalent bonds leads to an infinite array of complex organic molecules, which constitute all living things. A few major kinds of groupings are shown here. Note that each element forms a characteristic number of bonds: carbon, 4; nitrogen, 3; oxygen, 2; hydrogen, 1; sulfur, 2; and phosphorus, 5. Bonds left hanging (lines without atoms attached) indicate attachments to other atoms or groups of atoms.

Ionic Bonding

Another way in which atoms may achieve a stable electron configuration is to gain additional electrons to complete the filling of an orbital or to lose excess electrons in an incompleted orbital. In general, the maximum number of electrons that can be gained or lost by an atom is three. Therefore, an element's atomic number determines whether one or more electrons will be lost or gained. If an atom's outer orbital is one to three electrons short of being filled, it will always tend to gain additional electrons. If an atom has one to three electrons in excess of its last complete orbital, it will always tend to lose those electrons.

Of course, gaining or losing electrons results in the number of electrons in an atom being greater or less than the number of protons; the atom consequently has an electric charge. The charge will be one negative unit for each electron gained and one positive unit for each electron lost (Fig. C–4). A covalently bonded group of atoms may acquire an electric charge in the same way. An atom or group of atoms that has acquired an electric charge in this way is called an **ion**, positive or negative. Ions are designated by a superscript following the chemical symbol, which denotes the number of positive or negative charges. The absence of superscripts indicates that the atom or molecule is neutral. Some important ions are listed in Table C–2.

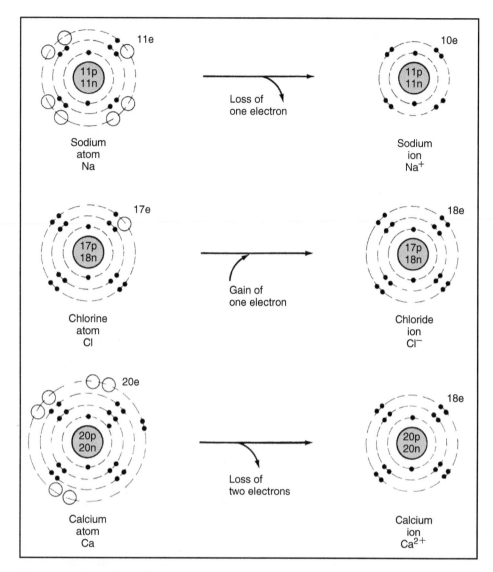

Figure C–4 **Formation of ions.** Many atoms will tend to gain or lose one or more electrons in order to achieve a state of complete (electron-filled) orbitals. In doing so, these atoms become positively or negatively charged ions, as indicated.

TABLE C–2 Ions of Particular Importance to Biological Systems			
Negative (–) Ions		**Positive (+) Ions**	
Phosphate	PO_4^{3-}	Potassium	K^+
Sulfate	SO_4^{2-}	Calcium	Ca^{2+}
Nitrate	NO_3^-	Magnesium	Mg^{2+}
Hydroxyl	OH^-	Iron	Fe^{2+}, Fe^{3+}
Chloride	Cl^-	Hydrogen	H^+
Bicarbonate	HCO_3^-	Ammonium	NH_4^+
Carbonate	CO_3^{2-}	Sodium	Na^+

Figure C–5 Crystals. Positive and negative ions bond together by their mutual attraction and form crystals.

Because unlike charges attract, positive and negative ions tend to join and pack together in dense clusters in such a way as to neutralize an atom's overall electric charge. This joining together of ions through the attraction of their opposite charges is called **ionic bonding**. The result is the formation of hard, brittle, more or less crystalline substances of which all rocks and minerals are examples (**Fig. C–5**).

It is significant to note that whereas covalent bonding leads to discrete molecules, ionic bonding does not. Any number and combination of positive and negative ions may enter into an ionic bond to produce crystals of almost any size. The only restriction is that the overall charge of positive ions be balanced by that of negative ions. Thus, substances bonded in an ionic fashion are properly called compounds but not molecules. When chemical formulas are used to describe such compounds, they define the ratio of various elements involved, not specific molecules.

Chemical Reactions

While atoms themselves do not change, the bonds between atoms may be broken and re-formed, with different atoms producing different compounds or molecules. This is essentially what occurs in all chemical reactions. What determines whether a given chemical reaction will occur? Earlier, we noted that atoms form bonds because they achieve a greater stability by doing so. However, some bonding arrangements may provide greater overall stability than others. Consequently, substances with relatively unstable bonding arrangements will tend to react to form one or more different compounds that have more stable bonding arrangements. Common examples are the reaction between hydrogen and oxygen to produce water and the reaction between carbon and oxygen to produce carbon dioxide (**Fig. C–6**).

Hydrogen + Oxygen — Energy → Water
Relatively unstable — Very stable

$$2H_2 + O_2 \longrightarrow 2H_2O$$
Balanced equation

Carbon Oxygen — Energy → Carbon dioxide
Unstable — Very stable

$$C + O_2 \longrightarrow CO_2$$
Balanced equation

Figure C–6 Stable bonding arrangements. Some bonding arrangements are more stable than others. Chemical reactions will go spontaneously toward more stable arrangements, releasing energy in the process. However, reactions may be driven in the opposite direction with suitable energy inputs.

Energy is always released when the constituents of a reaction gain greater overall stability, as indicated in the figure. Thus, when energy is released in a chemical reaction, the atoms achieve more stable bonding arrangements. Therefore, it may be said that chemical reactions always tend to go in a direction that releases energy as well as giving greater stability.

However, chemical reactions can be made to go in a reverse direction. With suitable energy inputs and under suitable conditions, stable bonding arrangements may be broken and less stable arrangements formed. As described in Chapter 3 of the text, this is the basis of the photosynthesis that occurs in green plants. Light energy causes the highly stable hydrogen-oxygen bonds of water to split and form less stable carbon-hydrogen bonds, thus creating high-energy organic compounds.

Obviously, much more could be said about the involvement of chemistry in environmental science. We would highly recommend a course (or several courses) in chemistry to the student who wants to gain a deeper understanding of how the subject is involved in environmental concepts and issues.

GLOSSARY

abiotic Pertaining to factors or things that are separate and independent from living things; nonliving.

abortion The termination of a pregnancy by some form of surgical or medicinal intervention.

acid Any compound that releases hydrogen ions when dissolved in water. Also, a water solution that contains a surplus of hydrogen ions.

acid deposition Any form of acid precipitation and also fallout of dry acid particles. (See **acid precipitation.**)

acid neutralizing capacity (ANC) In a water body, the capacity to neutralize acids due to the presence of **buffer** chemicals in solution.

acid precipitation Includes acid rain, acid fog, acid snow, and any other form of precipitation that is more acidic than normal (i.e., less than pH 5.6). Excess acidity is derived from certain air pollutants—namely, sulfur dioxide and oxides of nitrogen.

acquired immunodeficiency syndrome (AIDS) A fatal disease caused by the human immunodeficiency virus (HIV) and transmitted by sexual contact or the use of nonsterile needles (as in drug addiction).

activated-sludge system A system for removing organic wastes from water. The system uses microorganisms and active aeration to decompose such wastes. The system is used most as a means of secondary sewage treatment following the primary settling of materials.

active safety features Those safety features of nuclear reactors that rely on operator-controlled reactions, external power sources, and other features that are capable of failing. (See **passive safety features.**)

acute A reaction to a disease or chemical pollutant that brings on life-threatening reactions within hours or days.

adaptation An ecological or evolutionary change in structure or function that enables an organism to adjust better to its environment and hence enhances the organism's ability to survive and reproduce.

adiabatic cooling The cooling that occurs when warm air rises and encounters lower atmospheric pressure. **Adiabatic warming** is the opposite process, whereby cool air descends and encounters higher pressure.

Advanced Boiling-Water Reactor (ABWR) A third generation nuclear reactor design for power plants that incorporates many passive safety features. It is the design of choice for most new and planned reactors.

aeration *Soil:* The exchange within the soil of oxygen and carbon dioxide necessary for the respiration of roots. *Water:* The bubbling of air or oxygen through water to increase the amount of oxygen dissolved in the water.

aerosols Microscopic liquid and solid particles originating from land and water surfaces and carried up into the atmosphere.

Agenda 21 A definitive program to promote sustainable development that was produced by the 1992 Earth Summit in Rio de Janeiro, Brazil, and adopted by the UN General Assembly.

age structure Within a population, the different proportions of people who are old, middle aged, young adults, and children.

air pollutants Gases or aerosols in the atmosphere that have harmful effects on people or the environment.

Air Pollution Control Act Federal legislation introduced in 1955 that was the first attempt to bring air pollution under control.

air pollution disaster A short-term situation in industrial cities in which intense industrial smog brings about a significant increase in human mortality.

air toxics A category of air pollutants that includes radioactive materials and other toxic chemicals that are present at low concentrations but are of concern because they often are carcinogenic.

alga, pl. algae Any of numerous kinds of photosynthetic plants that live and reproduce while entirely immersed in water. Many species (the planktonic forms) exist as single cells or small groups of cells that float freely in the water. Other species (the seaweeds) may be large and attached.

algal bloom A relatively sudden development of a heavy growth of algae, especially planktonic forms. Algal blooms generally result from additions of nutrients, whose scarcity is normally limiting.

alkaline, alkalinity A *basic* substance; chemically, a substance that absorbs hydrogen ions or releases hydroxyl ions; in reference to natural water, a measure of the base content of the water.

altitude The vertical distance from sea level.

ambient standards Air-quality standards (set by the EPA) determining certain levels of pollutants that should not be exceeded in order to maintain environmental and human health.

amensalism An interaction between species whereby one species is harmed, while the other is unaffected.

American Recovery and Reinvestment Act of 2009 (Recovery Act) Legislation that provided money for a variety of programs, intended to stimulate the economy during the recent recession. Some $90 billion was directed into clean energy programs.

anaerobic Lacking oxygen.

anaerobic digestion The breakdown of organic material by microorganisms in the absence of oxygen. The process results in the release of methane gas as a waste product.

animal testing Procedures used to assess the toxicity of chemical substances, using rats, mice, and guinea pigs as surrogates for humans who might be exposed to the substances.

anthropogenic Referring to pollutants and other forms of impact on natural environments that can be traced to human activities.

AP1000 Advanced Passive Reactor A third generation nuclear power reactor manufactured by Westinghouse, the choice of most of the recent license applications in the United States.

aquaculture A propagation or rearing of any aquatic (water) organism in a more or less artificial system.

aquifer An underground layer of porous rock, sand, or other material that allows the movement of water between layers of nonporous rock or clay. Aquifers are frequently tapped for wells.

Arctic Climate Impact Assessment (ACIA) An assessment of the serious impacts of global warming on the Arctic region, published in 2004.

artificial selection Plant and animal breeders' practice of selecting individuals with the greatest expression of desired traits to be the parents of the next generation.

asthma A chronic disease of the respiratory system in which the air passages tighten and constrict, causing breathing difficulties; acute attacks may be life threatening.

Atlanta BeltLine A redevelopment initiative that employs an old railroad loop around the heart of Atlanta, providing parks, trails and rail transportation that will improve urban Atlanta.

Atlantic Meridional Overturning Circulation (AMOC) The pattern of ocean currents that involves global seawater movements between the surface and great depths. See **conveyor system.**

atmosphere The thin layer of gases surrounding Earth. Nitrogen, oxygen, water vapor, and carbon dioxide are major gases, while many minor gases are also present in trace amounts.

atmosphere-ocean general circulation model (AOGCM) A computer-based model for simulating long-term climatic conditions that combines global atmospheric circulation patterns with ocean circulation and cloud-radiation feedback.

atmospheric brown cloud (ABC) A 1- to 3-km-thick blanket of pollution that frequently sits over south and central Asia, made up of black carbon and soot from biomass and fossil fuel burning.

atom The fundamental unit of all elements.

atomic theory Theory that all matter is made up of particles called atoms, represented by more than 100 different elements in nature.

autotroph Any organism that can synthesize all its organic substances from inorganic nutrients, using light or certain inorganic chemicals as a source of energy. Green plants are the principal autotrophs.

Bacillus thuringensis (BT) A type of bacterium that produces a toxin that can kill the larvae of plant-eating insects; genes from this bacterium have been incorporated into plants using genomic techniques.

background radiation Radiation that comes from natural sources apart from any human activity. We are all exposed to such radiation.

bacterium, pl. bacteria Any of numerous kinds of prokaryotic microscopic organisms that exist as simple single cells that multiply by simple division. Along with fungi, bacteria constitute the decomposer component of ecosystems. A few species cause disease.

balance-of-trade deficit A deficit in money flow resulting from purchasing more from other countries than is sold to other countries.

BANANA ("build absolutely nothing anywhere near anything") An acronym expressing a common attitude about siting various facilities.

barrels of oil equivalent (BOE) A measurement that uses the energy content of a barrel of oil to compare different fossil fuel energy amounts.

Bar screen In a primary sewage treatment plant, a row of bars about one inch apart that provides initial screening of debris found in incoming sewage.

base Any compound that releases hydroxyl (OH–) ions when dissolved in water. A solution that contains a surplus of hydroxyl ions.

Basel Convention An international agreement that bans most international toxic-waste trade.

bed load The load of coarse sediment, mostly coarse silt and sand, that is gradually moved along the bottom of a riverbed by flowing water rather than being carried in suspension.

benefit-cost analysis A comparison of the benefits of any particular action or project to its costs. (See **cost-benefit ratio**.)

benthic plants Plants that grow under water and that are attached to or rooted in the bottom of the body of water. For photosynthesis, these plants depend on light penetrating the water.

benzene An organic chemical present in crude and refined oil products and tobacco smoke, a known human carcinogen.

best-demonstrated available technologies (BDATs) Treatment standards for hazardous wastes that have the effect of reducing their toxicity and mobility.

best management practice Farm management practice that serves best to reduce soil and nutrient runoff and subsequent pollution.

bioaccumulation The accumulation of higher and higher concentrations of potentially toxic chemicals in organisms. Bioaccumulation occurs in the case of substances that are ingested but that cannot be excreted or broken down (nonbiodegradable substances).

biochemical oxygen demand (BOD) The amount of oxygen that will be absorbed or "demanded" as wastes are being digested or oxidized in both biological and chemical processes. Potential impacts of wastes are commonly measured in terms of the BOD.

biodegradable Able to be consumed and broken down to natural substances, such as carbon dioxide and water, by biological

organisms, particularly decomposers. Opposite: **nonbiodegradable**.

biodiesel Diesel fuel made from a mixture of vegetable oil (largely soybean oil) and regular diesel oil.

biodiversity The diversity of living things found in the natural world. The concept usually refers to the different species but also includes ecosystems and the genetic diversity within a given species.

biodiversity hot spots Thirty-four locations around the world that are home to some 60% of the world's known biodiversity.

biofuel Any fuel, but usually liquids, derived from agricultural crops (e.g., ethanol and plant oils).

biogas The mixture of gases—about two-thirds methane, one-third carbon dioxide, and small portions of foul-smelling compounds—resulting from the anaerobic digestion of organic matter. The methane content enables biogas to be used as a fuel.

biogeochemical cycle The repeated pathway of particular nutrients or elements from the environment through one or more organisms and back to the environment. The cycles include the carbon cycle, the nitrogen cycle, the phosphorus cycle, and so on.

biological evolution The theory, attributed to Charles Darwin and Alfred Russell Wallace, that all species now on Earth descended from ancestral species through a process of gradual change brought about by natural selection.

biological nutrient removal (BNR) A process employed in sewage treatment to remove nitrogen and phosphorus from the effluent coming from secondary treatment.

biological wealth The life-sustaining combination of commercial, scientific, and aesthetic values imparted to a region by its biota.

biomagnification Bioaccumulation occurring through several levels of a food chain.

biomass The mass of biological material. Usually the total mass of a particular group or category (e.g., biomass of producers).

biomass energy Energy produced by burning plant-related materials such as firewood.

biomass fuels Fuels in the form of plant-related material (e.g., firewood, grasses, organic farm wastes).

biomass pyramid The structure that is obtained when the respective biomasses of producers, herbivores, and carnivores in an ecosystem are compared. Producers have the largest biomass, followed by herbivores and then carnivores.

biome A group of ecosystems that are related by having a similar type of vegetation governed by similar climatic conditions. Examples include prairies, deciduous forests, arctic tundra, deserts, and tropical rain forests.

biopesticide Naturally occurring substances that are designed to control pests; such substances usually clear the EPA registration process quickly. See **Bacillus thuringensis**.

bioremediation The use of microorganisms for the decontamination of soil or groundwater. Usually involves injecting organisms or oxygen into contaminated zones.

biosolid In sewage treatment, biosolids are the relatively stable organic matter that remains after anaerobic digestion has taken place in sludge digesters.

biosphere The overall ecosystem of Earth. The sum total of all the biomes and smaller ecosystems, which ultimately are all interconnected and interdependent through global processes such as the water cycle and the atmospheric cycle.

biota The sum total of all living organisms. The term usually is applied to the setting of natural ecosystems.

biotechnology The use of genetic engineering techniques, enabling researchers to introduce new genes into food crops and domestic animals and thereby produce valuable products and more nutritious crops.

biotic community All the living organisms (plants, animals, and microorganisms) that live in a particular area.

biotic potential Reproductive capacity. The potential of a species for increasing its population and/or distribution. The biotic potential of every species is such that, given optimum conditions, its population will increase. (Contrast **environmental resistance**.)

biotic structure   The organization of living organisms in an ecosystem into groups such as producers, consumers, detritus feeders, and decomposers.

birth control   Any means, natural or artificial, that may be used to reduce the number of live births.

bisphenol A (BPA)   A starter material for many plastics that is suspected of contributing to obesity, diabetes, altered sexual behavior, and cancer because of its estrogenic activity. See **endocrine disruptor**.

Blue Revolution   A proposed radical change in managing water supplies intended to make more water available for human use.

blue water   In the hydrologic cycle, precipitation and its further movement in infiltration, runoff, surface water, and groundwater; liquid water wherever it occurs.

BOD   See **biochemical oxygen demand**.

body mass index   A measurement used to calculate overweight and obesity; the ratio of weight in kilograms divided by the square of height in meters.

boiling-water reactor   A nuclear reactor that employs boiling water to create steam, which is circulated to turbines that generate electricity; the water is cooled and returned to the reactor tank.

bottle law, bottle bill   A law that provides for the recycling or reuse of beverage containers, usually by requiring a returnable deposit upon purchase of the item.

bottom-up regulation   Basic control of a natural population that occurs as a result of the scarcity of some resource.

breeder reactor   A nuclear reactor that, in the course of producing energy, also converts nonfissionable uranium-238 into fissionable plutonium-239, which can be used as fuel. Hence, a reactor that produces at least as much nuclear fuel as it consumes. Also called a **fast-neutron reactor**.

broad-spectrum pesticides   Chemical pesticides that kill a wide range of pests. These pesticides also kill a wide range of nonpest and beneficial species; therefore, they may lead to environmental disturbances and resurgences. The opposite of narrow-spectrum pesticides.

brownfields   Abandoned, idled, or underused industrial and commercial facilities whose further development is inhibited because of real or perceived chemical contamination.

BTU (British thermal unit)   A fundamental unit of energy in the English system. The amount of heat required to raise the temperature of 1 pound of water 1 degree Fahrenheit.

buffer   A substance that will maintain a constant pH in a solution by absorbing added hydrogen or hydroxyl ions. An example is the bicarbonate ion, the most important buffer in blood.

Bureau of Land Management (BLM)   A federal agency that manages public lands other than national forests and national parks. The agency leases land to ranchers for grazing, among other activities.

bush meat   Wild game that is harvested for food, especially in developing countries; often involves poaching and overexploitation.

calorie   A fundamental unit of energy. The amount of heat required to raise the temperature of 1 gram of water 1 degree Celsius. All forms of energy can be converted to heat and measured in calories. Calories used in connection with food are kilocalories, or "big" calories, the amount of heat required to raise the temperature of 1 liter of water 1 degree Celsius.

cancer   Any of a number of cellular changes that result in uncontrolled cellular growth.

cap-and-trade system   A form of market-based environmental policy that sets a maximum level of pollutant (the cap), distributes pollution permits, and allows industries to trade permits to achieve their allowable pollution.

capillary water   Water that clings in small pores, cracks, and spaces against the pull of gravity (e.g., water held in a sponge).

capital   In classical economic theory, one of the three factors of production (alongside land and labor); more broadly, any form of wealth. See **intangible capital, ecosystem capital** and **natural capital**.

carbon dioxide sinks   The oceans and terrestrial environments serve to absorb some of the carbon dioxide added to the atmosphere by human agency; these are called sinks.

carbon monoxide   A highly poisonous gas, the molecules of which consist of a carbon atom with one oxygen attached. Not to be confused with carbon dioxide, a natural gas in the atmosphere.

carbon tax   A tax levied on all fossil fuels in proportion to the amount of carbon dioxide that is released as they burn.

carcinogen, carcinogenic   Having the property of causing cancer, at least in animals and, by implication, in humans.

carnivore   An animal that feeds more or less exclusively on other animals.

carrying capacity   The maximum population of a given species that an ecosystem can support without being degraded or destroyed in the long run. Represented symbolically by K.

Cartagena Protocol on Biosafety   An international agreement governing trade in genetically modified organisms. The Cartagena Protocol was signed in January 2000.

Carter Doctrine   As stated by President Jimmy Carter in 1980, the assertion that the United States would use military force to ensure our access to Persian Gulf oil.

catalyst   A substance that promotes a given chemical reaction without itself being consumed or changed by the reaction. Enzymes are catalysts for biological reactions. Also, catalysts are used in some pollution control devices (e.g., the catalytic converter).

catalytic converter   The device used by vehicle manufacturers to reduce the amounts of carbon monoxide, hydrocarbons, and nitrogen oxides in a vehicle's exhaust. The converter contains catalysts that changes these compounds to less harmful gases as the exhaust passes through.

catch shares   See **individual quota system**.

cell   The basic unit of life; the smallest unit that still maintains all the attributes of life. Many microscopic organisms consist of a single cell. Large organisms consist of trillions of specialized cells functioning together.

cell respiration   The chemical process that occurs in all living cells whereby organic compounds are broken down to release energy required for life processes. For respiration, higher plants and animals require oxygen and release carbon dioxide and water as waste products, but certain microorganisms do not require oxygen.

cellulose   The organic macromolecule that is the prime constituent of plant cell walls and hence the major molecule in wood, wood products, and cotton. Cellulose is composed of glucose molecules, but because it cannot be digested by humans, its dietary value is only as fiber, bulk, or roughage.

center-pivot irrigation   An irrigation system consisting of a spray arm several hundred meters long, supported by wheels, pivoting around a central well from which water is pumped.

Centers for Disease Control and Prevention (CDC)   An agency within the United States Department of Health and Human Services that is the lead federal agency for protecting the health and safety of the public.

centrally planned economy   An economic system in which a ruling class makes most of the basic decisions about how the economy will be structured; typical of communist countries.

chain reaction   A nuclear reaction wherein each atom that fissions (splits) causes one or more additional atoms to fission.

character displacement   An effect of interspecific competition, whereby a physical change occurs in one or both competing species that lessens competition when the two species co-occur.

chemical energy   The potential energy that is contained in certain chemicals; most importantly, the energy that is contained in organic compounds such as food and fuels and that may be released through respiration or burning.

chemical treatment The use of pesticides and herbicides to control or eradicate agricultural pests.

chemosynthesis The process whereby some microorganisms utilize the chemical energy contained in certain reduced inorganic chemicals (e.g., hydrogen sulfide) to produce organic matter.

chlorinated hydrocarbons Synthetic organic molecules in which one or more hydrogen atoms have been replaced by chlorine atoms. Chlorinated hydrocarbons are hazardous compounds because they tend to be nonbiodegradable and therefore to bioaccumulate; many have been shown to be carcinogenic. Also called **organochlorides**.

chlorine catalytic cycle In the stratosphere, a cyclical chemical process in which chlorine monoxide breaks down ozone.

chlorofluorocarbons (CFCs) Synthetic organic molecules that contain one or more of both chlorine and fluorine atoms and that are known to cause ozone destruction.

chlorophyll The green pigment in plants responsible for absorbing the light energy required for photosynthesis.

chromosome In a living organism, one of a number of structures on which genes are arranged in a linear fashion.

chronic A reaction to infection or pollutants that leads to a gradual deterioration of health over a period of years.

chronic obstructive pulmonary disease (COPD) A progressive lung disease that makes it hard to breathe, involving three syndromes: asthma, bronchitis, and emphysema.

CITES (Convention on International Trade in Endangered Species) An international treaty conveying some protection to endangered and threatened species by restricting trade in those species or their products.

clay Any particles in soil that are less than 0.004 millimeters in size.

Clean Air Act of 1970 Amended in 1977 and 1990, the act is the foundation of U.S. air pollution control efforts.

Clean Air Interstate Rule (CAIR) EPA rule published in 2005 establishing cap-and-trade programs for sulfur dioxide and nitrogen oxides in 28 eastern states.

Clean Water Act of 1972 (CWA) The cornerstone federal legislation addressing water pollution.

clear-cutting In harvesting timber, the practice of removing an entire stand of trees, leaving an ugly site that takes years to recover.

climate A general description of the average temperature and rainfall conditions of a region over the course of a year.

Climate Change Science Compendium 2009 A report issued by the United Nations Environment Program that addresses many new findings in climate change science since the IPCC's Fourth Assessment.

Climate Change Science Program (CCSP) See Global Change Research Program (GCRP).

climate sensitivity The response of climate to greenhouse gas concentrations, usually measured as a rise in temperature as a consequence of a rise in greenhouse gas concentration.

climax ecosystem The last stage in ecological succession. An ecosystem in which populations of all organisms are in balance with each other and with existing abiotic factors.

cogeneration Also known as **combined heat and power (CHP)**, the joint production of useful heat and electricity. For example, furnaces may be replaced with gas turbogenerators that produce electricity, while the hot exhaust still serves as a heat source. An important avenue of conservation, cogeneration effectively avoids the waste of heat that normally occurs at centralized power plants.

combined heat and power (CHP) See **cogeneration**.

combustion The practice of disposing of wastes by incineration in a special facility designed to handle large amounts of waste; modern combustion facilities also capture some of the energy by generating electricity on the site.

command-and-control strategy The basic strategy behind most public policy having to do with air and water pollution. The strategy involves setting limits on pollutant levels and specifying control technologies that must be used to achieve those limits.

commensalism A relation between two species in which one is benefited and the other is not affected.

common good A recognition of the need for protection of the natural world and improvement of human welfare, especially as applied to public policy.

commons, common-pool resources Resources (usually natural ones) owned by many people in common or, as in the case of the air or the open oceans, owned by no one but open to exploitation.

community In ecological contexts, a community is defined as the group of populations of different species of plants, animals, and microbes living together in one area.

community supported agriculture An arrangement between farms and local citizens where the citizens are shareholders in the farm, supporting the farmers and gaining access to fresh farm produce.

compaction Packing down. *Soil*: Packing and pressing out air spaces present in the soil. Compaction reduces soil aeration and infiltration and thus diminishes the capacity of the soil to support plants. *Trash*: Packing down trash to reduce the space that it requires.

competition In ecology, the interaction between members of the same species or between different species for essential resources or access to those resources.

competitive exclusion principle The concept that when two species compete very directly for resources, one eventually excludes the other from the area.

composting compost The process of letting organic wastes decompose in the presence of air. A nutrient-rich humus, or compost, is the resulting product.

composting toilet A toilet that does not flush wastes away with water but deposits them in a chamber where they will compost. (See **composting**.)

compound Any substance (gas, liquid, or solid) that is made up of two or more different kinds of atoms bonded together. (Contrast **element**.)

Comprehensive Environmental Response, Compensation, and Liability Act of 1980 (CERCLA) See **Superfund**.

Comprehensive Everglades Restoration Plan (CERP) Multi-billion-dollar plan to restore the Florida Everglades by addressing water flow and storage.

concepts Valid explanations of data from the natural world that often allow predictions but do not reach the level of validity of natural laws.

condensation The collecting of molecules from the vapor state to form the liquid state, as, for example, when water vapor condenses on a cold surface and forms droplets. Opposite: **evaporation**.

condenser A device that turns turbine exhaust steam into water in a power plant.

conditions Abiotic factors (e.g., temperature) that vary in time and space but are not used up by organisms.

confined animal feeding operation (CAFO) Animal farming where the animals are kept in crowded pens, producing wastes that are hard to manage and creating other health threats.

coniferous forest biome A biome occupying northern regions or higher mountainous altitudes dominated by coniferous trees.

conservation The management of a resource in such a way as to ensure that it will continue to provide maximum benefit to humans over the long run. *Energy*: Saving energy by cutting back on the use of heating, air conditioning, lighting, transportation, and so on and also by increasing the efficiency of energy use.

conservation biology The branch of science focused on the protection of populations and species.

conservation reserve An imaginary source of energy that results from policies promoting greater efficiency of energy use, resulting in a reduced energy requirement.

Conservation Reserve Program (CRP) A federal program whereby farmers are paid to place highly erodible cropland in a reserve. A similar program, the **Conservation Stewardship Program**, encourages farmers to conserve soil and water resources on their lands.

consumers In an ecosystem, those organisms that derive their energy from feeding on other organisms or their products.

consumption In ecological use, the process of feeding on organic matter as a source of energy; all heterotrophs are consumers.

consumptive use The harvesting of natural resources in order to provide for people's immediate needs for food, shelter, fuel, and clothing.

consumptive water use The use of water for such things as irrigation, wherein the water does not remain available for potential purification and reuse.

containment building The reinforced concrete building housing a nuclear reactor. Designed to contain an explosion, should one occur.

continental drift See **plate tectonics**.

contour farming The practice of cultivating land along the contours across, rather than up and down, slopes. In combination with strip cropping, contour farming reduces water erosion.

contraceptive A device or method employed by couples during sexual intercourse to prevent the conception of a child.

control rods A part of the core of a nuclear reactor; the rods of neutron-absorbing material that are inserted or removed as necessary to control the rate of nuclear fissioning.

covalent bond A chemical bond between two atoms, formed by sharing a pair of electrons between the atoms. Atoms of all organic compounds are joined by covalent bonds.

convection/convection currents The vertical movement of air due to atmospheric heating and cooling, moving generally in a west-to-east pattern.

Convention on Biological Diversity The biodiversity treaty signed by 158 nations at the Earth Summit in Rio de Janeiro in 1992 calling for various actions and cooperative steps between nations to protect the world's biodiversity.

conversion losses Unavoidable energy losses in energy production, usually due to the loss of heat energy.

conveyor system The giant pattern of oceanic currents that moves water masses from the surface to the depths and back again, producing major effects on the climate.

cooling tower A massive tower designed to dissipate waste heat from a power plant (or other industrial facility) into the atmosphere by condensing turbine exhaust steam into water.

Copenhagen Accord The agreement signed at the 2009 Copenhagen meeting of delegates of the Framework Convention on Climate Change, pledging actions to limit global temperature increases to 2°C above preindustrial levels.

coral bleaching A condition, usually brought on by excessively high temperatures, in hard corals where the coral animals expel their symbiotic algae and become white in appearance.

corporate average fuel economy (CAFE) Fuel economy standards for vehicles set by the National Highway Traffic Safety Administration.

corrosion In a nuclear power plant, the deterioration of pipes receiving hot, pressurized water in a circulation system that conveys heat from one part of the unit to another.

cosmetic spraying The spraying of pesticides to control pests that damage only the surface appearance of fruits and vegetables.

cost-benefit analysis See **benefit-cost analysis**.

cost-benefit ratio, benefit-cost ratio The value of the benefits to be gained from a project, divided by the costs of the project. If the ratio is greater than unity, the project is economically justified; if the ratio is less than unity, the project is not economically justified.

cost-effectiveness analysis An alternative to benefit-cost analysis, this approach accepts the merits of a goal and attempts to achieve the goal with the least costly alternative.

credit associations Groups of poor people who individually lack the collateral to assure loans but who collectively have the wherewithal to assure each other's loans. Associated with microlending.

criteria maximum concentration (CMC) A water-quality standard; the highest single concentration of a water pollutant beyond which environmental impacts may be expected.

criteria pollutants Certain pollutants whose levels are used as a gauge for the determination of air (or water) quality.

criterion continuous concentration (CCC) A water-quality standard; the highest sustained concentration of a water pollutant beyond which undesirable impacts may be expected.

critical habitat Under the Endangered Species Act, an area provided for a listed species where it can be found or could likely spread as it recovers.

critical number The minimum number of individuals of a given species that is required to maintain a healthy, viable population of the species. If a population falls below its critical number, it will likely become extinct.

Cross State Air Pollution Rule The ruling by the EPA that replaces the Clean Air Interstate Rule, requiring reductions in NO_x and SO_2 to aid states in the East to achieve ozone and particulate matter reductions.

crude birthrate (CBR) The number of births per 1,000 individuals per year.

crude death rate (CDR) The number of deaths per 1,000 individuals per year.

cryptogamic crust Made up of primitive plants, called cryptogams, the crust develops on hardened soils and can stabilize soil but also prevents water infiltration and seed germination.

cryosphere Snow and sea ice in polar regions; it is significant in its contribution to the planetary albedo as it reflects sunlight.

crystal A solid form of matter made up of regularly repeating units of atoms, ionic compounds, or molecules.

cultural control A change in the practice of growing, harvesting, storing, handling, or disposing of wastes that reduces their susceptibility or exposure to pests. For example, spraying the house with insecticides to kill flies is a chemical control; putting screens on the windows to keep flies out is a cultural control.

cultural eutrophication The process of natural eutrophication accelerated by human activities. (See **eutrophication**.)

curie The unit of measurement of radioactivity; one gram of pure radium 226 gives off one curie per second, or 37 billion spontaneous disintegrations into particles and radiation.

d–t reaction A nuclear fusion reaction employing the hydrogen isotopes deuterium and tritium; the reaction takes extremely high temperatures and is very difficult to contain.

DALY (disability-adjusted life year) In assessing the disease burden of different health risks, 1 DALY equals the loss of one healthy year of a person's life (whether through disability or loss of life).

DDT (dichlorodiphenyltrichloroethane) The first and most widely used of the synthetic organic pesticides belonging to the chlorinated hydrocarbon class.

dead zone A region of an aquatic ecosystem (usually a marine coastal area) where oxygen is low or absent from the bottom up well into the water column. Also called a **hypoxic area**.

debt crisis Brought about by the great debt incurred by many less-developed nations, this crisis involves countries building up debts that can never be paid off.

debt relief Steps, including cancellation of debts and other means of reducing poverty, taken by the World Bank and donor nations to alleviate the heavy debt of many poor nations.

declining tax base The loss of tax revenues that occurs when affluent taxpayers and businesses leave an area and property values subsequently decline. Also referred to as an **eroding tax base**.

decommissioning The retirement of nuclear power plants from service after 25 or more years because the effects of radiation will gradually make them inoperable.

decomposers Organisms whose feeding action results in decay or rotting of organic material. The primary decomposers are fungi and bacteria.

deep-well injection A technique used for the disposal of liquid chemical wastes that involves putting them into deep dry wells where they permeate dry strata.

deforestation The process of removing trees and other vegetation covering the soil and converting the forest to another land use, often leading to erosion and loss of soil fertility.

Delaney clause A stipulation in the Federal Food, Drug, and Cosmetic Act of 1938 that prohibited the use of any food additive that is found to induce cancer in humans or animals; this has been replaced by the **negligible risk** standard.

demand-side policies Energy policies that emphasize conserving energy and using more renewable and nuclear energy in the future.

demographic dividend As a country goes through the demographic transition, there is a stage when the dependency ratio is low, giving the country the opportunity to spend more on poverty alleviation and economic growth.

demographic transition The transition of a human population from a condition of a high birthrate and a high death rate to a condition of a low birthrate and a low death rate. A demographic transition may result from economic or social development.

demography/demographer The study of population trends (growth, movement, development, and so on). People who perform such studies and make projections from them.

denitrification The process of reducing oxidized nitrogen compounds present in soil or water to nitrogen gas to the atmosphere, conducted by certain bacteria and now utilized in the treatment of sewage effluents.

density-dependent An attribute of population-balancing factors, such as predation, that increase and decrease in intensity in proportion to population density. May lead to population stability.

density-independent Mortality to a population that occurs regardless of the population density. Tends to be destabilizing to populations.

Department of Transportation regulations (DOT regs) Regulations intended to reduce the risk of spills, fires, and poisonous fumes by specifying the kinds of containers and methods of packing to be used in transporting hazardous materials.

dependency ratio In a human population, the ratio of the nonworking-age population (under 15 and over 65) to the working-age population.

desalination A process that purifies seawater into high-quality drinking water via distillation or microfiltration.

desert biome The pattern of living forms and habitat where rainfall is less than 25 centimeters (10 inches) per year.

desertification The formation and expansion of degraded areas of soil and vegetation cover in arid, semiarid, and seasonally dry areas, caused by climatic variations and human activities. Desertified land is most commonly traced to erosion due to human mismanagement.

desert pavement A covering of stones and coarse sand protecting desert soils from further wind erosion. The covering results from the differential erosion of finer material.

detritivores Organisms (fungi, soil insects, bacteria) that feed on dead or decaying organic matter, important in completing the breakdown of organic matter to inorganic constituents.

detritus The dead organic matter, such as fallen leaves, twigs, and other plant and animal wastes, that exists in any ecosystem.

detritus feeders See **detritivores**.

deuterium (^{2}H) A stable, naturally occurring isotope of hydrogen that contains one neutron in addition to the single proton normally in the nucleus.

developed countries The high-income industrialized countries—the United States, Canada, western European nations, Japan, Korea, Australia, and New Zealand, as well as many middle-income countries such as those in Latin America, China, eastern Europe, and many Arab states.

developing countries Countries in which the gross domestic product is less than $936 per capita. The category includes nations of Africa, India, other countries of southern Asia, and some former Soviet republics.

development A term referring to the continued improvement of human well-being, usually in the developing countries.

Diclofenac An anti-inflammatory drug often administered to animals but toxic to birds. Implicated in the die-off of vultures in the Indian subcontinent.

dioxin A synthetic organic chemical of the chlorinated hydrocarbon class. Dioxin is highly toxic and a widespread environmental pollutant given off in the combustion of many organic compounds.

discharge permit (technically called an **NPDES permit**) A permit that allows a company to legally discharge certain amounts or levels of pollutants into air or water.

discount rate In economics, a rate applied to some future benefit or cost in order to calculate its present real value.

dish-engine system A solar power system consisting of a set of parabolic concentrator dishes that focus sunlight onto a receiver, where the hot fluid is transferred to an engine that generates electricity.

disinfection The killing (as opposed to removal) of microorganisms in water or other media where they might otherwise pose a health threat. For example, chlorine is commonly used to disinfect water supplies.

dissolved oxygen (DO) Oxygen gas molecules (O_2) dissolved in water. Fish and other aquatic organisms depend on dissolved oxygen for respiration. Therefore, the concentration of dissolved oxygen is a measure of water quality.

distillation A process of purifying water or some other liquid by boiling the liquid and recondensing the vapor. Contaminants remain behind in the boiler.

disturbance A natural or human-induced event or process (e.g., a forest fire) that interrupts ecological succession and creates new conditions on a site.

DNA (deoxyribonucleic acid) The natural organic macromolecule that carries the genetic or hereditary information for virtually all organisms.

Doha Development Round Negotiations for trade begun in 2001 with the objective of lowering trade barriers around the world.

donor fatigue The tendency of donor organizations or countries to withhold their aid because of long-term misuse of aid funds in the recipient countries.

dose The mathematical product of the concentration of a hazardous material and the length of exposure to it. The effects of any given material or radiation correspond to the dose received.

dose-response assessment Part of risk assessment, establishing the number of cancers that might develop due to exposure to different doses of a chemical.

drip irrigation A method of supplying irrigation water through tubes that literally drip water onto the soil at the base of each plant.

drought A local or regional lack of precipitation such that the ability to raise crops and water animals is seriously impaired.

drylands Ecosystems characterized by low precipitation (25 to 75 cm per year) and often subject to droughts; some 41% of Earth's land is drylands.

Durban Platform An agreement forged at Durban in 2011 at the 17th Conference of the Parties to the FCCC where delegates agreed to begin negotiations leading to a binding agreement to curb greenhouse gas emissions by 2015.

easement In reference to land protection, an arrangement whereby a landowner gives up development rights into the future but retains ownership of the land.

ecdysone The hormone that promotes molting in insects.

ecological economist An economist who thoroughly integrates ecological and economic concerns; part of a new breed of economist who disagrees with classical economic theory.

ecological footprint A concept for measuring the demand placed on Earth's resources by individuals from different parts of the world, involving calculations of the natural area required to satisfy human needs.

ecological pest control Natural control of pest populations through understanding various ecological factors and, so far as possible, utilizing those factors, as opposed to using synthetic chemicals.

ecological risk assessment (ERA) Risk assessment by the EPA designed to protect natural organisms and ecosystems from adverse effects of human activities.

ecological succession The gradual or sometimes rapid change in the species that occupy a given area, with some species invading and becoming more numerous, while others decline in population and disappear. Succession is caused by a change in one or more abiotic or biotic factors that benefit some species at the expense of others.

ecologists Scientists who study ecology.

ecology The study of all processes influencing the distribution and abundance of organisms and the interactions between living things and their environment.

economic exclusion The cutting off of access of certain ethnic or economic groups to jobs, a good education, and other opportunities and thus preventing them from entering the economic mainstream of society—a condition that prevails in poor areas of cities.

economics The social science that deals with the production, distribution, and consumption of goods and services.

economic production As seen by ecological economists, economic production is the process of converting the natural world to the manufactured world.

Economic Simplified Boiling Water Reactor (ESBWR) A Generation III nuclear power reactor proposed by General Electric; it has many more passive safety feataures than current Advanced Boiling Water Reactors.

economic systems The social and legal arrangements people in societies construct in order to satisfy their needs and wants and improve their well-being.

economic threshold The level of pest damage that, to be reduced further, would require an application of pesticides that is more costly than the economic damage caused by the pests.

economy See **economic systems.**

ecosystem An interactive complex of communities and the abiotic environment affecting them within a particular area. Ecosystems have characteristic forms, such as deserts, grasslands, tundra, deciduous forests, and tropical rain forests.

ecosystem capital The sum of goods and services provided by natural and managed ecosystems, both free of charge and essential to human life and well-being.

ecosystem management The management paradigm, adopted by all federal agencies managing public lands, that involves a long-term stewardship approach to maintaining the lands in their natural state.

ecotone A transitional region between two adjacent ecosystems that contains some of the species and characteristics of each one and also certain species of its own.

ecotourism The enterprises involved in promoting tourism of unusual or interesting ecological sites.

edges Breaks between habitats that may expose sensitive species to predators.

electrical power The amount of work done by an electric current over a given time.

electric generator A device that converts mechanical energy into electrical energy by way of wire coils that are rotated in a magnetic field.

electrolysis The use of electrical energy to split water molecules into their constituent hydrogen and oxygen atoms. Hydrogen gas and oxygen gas result.

electrolyzer In a solar receptor that is designed to produce fuel from water using solar energy, a catalyst that uses the electron energy to split water into hydrogen and oxygen.

electrons Fundamental atomic particles that have a negative electrical charge and a very small mass, approximately 9.1×10^{-31} kg. Electrons surround the nuclei of atoms and thus balance the positive charge of protons in the nucleus. A flow of electrons in a wire is identical to an electrical current.

element A substance that is made up of one and only one distinct kind of atom. (Contrast **compound.**)

El Niño/La Niña Southern Oscillation (ENSO) A climatic phenomenon characterized by major shifts in atmospheric pressure over the central equatorial Pacific Ocean. An El Niño involves the movement of unusually warm surface water into the eastern equatorial Pacific Ocean, and a La Niña reverses the pattern. These phenomena result in extensive disruption of weather around the world.

eluviation In soils, the process of leaching many minerals due to the downward movement of water; the E in E horizon of soil profiles stands for eluviation.

embrittlement Becoming brittle. Pertains especially to the reactor vessel of nuclear power plants gradually becoming prone to breakage or snapping as a result of continuous bombardment by radiation.

Emergency Planning and Community Right-to-Know Act of 1986 (EPCRA) See **SARA.**

emergent vegetation Aquatic plants whose lower parts are underwater but whose upper parts emerge from the water.

endangered species A species whose total population is declining to relatively low levels such that, if the trend continues, the species will likely become extinct.

Endangered Species Act The federal legislation that mandates the protection of species and their habitats that are determined to be in danger of extinction.

endemic species A species that is found only in a particular geographic area or habitat.

endocrine See **hormone.**

endocrine disrupters Any of a class of organic compounds, often pesticides, that are suspected of having the capacity to interfere with hormonal activities in animals.

endocrine system The collection of all of the hormones and glands that produce them in animal bodies; they control metabolism, growth, and reproduction.

energy The capacity to do work. Common forms of energy are light, heat, electricity, motion, and the chemical bond energy inherent in compounds such as sugar, gasoline, and other fuels.

energy carrier Something (e.g., electricity) that transfers energy from a primary energy source to its point of use.

energy conservation and efficiency All of those steps that are taken to avoid or reduce the use of energy, such as raising the Corporate Average Fuel Economy standards for cars and trucks.

energy flow The movement of energy through ecosystems, starting with the capture of solar energy by primary producers and ending with the loss of heat energy.

Energy Independence and Security Act of 2007 Legislation establishing energy policy by emphasizing demand-side policies such as conserving energy and using renewable energy sources.

Energy Policy Act of 2005 Legislation establishing U.S. energy policy for years to come, encouraging greater use of fossil fuels and nuclear power, and providing some support for energy conservation and renewable energy.

Energy Star Program The EPA's program focusing on energy conservation in buildings and in appliances. An Energy Star tag signals that the device or building incorporates energy-saving technology.

enhanced recovery In the removal of oil from an oil field, a process that increases recovery beyond secondary recovery by injecting carbon dioxide or hydraulic fluids into wells.

enrichment With reference to nuclear power, the separation and concentration of uranium-235 so that, in suitable quantities, it will sustain a chain reaction.

entomologist A scientist who studies insects and their life cycles, physiology, behavior, and economic significance.

entropy A degree of disorder; increasing entropy means increasing disorder.

environment   The combination of all things and factors external to the individual or population of organisms in question.

environmental accounting   A process of keeping national accounts of economic activity that includes gains and losses of environmental assets.

environmental health   The study of the connections between hazards in the environment and human disease and death.

environmental impact   The effect on the natural environment caused by human actions. Includes indirect effects, for example, through pollution, as well as direct effects such as cutting down trees.

environmental impact statement   A study of the probable environmental impacts of a development project. The National Environmental Policy Act of 1968 (NEPA) requires such studies prior to proceeding with any project receiving federal funding.

environmentalism   An attitude or movement involving concern about pollution, resource depletion, population pressures, loss of biodiversity, and other environmental issues. Usually also implies action to address those concerns.

environmentalist   Any person who is concerned about the degradation of the natural world and is willing to act on that concern.

environmental justice   The fair treatment and meaningful involvement of all people, regardless of race, color, national origin, or income, with respect to the development, implementation, and enforcement of environmental laws and regulations.

environmental movement   The upwelling of public awareness and citizen action that began during the 1960s regarding environmental issues.

environmental public policy   All of a society's laws and regulations that deal with that society's interactions with the environment. Its purpose is to promote the common good.

environmental racism   Discrimination against people of color whereby hazardous industries are sited in nonwhite neighborhoods and towns.

environmental resistance   The totality of factors such as adverse weather conditions, shortages of food or water, predators, and diseases that tend to cut back populations and keep them from growing or spreading. (Contrast **biotic potential**.)

Environmental Revolution   In the view of some, a coming change in the adaptation of humans to the rising deterioration of the environment. The Environmental Revolution should bring about sustainable interactions with the environment.

environmental science   The multidisciplinary branch of science concerned with environmental issues.

environmental tobacco smoke (ETS)   See **secondhand smoke**.

enzyme   A protein that promotes the synthesis or breaking of chemical bonds.

EPA (U.S. Environmental Protection Agency)   The federal agency responsible for the control of all forms of pollution and other kinds of environmental degradation.

epidemiologic transition   In human populations, the pattern of change in mortality from high death rates to low death rates; contributes to the demographic transition.

epidemiology, epidemiological study   The study of the causes of disease (e.g., lung cancer) through an examination and comparison of large populations of people living in different locations or following different lifestyles or habits (e.g., smoking versus nonsmoking).

equilibrial species   See *K-strategists*

equilibrium   Referring to populations, the condition where births plus immigration are more or less equal to deaths plus emigration over time.

equilibrium climate sensitivity   The sustained change in mean global temperature that occurs if atmospheric carbon dioxide is held at double preindustrial values, or 550 parts per million.

equity   An ethical principle where people's needs are met in an impartial and just manner.

equity principle   An ethical principle claiming that those who produce the most pollution should compensate those who produce

less, especially because the less fortunate often suffer the most from, say, global climate change.

erosion   The process of soil particles being carried away by wind or water. Erosion moves the smaller particles first and hence degrades the soil to a coarser, sandier, stonier texture.

estimated reserves   See **reserves**.

estuary   A bay or river system open to the ocean at one end and receiving freshwater at the other. In the estuary, freshwater and saltwater mix, producing brackish water.

ethnobotany   The study of the relationships between plants and people.

ethyl alcohol   The main product of fermentation of sugars or starches, also called ethanol. It is a 2-carbon compound that can be burned in combustion engines as a substitute for gasoline.

euphotic zone   In aquatic systems, the layer or depth of water through which an adequate amount of light penetrates to support photosynthesis.

eutrophic   Characterized by nutrient-rich water supporting an abundant growth of algae or other aquatic plants at the surface.

eutrophication   The process of becoming eutrophic.

evaporation   The process whereby molecules leave the liquid state and enter the vapor or gaseous state, as, for example, when water evaporates to form water vapor. Opposite: **condensation**.

evaporative water loss   The loss of moisture from soil by evaporation; it can be lessened by covering the soil with detritus or plant cover.

evapotranspiration   The combination of evaporation and transpiration that restores water to the atmosphere.

evolution   See **biological evolution**.

e-waste   Any of a broad array of electronic devices that are discarded and often are hazardous to handle and difficult to recycle.

executive branch   That facet of the government in the United States consisting of the president, his cabinet, and all administrative agencies.

exotic species   A species introduced into a geographical area to which it is not native; also, species that are rare and subject to illegal trafficking.

experimentation   In the practice of science, the testing of hypotheses by setting up situations where cause and effect are investigated, using careful measurements of conditions and responses.

exponential increase   The growth produced when a base population increases by a given percentage (as opposed to a given amount) each year. An exponential increase is characterized by doubling again and again, each doubling occurring in the same period of time. It produces a J-shaped curve.

exposure assessment   A part of risk assessment, identifying human groups exposed to a chemical and calculating the doses and length of time of their exposure.

extended product responsibility   Voluntary or government programs that assign some responsibility for reducing the environmental impact of a product at various stages of its life cycle—especially at disposal.

external cost, externality   Any effect of a business process not included in the usual calculations of profit and loss. Pollution of air or water is an example of a *negative* externality—one that imposes a cost on society that is not paid for by the business itself.

extinction   The death of all individuals of a particular species. When this occurs, all the genes of that particular line are lost forever.

extreme poverty   Poverty that is defined as living on less than $1.25 a day. In 2012, some 1.4 billion were in this condition.

exurban migration   The pronounced trend since World War II of relocating homes and businesses from the central city and older suburbs to more outlying suburbs.

exurbs   New developments beyond the traditional suburbs, from which most residents still commute to the associated city for work.

facilitation   A mechanism of succession where earlier species create conditions that are more favorable to newer occupants and are replaced by them.

family planning Making contraceptives and other health and reproductive services available to couples in order to enable them to achieve a desired family size.

famine A severe shortage of food accompanied by a significant increase in the local or regional death rate.

FDA Food Safety Modernization Act A bill passed in 2010 that expanded the authority of the Food and Drug Administration over the food processing industry, in response to repeated outbreaks of food poisoning and pathogens in food.

fecal coliform test A test for the presence of *Escherichia coli*, the bacterium that normally inhabits the gut of humans and other mammals. A positive test result indicates sewage contamination and the potential presence of disease-causing microorganisms.

Federal Agricultural Improvement and Reform (FAIR) Act of 1996 Major legislation removing many subsidies and controls from farming.

Federal Food and Drug Administration (FDA) The federal agency with jurisdiction over foods, drugs, and all products that come in contact with the skin or are ingested.

feedback loops In ecological or environmental systems, feedback loops are processes that can amplify (positive loop) or dampen (negative loop) the behavior of the system. See **positive feedback**.

fermentation A form of respiration carried on by yeast cells and many bacteria in the absence of oxygen. Fermentation involves a partial breakdown of glucose (sugar) that yields energy for the yeast and the release of alcohol as a by-product.

fertility rate See **total fertility rate**.

fertility transition The pattern of change in birthrates in a human society from high rates to low; a major component of the demographic transition.

fertilizer Material applied to plants or soil to supply plant nutrients, most commonly nitrogen, phosphorus, and potassium but possibly others. *Organic* fertilizer is natural organic material, such as manure, that releases nutrients as it breaks down. *Inorganic* fertilizer, also called chemical fertilizer, is a mixture of one or more necessary nutrients in inorganic chemical form.

field scouts Persons trained to survey crop fields and determine whether applications of pesticides or other pest management procedures are actually necessary to avert significant economic loss.

FIFRA (Federal Insecticide, Fungicide, and Rodenticide Act) The key U.S. legislation passed to control pesticides.

fire climax ecosystems Ecosystems that depend on the recurrence of fire to maintain the existing balance.

first-generation pesticides Toxic inorganic chemicals that were the first used to control insects, plant diseases, and other pests. These pesticides included mostly compounds of arsenic and cyanide and various heavy metals, such as mercury and copper.

First Law of Thermodynamics The empirical observation, confirmed innumerable times, that energy is never created or destroyed but may be converted from one form to another (e.g., electricity to light). Also called the **Law of Conservation of Energy**. (See also **Second Law of Thermodynamics**.)

fishery Fish species being exploited, or a limited marine area containing commercially valuable fish.

fish ladder A stepwise series of pools on the side of a dam where the water flows in small falls that fish can negotiate.

fission The splitting of a large atom into two atoms of lighter elements. When large atoms such as uranium or plutonium fission, tremendous amounts of energy are released.

fission products Any and all atoms and subatomic particles resulting from splitting atoms in nuclear reactors or nuclear explosions. Practically all such products are highly radioactive.

fitness The state of an organism whereby it is adapted to survive and reproduce in the environment it inhabits.

flat-plate collector A solar collector that consists of a stationary, flat, black surface oriented perpendicular to the average angle of the sun. Heat absorbed by the surface is removed and transported by air or water (or some other liquid) flowing over or through the surface.

flood irrigation A technique of irrigation in which water is diverted from rivers by means of canals and is flooded through furrows in fields.

food aid Food of various forms that is donated or sold below cost to needy people for humanitarian reasons.

Food and Agriculture Organization of the United Nations (FAO) The UN agency responsible for coordinating international efforts to defeat hunger; also gathers and disseminates information about forests, fisheries, and farming.

food chain The transfer of energy and material through a series of organisms as each one is fed upon by the next.

Food Conservation and Energy Act of 2008 The latest farm bill, maintaining the existing high levels of support and subsidies to farms.

Food Quality Protection Act (FQPA) Passed in 1996, this act amended existing laws governing pesticide use and residues on foods, including the **Delaney clause**.

food security For families, the ability to meet the food needs of everyone in the family, providing freedom from hunger and malnutrition.

Forest Stewardship Council An alliance of organizations directed toward the certification of sustainable wood products.

food web The combination of all the feeding relationships that exist in an ecosystem.

fossil fuels Energy sources—mainly crude oil, coal, and natural gas—that are derived from the prehistoric photosynthetic production of organic matter on Earth.

FQPA (Food Quality Protection Act of 1996) Legislation that removed the Delaney clause and replaced many provisions of FIFRA.

fracking Refers to hydraulic fracturing, a technique for extracting natural gas and oil involving pumping fluids into a well to open up spaces that release gas or oil to be pumped back up the well.

fragile states Countries that are poor and conflict-prone, often lacking a stable government; an example is present-day Somalia.

fragmentation The division of a landscape into patches of habitat by road construction, agricultural lands, or residential areas.

Framework Convention on Climate Change (FCCC) A result of the 1992 Earth Summit, this international treaty was a start in negotiating agreements on steps to prevent future catastrophic climate change.

Framework Convention on Tobacco Control Adopted in 2003 and put into effect in 2005, this is a global treaty that aims to reduce the spread of smoking with the use of various strategies.

frankenfood A derogatory term used by opponents to genetic modification, applying to any food plant that has been developed with the use of genetic engineering.

free-market economy In its purest form, an economy in which the market itself determines what and how goods will be exchanged. The system is wholly in private hands.

freshwater Water that has a salt content of less than 0.1% (1,000 parts per million).

front The boundary where different air masses meet.

fuel cell A device that produces electrical energy by combining hydrogen and oxygen, used to power vehicles and other electrical machines.

fuel elements (fuel rods) The pellets of uranium or other fissionable material that are placed in tubes, or fuel rods, and that, together with the control rods, form the core of the nuclear reactor.

fuel load Dead trees and dense understories in many forestlands that tend to burn readily if ignited in a forest fire.

fuelwood The use of wood for cooking and heating; the most common energy source for people in developing countries.

fungus, pl. fungi Any of numerous species of molds, mushrooms, bracket fungi, and other forms of nonphotosynthetic plants. Fungi derive energy and nutrients by consuming other organic material. Along with bacteria, they form the decomposer component of ecosystems.

fusion The joining together of two atoms to form a single atom of a heavier element. When light atoms such as hydrogen are fused, tremendous amounts of energy are released.

gasohol A blend of 90% gasoline and 10% ethanol that can be substituted for straight gasoline. Gasohol serves to stretch gasoline supplies and enable gasoline to burn more cleanly.

gene A segment of DNA that codes for one protein, which in turn determines a particular physical, physiological, or behavioral trait.

gene pool The sum total of all the genes that exist among all the individuals of a species.

gene revolution The widespread development of genetically modified crops.

genetically modified organism (GMO) Any organism that has received genes from a different species through the techniques of genetic engineering; also called a transgenic organism.

genetic bank The concept that natural ecosystems with all their species serve as a repository of genes that may be drawn upon to improve domestic plants and animals and to develop new medicines, among other uses.

genetic control The selective breeding of a desired plant or animal to make it resistant to attack by pests. Also, attempting to introduce harmful genes—for example, those that cause sterility—into the pest populations.

genetic engineering The artificial transfer of specific genes from one organism to another.

Genuine Progress Indicator (GPI) An alternative measure of economic progress, the GPI calculates positive and negative economic activities, to reach a more realistic view of sustainable economic activity. It is an alternative to the **gross domestic product**.

geoengineering Large-scale schemes, proposed to reduce global climate change, involving major intrusions into climatic or ecological systems.

Geographic Informations Systems A digital technology enabling the location and imaging of landscapes by use of satellite signals. It employs hardware, software, and data to display many forms of geographic information.

geothermal Refers to the naturally hot interior of Earth, where heat is maintained by naturally occurring nuclear reactions.

geothermal energy Useful energy derived from water heated by the naturally hot interior of Earth.

geothermal heat pump An energy system whereby heat can be obtained or deposited via pipes buried in the ground and an exchange process that allows heated or cooled air to be circulated via ductwork.

GLASOD A map produced by the Global Assessment of Soil Degradation, prepared in the late 20th century and often cited but based on very suspect data.

Global Assessment of Land Degradation and Improvement (GLADA) A new assessment of land degradation based on satellite remote-sensing techniques.

Global Change Research Program (GCRP) The U.S. government-sponsored program that addresses a number of issues in climate change with research and reports.

global climate change The cumulative effects of rising levels of greenhouse gases on Earth's climate. These effects include global warming, weather changes, and a rising sea level.

Global Climate Change Initiative The Bush administration's voluntary response to climate change, involving a reduction in **emissions intensity**.

Global Forest Resources Assessment (FRA) A periodic assessment of forest resources conducted by the UN Food and Agricultural Organization (FAO) and made the basis of regular FAO *State of the World's Forest* reports.

Global Gag Rule The U.S. policy initiated by President Reagan and continued by other Republican presidents, whereby U.S. government aid is denied to any agency that provides abortions or abortion counseling.

globalization The accelerating interconnectedness of human activities, ideas, and cultures, especially evident in economic and information exchange.

glucose A simple sugar, the major product of photosynthesis. Glucose serves as the basic building block for cellulose and starches and as the major "fuel" for the release of energy through cell respiration in both plants and animals.

glyphosate (Roundup®) A herbicide that kills most varieties of plants, used to control weeds with crops that have been bioengineered with resistance to the glyphosate.

golden rice New strains of rice produced by genetic engineering that contain carotene (which the body uses to synthesize vitamin A) and iron, intended to compensate for nutritional deficiencies.

goods Products, such as wood and food, that are extracted from natural ecosystems to satisfy human needs.

Grameen Bank A banking network serving the poor with microloans, created by Muhammad Yunus of Bangladesh.

grassland biome Geographical regions that have seasonal rainfall of 10 to 60 inches/yr and are dominated by grass species and large grazing animals.

grassroots Environmental efforts that begin at the level of the populace, often in response to a perceived problem not being addressed by public policy.

gravitational water Water that is not held by capillary action in soil but that percolates downward by the force of gravity.

graying The increasing average age in populations in developed countries and in many developing countries that is occurring because of decreasing birthrates and increasing longevity.

gray water Wastewater, as from sinks and tubs, that does not contain human excrement. Such water can be reused without purification for some purposes.

greenhouse effect An increase in the atmospheric temperature caused by increasing amounts of carbon dioxide and certain other gases that absorb and trap heat, which normally radiates away from Earth.

greenhouse gases Gases in the atmosphere that absorb infrared energy and contribute to the air temperature. These gases are like a heat blanket and are important in insulating Earth's surface. Among the greenhouse gases are carbon dioxide, water vapor, methane, nitrous oxide, chlorofluorocarbons, and other halocarbons.

green products Manufactured products that are more environmentally benign than their traditional counterparts.

Green Revolution The development and introduction of new varieties of (mainly) wheat and rice that have increased yields per acre dramatically in many countries since the 1960s.

green water In the hydrologic cycle, water that is evaporated or transpired and returned as water vapor to the atmosphere; water in vapor form.

grit chamber A part of preliminary treatment in wastewater-treatment plants; a swimming pool–like tank in which the velocity of the water is slowed enough to let sand and other gritty material settle.

gross domestic product The total value of all goods and services exchanged in a year within a country.

groundwater Water that has accumulated in the ground, completely filling and saturating all pores and spaces in rock or soil. Free to move more or less readily, it is the reservoir for springs and wells and is replenished by infiltration of surface water.

groundwater remediation The repurification of contaminated groundwater by any of a number of techniques.

gully erosion Soil erosion produced by running water and resulting in the formation of gullies.

habitat The specific environment (woods, desert, swamp) in which an organism lives.

habitat destruction Known to be responsible for 36% of known extinctions, the destruction of natural habitats is one of the greatest threats to wild species and ecosystems.

Hadley cell A system of vertical and horizontal air circulation predominating in tropical and subtropical regions and creating major weather patterns.

half-life The length of time it takes for half of an unstable isotope to decay. The length of time is the same regardless of the starting amount. Also refers to the amount of time it takes compounds to break down in the environment.

halogenated hydrocarbon A synthetic organic compound containing one or more atoms of the halogen group, which includes chlorine, fluorine, and bromine.

hard water Water that contains relatively large amounts of calcium or certain other minerals that cause soap to precipitate. (Contrast **soft water**.)

hazard Anything that can cause (1) injury, disease, or death to humans; (2) damage to property; or (3) degradation of the environment. *Cultural* hazards include factors that are often a matter of choice, such as smoking or sunbathing. *Biological* hazards are pathogens and parasites that infect humans. *Physical* hazards are natural disasters like earthquakes and tornadoes. *Chemical* hazards refer to the chemicals in use in different technologies and household products.

hazard communication standard The outcome of amendments to the Occupational Safety and Health Act of 1970, this law guarantees the workers' right to know about hazardous materials they encounter.

hazard identification The process of examining evidence linking a potential hazard to its possible harmful effects; a major element of risk assessment by the EPA.

hazardous material (HAZMAT) Any material having one or more of the following attributes: ignitability, corrosivity, reactivity, and toxicity.

health According to the World Health Organization, "a state of complete physical, social, and mental well-being and not merely the absence of disease or infirmity."

heavy metal Any of the high-atomic-weight metals, such as lead, mercury, cadmium, and zinc. All may be serious pollutants in water or soil because they are toxic in relatively low concentrations and they tend to bioaccumulate.

heavy water Deuterium oxide (D_2O), a form of water incorporating a heavy isotope of hydrogen.

herbicide A chemical used to kill or inhibit the growth of undesired plants.

herbivore An organism such as a rabbit or deer that feeds primarily on green plants or plant products such as seeds or nuts. Such an organism is said to be herbivorous. (Synonym: **primary consumer**.)

herbivory The feeding on plants that occurs in an ecosystem. The total feeding of all plant-eating organisms.

heterotroph Any organism that consumes organic matter as a source of energy. Such an organism is said to be heterotrophic.

high-level wastes In a nuclear reactor, the direct products of fission produce highly radioactive isotopes that make the management of reactor wastes difficult and hazardous.

Highway Trust Fund The monies collected from the gasoline tax and designated for the construction of new highways.

HIPPO An acronym for the major threats to biodiversity: Habitat destruction, Invasive species, Pollution, Population, and Overexploitation.

hormones Natural chemical substances that control the development, physiology, and behavior of an organism. Hormones are produced internally and affect only the individual organism. Hormones are coming into use in pest control. (See also **pheromones**.)

host In feeding relationships, particularly parasitism, refers to the organism that is being fed upon (i.e., the organism that is supporting the feeder).

host-parasite relationship The relationship between a parasite and the organism upon which it feeds.

hot spots See **biodiversity hot spots**.

household hazardous wastes An important component of the hazardous-waste problem in the United States.

Hubbert Peak The concept proposed by M. King Hubbert that peak oil production will follow a bell-shaped curve when half of available oil would have been withdrawn.

human capital See **intangible capital**.

Human Poverty Index, Human Development Index Based on life expectancy, literacy, and living standards, these indices are used by the United Nations Development Program to measure progress in alleviating poverty.

human system The entire system that humans have created for their own support, consisting of agriculture, industry, transportation, communication networks, and so on.

humidity The amount of water vapor in the air. (See also **relative humidity**.)

humus A dark brown or black, soft, spongy residue of organic matter that remains after the bulk of dead leaves, wood, or other organic matter has decomposed. Humus does oxidize, but relatively slowly. It is extremely valuable in enhancing the physical and chemical properties of soil.

hunger A condition wherein the basic food required for meeting nutritional and energy needs is lacking and the individual is unable to lead a normal, healthy life.

hunter-gatherers Humans surviving by hunting wild game and gathering seeds, nuts, berries, and other edible things from the natural environment.

hybrid A plant or animal resulting from a cross between two closely related species that do not normally cross.

hybrid electric vehicle An automobile combining a gasoline motor and a battery-powered electric motor that produces less pollution and gets higher gasoline mileage than do conventional gasoline-powered vehicles.

hybridization Cross-mating between two more or less closely related species.

hydrocarbons *Chemistry*: Natural or synthetic organic substances that are composed mainly of carbon and hydrogen. Crude oil, fuels from crude oil, coal, animal fats, and vegetable oils are examples. *Pollution*: A wide variety of relatively small carbon-hydrogen molecules resulting from incomplete burning of fuel that are emitted into the atmosphere. (See **volatile organic compounds**.)

hydroelectric dam A dam and an associated reservoir used to produce electrical power by letting the high-pressure water behind the dam flow through and drive a turbogenerator.

hydroelectric power Electric power that is produced from hydroelectric dams or, in some cases, natural waterfalls.

hydrogen bonding A weak attractive force that occurs between a hydrogen atom of one molecule and, usually, an oxygen atom of another molecule. Hydrogen bonding is responsible for holding water molecules together to produce the liquid and solid states.

hydrogen economy A future economy where renewable energy via hydrogen as a major energy carrier prevails.

hydrogen ions Hydrogen atoms that have lost their electrons (chemical symbol, H+).

hydrologic cycle The movement of water from points of evaporation, through the atmosphere, through precipitation, and through or over the ground, returning to points of evaporation.

hydrosphere The water on Earth, in all of its liquid and solid compartments: oceans, rivers, lakes, ice, and groundwater.

hydroxyl radical The hydroxyl group (OH), missing the electron. The hydroxyl radical is a natural cleansing agent of the atmosphere. It is highly reactive, readily oxidizes many pollutants upon contact, and thus contributes to their removal from the air.

hygiene hypothesis The theory that human immune systems need to encounter microbes and even worms at early ages in order to stimulate a regulated anti-inflammatory network; this reduces incidences of allergies and asthma.

hypothesis A tentative guess concerning the cause of an observed phenomenon that is then subjected to experiment to test its logical or empirical consequences.

hypoxia See **dead zone**.

ICPD (International Conference on Population and Development) A UN-sponsored conference held in 1994 in Cairo, Egypt, that produced a program of action that was drafted and later adopted by the United Nations.

immigration The movement of people from countries of their birth to other countries, usually with the intent to reside there permanently.

ImPACT A refinement of the IPAT formula that separates the effects of Technology (T in the equation) into two components that incorporate the different effects of consumption of resources.

incremental value In the measurement of the value of ecosystem services, the incremental value of a service may be calculated when changes in that service occur.

indicator organism An organism, the presence or absence of which indicates certain conditions. For example, the presence of *Escherichia coli* indicates that water is contaminated with fecal wastes and that pathogens may be present.

individual quota system A system of fishery management wherein a quota is set and individual fishers are given or sold the right to harvest some proportion of the quota. Also called **catch shares**.

industrialized agriculture The use of fertilizer, irrigation, pesticides, and energy from fossil fuels to produce large quantities of crops and large numbers of livestock with minimal labor for domestic and foreign sale.

Industrial Revolution During the 19th century, the development of manufacturing processes using fossil fuels and based on applications of scientific knowledge.

industrial smog The grayish mixture of moisture, soot, and sulfurous compounds that occurs in local areas in which industries are concentrated and coal is the primary energy source.

infant mortality The number of babies that die before one year of age, per 1,000 babies born.

infiltration The process in which water soaks into soil as opposed to running off the surface of the soil.

infiltration-runoff ratio The ratio of the amount of water soaking into the soil to that running off the surface. The ratio is obtained by dividing the first amount by the second.

infrared radiation Radiation of somewhat longer wavelengths than red light, which comprises the longest wavelengths of the visible spectrum. Such radiation manifests itself as heat.

infrastructure The sewer and water systems, roadways, bridges, and other facilities that underlie the functioning of a city or a society.

inherently safe reactor In theory, a nuclear reactor that is designed in such a way that any accident would be automatically corrected, with no radioactivity released.

inorganic chemical In classifying chemical pollutants, some are inorganic, such as the heavy metals (lead, mercury and so forth) and salts.

inorganic compounds/molecules *Classical definition*: All things such as air, water, minerals, and metals that are neither living organisms nor products uniquely produced by living things. *Chemical definition*: All chemical compounds or molecules that do not contain carbon atoms as an integral part of their molecular structure. (Contrast **organic compounds/molecules**.)

inorganic fertilizer See **fertilizer**.

instrumental value The value that living organisms or species have by virtue of their benefit to people; the degree to which they benefit humans. (Contrast **intrinsic value**.)

insurance spraying The spraying of pesticides when it is not really needed, in the belief that it will ensure against loss due to pests.

intangible capital One component of the wealth of nations. Comprises the *human capital*, or the population and its attributes; the *social capital*, or the social and political environment that people have created in a society; and the *knowledge assets*, or the human fund of knowledge.

integrated gasification combined cycle (IGCC) plant A coal-fired technology where coal is mixed with water and oxygen and heated under pressure to produce a synthetic gas.

integrated pest management (IPM) A program consisting of two or more methods of pest control carefully integrated and designed to avoid economic loss from pests. The objective of IPM is to minimize the use of environmentally hazardous synthetic chemicals.

Integrated Risk Information System (IRIS) A compendium of risk information published by the EPA providing data on chemical hazards; available on the Internet.

integrated waste management The approach to municipal solid waste that provides for several options for dealing with wastes, including recycling, composting, waste reduction, and landfilling, as well as incineration where unavoidable.

Interdecadal Pacific Oscillation (IPO) One of several ocean-atmosphere cycles, a warm-cool cycle that swings back and forth across the Pacific over periods of several decades.

intergenerational equity Meeting the needs of the present without jeopardizing the ability of future generations to meet their needs in an equitable way.

Intergovernmental Panel on Climate Change (IPCC) The UN-sponsored organization charged with continually assessing the science of global climate change, its potential impacts, and the means of responding to the threat.

International Whaling Commission (IWC) The international body that regulates the harvesting of whales; the IWC placed a ban on all whaling in 1986.

interspecific competition Competition for resources between members of two or more species.

intragenerational equity The attempt to achieve an equitable distribution of assets within a given generation or across existing people groups.

intraspecific competition Competition for resources between members of the same species.

intrinsic value The value that living organisms or species have in their own right; in other words, organisms and species do not have to be useful to have value. (Contrast **instrumental value**.)

invasive species An introduced species that spreads out and often has harmful ecological effects on other species or ecosystems.

inversion See **temperature inversion**.

inverter In a photovoltaic (PV) system, the device that acts as an interface between the solar PV modules and the electric grid or batteries.

ion An atom (or a group of atoms) that has lost or gained one or more electrons and, consequently, has acquired a positive or negative charge. Ions are designated by "+" or "−" superscripts following the chemical symbol for the element(s) involved.

ion-exchange capacity See **nutrient-holding capacity**.

ionic bond The bond formed by the attraction between a positive and a negative ion.

ionizing radiation Radiation that displaces ions in tissues as it penetrates them, leaving behind charged particles (ions).

IPAT formula A conceptual formula relating environmental impact (I) to population (P), affluence (A), and technology (T).

isotope A form of an element in which the atoms have more (or less) than the usual number of neutrons. Isotopes of a given element have identical chemical properties but differ in mass (weight) as a result of the superfluity (or deficiency) of neutrons. Many isotopes are unstable and radioactive. (See **radioactive decay**, **radioactive emissions**, and **radioactive materials**.)

ISTEA (Intermodal Surface Transportation Efficiency Act) Legislation that provides for the funding of alternative transportation (e.g., mass transit or bicycle paths) using money from the Highway Trust Fund. Succeeded by the Transportation Equity Act for the Twenty-first Century (TEA–21) and then the Safe, Accountable, Flexible, Efficient Transportation Equity Act (SAFETEA).

IUCN (International Union for Conservations of Nature) Formerly the **World Conservation Union**. An international organization that maintains a Red List of threatened species worldwide.

jet stream A river of air, generated by Earth's rotation and air-pressure gradients, high in the troposphere that flows eastward at high speeds but meanders considerably.

judicial branch   One of the three branches of government set up by the U.S. constitution, involving a system of judges at various levels on up to the Supreme Court.

junk science   Information presented as valid science but unsupported by peer-reviewed research. Often, politically motivated and biased results are selected to promote a particular point of view.

juvenile hormone   The insect hormone that, at sufficient levels, preserves the larval state. Pupation requires diminished levels of juvenile hormone; hence, artificial applications of the hormone may block pupal development.

keystone species   A species whose role is essential for the survival of many other species in an ecosystem.

kinetic energy   The energy inherent in motion or movement, including molecular movement (heat) and the movement of waves (hence, radiation and therefore light).

knowledge assets   See **intangible capital**.

K-strategist   A reproductive strategy for a species whereby there is a low reproductive rate but good survival of young due to care and protection by adults. Such species often have populations close to the carrying capacity.

Kyoto Protocol   An international agreement among the developed nations to curb greenhouse gas emissions. The Kyoto Protocol was forged in December 1997 and became binding in 2004.

labor   In classical economic theory, one of the three elements that constitute the factors of production: the work done by people as they produce goods or services.

Lacey Act   Passed in 1900, the first national act that gave protection to wildlife by forbidding interstate commerce in illegally killed animals.

land   In classical economic theory, one of the three elements that constitute the factors of production: the natural resources used in the production of goods and services.

land degradation   The processes where land is rendered less capable of supporting plant growth, often through soil erosion.

land ethic   First described by Aldo Leopold, this is an ethic that promotes protection of natural areas based on their integrity, stability, and beauty.

landfill   A site where municipal, industrial, or chemical wastes are disposed of by burying them in the ground or placing them on the ground and covering them with earth.

landscape   A group of interacting ecosystems occupying adjacent geographical areas.

land subsidence   The gradual sinking of land. The condition may result from the removal of groundwater or oil, which is frequently instrumental in supporting the overlying rock and soil.

land trust   Land that is purchased and held by various private organizations specifically for the purpose of protecting the region's natural environment and the biota that inhabit it.

La Niña   See **El Niño/La Niña Southern Oscillation (ENSO)**.

larva, pl. larvae   A free-living immature form that occurs in the life cycle of many organisms and that is structurally distinct from the adult. For example, caterpillars are the larval stage of moths and butterflies.

latitude   In biomes, latitude is the distance from the equator, which determines the average temperature for a region.

Law of Conservation of Energy   See **First Law of Thermodynamics**.

Law of Conservation of Matter   The law stating that, in chemical reactions, atoms are neither created nor changed nor destroyed; they are only rearranged.

law of limiting factors   The law stating that a system may be limited by the absence or minimum amount (in terms of that needed) of any required factor. Also known as **Liebig's law of minimums**. (See **limiting factor**.)

leachate   The mixture of water and materials that are leaching.

leaching   The process in which materials in or on the soil gradually dissolve and are carried by water seeping through the soil. Leaching may eventually remove valuable nutrients from the soil, or it may carry buried wastes into groundwater, thereby contaminating it.

lead   One of the heavy metal pollutants, lead was once added to gasoline to improve combustion. It is toxic in very small quantities and has been removed from all but aviation gasoline.

legislative branch   One of the three branches of government set up by the U.S. constitution, the legislative branch consists of the House of Representatives and the Senate, all members of which are voted into office by the people of different states.

legumes   The group of pod-bearing land plants that is virtually alone in its ability to fix nitrogen; legumes include such common plants as peas, beans, clovers, alfalfa, and locust trees but no major cereal grains. (See **nitrogen fixation**.)

Liebig's law of minimums   See **law of limiting factors**.

life expectancy   The number of years a newborn can expect to live under mortality rates current for its country of residence.

life history   The progression of changes an organism undergoes in its life from birth to death.

light-water reactor (LWR)   A reactor that uses extra-pure ordinary water as a moderator. Nuclear plants in the United States are all LWRs.

limiting factor   A factor primarily responsible for determining the growth or reproduction of an organism or a population. The limiting factor in a given environment may be a physical factor such as temperature or light, a chemical factor such as a particular nutrient, or a biological factor such as a competing species.

limits of tolerance   The extremes of any factor (e.g., temperature) that an organism or a population can tolerate and still survive and reproduce.

lipids   A class of natural organic molecules that includes animal fats, vegetable oils, and phospholipids, the last being an integral part of cellular membranes.

lithosphere   The Earth's crust, made up of rocks and minerals.

litter   In an ecosystem, the natural cover of dead leaves, twigs, and other dead plant material. This natural litter is subject to rapid decomposition and recycling in the ecosystem, whereas human litter—such as bottles, cans, and plastics—is not.

livability   A subjective index of how enjoyable a city is to live in.

loam   A soil texture consisting of a mixture of about 40% sand, 40% silt, and 20% clay; loam is usually good soil.

locavore   People who try to purchase or grow most of their food within their own region; eating locally.

logistic growth   A pattern of growth of a population that results in an S-shaped curve plotted over time, such that the population levels off at the carrying capacity (K).

longevity   The maximum life span of individuals of a given species. The known record for humans is 122 years.

loss-of-coolant accident (LOCA)   A situation in a nuclear reactor where an accident causes the loss of the water from around the reactor, resulting in overheating and a possible meltdown of the nuclear core.

low-level wastes   Radioactive wastes from nuclear power plants and other facilities that employ radioisotopes; they are easier to manage than the high-level wastes.

low-till farming   Similar to no-till farming, except that instead of using herbicides, farmers plow just once over residues of a previous crop and plant their new crop.

LULU ("locally unwanted land use")   An acronym expressing the difficulty in siting a facility that is necessary but that no one wants in his or her immediate locality.

macromolecules   Very large organic molecules, such as proteins and nucleic acids, that constitute the structural and functional parts of cells.

Magnuson Act   An act passed in 1976 that extended the limits of jurisdiction over coastal waters and fisheries of the United States to 200 miles offshore. Reauthorized in 2006 as the **Magnuson-Stevens Fishery Conservation and Management Reauthorization Act**.

malnutrition   The lack of essential nutrients such as vitamins, minerals, and amino acids. Malnutrition ranges from mild to severe and life threatening.

marine protected area   An area of the coast or open ocean that is closed to commercial fishing and mineral mining; marine reserves.

marker-assisted breeding   The science of locating genes with desirable traits using DNA sequencing and then using cross-breeding with standard crop lines, thus avoiding the use of transgenics.

market-based policy   An approach to environmental regulation that allows the use of markets to achieve a desired outcome (e.g., a **cap-and-trade system** for reducing emissions of a pollutant).

mass number   The number that accompanies the chemical name or symbol of an element or isotope. The mass number represents the number of neutrons and protons in the nucleus of the atom.

material safety data sheets (MSDS)   Documents that contain information on the reactivity and toxicity of more than 600 chemicals and that must accompany the shipping, storage, and handling of these chemicals.

materials recovery facility (MRF)   A processing plant in which regionalized recycling is carried out. Recyclable municipal solid waste, usually presorted, is prepared in bulk for the recycling market.

matter   Any gas, liquid, or solid that occupies space and has mass. (Contrast **energy**.)

maximum achievable control technology (MACT)   The best technology available for reducing the output of especially toxic industrial pollutants.

maximum contaminant level (MCL)   A drinking water standard; the highest allowable concentration of a pollutant in a drinking water source.

maximum sustainable yield (MSY)   The maximum amount of a renewable resource that can be taken year after year without depleting the resource. The maximum sustainable yield is the maximum rate of use or harvest that will be balanced by the regenerative capacity of the system.

MDG Support Team   The successor to the Millennium Project, this team works with developing countries to achieve the targets of the Millennium Development Goals (MDGs).

Medical Revolution   Medical advances and public sanitation led to spectacular reductions in mortality, beginning in the late 1800s and extending to the present.

Megatons to Megawatts Program   An exchange program between the United States and Russia whereby weapons-grade uranium from Russia is diluted to produce power-plant uranium that is used in U.S. power plants.

meltdown   The event of a nuclear reactor's getting out of control or losing its cooling water so that it melts from its own production of heat. The melted reactor would continue to produce heat and could melt its way out of its containment vessel and eventually down into groundwater, where it would cause a violent eruption of steam that could spread radioactive materials over a wide area. (See **loss-of-coolant accident (LOCA)**.)

Mercury and Air Toxics Standards   Rules published by the EPA in 2011 that require all coal- and oil-fired power plants to limit their emissions of mercury and other toxic pollutants; industries have four years to comply with the rules.

mesosphere   A layer of atmosphere beyond the stratosphere where only very small quantities of gas are found.

metabolism   The sum of all the chemical reactions that occur in an organism.

meteorology   The scientific study of the atmosphere, involving both weather and climate.

methane   A gas, CH_4. Methane is the primary constituent of natural gas and is also a product of fermentation by microbes. Methane is one of the greenhouse gases.

methyl bromide   A soil fumigant to control agricultural pests; its use releases bromine to the atmosphere, and it destroys ozone when it gets up into the stratosphere.

microbe   Any microscopic organism, although primarily a bacterium, a virus, or a protozoan.

microbial   Of or pertaining to microbes.

microclimate   The actual conditions experienced by an organism in its particular location. Owing to numerous factors—such as shading, drainage, and sheltering—the microclimate may be quite distinct from the overall climate.

microfiltration   A technology for desalination, based on forcing seawater through very small pores in a membrane filter that removes the salt.

microlending   The process of providing very small loans (usually \$50–\$500) to poor people to facilitate their starting a small enterprise and becoming economically self-sufficient.

microorganism   See **microbe**.

midnight dumping   The illicit dumping of materials, particularly hazardous wastes, frequently under the cover of darkness.

Milankovitch cycle   A cycle of major oscillations in the Earth's orbit, taking place over frequencies of thousands of years and known to influence the distribution of solar radiation and therefore global weather patterns.

Millennium Development Goals (MDGs)   A comprehensive set of goals aimed at addressing the most important needs of people in the developing countries to improve their well-being, adopted by the United Nations at the UN Millennium Summit in 2000.

Millennium Ecosystem Assessment (MA)   A four-year effort by over 1,360 scientists to produce reports on the state of Earth's ecosystems. The reports are aimed at policy makers and the public and are all available on the Internet.

Millennium Project   A UN-commissioned project given a mandate to develop an action plan to coordinate the efforts of various agencies and organizations to achieve the Millennium Development Goals. Succeeded by the **MDG Support Team**.

Minamata disease   A disease named for a fishing village in Japan where an "epidemic" was first observed. Symptoms—which included spastic movements, mental retardation, coma, death, and crippling birth defects in the next generation—were found to be the result of mercury poisoning.

mineral   Any hard, brittle, stone-like material that occurs naturally in Earth's crust. All minerals consist of various combinations of positive and negative ions held together by ionic bonds. A pure mineral, or crystal, is one specific combination of elements. Common rocks are composed of mixtures of two or more minerals.

mineralization   The process of gradual oxidation of the organic matter (humus) present in soil that leaves just the gritty mineral component of the soil.

mitigation   Reducing greenhouse gas emissions by a variety of strategies and policies.

mixture   A combination of elements in which there is no chemical bonding between the molecules. For example, air contains (is a mixture of) oxygen, nitrogen, and carbon dioxide.

model   In the scientific method, observations may be put together to form a larger picture of how a system works, called a model.

moderator   In a nuclear reactor, any material that slows down neutrons from fission reactions so that they are traveling at the right speed to trigger another fission. Water and graphite are two types of moderators.

molecule   The smallest unit of two or more atoms forming a compound. A molecule has all the characteristics of the compound of which it is a unit.

monsoon   The seasonal airflow created by major differences in cooling and heating between oceans and continents, usually bringing extensive rain.

Montreal Protocol   An agreement made in 1987 by a large group of nations to cut back the production of chlorofluorocarbons in order to protect the ozone shield. A 1990 amendment called for the complete phaseout of these chemicals by 2000 in developed nations and by 2010 in less-developed nations.

morbidity   The incidence of disease in a population.

mortality   The incidence of death in a population.

mountaintop removal mining   A form of **strip mining** for coal that takes off whole tops of mountains to get at the seams of coal that are buried as deeply as 1,000 feet below the surface.

municipal solid waste (MSW) The entirety of refuse or trash generated by a residential and business community. Distinct from agricultural and industrial wastes, municipal solid waste is the refuse that a municipality is responsible for collecting and disposing of.

mutagenic Causing mutations.

mutation A random change in one or more genes of an organism. Mutations may occur spontaneously in nature, but their number and degree are vastly increased by exposure to radiation or certain chemicals. Mutations generally result in a physical deformity or metabolic malfunction.

mutualism A close relationship between two organisms from which both derive a benefit.

mycorrhiza, pl. mycorrhizae The mycelia of certain fungi that grow symbiotically with the roots of some plants and provide for additional nutrient uptake.

National Ambient Air Quality Standards (NAAQS) The allowable levels of ambient criteria air pollutants set by EPA regulation.

National Center for Environmental Assessment (NCEA) An agency within the EPA that performs and publishes risk assessments of substances and processes that are widely released in the environment.

National Emission Standards for Hazardous Air Pollutants (NESHAPs) The standards for allowable emissions of certain toxic substances.

National Energy Policy Report The 2001 report by a task force chaired by Vice President Cheney that emphasized dependence on **supply-side policies** to generate the energy needed by the United States into the future.

national forests Public forests and woodlands administered by the National Forest Service for multiple uses, such as logging, mineral exploitation, livestock grazing, and recreation.

national parks Lands and coastal areas of great scenic, ecological, or historical importance administered by the National Park Service, with the dual goals of protecting them and providing public access.

National Pollution Discharge Elimination System (NPDES) An EPA-administered program that addresses point-source water pollution through the issuance of permits that regulate pollution discharge.

National Priorities List (NPL) A list of the chemical waste sites presenting the most immediate and severe threats. Such sites are scheduled for cleanup ahead of other sites.

national wildlife refuges Administered by the U.S. Fish and Wildlife Service, these lands are maintained for the protection and enhancement of wildlife and for the provision of public access.

natural capital The natural assets and the services they perform. One form of the wealth of a nation is its complement of natural capital.

natural chemical control The use of one or more natural chemicals, such as hormones or pheromones, to control a pest.

natural enemies All the predators and parasites that may feed on a given organism. Organisms used to control a specific pest through predation or parasitism.

natural goods The food, fuel, wood, fibers, oils, alcohols, and the like derived from the natural world, on which the world economy and human well-being depend.

natural increase The number of births minus the number of deaths in a given population. The natural increase does not take into account immigration and emigration and is the percent of growth (or decline) of a given population during a year. It is found by subtracting the crude death rate from the crude birthrate and changing the result to a percent.

natural laws Generalizations derived from our observations of matter, energy, and other phenomena. Though not absolute, natural laws have been empirically confirmed to a high degree and are often derivable from higher-level theory.

natural organic compounds The organic compounds that make up living organisms, to be distinguished from synthetic organic compounds, like plastics.

Natural Resources Conservation Service (NRCS) Formerly the Soil Conservation Service, a nationwide network of offices that provides extension services to farmers and encourage soil and water conservation throughout the United States.

natural resources Features of natural ecosystems and species that are of economic value and that may be exploited. Also, features of particular segments of ecosystems, such as air, water, soil, and minerals.

natural sciences Those scientific disciplines that study the natural world, from subatomic particles to the cosmos.

natural selection The evolutionary process whereby the natural factors of environmental resistance tend to eliminate those members of a population that are least well adapted to cope with their environment and thus, in effect, tend to select those best adapted for survival and reproduction.

natural services Functions performed free of charge by natural ecosystems, such as control of runoff and erosion, absorption of nutrients, and assimilation of air pollutants.

negligible risk standard A new safety standard based on risk analysis, established by the **FQPA** of 1996, that replaces the **Delaney clause** in dealing with pesticide residues on food products.

Neolithic Revolution The development of agriculture begun by human societies around 12,000 years ago, leading to more permanent settlement and population increases.

net metering The practice of allowing individuals on the power grid to subtract the cost of the energy they get from photovoltaics or wind turbines from their electric bills.

neutron A fundamental atomic particle found in the nuclei of atoms (except hydrogen) and having one unit of atomic mass but no electrical charge.

new forestry Now part of the U.S. Forest Service's management practice, a forestry management strategy that places priority on protecting the ecological health and diversity of forests rather than maximizing the harvest of logs.

niche (ecological) The total of all the relationships that bear on how an organism copes with the biotic and abiotic factors it faces.

NIMBY ("not in my backyard") A common attitude regarding undesirable facilities such as incinerators, nuclear facilities, and hazardous-waste treatment plants whereby people do everything possible to prevent such facilities from being located near their residences.

NIMTOO ("not in my term of office") An attitude expressing the reluctance of officeholders to make unpopular decisions on matters such as siting waste facilities.

nitric acid A secondary air pollutant and a major component of acid deposition, nitric acid is produced when NO_x in the air reacts with the hydroxyl radical and water.

nitrogen cascade The detrimental complex of ecological effects brought on by reactive nitrogen (Nr) that has been added to natural systems by the burning of fossil fuels and the fertilization of agricultural crops.

nitrogen fixation The process of chemically converting nitrogen gas (N_2) from the air into compounds such as nitrates (NO_3) or ammonia (NH_3) that can be used by plants in building amino acids and other nitrogen-containing organic molecules.

nitrogen oxides (NO_X) A group of nitrogen-oxygen compounds formed when some of the nitrogen gas in the air combines with oxygen during high-temperature combustion. Nitrogen oxides are a major category of air pollutants and, along with hydrocarbons, are a primary factor in the production of ozone and other photochemical oxidants that are the most harmful components of photochemical smog. Nitrogen oxides also contribute to acid precipitation.

nitrous oxide A gas (N_2O). Nitrous oxide, which comes from biomass burning, fossil fuel burning, and the use of chemical fertilizers, is of concern because it is a greenhouse gas in the troposphere and it contributes to ozone destruction in the stratosphere.

nonbiodegradable Not able to be consumed or broken down by biological organisms. Nonbiodegradable substances include plastics, aluminum, and many chemicals used in industry and agriculture. Particularly dangerous are synthetic chemicals that are also toxic and tend to accumulate in organisms. (See **biodegradable** and **bioaccumulation.**)

nonconsumptive water use The use of water for such purposes as washing and rinsing, wherein the water, albeit polluted, remains available for further uses. With suitable purification, such water may be recycled indefinitely.

nongovernmental organization (NGO) Any of a number of private organizations involved in studying or advocating action on different environmental issues.

nonpersistent Said of chemicals that break down readily to harmless compounds, as, for example, natural organic compounds that break down to carbon dioxide and water; applied to pesticides, any pesticide that breaks down within days or a few weeks into nontoxic products.

nonpoint sources Sources of pollution such as the general runoff of sediments, fertilizers, pesticides, and other materials from farms and urban areas, as opposed to specific points of discharge such as factories. Also called **diffuse sources.** (Contrast **point sources.**)

nonreactive nitrogen The main reservoir of nitrogen as nitrogen gas in the atmosphere.

nonrenewable resources Resources, such as ores of various metals, oil, and coal that exist as finite deposits in Earth's crust and that are not replenished by natural processes as they are mined. (Contrast **renewable resources.**)

North Atlantic Deep Water (NADW) The cold, saline water that sinks in the high-latitude North Atlantic and initiates a deep current that spreads the waters throughout the oceans. See **Atlantic Meridional Overturning Circulation.**

North Atlantic Oscillation (NAO) One of several ocean-atmosphere oscillations where atmospheric pressure centers switch back and forth across the Atlantic, with many impacts on winds and storms.

no-till agriculture The farming practice in which weeds are killed with chemicals (or other means) and seeds are planted and grown without resorting to plowing or cultivation. The practice is highly effective in reducing soil erosion.

NRCS (Natural Resources Conservation Service) Formerly the U.S. Soil Conservation Service). The NRCS provides information to landowners regarding soil and water conservation practices.

nuclear power Electrical power generated by using a nuclear reactor to boil water and produce steam that in turn drives a turbogenerator.

Nuclear Regulatory Commission (NRC) The agency within the U.S. Department of Energy that sets and enforces safety standards for the operation and maintenance of nuclear power plants.

Nuclear Waste Policy Act of 1982 A law that committed the federal government to begin receiving nuclear wastes from commercial power plants by 1998. This has not happened yet, as the nation debates where to take the wastes.

nucleic acids The class of natural organic macromolecules that function in the storage and transfer of genetic information.

nucleus *Biology:* The large body residing in most living cells that contains the genes or hereditary material (DNA). *Physics:* The central core of atoms, which is made up of neutrons and protons. Electrons surround the nucleus.

nutrient *Animal:* Material such as protein, vitamins, and minerals required for growth, maintenance, and repair of the body and material such as carbohydrates required for energy. *Plant:* An essential element (C, P, N, Ca) in a particular ion or molecule that can be absorbed and used by the plant.

nutrient-holding capacity The capacity of a soil to bind and hold nutrients (fertilizer) against their tendency to be leached from the soil.

observations Things or phenomena that are perceived through one or more of the basic five senses in their normal state. In addition, to be accepted as factual, observations must be verifiable by others.

Occupational Safety and Health Act of 1970 (OSHA) The act protecting the rights of workers to know about hazards in their workplace.

ocean acidification An outcome of the rise in atmospheric carbon dioxide; as the oceans take up more and more of the CO_2, the carbonate ion concentration is reduced, making it more difficult for coral animals to build their calcium carbonate skeletons.

ocean thermal-energy conversion (OTEC) The concept of harnessing the difference in temperature between surface water heated by the Sun and colder deep water to produce power.

Official Development Assistance (ODA) Financial assistance provided to developing countries from the developed countries and coordinated by United Nations agencies.

oil field The underground area in which exploitable oil is found.

oil sand Sedimentary material containing bitumen, a tar-like hydrocarbon that is subject to exploitation under favorable economic conditions.

oil shale A natural sedimentary rock that contains kerogen, a material that can be extracted and refined into oil and oil products.

oligotrophic Nutrient poor and hence unable to support much phytoplankton (said of a body of water).

omnivore An animal that feeds on both plant material and other animals.

OPEC (Organization of Petroleum Exporting Countries) A cartel of oil-producing nations that attempts to control the market price of oil.

optimal population The population of a harvested biological resource that yields the greatest harvest for exploitation; according to maximum-sustained-yield equations, the optimal population is half the carrying capacity.

optimal range With respect to any particular factor or combination of factors, the maximum variation that still supports optimal or near-optimal growth of the species in question.

optimum The condition or amount of any factor or combination of factors that will produce the best result. For example, the amount of heat, light, moisture, nutrients, and so on that will produce the best plant growth.

organically grown Grown without the use of hard chemical pesticides or inorganic fertilizer. Any produce grown according to USDA standards for organic foods is organically grown.

organic chemical In classifying pollutants, some are organic, synthetic chemicals that served some purpose but have been released into the environment and pose some serious problems.

organic compounds/molecules *Classical definition:* All living things and products that are uniquely produced by living things, such as wood, leather, and sugar. *Chemical definition:* All chemical compounds or molecules, natural or synthetic, that contain carbon atoms as an integral part of their molecular structure. The structure of organic compounds is based on bonded carbon atoms with hydrogen atoms attached. (Contrast **inorganic compounds.**)

organic fertilizer See **fertilizer.**

organic food/gardening/farming Gardening or farming without the use of inorganic fertilizers, synthetic pesticides, or other human-made materials; food raised with organic farming techniques.

Organic Foods Protection Act A law passed in 1990 that established the National Organic Standards Board, the agency that certifies organic foods.

organic phosphate Phosphate (PO_4–3) bonded to an organic molecule.

orphan site The location of a hazardous waste site abandoned by former owners.

OSHA (Occupational Safety and Health Administration) The federal agency that promulgates regulations to protect workers.

osmosis The phenomenon whereby water diffuses through a semipermeable membrane toward an area where there is more material in solution (i.e., where there is a relatively lower concentration of water). Osmosis has particular application in the salinization of those soils in which plants are unable to grow because of osmotic water loss.

outbreak A population explosion of a particular pest. Often caused by an application of pesticides that destroys the pest's natural enemies.

overexploitation The overharvesting of a species or ecosystem that leads to its decline.

overgrazing The phenomenon of grazing animals in greater numbers than the land can support in the long term.

overnourishment The condition of obesity and overweight that results from overeating.

oxidation A chemical reaction that generally involves a breakdown of some substance through its combining with oxygen. Burning and cellular respiration are examples of oxidation. In both cases, organic matter is combined with oxygen and broken down to carbon dioxide and water.

ozone A gas, O_3, that is a secondary air pollutant in the lower atmosphere but that is necessary to screen out ultraviolet radiation in the stratosphere. May also be used for disinfecting water.

ozone hole First discovered over the Antarctic, a region of stratospheric air that is severely depleted of its normal levels of ozone during the Antarctic spring because of CFCs from anthropogenic (human-made) sources.

ozone shield The layer of ozone gas (O_3) in the stratosphere that screens out harmful ultraviolet radiation from the Sun.

parasites Organisms (plant, animal, or microbial) that attach themselves to another organism, the host, and feed on it over a period of time without killing it immediately, although usually doing harm to it. Parasites are commonly divided into ectoparasites—those that attach to the outside of their hosts—and endoparasites—those that live inside their hosts.

parasitoid Any parasitic insect, usually a wasp, that attacks other insects and can be responsible for bringing pest insects under control.

parent material Rock material whose weathering and gradual breakdown are the source of the mineral portion of soil.

particulates See **PM$_{2.5}$** and **PM$_{10}$** and **suspended particulate matter.**

parts per million (ppm) A frequently used expression of concentration. The number of units of one substance present in a million units of another. Equivalent to milligrams per liter.

passive safety features Those safety features of nuclear facilities that involve processes that are not vulnerable to operator intrusion or electrical power failures. Passive safety features enhance the degree of safety of nuclear reactors. (See **active safety features.**)

pasteurization The process of applying enough heat to milk or some other substance to kill pathogens and sufficient other bacteria to extend the shelf life of the product.

pastoralist One involved in animal husbandry, usually in subsistence agriculture.

pathogen An organism, usually a microbe, that is capable of causing disease. Such an organism is said to be pathogenic.

pathogen pollution A situation where human wastes spread diseases to wild species.

Payments for Ecosystem Services (PES) A market-based system that pays owners who hold properties that provide valuable services.

PAYT (pay as you throw) A system for collecting municipal wastes that charges residents by the container for nonrecycled wastes.

peat Compacted plant material that accumulates in wet environments where oxygen is lacking; it may be used for fuel or extracted for use in gardening.

percolation The process of water seeping downward through cracks and pores in soil or rock.

permafrost The ground of arctic regions that remains permanently frozen. Defines tundra because only small herbaceous plants can be sustained on the thin layer of soil that thaws each summer.

permanent polyculture A sustainable agriculture venture where a group of perennial plants of different species are grown together to produce food and fuel.

peroxyacetyl nitrates (PANs) A group of compounds present in photochemical smog that are extremely toxic to plants and irritating to the eyes, nose, and throat membranes of humans.

persistent organic pollutants (POPs) Any members of a class of organic pollutants that are resistant to biodegradation and that are often toxic; for example, DDT, PCBs, and dioxin are persistent organic pollutants. Such chemicals may remain present in the environment for periods of years.

pest Any organism that is noxious, destructive, or troublesome; usually an agricultural pest.

pesticide A chemical used to kill pests. Pesticides are further categorized according to the pests they are designed to kill—for example, herbicides kill plants, insecticides kill insects, fungicides kill fungi, and so on.

pesticide treadmill The idea that use of chemical pesticides simply creates a vicious cycle of "needing more pesticides" to overcome developing resistance and secondary outbreaks caused by the pesticide applications.

pH The scale used to designate the acidity or basicity (alkalinity) of solutions or soil, expressed as the logarithm of the concentration of hydrogen ions (H^+). pH 7 is neutral; values decreasing from 7 indicate increasing acidity, and values increasing from 7 indicate increasing basicity. Each unit from 7 indicates a tenfold increase over the preceding unit.

pharma crops Crop plants that produce pharmaceutical products with the use of genomics.

pheromones Chemical substances secreted externally by certain members of a species that affect the behavior of other members of the same species. The most common examples are sex attractants, which female insects secrete to attract males. Pheromones are coming into use in pest control. (See also **hormones.**)

phosphorus, phosphate An ion composed of a phosphorus atom with four oxygen atoms attached. Denoted PO_4^{-3}, phosphate is an important plant nutrient. In natural waters, it is frequently the limiting factor; therefore, additions of phosphate to natural water are often responsible for algal blooms.

photochemical oxidants A major category of secondary air pollutants, including ozone, that are highly toxic and damaging, especially to plants and forests. Formed as a result of interactions between nitrogen oxides and hydrocarbons driven by sunlight.

photochemical smog The brownish haze that frequently forms on otherwise clear, sunny days over large cities with significant amounts of automobile traffic. Photochemical smog results largely from sunlight-driven chemical reactions among nitrogen oxides and hydrocarbons, both of which come primarily from auto exhausts.

photosynthesis The chemical process carried on by green plants through which light energy is used to produce glucose from carbon dioxide and water. Oxygen is released as a by-product.

photovoltaic cell (PV cell) A device that converts light energy into an electrical current.

phthalates A group of chemicals used to soften plastic toys and suspected of being hormone disrupters.

phytoplankton Any of the many species of photosynthetic microorganisms that consist of single cells or small groups of cells that live and grow freely suspended near the surface in bodies of water.

phytoremediation The use of plants to accomplish the cleanup of some hazardous chemical wastes.

planetary albedo The reflection of solar radiation back into space due to cloud cover, snow and ice, contributing to the cooling of the atmosphere.

planetary boundaries Safe limits on a variety of conditions on Earth that, if crossed, could become tipping points and lead to very undesirable changes that would be difficult to reverse. See **tipping point.**

plankton Any and all living things that are found freely suspended in the water and that are carried by currents, as opposed to being able to swim against currents. Plankton includes both plant (phytoplankton) and animal (zooplankton) forms.

plant community The array of plant species, including their numbers, ages, and distribution, that occupy a given area.

plant-incorporated protectants In genetically modified crops, substances that have been bioengineered to incorporate substances that would repel or kill pests.

plate tectonics The theory, proposed by Alfred Wegener, that postulates the movement of sections of the Earth's crust, creating earthquakes, volcanic activity, and the buildup of continental masses over long periods of time, also known as continental drift.

$PM_{2.5}$ and PM_{10} Standard criterion pollutants for suspended particulate matter. PM_{10} refers to particles smaller than 10 micrometers in diameter; $PM_{2.5}$ refers to particles smaller than 2.5 micrometers in diameter. The smaller particles are readily inhaled directly into the lungs.

point sources Specific points of origin of pollutants, such as factory drains or outlets from sewage-treatment plants. (Contrast **nonpoint sources**.)

policy life cycle The typical course of events occurring over time in the recognition of, formulation of an approach to, implementation of a solution to, and control of an environmental problem requiring public policy action.

pollutant A substance that contaminates air, water, or soil.

polluter-pays principle An ethical principle whereby those who pollute the environment should pay for the damage their pollution causes.

pollution According to the EPA, "the presence of a substance in the environment that, because of its chemical composition or quantity, prevents the functioning of natural processes and produces undesirable environmental and health effects."

Pollution Prevention Act of 1990 A law that mandates collection of data on toxic chemicals that are released to the environment, treated on site, recycled, or combusted. See **Toxics Release Inventory**.

polychlorinated biphenyls (PCBs) A group of widely used industrial chemicals of the chlorinated hydrocarbon class. PCBs have become serious and widespread pollutants because they are resistant to breakdown and are subject to bioaccumulation. They are also carcinogenic.

population A group within a single species whose individuals can and do freely interbreed.

population density The number of individuals per unit of area.

population equilibrium A state of balance between births and deaths in a population.

population explosion The exponential increase observed to occur in a population when conditions are such that a large percentage of the offspring are able to survive and reproduce in turn. A population explosion frequently leads to overexploitation and eventual collapse of the ecosystem.

population growth rate The change in population numbers divided by the time over which that change occurs.

population momentum A property whereby a rapidly growing human population may be expected to grow for 50–60 years after replacement fertility (2.1 live births per female) is reached. Momentum is sustained because of increasing numbers entering reproductive age.

population profile A bar graph that shows the number of individuals at each age or in each five-year age group, starting with the youngest ages at the bottom of the profile.

population structure See **age structure**.

positive feedback A phenomenon where some process leads to even more intensification of that process; an example is the evaporative rise in water vapor with global warming, adding water, a greenhouse gas, to the atmosphere.

potential energy The ability to do work that is stored in some chemical or physical state. For example, gasoline is a form of potential energy because the ability to do work is stored in the chemical state and is released as the fuel is burned in an engine.

poverty trap In a developing country, the situation where people are so poor that they are unable to earn or work their way out of their poverty and their condition deteriorates.

power grid The combination of central power plants, high-voltage transmission lines, poles, wires, and transformers that makes up an electrical power system.

power tower A solar energy converter that collects solar energy with an array of Sun-tracking mirrors and focuses the energy onto a receiver on a tower in the center of the array, where the heat energy drives a conventional turbogenerator.

prairie biome See **grassland biome**.

precautionary principle The principle that says that where there are threats of serious or irreversible damage, the absence of scientific certainty shall not be used as a reason for postponing cost-effective measures to prevent environmental degradation.

precipitation Any form of moisture condensing in the air and depositing on the ground.

predation A conspicuous process in all ecosystems, any situation where one organism feeds on another living organism.

predator An animal that feeds on another living organism, either plant or animal.

predator-prey relationship A feeding relationship existing between two kinds of organisms. The predator is the animal feeding on the prey. Such relationships are frequently instrumental in controlling populations of herbivores.

preservation In protecting natural areas, the objective of preservation is to ensure the continuity of species and ecosystems, regardless of their potential utility.

pressurized-water reactor A nuclear power plant where two loops are employed; one where water is heated in the reactor but does not boil because it is under high pressure, and a second where the pressurized water is circulated through a heat exchanger, where it boils other unpressurized water that then produces steam to drive the turbogenerator.

prey An organism that is fed on by a predator.

primary air pollutants Pollutants released directly into the atmosphere, mainly as a result of burning fuels and wastes, as opposed to **secondary air pollutants**.

primary clarifier In a sewage-treatment system, a large tank that allows particulate matter to settle to the bottom before the water moves on to **secondary treatment**.

primary consumer An organism, such as a rabbit or deer, that feeds more or less exclusively on green plants or their products, such as seeds and nuts. (Synonym: **herbivore**.)

primary energy sources Fossil fuels, radioactive material, and solar, wind, water, and other energy sources that exist as natural resources subject to exploitation.

primary producers/primary production Photosynthetic organisms. The activities of these organisms in creating new organic matter in ecosystems.

primary recovery In an oil well or oil field, the oil that can be removed by conventional pumping. (See **secondary recovery**.)

primary recycling A form of recycling where the original waste material is made back into the same material.

primary succession The gradual establishment, through a series of stages, of a climax ecosystem in an area that has not been occupied before (e.g., a rock face).

primary treatment The process that consists of passing the wastewater very slowly through a large tank so that the particulate organic material can settle out. The settled material is **raw sludge**, which is treated separately.

prior informed consent (PIC) A UN-approved procedure whereby countries exporting pesticides must inform importing countries of actions the exporting countries have taken to restrict the use of the pesticides.

private land trust See **land trust**.

produced capital   The stock of buildings, machinery, vehicles, and other elements of a country's infrastructure that are essential to the production of economic goods and services. One component of the wealth of nations.

producers   In an ecosystem, those organisms (mostly green plants) that use light energy to construct their organic constituents from inorganic compounds.

productive use   The exploitation of ecosystem resources for economic gain.

productivity   See **primary producers/primary production.**

property taxes   Taxes that the local government levies on privately owned properties, proportional to the value of the property. Property taxes are the major source of revenue for local governments.

protein   Organic macromolecules made up of amino acids; the major structural component of all animal tissues as well as enzymes in both plants and animals.

proton   A fundamental atomic particle with a positive charge, found in the nuclei of atoms. The number of protons present equals the atomic number and is distinct for each element.

protozoon, pl. protozoa   Any of a large group of eukaryotic microscopic organisms that consist of a single, relatively large complex cell or, in some cases, a small groups of cells. All have some means of movement. Amoebae and paramecia are examples.

proved reserves   See **reserves.**

proxies   These are measurable records, like tree rings, ice cores, and marine sediments, that can provide extensions back in time of climatic factors including temperatures and greenhouse gases.

public good   A category of ecosystem services that is not used up when people use it and cannot be marketed, like the air we breathe.

Public Trust Doctrine   The legal arrangement whereby wildlife resources are considered to be public resources, held in trust for all the people and protected or managed by state or federal agencies.

pumped-storage power plant   A hydroelectric plant component that pumps water up to an elevated reservoir when power demand is low and allows it to return to a lower reservoir and generate electricity when demand is higher.

purification   For water, purification occurs whenever water is separated from the solutes and particles it contains.

radiation sickness   The outcome of a high dose of radiation, often leading to death.

radiative forcing   Refers to the internal or external factors of the climate system that can influence the climate, usually to promote warming or cooling of the atmosphere as they affect the Earth's energy balance.

radioactive decay   The reduction in radioactivity that occurs as an unstable isotope (radioactive substance) gives off radiation, ultimately becoming stable.

radioactive emissions   Any of various forms of radiation or particles that may be given off by unstable isotopes. Many such emissions have very high energy and can destroy biological tissues or cause mutations leading to cancer or birth defects.

radioactive materials   Substances that are or that contain unstable isotopes and that consequently give off radioactive emissions. (See **isotope** and **radioactive emissions.**)

radioactive wastes   Waste materials that contain, are contaminated with, or are radioactive substances. Many materials used in the nuclear industry become radioactive wastes because of such contamination.

radioisotope   An isotope of an element that is unstable and that gives off radioactive emissions. (See **isotope** and **radioactive decay.**)

radon   A radioactive gas produced by natural processes in Earth that is known to seep into buildings. Radon can be a major hazard within homes and is a known carcinogen.

rain shadow   The low-rainfall region that exists on the leeward (downwind) side of a mountain range. This rain shadow is the result of the mountain range causing precipitation on the windward side.

range of tolerance   The range of conditions within which an organism or population can survive and reproduce—for example, the range from the highest to the lowest temperature that can be tolerated. Within the range of tolerance is the optimum, or best, condition.

raw sewage (raw wastewater)   The water from a sewer system as it reaches a sewage-treatment plant.

raw sludge   The untreated organic matter that is removed from sewage water by letting it settle. Raw sludge consists of organic particles from feces, garbage, paper, and bacteria.

REACH (Registration, Evaluation and Authorization of Chemicals)   The European Union's new, rigorous approach to screening hazardous chemicals for toxicity.

reactive nitrogen   All forms of nitrogen in ecosystems that are usable by organisms, as opposed to the nonreactive nitrogen in the form of nitrogen gas.

reactor vessel   A steel-walled vessel that contains a nuclear reactor.

reasonably available control technology (RACT)   Applied to the goals of the Clean Air Act, EPA-approved forms of technology that will reduce the output of industrial air pollutants. (See **maximum achievable control technology.**)

recharge area   The area over which groundwater will infiltrate and resupply an aquifer.

recruitment   The maturation and successful entry of young into an adult breeding population.

recycling   The recovery of materials that would otherwise be buried in landfills or be combusted. Primary recycling involves remaking the same material from the waste; in secondary recycling, waste materials are made into different products.

redlining   The practice of discriminatory lending and real estate showing designed to keep minorities out of white suburbs.

Red List   A list of threatened and endangered species maintained by the International Union for Conservation of Nature (IUCN) and accessible on the Internet.

relative humidity   The percentage of moisture in the air compared with how much the air can hold at the given temperature.

rem   An older unit of measurement of the ability of radioactive emissions to penetrate biological tissue. (See **sievert.**)

remittances   Money sent back to the country of birth by guest workers and immigrants to help family and friends meet their financial needs.

remote sensing   A system of imaging the Earth from satellites, or of accessing data from devices that are distant from the scientist.

renewable fuel standard (RFS)   A policy that requires a minimum volume of renewable fuel in gasoline.

renewable portfolio standard   A policy that requires utilities to provide a percentage of power from renewable energy sources.

renewable resources   Biological resources, such as trees, that may be renewed by reproduction and regrowth. Conservation to prevent overcutting and to protect the environment is still required, however. (Contrast **nonrenewable resources.**)

replacement fertility rate/level   The fertility rate (level) that will just sustain a stable population. It is 2.1 for developed countries.

reprocessing   The recovery of radioactive materials from nuclear reactors and the conversion of those materials into useful nuclear fuel.

reproductive health   Health care directed primarily toward the needs of women and infants, strongly emphasized in the 1994 Cairo population conference.

reproductive isolation   One of the processes of speciation, involving anything that keeps individuals or subpopulations from interbreeding.

reproductive strategy   A life history property of a species that involves a balance between reproduction and death. (See **r-strategist** and **K-strategist.**)

reserves   The amount of a mineral resource (including oil, coal, and natural gas) remaining in Earth that can be exploited using current technologies and at current prices. Usually given as **proved reserves** (those that have been positively identified) and **undiscovered reserves** (reserves from fields that have not yet been found).

resilience   The tendency of ecosystems to recover from disturbances through a number of processes known as resilience mechanisms (e.g., succession after a fire).

resistance   The development of more hardy pests through the effects of the repeated use of pesticides in selecting against sensitive individuals in a pest population.

resource partitioning   The outcome of competition by a group of species where natural selection favors the division of a resource in time or space by specialization of the different species.

resources   Biotic and abiotic factors that are consumed by organisms.

Resource Conservation and Recovery Act of 1976 (RCRA)   The cornerstone legislation to control indiscriminate land disposal of hazardous wastes.

respiration   See **cell respiration**.

restoration ecology   The branch of ecology devoted to restoring degraded and altered ecosystems to their natural state.

resurgence   The rapid comeback of a population (especially of pests after a severe die-off, usually caused by pesticides) and the return to even higher levels than before the treatment.

reverse osmosis   See **microfiltration**.

risk   The probability of suffering injury, disease, death, or some other loss as a result of exposure to a hazard.

risk assessment/analysis   The process of evaluating the risks associated with a particular hazard before taking some action.

risk characterization   The process of determining the level of a risk and its accompanying uncertainties after hazard assessment, dose-response assessment, and exposure assessment have been accomplished.

risk management   The task of regulators whose job is to review risk data and make regulatory decisions based on the data. The process often is influenced by considerations of costs and benefits as well as by public perception.

risk perception   Nonexperts' intuitive judgments about risks, which often are not in agreement with the level of risk as judged by experts.

roadless rule   A moratorium placed on building new roads in the national forests, put in place by the Clinton administration and contested by subsequent administrations.

rotavirus   A little-known virus that causes many childhood deaths, responsible for most cases of severe diarrhea.

Roundup®   See **glyphosate**.

r-strategist   A reproductive strategy of a species that involves producing large numbers of young (a high reproductive rate) and survival of smaller numbers over time. Also called **opportunistic species**.

Rust Belt   Cities and their outskirts, often in the Midwest, that once specialized in heavy manufacturing and have since suffered a decline, characterized by abandoned factories and crumbling buildings.

Safe, Accountable, Flexible, Efficient Transportation Equity Act of 2005 (SAFETEA)   Successor to TEA–21 and ISTEA, this act authorizes funding for highway and transit programs.

Safe Drinking Water Act (SDWA) of 1974   Legislation to protect the public from the risk that toxic chemicals will contaminate drinking water supplies. The act mandates regular testing of municipal water supplies.

safety net   In a society, the availability of food and other necessities extended to people who are unable to meet their own needs for a variety of reasons.

salinization   The process whereby soil becomes saltier and saltier until, finally, the salt prevents the growth of plants. Salinization is caused by irrigation because salts brought in with the water remain in the soil as the water evaporates.

saltwater intrusion, saltwater encroachment   The phenomenon of seawater moving back into aquifers or estuaries. Such intrusion occurs when the normal outflow of freshwater is diverted or removed for use.

salvage logging   Established by the Bush administration, this refers to harvesting timber from recent burns in national forestlands; it is controversial because it is suspected of preventing natural regeneration of trees on the burned land.

sand   Mineral particles 0.063 to 2.0 mm in diameter.

sanitary sewer   A separate drainage system used to receive all the wastewater from sinks, tubs, and toilets.

SARA (Title III)   A section of the Superfund Amendments and Reauthorization Act that addresses hazardous waste accidents and promulgates community right-to-know requirements. Also known as the **Emergency Planning and Community Right-to-Know Act of 1986 (EPCRA)**. (See **Toxics Release Inventory (TRI)**.)

scale insect   Any of a group of minute insect pests that suck the juices from plant cells.

scientific method   The process of making observations and logically integrating those observations into a model of how the world works. Often involves forming hypotheses, experimenting, and conducting further testing for confirmation.

secondary air pollutants   Air pollutants resulting from reactions of primary air pollutants resident in the atmosphere. Secondary air pollutants include ozone, other reactive organic compounds, and sulfuric and nitric acids. (See **ozone, peroxyacetyl nitrates**, and **photochemical oxidants**.)

secondary clarifier   In activated sludge sewage treatment, the tank where organisms and other particles settle out after the aeration tank.

secondary consumer   An organism such as a fox or coyote that feeds more or less exclusively on other animals that feed on plants.

secondary pest outbreak   The phenomenon of a small and therefore harmless population of a plant-eating insect suddenly exploding to become a serious pest problem. Often caused by the elimination of competitors through the use of pesticides.

secondary recovery   In an oil well or oil field, the oil that can be removed by manipulating pressure in the oil reservoir by injecting brine or other substances; more costly than **primary recovery**.

secondary recycling   Recycling processes wherein waste materials are made into different products than the starting materials, for example, wastepaper to cardboard.

secondary succession   The reestablishment, through a series of stages, of a climax ecosystem in an area from which it was previously cleared.

secondary treatment   Also called **biological treatment**. A sewage-treatment process that follows primary treatment. Any of a variety of systems that remove most of the remaining organic matter by enabling organisms to feed on it and oxidize it through their respiration. Trickling filters and activated-sludge systems are the most commonly used secondary-treatment methods.

second-generation pesticides   Synthetic organic compounds used to kill insects and other pests, replacing the first-generation pesticides. Started with the use of DDT in the 1940s.

Secondhand smoke   Smoke experienced by those breathing air contaminated with tobacco smoke from others; classified as a known human carcinogen.

Second Law of Thermodynamics   The empirical observation, confirmed innumerable times, that in every energy conversion (e.g., from electricity to light), some of the energy is converted to heat and some heat always escapes from the system because it always moves toward a cooler place. Therefore, in every energy conversion, a portion of energy is lost, and since, by the **First Law of Thermodynamics**, energy cannot be created, the functioning of any system requires an energy input.

secure landfill   A landfill with suitable barriers, leachate drainage, and monitoring systems such that it is deemed secure against contaminating groundwater with hazardous wastes.

sediment Soil particles—namely, sand, silt, and clay—carried by flowing water. The same material after it has been deposited. Because of different rates of settling, deposits generally are pure sand, pure silt, or pure clay.

sedimentation The filling in of lakes, reservoirs, stream channels, and so on with soil particles, mainly sand and silt. The soil particles come from erosion. Also called **siltation**.

seep An area where groundwater seeps from the ground. Contrast with a **spring**, which is a single point from which groundwater exits.

selective cutting In forestry, the practice of cutting some mature trees from a stand but leaving enough to maintain normal ecosystem functions and a diverse biota.

selective pressure An environmental factor that causes individuals with certain traits that are not the norm for the population to survive and reproduce more than the rest of the population. The result is a shift in the genetic makeup of the population. Selective pressure is a fundamental mechanism of evolution.

septic system An on-site method of treating sewage that is widely used in suburban and rural areas. Requires a suitable amount of land and porous soil.

services Ecosystem functions that are essential to human life and economic well-being, such as waste breakdown, climate regulation, and erosion control. These can be further categorized as regulating, supporting, and provisioning services.

sex attractant A natural chemical substance (see **pheromones**) secreted by the female of many insect species that serves to attract males for the function of mating. Sex attractants may be used by humans in traps or to otherwise confuse insect pests in order to control them.

shadow pricing In cost-benefit analysis, a technique used to estimate benefits when normal economic analysis is ineffective. For example, people could be asked how much they might be willing to pay monthly to achieve some improvement in their environment.

sheet erosion The loss of a more or less even layer of soil from the land surface due to the impact of rain and runoff from a rainstorm.

shelterbelts Rows of trees around cultivated fields for the purpose of reducing wind erosion.

shelter-wood cutting In forestry practice, the strategy of cutting the mature trees in groups over a period of years, leaving enough trees to provide seeds and give shelter to growing seedlings.

sievert A unit of measurement of the ability of radioactive emissions to penetrate biological tissues. 1 sievert = 100 rem.

silt Soil particles between the size of sand particles and that of clay particles—namely, particles 0.004 to 0.063 mm in diameter.

siltation See **sedimentation**.

silviculture A term used to denote the practice of forest management.

simplification The human use of habitats that removes natural objects, such as maintaining a forest to produce one kind of tree or removing fallen logs.

sinkhole A large hole in the ground resulting from the collapse of an underground cavern.

slash-and-burn agriculture The practice, commonly found in tropical regions, of cutting and burning vegetation to make room for agriculture. The process destroys soil humus and may lead to rapid degradation of the soil.

sludge cake Treated sewage sludge that has been dewatered to make a moist solid.

sludge digesters Large tanks in which raw sludge (removed from sewage) is treated through anaerobic digestion by bacteria.

slum A concentrated habitation where squalor and disease reign, usually consisting of flimsy shacks and characterized by an almost complete lack of public amenities.

smart grid Control systems for power plants and electricity transmission lines with the ability to monitor problems, react to trouble quickly, and isolate trouble areas.

Smart Growth A movement that addresses urban sprawl by protecting sensitive lands and directing growth to limited areas, creating attractive, sustainable communities.

smog See **industrial smog** and **photochemical smog**.

social capital See **intangible capital**.

social modernization A process of sustainable development that leads developing countries through the demographic transition by promoting education, family planning, and health improvements rather than simply economic growth.

soft water Water with little or no calcium, magnesium, or other ions in solution that will cause soap to precipitate. (The soap would otherwise form a curd that makes a "ring" around the bathtub.) (Contrast **hard water**.)

soil A dynamic terrestrial system involving three components: mineral particles, detritus, and soil organisms feeding on the detritus.

soil classes Taxonomically arranged major groupings of soil that define the properties of the soils of different regions.

soil erosion The loss of soil caused by particles being carried away by wind or water.

soil fertility A soil's ability to support plant growth; often refers specifically to the presence of proper amounts of nutrients. The soil's ability to fulfill all the other needs of plants is also involved.

soil horizons Distinct layers within a soil that convey different properties to the soil and that derive from natural processes of soil formation.

soil order The highest group in the taxonomy of soils; there are 12 major orders of soil worldwide.

soil profile A description of the different naturally formed layers, called horizons, within a soil.

soil structure The composition of soil in terms of particles (sand, silt, and clay) stuck together to form clumps and aggregates, generally with considerable air spaces in between. Soil structure affects infiltration and aeration and develops as organisms feed on organic matter in and on the soil.

soil texture The relative size of the mineral particles that make up the soil. Generally defined in terms of the soil's sand, silt, and clay content.

solar cells See **photovoltaic cells**.

solar constant The radiant energy reaching the top of Earth's atmosphere from the Sun, measured at 1,366 watts per square meter.

solar energy Energy derived from the Sun; includes direct solar energy (the use of sunlight directly for heating or the production of electricity) and indirect solar energy (the use of wind, which results from the solar heating of the atmosphere, and biological materials such as wood, which result from photosynthesis).

solar-trough collectors Reflectors, in the shape of a parabolic trough, that reflect sunlight onto a tube of oil at the focal point of the trough. Thus heated, the oil is used to boil water to drive a steam turbine.

solar variability One proposed mechanism for global warming involving increases in solar output; this explanation has been discredited because of lack of convincing data.

solid waste The total of materials discarded as "trash" and handled as solids, as opposed to those that are flushed down sewers and handled as liquids.

solution A mixture of molecules (or ions) of one material in another; most commonly, molecules of air or ions of various minerals in water. For example, seawater contains salt in solution.

sound science *The basis for our understanding of how the world works and how human systems interact with it.* It stems from scientific work based on peer-reviewed research and is one of the unifying themes of this text.

source reduction According to the EPA, "the practice of designing, manufacturing, purchasing, or using materials in ways that reduce the amount or toxicity of trash created."

special-interest group In politics, people organized around a particular issue who lobby for their cause and exert their influence on the political process to bring about changes they favor.

specialization In evolution, the phenomenon whereby species become increasingly adapted to exploit one particular niche but thereby are less able to exploit other niches.

speciation The evolutionary process whereby populations of a single species separate and, through being exposed to different forces of natural selection, gradually develop into distinct species.

species All the organisms (plant, animal, or microbe) of a single kind. The "single kind" is determined by similarity of appearance or by the fact that members do or can mate and produce fertile offspring. Physical, chemical, or behavioral differences block breeding between species.

splash erosion The compaction of soil that results when rainfall hits bare soil.

springs Natural exits of groundwater to the surface.

stakeholders Groups of people who have an interest in the management of a given environmental resource, from those dependent on the resource to those managing or studying the resource.

standing crop biomass The biomass of primary producers in an ecosystem at any given time.

state capitalism A hybrid economic system with elements of both central planning and free-market economic systems, seen in China, Russia, and many Gulf oil states.

Statement on Forest Principles One of the treaties signed at the 1992 Earth Summit wherein the signatory countries agreed to a number of nonbinding principles stressing sustainable management.

steward/stewardship A steward is one to whom a trust has been given. As one of the unifying themes of this text, stewardship is *the actions and programs that manage natural resources and human well-being for the common good.*

Stockholm Convention on Persistent Organic Pollutants An international treaty that works toward the banning of most uses of the persistent organic pollutants.

storm drains Separate drainage systems used for collecting and draining runoff from precipitation in urban areas.

stratosphere The layer of Earth's atmosphere between 10 and 40 miles above the surface that contains the ozone shield. This layer mixes only slowly; pollutants that enter it may remain for long periods of time. (See **troposphere**.)

strip mining A mining procedure in which all the earth covering a desired material, such as coal, is stripped away with huge power shovels in order to facilitate removal of the material.

submerged aquatic vegetation (SAV) Aquatic plants rooted in bottom sediments and growing underwater. Submerged aquatic vegetation depends on the penetration of light through the water for photosynthesis.

subsidy A payment or other support of produced goods that helps the producers to maintain their production and earn income above what the market would normally provide.

subsistence farming Farming that meets the food needs of farmers and their families but little more. Subsistence farming involves hand labor and is practiced extensively in the developing world.

subsoil In a natural situation, the soil beneath topsoil. In contrast to topsoil, subsoil is compacted and has little or no humus or other organic material, living or dead. In many areas, topsoil has been lost or destroyed as a result of erosion or development, and subsoil is at the surface.

succession See **ecological succession**.

sulfur dioxide (SO_2) A major air pollutant and toxic gas formed as a result of burning sulfur. The major sources are burning coal (in coal-burning power plants) that contains some sulfur and refining metal ores (in smelters) that contain sulfur.

sulfuric acid (H_2SO_4) The major constituent of acid precipitation. Formed when sulfur dioxide emissions react with water vapor in the atmosphere. (See **sulfur dioxide**.)

Superfund The popular name for the **Comprehensive Environmental Response, Compensation, and Liability Act of 1980 (CERCLA)**. This act is the cornerstone legislation that provides the mechanism and funding for the cleanup of potentially dangerous hazardous-waste sites and the protection of groundwater.

Superfund Amendments and Reauthorization Act of 1986 (SARA) Amendments that strengthened the Superfund program for identifying and cleaning up hazardous waste sites.

supply-side policies Those energy policies that emphasize providing greater amounts of energy through more development of oil, coal, and gas resources.

surface impoundments Closed ponds used to collect and hold liquid chemical wastes.

surface water All bodies of water, lakes, rivers, ponds, and so on that are on Earth's surface. Contrast with **groundwater**, which lies below the surface.

suspended particulate matter (SPM) A category of major air pollutants consisting of solid and liquid particles suspended in the air. (See $PM_{2.5}$ and PM_{10}.)

sustainability A property whereby a process can be continued indefinitely without depleting the energy or material resources on which it depends. As one of the unifying themes of the text, *sustainability is the practical goal toward which our interactions with the natural world should be working.*

sustainable agriculture Agriculture that maintains the integrity of soil and water resources such that it can be continued indefinitely.

Sustainable Communities and Development Program in the United States that provides grants to encourage the development of more livable urban neighborhoods.

sustainable development Development that provides people with a better life without sacrificing or depleting resources or causing environmental impacts that will undercut the ability of future generations to meet their needs.

sustainable forest management The management of forests as ecosystems wherein the primary objective is to maintain the biodiversity and function of the ecosystem.

sustainable society A society that functions in a way so as not to deplete the energy or material resources on which it depends. Such a society interacts with the natural world in ways that maintain existing species and ecosystems.

sustainable yield The taking of a biological resource (e.g., fish or forests) in a manner that does not exceed the capacity of the resource to reproduce and replace itself.

sustained yield In forestry, the objective of managing a forest to harvest wood continuously over time without destroying the forest.

symbiosis The intimate living together or association of two kinds of organisms.

synergism The phenomenon whereby two factors acting together have a greater effect than would be indicated by the sum of their effects separately—as, for example, the sometimes fatal mixture of modest doses of certain drugs in combination with modest doses of alcohol.

synergistic effects Where two or more factors interact to affect organisms in a way that makes the impact greater than from the two acting separately.

syngas A combustible gas produced in an integrated gasification combined cycle plant by burning coal; the syngas is then burned in a gas turbine to produce electricity.

synthetic organics Any of a large group of organic compounds that may be synthesized in chemical laboratories and are known by the difficulty with which they degrade in the environment.

tariff Any tax placed on imported goods that raises the price of those goods in the recipient country.

taxonomy The science of identifying and classifying organisms according to their presumed natural relationships.

tectonic plates The huge slabs of rock in the lithosphere that have moved around and produced major changes in the surface of Earth; they are still moving, creating earthquakes and tsunamis when they do. See **plate tectonics**.

temperate deciduous forest A biome in the temperate zone characterized by deciduous trees, found where annual precipitation is 30–80 inches per year.

temperature inversion   The weather phenomenon in which a layer of warm air overlies cooler air near the ground and prevents the rising and dispersion of air pollutants.

tenure   Property rights over land and water resources that involve different patterns of use of those resources.

teratogenic   Causing birth defects.

terracing   The practice of grading sloping farmland into a series of steps and cultivating only the level portions in order to reduce erosion.

territoriality   The behavioral characteristic exhibited by many animal species, especially birds and mammalian carnivores, to mark and defend a given territory against other members of the same species. A form of intraspecific competition.

territory   The area defended by an animal in territorial behavior.

TESRA (Threatened and Endangered Species Recovery Act)   One of a number of acts proposed in Congress in an attempt to weaken the Endangered Species Act.

theory   A conceptual formulation that provides a rational explanation or framework for numerous related observations.

thermal pollution   The addition of abnormal and undesirable amounts of heat to air or water. Thermal pollution is most significant with respect to the discharging of waste heat from electric generating plants—especially nuclear power plants—into bodies of water.

thermohaline   Refers to temperature and salinity, specifically the cold temperature and high salinity of waters that sink in the North Atlantic and initiate the Atlantic Meridional Overturning Circulation.

thermosphere   The highest layer in the atmosphere, between the mesosphere and outer space.

third world   A dated term for **developing countries**.

threatened species   A species whose population is declining precipitously because of direct or indirect human impacts.

threshold level   The maximum degree of exposure to a pollutant, drug, or some other factor that can be tolerated with no ill effect. The threshold level varies, depending on the species, the sensitivity of the individual, the length of exposure, and the presence of other factors that may produce synergistic effects.

tidal barrage   A form of renewable energy where barriers are placed across the mouth of a coastal bay and turbines are able to convert tidal water flow to power.

tilth   In farming, the ability of a soil to support crop growth.

tipping point   A situation in a human-impacted ecosystem where a small action or reaction is the catalyst for a major change in the state of the system.

Tobacco Control Act   A law passed in 2009 giving the Food and Drug Administration greater authority to regulate tobacco products.

top-down regulation   Basic control of a population (or species) occurs as a result of predation.

topsoil   The surface layer of soil, which is rich in humus and other organic material, both living and dead. As a result of the activity of organisms living in the topsoil, it generally has a loose, crumbly structure, as opposed to being a compact mass.

total allowable catch (TAC)   In fisheries management, a yearly quota set for the harvest of a species by managers of fisheries.

total fertility rate   The average number of children that will be born alive to each woman during her total reproductive years if her fertility is average at each age.

Total Maximum Daily Load (TMDL) program   An EPA-administered program to address nonpoint-source water pollution that sets pollution limits according to the ability of a body of water to assimilate different pollutants.

total product life cycle   The sum of all steps in the manufacture of a product, from obtaining the raw materials through producing, using, and, finally, disposing of the product. By-products and the pollution resulting from each step are taken into account in a consideration of the total product life cycle.

toxicity   The condition of being harmful, deadly, or poisonous.

toxicology   The study of the impacts of toxic substances on human health and the pathways by which such substances reach humans.

Toxics Release Inventory (TRI)   An annual record of releases of toxic chemicals to the environment and the locations and quantities of toxic chemicals stored at all U.S. sites. Required by the **Emergency Planning and Community Right-to-Know Act of 1986 (EPCRA)**. See SARA.

Toxic Substances Control Act of 1976 (TSCA)   A law requiring the assessment of the potential hazards of a chemical before the chemical is put on the market.

trace elements   Those essential elements, like copper or iron, that are needed in only very small amounts.

trade winds   The more or less constant winds blowing in horizontal directions over the surface as part of Hadley cells.

traditional agriculture   Farming methods as they were practiced before the advent of modern industrialized agriculture.

TRAFFIC network   An acronym for the Trade Records Analysis for Flora and Fauna in International Commerce network, monitoring trade in wildlife and wildlife parts.

tragedy of the commons   The overuse or overharvesting and consequent depletion or destruction of a renewable resource that tends to occur when the resource is treated as a commons—that is, when it is open to be used or harvested by any and all with the means to do so.

trait   Any physical or behavioral characteristic or talent that an individual is born with.

transgenic organism   Any organism with genes introduced from other species via biotechnology to convey new characteristics.

transpiration   The loss of water vapor from plants. Water evaporates from cells within the leaves and exits through the stomata.

trapping technique   The use of sex attractants to lure male insects into traps.

treadle pump   A pump worked like a step exercise machine that pulls water up from groundwater for irrigation, commonly used in developing countries.

treated sludge   Solid organic material that has been removed from sewage and treated so that it is nonhazardous.

trickling-filter system   A system in which wastewater trickles over rocks or a framework coated with actively feeding microorganisms. The feeding action of the organisms in a well-aerated environment results in the decomposition of organic matter. Used in secondary or biological treatment of sewage.

tritium (^{3}H)   An unstable isotope of hydrogen that contains two neutrons in addition to the usual single proton in the nucleus. Tritium does not occur in significant amounts in nature.

trophic level   A feeding level defined with respect to the primary source of energy. Green plants are at the first trophic level, primary consumers at the second, secondary consumers at the third, and so on.

trophic structure   The major feeding relationships between organisms within ecosystems, organized into trophic levels.

tropical rain forest   Biome in the tropic zone where rainfall averages over 95 inches/yr; locations of great biodiversity.

troposphere/tropopause   The layer of Earth's atmosphere from the surface to about 10 miles in altitude. The tropopause is the boundary between the troposphere and the stratosphere above. The troposphere is well mixed and is the site and source of our weather as well as the primary recipient of air pollutants. (See also **stratosphere**.)

tsunami   A series of ocean waves (often called tidal waves) originating with underwater or coastal earthquakes and moving rapidly across ocean expanses, often resulting in major inundations of coastal areas.

tundra biome   In cold latitudes and high altitudes, the pattern of plants and animals able to live where permafrost persists; dominated by low-growing sedges, shrubs, lichens, mosses, and grasses.

turbid   Cloudy due to particles present. (Said of water and water purity.)

turbine A rotary engine driven at a very high speed by steam, water, or exhaust gases from combustion, employed in generating electrical energy.

turbogenerator A turbine coupled to and driving an electric generator. Virtually all commercial electricity is produced by such devices.

ultraviolet radiation Radiation similar to light but with slightly shorter wavelengths and with more energy than violet light. Its greater energy causes ultraviolet light to severely burn and otherwise damage biological tissues.

underground storage tanks (USTs) Tanks used to store petroleum products at service stations, now subject to mandated protection against leakage. (See **UST legislation.**)

undernourishment A form of hunger in which the individual lacks adequate food energy, as measured in calories. Starvation is the most severe form of undernourishment.

underweight The world's number one health risk factor, this refers to the effects of undernourishment on children that prevent their normal growth.

undiscovered resources Estimates of oil and natural gas based on geological science but not explored to confirm their presence; the estimates may be way off the mark.

United Nations Convention to Combat Desertification (UNCCD) A UN agency with the mission of helping drylands countries take steps to reduce soil degradation.

United Nations Development Program (UNDP) A UN agency with offices in 131 countries, with the mission of helping developing countries to attract and use development aid effectively and, in particular, to reach the Millennium Development Goals.

United Nations Environment Program (UNEP) A UN agency with the mission of providing leadership and encouraging partnership in caring for the environment by inspiring, informing, and enabling nations and peoples to improve their quality of life without compromising that of future generations.

United Synthesis Product (USP) The 2009 report, *Global Change Impacts in the United States*, drawing from 19 existing Climate Change Science Program reports, providing a detailed look at the impacts of climate change on various sectors and regions in the U.S.

unmet need A situation where women who would like to postpone or prevent childbearing are not currently using contraception, often because it is not available to them.

upwelling In oceanic systems, the upward vertical movement of water masses, caused by diverging currents and offshore winds, bringing nutrient-rich water to the surface.

urban blight/decay The general deterioration of structures and facilities such as buildings and roadways, in addition to the decline in quality of services such as education, that has occurred in inner-city areas.

urban food forest A new design for urban landscapes where perennial plants and trees are grown with the intention of allowing people to forage them for food.

urban foragers Those urban dwellers who forage for fruits, berries, mushrooms, and other foods in urban landscapes.

urban sprawl The widespread expansion of metropolitan areas through building houses and shopping centers farther and farther from urban centers and lacing them together with more and more major highways, usually without planning.

USDA Organic A food that is certified by the U.S. Department of Agriculture to have been produced without the use of chemical fertilizers, pesticides, or antibiotics.

UST legislation Amendments to the Resources Conservation and Recovery Act of 1976 passed in 1984 to address the mounting problem of leaking underground storage tanks (USTs).

value In ethical considerations, a property attributed to objects, species, or individuals that implies a moral duty to the one assigning the value; intrinsic value and instrumental value are two types of value.

value added The increase in value from raw materials to final production.

vector/vector control An agent, such as an insect or tick, that carries a parasite from one host to another; methods of controlling a parasite or disease by attacking the vector.

virtual water In place of shipping water to water-stressed regions, food may be exported to those regions, thus preventing the direct need for water and replacing it with "virtual" water.

vitamin A specific organic molecule that is required by the body in small amounts but that cannot be made by the body and therefore must be present in the diet.

volatile organic compounds (VOCs) A category of major air pollutants present in the air in the vapor state. The category includes fragments of hydrocarbon fuels from incomplete combustion and evaporated organic compounds such as paint solvents, gasoline, and cleaning solutions. Volatile organic compounds are major factors in the formation of photochemical smog.

vulnerability A measure of the likelihood of exposure to a hazard.

Waste Isolation Pilot Plant (WIPP) A facility built by the U.S. Department of Energy in New Mexico to receive defense-related nuclear wastes.

waste-to-energy combustion A process of combustion of solid wastes that also generates electrical energy.

WasteWise An EPA-sponsored program that targets the reduction of municipal solid waste by a number of partnerships.

water cycle See **hydrologic cycle**.

water-holding capacity The ability of a soil to hold water so that it will be available to plants.

waterlogging The total saturation of soil with water. Waterlogging results in plant roots not being able to get air and dying as a result.

watershed The total land area that drains directly or indirectly into a particular stream or river. The watershed is generally named from the stream or river into which it drains.

water table The upper surface of groundwater, rising and falling with the amount of groundwater.

water vapor Water molecules in the gaseous state.

weather The day-to-day variations in temperature, air pressure, wind, humidity, and precipitation mediated by the atmosphere in a given region.

weathering The gradual breakdown of rock into smaller and smaller particles, caused by natural chemical, physical, and biological factors.

weed Any plant that competes with agricultural crops, forests, lawns, or forage grasses for light and nutrients.

wet cleaning A water-based alternative to dry cleaning that avoids the use of hazardous chemicals.

wetlands Areas that are constantly wet and are flooded at more or less regular intervals—especially marshy areas along coasts that are regularly flooded by tides.

wetland system A biological aquatic system (usually a restored wetland) used to remove nutrients from treated sewage wastewater and return it virtually pure to a river or stream. Wetland systems are sometimes used when the application of treated wastewater for irrigation is not feasible.

Wild and Scenic Rivers Act of 1968 Legislation that protects rivers designated as "wild and scenic," preventing them from being dammed or otherwise harmfully affected.

wilderness Land that is undeveloped and wild; in the U.S., land that is protected by the Wilderness Act.

Wilderness Act of 1964 Federal legislation that provides for the permanent protection of undeveloped and unexploited areas so that natural ecological processes can operate freely in them.

Wildlife Services An agency within the U.S. Department of Agriculture that removes "nuisance" animals for landowners; the agency dispatches more than 2 million animals and birds yearly.

wind farms Arrays of numerous, modestly sized wind turbines for the purpose of producing electrical power.

windrows Piles of organic material extended into long rows to facilitate turning and aeration in order to enhance composting.

wind turbines Large "windmills" designed for the purpose of producing electrical power.

workability The relative ease with which a soil can be cultivated.

World Bank A branch of the United Nations that acts as a conduit for handling loans to developing countries.

World Food Program (WFP) A UN administration that receives donations of money and food from donor countries and distributes food aid to needy regions and countries.

World Trade Organization (WTO) A body that sets the rules for international trade agreements, made up of representatives from many countries and often dominated by the rich nations.

xeriscaping Landscaping with drought-resistant plants that need no watering.

yard wastes Grass clippings and other organic wastes from lawn and garden maintenance; major target for composting.

yellowcake So called because of its yellowish color, uranium ore that has been partially purified and is ready for further purification and enrichment.

Younger Dryas event A rapid change in global climate between 10,000 and 12,000 years ago that brought on 1,500 years of colder weather.

Yucca Mountain A remote location in Nevada chosen to be the nation's commercial nuclear waste repository; although well along in development, its future is uncertain.

zones of stress Regions where a species finds conditions tolerable but suboptimal. The species survives but is under stress.

zoonotic Diseases that may be transmitted between animals and humans.

zooplankton Any of a number of animal groups, including protozoa, crustaceans, worms, mollusks, and cnidarians, that live suspended in the water column and that feed on phytoplankton and other zooplankton.

zooxanthellae Photosynthetic algae that live within the tissues of coral species and enable them to grow productively in warm, shallow coastal areas.

CREDITS

Photo Credits

Frontmatter
Iii: Photodisc/Getty Images/Houghton Mifflin Harcourt; vi: KIM STALLKNECHT/ AFP/Newscom; vii: Altmarkfoto/iStockphoto; viii: David Grossman / Alamy; x: AP Photo/Anonymous; xi: Mircea Bezerghean/Shutterstock; xii: altrendo travel/Getty Images; xix: AFP/Getty Images

Chapter 1
Page 1 (top left): Silia Photo/Shutterstock; (bottom right): Photodisc/Getty Images/ Houghton Mifflin Harcourt; Page 2 (top right): Joseph Sohm/Visions of America/ Glow Images, Inc.; (bottom right): Steve Byland / Fotolia; Page 3 (top left): Rachel Carson Counci/Newscom; Page 3 (top right): brt COMM / Alamy; Page 8 (top right) John Sylvester / Alamy; (top left): Casper Wilkens/iStockphoto; Page 11 (bottom left): AP Photo/Las Cruces Sun-News, Norm Dettlaff; (bottom center): Science Images/UIG/Getty Images; (top center): Joseph Sohm/Visions of America/Glow Images, Inc.; Page 15 (top left): Michael Amaranthus/Mycorrhizal Applications, Inc.; Page 18 (top left): Goldman Environmental Prize; (top right): AFP/Getty Images; Page 19 (top left): Sveta/iStockphoto; Page 21 (top left): globestock/ iStockphoto

Chapter 2
Page 23 (top): Lou Linwei / Alamy; (bottom left): Martha Bayona/iStockphoto; Page 24: PETER PARKS/AFP/Getty Images/Newscom; Page 27: KIM STALLKNECHT/ AFP/Newscom; Page 30 (left): Toklo/iStockphoto; (center): Noah Poritz/MacroWorld/ Photo Researchers, Inc.; (right): David Weintraub/Photo Researchers, Inc.; Page 35 (left): fstockfoto/Shutterstock; (center): Frontpage/Shutterstock; (top right): VisualField/iStockphoto; Page 37 (top right): AP Photo; Page 39 (top left): John Craig/Bureau of Land Management; (top right): Dainis Derics/Shutterstock

Chapter 3
Page 49 (top left): Altmarkfoto/iStockphoto; (bottom right): GlobalP/iStockphoto; Page 50 (top right): Mifippo/iStockphoto; (bottom right): Alex Staroseltsev/ Shutterstock; Page 52 (center left): Olga Khoroshunova/Fotolia; (center): Pete Oxford/Nature Picture Library; (bottom right): LYNN M. STONE/Nature Picture Library; Page 53 (top left): Jerry and Marcy Monkman/EcoPhotography.com/ Alamy; (bottom right): Richard T. Wright; Page 54 (bottom right): louise murray / Alamy; Page 57: Derek Croucher / Alamy; Page 59 (bottom left): Pascal Goetgheluck / Photo Researchers, Inc.; Page 63 (top): khunaspix/Fotolia; Page 64 (top right): Olga Khoroshunova/Fotolia

Chapter 4
Page 75 (top left): Justin Black/Shutterstock; (bottom left): Joel Sartore/Getty Images; Page 78 (top right): Kokhanchikov/Shutterstock; Page 81 (top left): The Natural History Museum / The Image Works; (center left): Nigel Hicks/Dorling Kindersley; Page 82 (top left): galam/Fotolia; (top right): Phanie / SuperStock; (bottom left): James L. Amos/National Geographic/Getty Images; (bottom right): John Watney / Photo Researchers, Inc.; Page 84 (bottom left): Images of Africa Photobank / Alamy; (bottom right): Michael S. Nolan / age fotostock / SuperStock; Page 85 (bottom left): William Leaman / Alamy; (top right): Charles Stirling (Diving) / Alamy; Page 87 (center): Stubblefield Photography/Shutterstock; (left): David Hosking / Alamy; Page 88 (top left): Stephen P. Parker/Photo Resesearchers, Inc.; (top right): Bernard J. Nebel; (bottom left): Pj Malsbury/iStockphoto; Page 89 (bottom left): Susanna Sez El Pais Photos/Newscom; Page 90 (top left): Bernard J. Nebel; (top right): Natural Visions / Alamy; Page 94 (bottom left): Jeff Lepore/Photo Researchers, Inc.; (bottom center): Craig K. Lorenz/Photo Researchers, Inc.; Page 96 (center right): Andreas Von Einsiedel/Dorlng Kindersley; (bottom right): Krys Bailey / Alamy; Page 97 (top left): LightScribe/iStockphoto; (bottom left): Doug Smith/MCT/Newscom; (bottom right): NHPA /SuperStock; Page 98 (right): John W. Bova/Photo Researchers, Inc.

Chapter 5
Page 101 (top left): Martin Rietze/Stocktrek Images/Alamy Limited; (bottom left): iStockphoto; Page 102 (center left): Kai Horstmann / vario images GmbH & Co.KG/ Alamy; (top left): ROBERT T. WELLS/UNEP / Still Pictures / The Image Works Page 107 (bottom left): Reproduced from Transmission electron micrograph by Breznak & Pankratz (1977) with permission of the American Society for Microbiology.; Page 111: Oksana.perkins/Shutterstock; Steve Geer/iStockphoto; Dmitry Savinov/Shutterstock; Galyna Andrushko/Shutterstock; Yuriy Kulyk/Shutterstock; © TTphoto/Shutterstock; Page 114: Mikedabell/iStockphoto; Johnny Lye/iStockphoto; Angelo Garibaldi/Shutterstock; Cedric Schmidt/Fotolia; iStockphoto; Mr. Eckhart/ IStockphoto; Page 116 (top left) Bernard J. Nebel; (bottom right): Bernard J. Nebel; (top left): Bernard J. Nebel; (bottom right): Piotr Gatlik/Shutterstock; Page 118 (bottom left): Anna Galejeva/Shutterstock: Page 119 (top left): szefei/Shutterstock; (top right): Tupungato/Shutterstock; Page 120: Everett Collection Inc / Alamy

Chapter 6
Page 129 (bottom left): Varin-Visage/Photo Researchers, Inc.; (top left): Jacana/ Photo Researchers, Inc.; Page 130 (bottom right): STEPHANIE STONE/AFP/Getty Images/Newscom; Page 131 (bottom right): Ryan M. Bolton/Shutterstock; Page 132 (bottom right): AP Photo/George Osodi; Page 133 (bottom left): WILDLIFE GmbH / Alamy; Page 134 (center left): iStockphoto; (center): Jeremy Woodhouse/ Blend Images/Getty Images; (center left): blickwinkel/Rose/Alamy; Page 139 (top): James P. Blair/NATIONAL GEOGRAPHIC IMAGE COLLECTION/Getty Images; (bottom left): Nagy Melinda/Shutterstock; Page 141 (top left): James H Robinson/Photo Researchers/Getty Images; (top right): mkimages/Alamy; Page 142 (top left): blickwinkel / Alamy; (bottom right): AP Photo/The Daily News-Record, Pete Marovich; Page 143 (bottom left): Piotr Gatlik/Shutterstock; (bottom left): Premaphotos/Alamy; Page 144 (center right): AP Photo/John Kuntz/The Plain Dealer; Page 145 (top right): Roberta Olenick/All Canada Photos/SuperStock; Page 146 (bottom right): AndreyKlepikov/Shutterstock; Page 148 (top): AP Photo/ The El Paso Times, Rudy Gutierrez; Page 149 (top right): Marvin Dembinsky Photo Associates/Alamy; (top center): kuma/Shutterstock; (top right): David Norris/ Photo Researchers, Inc.; (center left): A.H. Rider/Photo Researchers, Inc.; (center): Jeff Lepore/Photo Researchers, Inc.; (center right): Canon Bob/iStockphoto.com; (bottom left): Tom McHugh/Steinhart Aquarium/Photo Researchers, Inc.; (bottom center): Gorshkov25/Shutterstock; (bottom right): Nicolas Larento/Fotolia
Page 152 (top right): Richard Langs/Shutterstock;
Page 153 (top left): Tom Lynn/MCT/Newscom

Chapter 7
Page 158 (top): Rich Carey / Shutterstock; (bottom): Reinhard Dirscherl/Robert Harding World Imagery; Page 161 (top left): think4photop/Shutterstock; Page 162: Andre Seale/Alamy; Page 163 (top left): Daniel Heuclin/NHPA/Photoshot; (bottom right): Jim West / Alamy; Page 164: Norma Jean Gargasz/Alamy; Page 167: Image Quest Marine; Page 169 (bottom right): jeremy sutton-hibbert/Alamy; Page 171 (bottom left): Tim Hall/Robert Harding World Imagery; Page 173 (top right): Robert Brook/Photo Researchers, Inc.; Page 176 (top left): AP Photo; Page 177 (top left): Kurt Lackovic / Alamy; (bottom right): Georgette Douwma / Photo Researchers, Inc.

Chapter 8
Page 186 (top right): David Grossman / Alamy; (bottom left) TED ALJIBE/AFP/ Getty Images/Newscom; Page 187 (left): L Ancheles/Getty Images; Ron Giling/ Lineair/Still Pictures/Specialist Stock; (right): James Baigrie/FoodPix/Getty Images; Page 190 (bottom right): Peter Johnson/CORBIS/Glow Images, Inc.; Page 191 (bottom left): Library of Congress Prints and Photographs Division [LC-DIG-nclc-01537]; Page 192 (top left): The National Archives/SSPL/Getty Images; (bottom right): NARINDER NANU/AFP/Getty Images; Page 201 (top right): Evelyn Hockstein/MCT/Newscom; Page 202 (bottom left): ASTER Science Team/ Nasa Images; (bottom right): J.m._Vidal European Press Agency/Newscom; Page 203 (top right): imagebroker.net / SuperStock

Chapter 9
Page 216 (top right): Thor Jorgen Udvang/Shutterstock; (bottom right): foto76/ Fotolia; Page 219 (center right): Amit Bhargava/Bloomberg via Getty Images; Page 221 (bottom left): F1online/Getty Images; (bottom right): Images & Stories / Alamy; Page 225 (top right): Alex Segre/Alamy; Page 227 Gallo Images / Alamy; Page 228 (top left): Courtesy of The World Bank; AP Photo/Julie Plasencia; Page 229: Caro / Alamy; Page 232: Fabienne Fossez/Alamy; Page 233: Xinhua /Landov; Page 235 (top left): Peter D. O'Neill TW : EEC/Alamy; (bottom right): STR/AFP/ Getty Images/Newscom

Chapter 10
Page 239 (top left): FOREST LUGH/EPA/Newscom; (bottom left): Stringer Shanghai/REUTERS; Page 241 (top left): Fotolia; (top right): Andrew Woodley / Alamy; Page 247: Dead Shot Keen / Alamy; Page 248: Caro / Alamy; Page 252: Alison Jones / DanitaDelimont.com Danita Delimont Photography/Newscom; Page 254: PacifiCorp/AP Images; Page 255 (top right): Stephen Mcsweeny/Shutterstock; (center right): Francois Gohier/Photo Researchers, Inc.; Page 256 (top): AP Photo/ Dale Wilson; Page 258 Eitan Simanor / Alamy; Page 259 (bottom left): Lowell Georgia/Photo Researchers, Inc.; (bottom right): Jake Lyell / Alamy; Page 260 (top right): berna namoglu/Shutterstock; Page 262 AP Photo/Gary Kazanjian

Chapter 11
Page 266 (bottom right): fotolE/iStockphoto; (top right): National Archives; Page 267: Ted Foxx / Alamy; Page 274 (bottom left): Bernard J. Nebel; (bottom right): Richard T. Wright; Page 275: Eye of Science / Photo Researchers, Inc.; Page 276: Philippe Psaila / Photo Researchers, Inc.; Page 278 (top): Charles R. Belinky/Photo Researchers, Inc.; (center right): Jon Arnold Images Ltd/Alamy; Page 279: Edwin Remsberg/Alamy; Page 280 (top left): U.S. Department of Agriculture; (center left):

David Wall/Alamy; Page 281: Leng Yuehan - CNImaging/Newscom; Page 282 (top left): Betty Derig/Photo Researchers; (top right): DAVID GRAY/REUTERS/Newscom; Page 284 (top right): Richard Lord/PhotoEdit; Page 285 (bottom left): Issouf Sanogo/AFP/Getty Images

Chapter 12

Page 289 (top left): AP Photo/Carrie Antlfinger; (bottom left): Basel101658/Shutterstock; Page 290 (bottom right): iStockphoto; Page 291 (top left): Pete Oxford/Danita Delimont, Agent/Alamy; Page 292 (top left): Garry D. McMichael/Photo Researchers, Inc.; (top right): Fotokostic/Shutterstock; Page 293 (top right): FDR Library; Page 294 (top): Kip Ross/National Geographic/Getty Images; Page 295 (top right): Jim West / Alamy; Page 296 (top left): Wayne Hutchinson/Alamy; (top right): James Steidl/Shutterstock; Page 298 (top left): Bill Barksdale/Age Fotostock; Page 299 (top left): Courtesy Danforth Plant Science Center; (bottom right): kurt_G/Shutterstock; Page 300 (bottom right): MICHEL GANGNE/AFP/Getty Images/Newscom; Page 301 (top right): Golden Rice Humanitarian Board. www.goldenrice.org, Page 304 (top right): Dorthea Lange/[LC-DIG-fsa-8b29516]/Library of Congress Prints and Photographs Division; Page 305 (bottom left): Susan Kuklin / Photo Researchers, Inc.; (bottom center): Todd Bannor/Alamy; (bottom right): NASA Images; Page 307 (top center): John Takai/Fotolia; Page 308 (top left): David Cole/Alamy; Page 314 (top left): John Birdsall/Age Fotostock; (top right): www.NASA Images.gov; (center left): Bloomberg/Getty Images; (center right): AP Photo/Orlin Wagner

Chapter 13

Page 317 (top left): Katja Heinemann/Aurora Photos/Alamy; (bottom left): Oxford Scientific/Getty Images; Page 319 (top left): Nigel Cattlin/Alamy; (top right): Richard T. Wright; (center left): Richard T. Wright; (center right): Arco Images GmbH/Alamy; (left): Nick Greaves/Alamy; (right): Allik Camazine/Alamy; (bottom left): Roger Eritja/Alamy; (bottom right): Photo Researchers, Inc.; Page 320 (top left): Drake Fleege/Alamy; (top right): U.S. Customs and Border Protection; Page 322 (top right): Ian Berry/Magnum Photos; Page 323 (bottom right): courtesy/everett collection inc/AGE Fotostock; (top right): John de la Bastide/Shutterstock; Page 325 (top left): Nigel Cattlin / Photo Researchers, Inc.; (bottom left): Ronnie Howard/Shutterstock; Page 327 (bottom left): James H. Robinson / Photo Researchers, Inc.; Page 328 (bottom right): R Koenig/Blickwinkel/AGE Fotostock; Page 330 (bottom right): Richard T. Wright; Page 331 (center right): USDA/APHIS Animal And Plant Health Inspection Service; (bottom left): Harry Rogers/Photo Researchers, Inc.; Page 332 (bottom left): juulijs/Fotolia; (bottom right): Louis Quitt/Photo Researchers, Inc.; Page 333 (top left): Christopher M. Ranger, Penn State University; (top right): A3386 Uli Deck Deutsche Presse-Agentur/Newscom; Page 334 (top right): Sonda Dawes/The Image Works; Page 336 (top right): Nigel Cattlin/Holt Studios International/Photo Researchers, Inc.

Chapter 14

Page 342 (top right): Stock Connection/SuperStock; (bottom left): Elzbieta Sekowska/Shutterstock; Page 343 (top left): AP Photo/Anonymous, (bottom left): Jason Verschoor/iStockphoto; Page 344: Handout/Reuters; Page 345: Douglas Lander/Alamy; Page 347 (center right): Mark Jensen/iStockphoto; Page 350 Martin Muránsky/Shutterstock; Page 357 AP Photo/Kevin Frayer; Page 362 AP Photo/Str; Page 363 Jim West/PhotoEdit; Page 366 iStockphoto

Chapter 15

Page 369 (top left): Aflo/Mainichi Newspaper/epa/Newscom; (bottom left): Dalibor Zivotic/iStockphoto; Page 370: Kyodo/Newscom; Page 372: AP Photo/Tennessee Valley Authority; Page 375 (center left): Erich Hartmann/Magnum Photos; Page 381 (top left): AP Photo/Holtec International; (bottom right): Everett Collection Historical / Alamy; Page 382: AP Photo; Page 383: (top right): ITAR-TASS Photo Agency / Alamy; Page 387: AP Photo/Robert F. Bukaty, File; Page 388: The National Ignition Facility

Chapter 16

Page 392 (top right): Meyerbroeker/Caro/Alamy; (bottom right): Sebastien Burel/Shutterstock; Page 393 (top left): Armen Gharibyan/Alamy; (top right): MaxFX/Shutterstock; Page 398 (top left): Bernard J. Nebel; Page 399 (top left): National Renewable Energy Laboratory; (top right): Ethan Miller/Getty Images; Page 400: (bottom left): Robyn Beck/Afp/Getty Images/Newscom; Page 402: Iofoto/Shutterstock; Page 404 (top left): Planetpix/Alamy; Page 404 (bottom right): Creative Energy Corporation; Page 405 (top right): Joerg Boethling / Alamy; Page 406: Ideeone/iStockphoto; Page 408 (bottom right): Transtock Inc. / Alamy; Page 409: Courtesy of Pacific Gas and Electric Company

Chapter 17

Page 414: (top right): Mircea Bezerghean/Shutterstock; (bottom left): PhilAugustavo/iStockphoto; Page 415 (top left): Capifrutta/Shutterstock.com; (bottom left): Pasieka/Science Photo Library/Alamy; Page 423 (top left): Aflo Foto Agency/Alamy; (top right): Pammy1140/Fotolia; (center left): Mark Pearson/Alamy; (center right): Ryan McGinnis/Alamy; Page 425 (top left): Calvin Larsen/Photo Researchers, Inc.; (top right): Robert Harding/Glow Images, Inc.; (center left): Tomas Sereda/Fotolia; (center right): Bloomberg/Getty Images; Page 427: Ulrich Doering/Alamy; Page 428: AP Photo; Page 431: Jake Lyell / Alamy

Chapter 18

Page 441 (top left): Kyodo /Landov; (bottom left): Jack F/Fotolia; Page 442 (top left): Shahee Ilyas/Alamy; (center left): GABRIEL BOUYS/AFP/Getty Images; (top

center): Office of Science and Technology Policy Executive Office of the President/NASA Images; Page 454 (top right): National Snow and Ice Data Center; (top right): National Snow and Ice Data Center

Chapter 19

Page 472 (top right): Ronaldo Schemidt/AFP/Getty Image; (bottom right): Tomas Sereda/Fotolia; Page 473: Bettmann/Corbis; Page 476 (top left): Ekash/iStockphoto; (top right): Daniel Stein/iStockphoto: Page 478: Richard T. Wright; Page 480 (top right): Les Cunliffe/Fotolia; (center right): Alexandra Gl/Fotolia; (center): hartphotography/Fotolia; (right): Elenathewise/Fotolia; (bottom): Stefan Redel/Fotolia; (bottom): martin33/Fotolia; Page 485 (top left): Grapes - Michaud/Photo Researchers, Inc.; (center): Matt Meadows/Peter Arnold/Getty Images; (center left): Matt Meadows/Peter Arnold/Getty Images; Page 487: Seth Joel/Photographer's Choice/Getty Images; Page 488: AS Heagle/United States Department of Agriculture; Page 490: Balliolman/Fotolia; Page 492: AP Photo

Chapter 20

Page 506 (top right): Courtesy of NASA Images Images; (bottom right): Science Photo Library / Alamy; Page 508 (center left): richard ellis/Alamy; Page 509 (top left): AP Photo, Page 510: Robert Harding Picture Library / SuperStock; Page 511 (left): Bob Hudson/George Waclawin/Bernard J. Nebel; (center left): Bob Hudson/George Waclawin/Bernard J. Nebel; (center): Bob Hudson/George Waclawin/Bernard J. Nebel; (center right): Bob Hudson/George Waclawin/Bernard J. Nebel; Page 513: Thomas R. Fletcher / Alamy; Page 514 (bottom): Charles R. Belinky/Photo Researchers, Inc.; Page 515: Bernard J. Nebel; Page 518 (top right): Bernard J. Nebel; Page 520: eric fowke/alamy; Page 521 (top left): Bernard J. Nebel; (top right): Bernard J. Nebel; Page 522 (top left): Scott Smith/Sancor Industries Ltd; (top right): Scott Smith/Sancor Industries Ltd; Page 525 (bottom right): G. Avila / Alamy; Page 528: Jennifer Weinberg / Alamy

Chapter 21

Page 532 (top right): Jack Plunkett/Bloomberg/Getty Images; (bottom right): imagestock/iStockphoto; Page 533: Photo © Cymie Payne, courtesy of Cambridge Arts Council; Page 534: Van D. Bucher/Photo Researchers, Inc.; Page 535: Jim West / Alamy; Page 537: NYC Parks Department; Page 540: D. Hurst/Alamy; Page 541: Trex, Inc.; Page 542: Justin Sullivan/Getty Images; Page 543: John Griffin/The Image Works; Page 545: Jim R. Bounds/Bloomberg/Getty Images; Page 547: Richard T. Wright

Chapter 22

Page 551 (top left): M.Sobreira/Alamy; (bottom): Gresei/Fotolia; Page 558: imagebroker / Alamy; Page 559 (top right): AP Photo/Jackie Johnston; (bottom left): U.S. Environmental Protection Agency Headquarters; Page 560 (bottom right): Joe Traver/Liaison/Getty Images; (top left): Nancy J. Pierce/Photo Researchers, Inc.; (bottom left): Van Bucher/Photo Researchers, Inc.; Page 563 (bottom left): Richard T. Wright; Page 565 (center right): Tetra Tech EM Inc; Page 567: BEDI/AFP/Getty Images/Newscom

Chapter 23

Page 573 (top left): Curtis W. Richter/Getty Images; (bottom right): Reinhold Foeger/Shutterstock; Page 574 (top right): JRC, Inc./Alamy; (bottom): Age Fotostock/SuperStock; Page 575: ERIK S. LESSER/EPA/Landov Media; Page 576 (top left): Richard Thornton/Shutterstock; (center left): Esbin-Anderson/The Image Works; Page 577 (top left): MaxFX/Shutterstock; (bottom left): Johnny Stockshooter/Alamy; (center right): Shaun Cunningham / Alamy; (bottom right): asterix0597/iStockphoto; Page 583: Cameron Davidson /Getty Images; (center right): Bernard J. Nebel; Page 584 (top left): Bernard J. Nebel; (top right): altrendo travel/Getty Images; Page 585: Marcia Chambers /dbimages / Alamy; Page 586 (top left): Medioimages/Photodisc/Getty Images; (top right): steinphoto/iStockphoto; (bottom right): Warwick Kent/Photolibrary/Getty Images; Page 588: Andrew Murphy/Alamy; Page 589 (bottom left): Chattanooga Area Convention and Visitors Bureau; Page 591 (center right): Jeffrey Pohorski; Page 592: Ilene MacDonald / Alamy

Text Credits

Chapter 1

Pages 3–4, 6: Source: *Silent Spring* by Rachel Carson. Published 1962 by Houghton Mifflin; Pages 49–50, Table 1-1: Source: Based on "Millennium Ecosystem Assessment, Ecosystems and Human Well-Being: Synthesis" from Millennium Ecosystem Assessment website; Figure 1.4: "Worldwide trends in the Human Development index," from *2010 Human Development Report*. Copyright © 2010 by United Nations Publications. Reprinted with permission. All rights reserved.; Figure 1.5: "Atmospheric CO2 at Mauna Loa Observatory (Fig. 1.5)," Scripps CO2 Program, Scripps Institution of Oceanography, La Jolla, CA. Reprinted with permission.

Chapter 2

Page 53, Table 2.1: "Total Wealth and Per Capita Wealth By Type of Wealth, 2005 (Table 2.1)," from *World Bank: World Development Report*; Page 25, Figure 2.2: Source: Based on World Development Report 1992; Page 33, Figure 2.7: Source: Based on "The Genuine Progress Indicator 2006: A Tool for Sustainable

Development," by John Talberth, Clifford Cobb, and Noah Slattery, from Redefining Progress, 2006; Figure 2.15: Source: Office of Management and Budget.

Chapter 4

Page 87, Figure 4.13: "Evolution of Character Displacement in Darwin's Finches" by Peter R. Grant and B. Rosemary Grant, from SCIENCE, July 2006, Volume 313(5784). Copyright © 2006 by AAAS. Reprinted with permission.; Page 95, Figure 4.21: Figure from *Geosystems: an Introduction to Physical Geography,* 6th Edition by Robert W. Christopherson, 2006. Copyright © 2006 by Pearson Education, Inc. Reprinted by permission. All rights reserved.

Chapter 5

Page 113, Figure 5.10: Source: United States Department of Agriculture: Natural Resources Conservation Service; Page 117, Figure 5.13: *Biology: Concepts and Connections,* 4th Edition, by Neil A. Campbell, Jane B. Reece, Lawrence G. Mitchell and Martha R. Taylor. Copyright © 2003 by Pearson Education. Reprinted with permission.; Table 5.3: "Ecosystem Services and Function," in *The Value of the World's Ecosystem,* by Robert Costanza, Ralph D. Arge and Rudolf de Groot. Reprinted with permission.

Chapter 6

Page 89, Table 6.2: "Preventing Childhood Obesity and Type II Diabetes," by Sharron Dalton from *Our Overweight Children: What Parents, Schools, and Communities Can Do to Control the Fatness Epidemic,* University of California Press. Copyright © 2004 by the Regents of the University of California. Reprinted with permission.; Page 117, Table 6.4: Source: U.S. Fish and Wildlife Service.

Chapter 7

Table 7.2: Source: Data from "Living Beyond Our Means: Natural Assets and Human Well-Being," from Millennium Ecosystem Assessment (Statement of the Millennium Ecosystem Assessment Board, 2005); Figure 7.8: Source: based on "Global Forest Resources Assessment 2010" from Food and Agriculture Organization of the United Nations; Figure 7.10: Source: based on "Global Forest Resources Assessment 2010" from Food and Agriculture Organization of the United Nations; Page 176, 7.12: "A Global Map of Human Impacts to Marine Ecosystems," from *National Center for Ecological Analysis and Synthesis* website, 2010. Copyright © 2010 by The Regents of the University of California. Reprinted with permission. All Rights Reserved.; Page 184, Figure 7.19: Source: National Atlas website.

Chapter 8

Figure 8.7: "Changes in Country Classification" from the World Bank Website, July 1, 2011. Copyright © 2011 by The World Bank Group, All Rights Reserved. Reprinted with permission; Figure 8.8: Total Population poster from *Worldmapper* website. Copyright © 2006 by SASI Group (University of Sheffield) and Mark Newman (University of Michigan). Reprinted with permission; Figure 8.9: "Population Growth in Different World Regions," from *World Population Prospects: 2010 Revision.* Copyright © 2010 by United Nations. Reprinted with permission. All rights reserved; Figure 8.10: "Total Fertility Rates Around the World," from World Population Prospects: 2010 Revision. Copyright © 2010 by United Nations Publications. Reprinted with permission; Table 8.2: Source: based on data from 2011 World Population Data Sheet from Population Reference Bureau; Figure 8.1: "Growing Cities," from *World Organization Prospects: 2009 Revision.* Copyright © 2009 by United Nations. Reprinted with permission. All rights reserved; Figure 8.15: Source: Data from: "The World Population Growth Rate: Why Declines Stalled in the 1980s" by Shiro Horiuchi, from *Population Today,* Volume 21(6) and "World Population Expected to Reach 6 Billion in Early 1999" by Carl Haub, *Population Today,* June/July 1996, Volume 24(6/7). Population Reference Bureau; and *World Population Prospects the 2008 Revision.* United Nations; Figure 8.16: "Population of the world, 1950-2100, according to different projections and variants," from *World Population Prospects: The 2010 Revision.* Volume 1: Comprehensive Tables. Copyright © 2010 by United Nations. Reprinted with permission. All rights reserved; Figure 8.17: Source: *The 2010 Revision,* Volume II: Demographic Profiles from United Nations Department of Economic and Social Affairs/Population Division; Figure 8.19: Figures from *World Population Prospects: the 2010 Revision,* Volume II: Demographic Profiles. Reprinted with permission. All rights reserved. Figure 8.20: Source: U.S. Population Projections. United States Census Bureau; Figure 8.21a-d: Figures from *World Population Prospects: The 2010 Revision,* Volume II: Demographic Profiles. Copyright © 2010 by United Nations. Reprinted with permission. All rights reserved; Figure 8.21e-h: Figures from *World Population Prospects: The 2010 Revision,* Volume II: Demographic Profiles. Copyright © by United Nations. Reprinted with permission. All rights reserved; Figure 8.22: Adapted from "Demographic transition in developed and developing countries," from Population Reference Bureau; Figure 8.23: "World Population Growing at Record Speed," by Carl Haub and James Gribble, from *Population Bulletin: The World at 7 Billion,* July 2011, Volume 66(2). Copyright © 2011 by Population Reference Bureau. Reprinted with permission.

Chapter 9

Table 9.1: Source: based on data from various World Population Data Sheets. Source: Based on "Population, Human Resources, Health, and the Environment: Getting the Balance Right." by Anthony J. McMichael, from *Environment,* January/February 2008, Volume 50(1); Figure 9.1: Sources: Data from 2008 *World Population Data Sheet* and 2011 *World Population Data Sheet.* Population

Reference Bureau; Figure 9.2: "Technology & Development" Kavita Watsa from *Global Economic Prospects 2008: Technology Diffusion in the Developing World.* Copyright © 2008 by The International Bank for Reconstruction and Development / The World Bank. Reprinted with permission; Figure 9.3: *World Development Report 2012: Gender and Equality Development.* Copyright © 2012 by the World Bank Group. Reprinted with permission; Figure 9.4: *World Development Report 2003.* Copyright © 2003 by World Bank Group. Reprinted with permission; Figure 9.5: Source: based on data from *World Data Sheet 2011.* Population reference Bureau; and *World Economic Outlook Database-September 2011.* International Monetary Fund; Figure 9.8: Source: based on data from *World Data Sheet 2011.* Population reference Bureau; Figure 9.10: "Proportion of people living on less than $1.25 a day, 1990 and 2005 (Percentage)," from *The Millennium Development Goals Report 2011.* Copyright © 2011 by United Nations. Reprinted with permission. All rights reserved; Figure 9.11: "Under-five mortality rate, 1990 and 2009 (Deaths per 1,000 live births)," from *The Millennium Development Goals Report 2011.* Copyright © 2011 by United Nations. Reprinted with permission. All rights reserved; Figure 9.13: List of five World Bank Group organizations from the World Bank website. Copyright © 2012 The World Bank Group, All Rights Reserved. Reprinted with permission; Figure 9.16: "Haiti Aid Facts," by David Roodman, from *Center for Global Development* website, January 15, 2010. Copyright © 2010 by Center for Global Development. Reprinted with permission; Figure 9.18: Source: Based on data from *Projections of Mortality and Burden of Disease, 2002–2030.* World Health Organization.

Chapter 10

Page 43: Source: *World Water Vision* by William J. Cosgrove and Frank R. Rijsberman, 2000. Copyright © 2000 by World Water Council. Table 10.2: Source: U.S. Geological Survey. Page 246, Figure 10.1: Source: based on pie chart from USGS; Figure 10.5: *Elemental Geosystems,* 7th Edition, by Robert W. Christopherson. Copyright © 2013 by Pearson Education. Reprinted with permission; Figure 10.11: Adapted from "Water Poverty Index," by C. A. Sullivan, et al., *Report to DFID, 2000.* Copyright © by Centre for Ecology & Hydrology. Reprinted with permission; Figure 10.12: Source: Adaptation of Figure 13 from *Estimated Use of Water in the United States in 2005* (Circular 1344) by Joan F. Kenny, et al. United states Geological Survey, 2009; Figure 10.16: Source: CorpsMap, National Inventory of Dams website. United States Army Corps of Engineers. NOAA.

Chapter 11

Figure 11.3: "Relative Size of Soil Particles," from *CMG Garden Notes.* Copyright © by Colorado State University Extension. Reprinted with permission; Page 275, Figure 11.6: Source: "Global Soil Regions" by Natural Resources Conservation Service, November 2005. United States Department of Agriculture; Figure 11.14: Based on "Production Scenarios and the Effect of Soil Degradation on Long-Term Food Security in China," by Liming Ye and Eric Van Ranst, from *Global Environment Change,* October 2009, Volume 19(4). Copyright © 2009 by Elsevier. Reprinted with permission. All rights reserved.

Chapter 12

Page 300: Source: "20 questions on genetically modified foods," World Health Organization; Page 312: Source: *The Doubly Green Revolution: Food for All in the 21st Century* by Gordon Conway. Source: "Farming Needs 'Climate-smart' Revolution, Says Report" by Richard Black, from BBC News website, March 28, 2012; Page 306, Figure 12.12: Adapted from "Global Status of Commercialized Biotech/GM Crops: 2007," from ISAA BRIEF, Number 37. Copyright © 2007 by ISAAA. Reprinted with permission; Page 314, Figure 12.17: Source: MyPyramid from ChooseMyPlate.gov. United States Department of Agriculture.; Page 316, Figure 12.19: "Proportion of children under age five who are underweight, 1990 and 2006 (Percentage)," from *The Millennium Development Goals Report 2008.* Copyright © 2011 by United Nations. Reprinted with permission. All rights reserved; Page 318, Figure 12.20: Source: Data from World Food Programme; United States Department of Agriculture, Food Aid Information System; Food and Agriculture Organization of the United Nations; Figure 304, Figure 12.21: Figure from the Food and Agriculture Organization of the United Nations. Reprinted with permission; Figure 12.22b: **www.nasa.gov**; Figure12.22c: NASA.

Chapter 13

Page 318: "Definition of Pest" from *Random House Webster's College Dictionary,* April 27, 1999. Copyright © 1999 by Random House, Inc. Reprinted with permission; Table 13.1: Source: "Private Pesticide Applicator Training Manual" from Environmental Protection Agency; Page 325, Figure 13.4: Source: Environmental Protection Agency.

Chapter 14

Table 14.2: Source: based on data from BP Statistical Review of World Energy; Figure 14.6: Figure from *Benchmarking Air Emissions of the 100 Largest Electric Poser Producers in the United States,* by M. J. Bradley & Associates, June 2010. Copyright © 2010 by Natural Resources Defense Council. Reprinted with permission; Figure 14.9: Adaptation from "Estimated U.S. energy Use in 2010: ~98.0 Quads" from *Lawrence Livermore National Library.* Copyright © 2011 by Lawrence Livermore National Library. Reprinted with permission; Figure 14.12: Source: Annual Energy Review 2010, from the Department of Energy; Figure 14.13: Source: Department of Energy; Figure 14.15: Source: Based on ASPO Newsletter No. 100, April 2009; Figure 14.16: Source: U.S. State Department.

Chapter 15

Table 15.1: Source: based on data from NRC; Page 375, Figure 15.2: Source: Data from U.S. Department of Energy; Figure 15.4: Source: Data from International Atomic Energy Agency; Figure 15.17: Source: Data from International Atomic Energy Agency.

Chapter 16

Table 16.1: Source: REN21. Global Status Report 2011; Page 403, Figure 16.10: *Renewables Global Status Report, 2009 Update, REn 21,* Secretariat, United Nations Environment Programme; Figure 16.11: National Renewable Energy Laboratory; Figure 16.15: Data from GWEC.

Chapter 17

Page 414: Source: *Red Sky at Morning: America and the Crisis of the Global Environment,* by James Gustave Speth. Published by Yale University Press, 2004; Page 419: Source: Mission Statement of the Centers for Disease Control and Prevention; Page 45–6: Source: "Risk communication: Evolution and Revolution" by Vincent Covello and Peter M. Sandman, from *Solutions to an Environment in Peril,* edited by Anthony Wolbarst. Published by John Hopkins University Press, 2001; Table 17.1: Source: based on data from The Global Burden of Disease: 2008; Table 17.2: Source: based on data from the OFDA/CRED International Disaster Database; Table 17.3: Source: based on "Risk-Benefit Analysis" by R. Wilson and E.A. Crouch; Table 17.4: "Ten Leading Selected Risk Factors as Percentage Causes of Disease Burden, Measured in DALYs," from *World Health Report 2009.* Reprinted with permission; Figure 17.1: "Timeline: Pandemic (H1N1) 2009 laboratory confirmed cases and number of deaths as reported to WHO. Status as of: 15 August 2010," from World Health Organization website. Copyright © 2010 by World Health Organization. Reprinted with permission; Page 427, Figure 17.3: Sources: Data from: "Deaths: Preliminary Data for 2009" by Kenneth D. Kochanek, et al., from *National Vital Statistics Reports,* March 16, 2011, Volume 59(4); Centers for Disease Control; and American Medical Association; Figure 17.4: Source: U.S. Department of Health & Human Services; Figure 17.5: Table from World Health Organization report: Global Tuberculosis Control 2011. Copyright © 2011 by World Health Organization. Reprinted with permission; Figure 434, Figure 17.11: Source: Centers for Disease Control and Prevention; Figure 17.16: "Loss of life expectancy of the Danes related to various risk factors. Loss of life expectancy (years) for men and women," by Krud Juel, Jan Sørensen, and Henrick Brønnum-Hansen, from *Risk Factors and Public Health in Denmark—Summary Report,* National Institute of Public Health, 2007. Copyright © 2007 by National Institute of Public Health, Denmark. Reprinted with permission; Figure 17.17: Source: Environmental Protection Agency.

Chapter 18

Table 18.3: "Climate Change 2007: Synthesis Report. Contribution of Working Groups I, II and III to the Fourth Assessment Report of the Intergovernmental Panel on Climate Change, Table SPM.6." IPCC, Geneva, Switzerland; Figure 18.14a: National Snow and Ice Data Center; Figure 18.14b: National Snow and Ice Data Center; Figure 18.5: The Stern Review Report © Crown Copyright 2006 The Economics of Climate Change: The Stern Review © Cambridge University Press 2007. Source: "Global Land-Ocean Temperature Index" graph from NASA website. Based on Fig 1A from "Global Temperature Change," by James Hansen, from *Proceedings of the National Academy of Sciences,* July 2006, Volume 103. Copyright © 2006 by National Academy of Sciences. Reprinted with permission; Figure 18.6: Source: Data from "Atmospheric carbon dioxide concentrations," NOAA; Figure 18.7a: Adapted from The Niels Bohr Institute Archives; Figure 18.7b & c: *Elemental Geosystems,* 5th Edition, by Robert W. Christopherson. Copyright © 2007 by Pearson Education. Reprinted with permission; Page 456, Figure 18.8: *Our Changing Planet: An Introduction to Earth System Science and Global Environmental Change,* 2nd Edition, by Fred T. Mackenzie. Copyright © 1998 by Pearson Education. Reprinted with permission; Page 460, Figure 18.10: Source: Graph by Robert Simmon from "Correcting Ocean Cooling" by Rebecca Lindesy, from Earth Observatory website, February 2007. National Aeronautics and Space Administration; Figure 18.11: Adapted from "The Rise In Global Mean Sea Level (2011_re14)," from *CU Sea Level Research Group* website. Copyright © 2011 by University of Colorado. Reprinted with permission; Figure 18.12: Source: National Snow and Ice Data Center. Source: National Snow and Ice Data Center; Figure 18.13: Source: NOAA Arctic Report Card: Update for 2011; Figure 18.15: Source: Carbon Dioxide Information Analysis Center; Page 465, Figure 18.16: Source: U.S. Energy Information Administration; Figure 18.17: Source: "The Cooperative Global Air Sampling Network Newsletter" from NOAA Earth System Research Laboratory, Spring 2011; Page 465, Figure 18.18: Source: Carbon Cycling and Biosequestration: Report from the March 2008 Workshop, DOE/SC-108, U.S. Department of Energy Office of Science; Page 467, Figure 18.19: "Climate Change 2007: The Physical Science basis. Working Group I Contribution to the Fourth Assessment Report of the Intergovernmental Panel on Climate Change, Figure SPM.2." Cambridge University Press. Reprinted with permission; Page 467, Figure 18.19: "Climate Change 2007: The Physical Science Basis, Contribution of Working Group I to the Fourth Assessment Report of the Intergovernmental Panel on Climate Change, Figure TS.32." Cambridge University Press. Reprinted with permission; Page 467, Figure 18.19: "Climate Change 2007: The Physical Science Basis, Contribution of Working Group I to the Fourth Assessment Report of the Intergovernmental Panel on Climate Change, Figure TS.32." Cambridge University Press. Reprinted with permission; Page 469, Figure 18.22: "How Urgent Is Climate Change?" by Richard A. Kerr, from *Science,*

November 2007, Volume 318(5854). Copyright © 2007 by AAAS. Reprinted with permission; Page 471, Figure 18.23: Adapted from "Water Poverty Index," by C. A. Sullivan, et al., *Report to DFID, 2000,* from Copyright © by Centre for Ecology & Hydrology. Reprinted with permission; Page 473, Figure 18.24: "Climate Change 2007: Synthesis Report. Contribution of Working Groups I, II and III to the Fourth Assessment Report of the Intergovernmental Panel on Climate Change, Figure 5.1," Cambridge University Press. Reprinted with permission; Figure 18.25: "Global Pathways" from Climate Action Tracker website. Copyright © 2011 by Climate Action Tracker Partners. Reprinted with permission.

Chapter 19

Figure 19.3: Source: "National Ambient Air Quality Standards" from Environmental Protection Agency, October 2011; Table 19.4: Source: "Scientific Assessment of Ozone Depletion: 2010," from *Global Ozone Research and Monitoring Project Report,* No. 52, Geneva, Switzerland: World Meteorological Organization, 20; Page 489, Figure 19.9: Source: "National Emissions Inventory (NEI) Air Pollutant Emissions Trends Data" from U.S. Environmental Protection Agency website; Page 490, Figure 19.10: Source: "National Emissions Inventory (NEI) Air Pollutant Emissions Trends Data" from U.S. Environmental Protection Agency website; Page 490, Figure 19.11: Source: "Air Quality Trends" from U.S. Environmental Protection Agency website; Figure 19.15: Source: "NADP Data and Information Use Conditions" from National Atmospheric Deposition Program website; Figure 19.16: Source: "Coal plants without scrubbers account for a majority of U.S. SO2 emissions" from *Today in Energy,* from U.S. Energy Information Agency website; Page 498, Figure 19.20: Source: "Effects of Ozone Air Pollution on Plants" from U.S. Department of Agriculture website; Figure 19.25: Source: Environmental Protection Agency; Figure 19.26: Source: Environmental Protection Agency; Figure 19.27: Source: "United States Geological Survey (USGS): Water Resources of New York" from the USGS website; Page 510, Figure 19.29: Source: Report by the U.S. Climate Change Science Program and the Subcommittee on Global Change Research; Page 513, Figure 19.31: Source: "Ozone Hole Watch" from the NASA website; Page 514, Figure 19.32: "Production and presence of ozone-depleting substances in the atmosphere: past, present, and future," from *Scientific Assessment of Ozone Depletion.* Copyright © 2006 by United Nations. Reprinted with permission. All rights reserved.

Chapter 20

Page 506: NASA. Table 20.2: Source: "Guidance for Water Quality-Based Decisions: The TMDL Process" from Environmental Protection Agency; Figure 20.1: Source: "The Mississippi River/Gulf of Mexico Watershed Nutrient Task Force" from the Environmental Protection Agency website; Figure 20.5: *Progress on Drinking Water and Sanitation, 2012 Update.* Copyright © 2012 by World Health Organization. Reprinted with permission.

Chapter 21

Table 21.1: Source: "Interstate Shipment of Municipal Solid Waste: 2007 Update" by James E. McCarthy, from *CRS Report for Congress,* June 13, 2007; Page 547, Figure 21.2: Source: data from Environmental Protection Agency, Office of Solid Waste, Municipal Solid Waste in the United States: 2010 Facts and Figures; Page 457, Figure 21.3: Source: data from Environmental Protection Agency, Office of Solid Waste, Municipal Solid Waste in the United States: 2010 Facts and Figures; Figure 21.9: Data from EPA, Office of Solid Waste, Municipal Solid Waste in the United States: Non-Hazardous Waste Management Hierarchy; Figure 21.12: Source: data from the Environmental Protection Agency, Municipal Solid Waste Generation, Recycling, and Disposal in the United States: Facts and Figures for 2010.

Chapter 22

Page 569: Source: data from *Environmental Protection Agency, Final Guidance for Incorporating Environmental Justice Concerns in EPA's NEPA Compliance Analyses;* Table 22.1: "The "Dirty Dozen" Persistent Organic Pollutants," from Report on DDT, Aldrin, Dieldrin, Endrin, Chlordane, Heptachlor, Hexachlorobenzene, Mirex, Toxaphene, Polychlorinated Biphenyls, Dioxins, and Furans, International Programme on Chemical Safety. Copyright © 1995 by United Nations. Reprinted with permission. All rights reserved; Figure 22.5: Source: "2010 Toxics Release Inventory" from the Environmental Protection Agency, January 2012; Figure 22.08: "U.S. Environmental Protection Agency Headquarters."

Chapter 23

Page 574: "Map of Atlanta BeltLine," from *Atlanta Beltline 2010 Annual Report.* Copyright © 2010 by Atlanta BeltLine. Reprinted with permission. All rights reserved; Page 591: *The Waterman's Stewardship Covenant* by Susan Drake Emmerich. Copyright © by Dr. Susan D. Emmerich. Reprinted with permission. Table 23.1: Source: U.S. Census Bureau; Table 23.2: "Ten Most Sprawling Metropolitan Regions," by Reid Ewing, Rolf Pendall, and Don Chen, adapted from *Measuring Sprawl and Its Impact.* Copyright © 2012 by Smart Growth America. Reprinted with permission; Page 593: Source: Edmund Burke, Irish orator, philosopher, and politician (1729–1797); Page 595, Figure 23.7: "Sprawl scores for 83 metropolitan regions," adapted from *Measuring Sprawl and Its Impact. Copyright* © 2012 by Smart Growth America. Reprinted with permission; Figure 23.8: Source: U.S. Department of Agriculture. 2007 National Resources Inventory, Natural Resources Conservation Service, Washington, D.C. and Center for Survey Statistics and Methodology, Iowa State University, Ames, Iowa. July 2009; Page 605, Figure 23.16: "Boston, Massachusetts Map," from Rose Fitzgerald Kennedy Greenway Conservancy. Reprinted with permission.

INDEX